The Chemistry of
Metal Cluster Complexes

Edited by

**Duward F. Shriver
Herbert D. Kaesz
Richard D. Adams**

VCH

38814 90

CHEMISTRY

Duward F. Shriver
Department of Chemistry
Northwestern University
Evanston, Illinois
60208-3113

Herbert D. Kaesz
Department of Chemistry
University of California
—Los Angeles
Los Angeles, CA 90024-1569

Richard D. Adams
Department of Chemistry
University of South Carolina
Columbia, South Carolina 29208

Library of Congress Cataloging-in-Publication Data

The Chemistry of metal cluster complexes / edited by Duward F.
  Shriver, Herbert D. Kaesz, Richard D. Adams.
      p.   cm.
  Includes bibliographical references.
  ISBN 1-56081-012-2
  1. Metal crystals.   2. Metal-metal bonds.   3. Organometallic
compounds.   I. Shriver, D. F. (Duward F.), 1934–   II. Kaesz,
Herbert D.   III. Adams, Richard D.
QD921.C424   1990
547′.05--dc20

89-21490
CIP

British Library Cataloguing in Publication Data

The chemistry of metal cluster complexes.
  1. Organometallic compounds. Chemical analysis
  I. Shriver, D. F. (Duward Felix), 1934–   II. Kaesz,
Herbert D.   III. Adams, Richard D.
547.0504

  ISBN 3-527-28047-2

Printed in the United States of America.
ISBN-1-56081-01202 VCH Publishers
ISBN-3-527-28047-2 VCH Verlagsgesellschaft

Printing History:
10 9 8 7 6 5 4 3 2 1

Published jointly by:

VCH Publishers, Inc.
220 East 23rd Street
Suite 909
New York, New York 10010

VCH Verlagsgesellschaft mbH
P.O. Box 10 11 61
D-6940 Weinheim
Federal Republic of Germany

VCH Publishers (UK) Ltd.
8 Wellington Court
Cambridge CB1 1HW
United Kingdom

Contributors

Richard D. Adams ■ Department of Chemistry, University of South Carolina, Columbia, South Carolina 29208, USA

Michael I. Bruce ■ Department of Physical and Inorganic Chemistry, University of Adelaide, South Australia 5001

Donald J. Darensbourg ■ Department of Chemistry, Texas A&M University, College Station Texas 77489, USA

Wayne L. Gladfelter ■ Department of Chemistry, University of Minnesota, Minneapolis, Minnesota 55455, USA

Brian F. G. Johnson ■ University Chemical Laboratory, Lensfield Road, Cambridge University, Cambridge CB2 1EW, United Kingdom

Herbert D. Kaesz ■ Department of Chemistry, University of California—Los Angeles, Los Angeles, California 90024-1569, USA

Guy Lavigne ■ Laboratoire de Chimie de Coordination, 205 route de Narbonne, 31077 Toulouse Cedex, France

Andrew S. May ■ Inorganic Chemistry Laboratory, University of Oxford, Oxford OX1 3QR, United Kingdom

D. Michael P. Mingos ■ Inorganic Chemistry Laboratory, University of Oxford, Oxford OX1 3QR, United Kingdom

Alison Rodger ■ University Chemical Laboratory, Lensfield Road, Cambridge University, Cambridge CB2 1EW, United Kingdom

Kevin J. Roesselet ■ Department of Chemistry, University of Minnesota, Minneapolis, Minnesota 55455, USA

Duward F. Shriver ■ Department of Chemistry, Northwestern University, Evanston, Illinois 60208-3113, USA

Preface

A major development in the burgeoning field of inorganic chemistry is the discovery and evolution of organometallic cluster chemistry. This book presents a coordinated set of chapters written by leading experts, who provide their perspective on fundamentals of structure, bonding, and reactivity of metal cluster complexes. Thorough introductions in each chapter make the material accessible to individuals who are meeting the field for the first time. This book should be of special interest to students and teachers of inorganic chemistry and to research workers in organometallic chemistry and catalysis. It also provides active research workers in the field of metal cluster chemistry with a thought-provoking summary and useful reference work. We anticipate that future volumes in this series will cover more specialized aspects of metal cluster chemistry.

1989

Duward F. Shriver
Herbert D. Kaesz
Richard D. Adams

Contents

Introduction

Herbert D. Kaesz and Duward F. Shriver

A distinctive characteristic of inorganic chemistry is the wide occurrence of closed polyhedral species, such as the tetrahedral P_4 molecule, the polyhedral boron hydrides and carboranes, metal cluster halides (Figure 1.1a,b), cluster carbonyls (Figure 1.1c), and ligand-free cluster ions of the p-block elements (Figure 1.1d). Nowhere is cluster formation more strongly expressed than in the organometallic cluster compounds of the d-block elements, which form the subject of this volume. Organometallic cluster compounds have been intensively investigated for over two decades and the time is ripe for a summary of what is known about their synthesis, stoichiometry, structures, and reactions.

Throughout this book we adhere to the definition of a metal cluster compound as containing "a finite group of metal atoms that are held together mainly or at least to a significant extent, by bonds directly between metal atoms, even though some non-metal atoms may also be intimately associated with the cluster."[1] This definition excludes cage compounds in which several metal atoms are held together exclusively by ligand bridges. Much of the emphasis in this volume is on cluster complexes containing three or more metal atoms, but two-metal systems are mentioned whenever appropriate. Part of the reason for focusing on the larger cluster complexes is that the chemistry of binuclear metal-metal bonded systems is described in recent books.[2,3]

The beginnings of organometallic cluster chemistry can be traced to the discovery of $Co_2(CO)_8$,[4] $Fe_2(CO)_9$,[5] and $Fe_3(CO)_{12}$[6] in the early part of the century, but the field was first set in motion by Walter Hieber in Munich (from about 1930 through the 1950s) with his discovery of many neutral and anionic carbonyl compounds containing more than one metal.[7] The structures of these compounds were unknown at that time so a full development of their chemistry was not possible. It was clear that Hieber had struck a rich vein, which could only be mined when the proper tools were available. Similarly low oxidation state metal halides of the

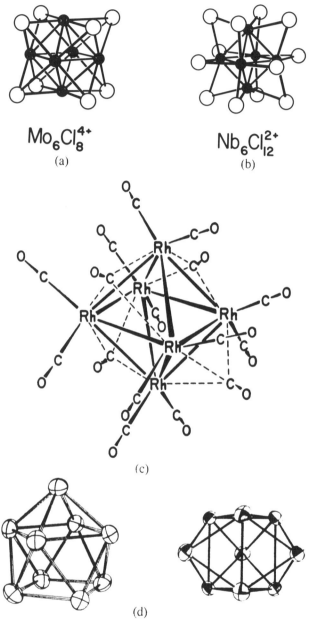

Figure 1.1 ▪ (a) The structure of the complex ion $[Mo_6Cl_8]^{4+}$, (b) the structure of $[Ta_6Cl_{12}]^{2+}$, (c) structure of the carbonyl complex $Rh_6(CO)_{16}$, (d) structures of the homopolyatomic zintl ions $[Sn_9]^{4-}$ and $[Sn_9]^{3-}$. Reproduced by permission from: L. Pauling, *Nature of the chemical bond*, Cornell University Press, Ithaca, NY, 1960, (a) and (b); E. R. Corey, L. F. Dahl and W. Beck, *J. Am. Chem. Soc.*, 1963, **85**, 1202, (c); J. D. Corbett, *Chem. Rev.*, 1985, **85**, 387, (d).

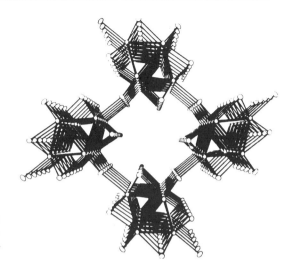

Figure 1.2 ▪ A perspective view of four chains of Sc_4Cl_6B, reproduced by permission from reference 8.

early d-block elements were known and a few early structures were available, but this area did not blossom until recently.[8]

1.1. Structures

As with most of inorganic chemistry, the foremost structural tool in cluster chemistry is X-ray diffraction, because the variety and size of the cluster complexes reduces the value of spectroscopic methods for primary structure determination. Once a basic structural pattern is determined by diffraction, NMR and IR spectroscopic studies provide information on the structures in solution and aid in the structure determination of derivatives. These two spectroscopic techniques also provide the means to follow the course of reactions in synthetic cluster chemistry.

The structure of $Fe_2(CO)_9$ (Figure 1.3) was reported in 1939 by Powell and Ewens, who collected X-ray data on film and processed it by hand.[9] This structure provided the first inkling of the constitution of cluster complexes, for example the close approach of the iron atoms (2.46 Å) indicating the possibility of an M—M bond accompanied by bridging CO ligands. Such features were later discovered in many larger metal cluster compounds. A landmark structure showing the existence of a metal-metal bond in a molecular complex *not* accompanied by any bridging ligands is that of $Mn_2(CO)_{10}$ (Figure 1.4). X-ray diffraction studies since the late 1950s have been greatly facilitated first by computer analysis of the data and later by automated diffractometers.

X-ray diffraction is now an integral part of any major research project in metal cluster chemistry. Much of the early structural work on cluster complexes was performed by Lawrence Dahl (USA) who for example determined the structure of $Rh_6(CO)_{16}$ (Figure 1.1c) and $Fe_3(CO)_{12}$ (Figure 1.5).[10] The latter compound presented serious difficulties because the triangular Fe_3 metal array is disordered into a pseudo 6-fold array in the crystal.[11] When these difficulties were overcome,

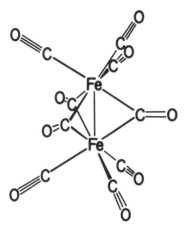

Figure 1.3 ▪ The structure of $Fe_2(CO)_9$.

it was found that the structure contains three metal atoms in a triangular array, with one edge bridged by two CO ligands.

Another landmark structure was that for $Fe_5(CO)_{15}C$ (Figure 1.6) which was reported by Braye, Dahl, Hubel, and Wampler in 1962.[12] Of great interest here is the presence of a carbide atom in the base of the square pyramidal array of iron atoms. Subsequently many transition metal clusters have been recognized to

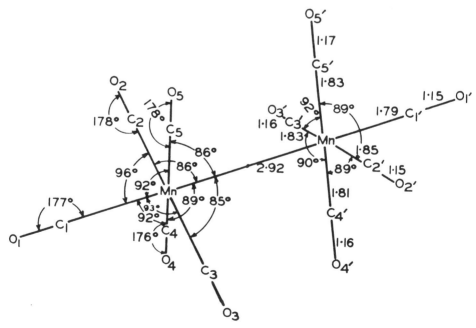

Figure 1.4 ▪ The structure of $Mn_2(CO)_{10}$, reproduced by permission from L. F. Dahl and R. E. Rundle, *Acta Cryst.*, 1963, **16**, 419.

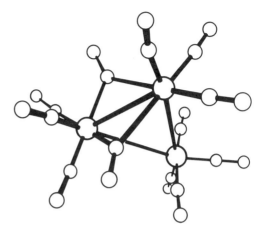

Figure 1.5 ▪ The structure of $Fe_3(CO)_{12}$.

contain more than one p-block element in the cluster framework. This area of research is undergoing rapid expansion and although it is not described here, a recent review provides thorough coverage.[13]

Simultaneous with the discovery and structural characterization of d-block cluster complexes structural regularities have been observed and bonding models have been developed. Although metal-metal bonding in the simplest cluster complexes can be represented by conventional localized two-electron bonds, clusters containing six or more metal atoms require a delocalized description. The bonding models that have been developed provide some very useful and simple relationships between valence electron count and the shape of the metal polyhedron. A simple but important structural correlation is that *for two metal clusters containing the*

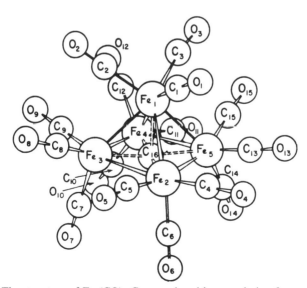

Figure 1.6 ▪ The structure of $Fe_3(CO)_{15}C$, reproduced by permission from reference 12.

same number of metal atoms but different numbers of valence electrons the one with the higher electron count has the more open structure. An account of the polyhedral structures of metal complexes and bonding models is given by Mingos and May in Chapter 2.

1.2. Reactions

1.2.1. Synthesis and Kinetic Studies

With the availability of structural data it became possible to develop the synthesis of new cluster compounds in a rational way. One of the great pioneers in this area, Paulo Chini, synthesized a wide range of metal carbonyl cluster compounds in conjunction with an expert group of co-workers in Milan from the 1960s until his untimely death in 1980. One of their accomplishments was the recognition of the way in which cluster size could be adjusted with changes in redox level of the system. Chini coined the term redox condensation[14] to characterize reactions such as the following, which was first observed by Hieber:[15]

$$[Fe_3(CO)_{11}]^{2-} + Fe(CO)_5 \xrightarrow[THF]{25°C} [Fe_4(CO)_{13}]^{2-} + 3CO \qquad (1.1)$$

Examples from the work of Chini and co-workers[14] are as follows:

$$[Rh_6(CO)_{15}]^{2-} + Rh_6(CO)_{16} \xrightarrow[THF]{25°C} [Rh_{12}(CO)_{30}]^{2-} + CO \qquad (1.2)$$

$$2[Co_6(CO)_{15}C]^{2-} + Co_4(CO)_{12} \xrightarrow[Et_2O]{25°C} 2[Co_8(CO)_{18}C]^{2-} + 6CO \qquad (1.3)$$

Systematics in the synthesis of metal cluster compounds are presented in Chapter 3. The formation of cluster compounds is recognized to occur when one or more ligands are eliminated from coordinately saturated mononuclear metal complexes: for example, in the series $Fe(CO)_5$, $Fe(CO)_4 \cdot Fe(CO)_5$ [i.e., $Fe_2(CO)_9$], and $[Fe(CO)_4]_3$. Systematic methods for the removal of one or more ligands from coordinatively saturated starting complexes thus leads to systematic build-up of the metal cluster complexes. Included in this methodology are reactions in which coordinated CO is converted (and removed) as CO_2 by Me_3NO, among other chemical conversions of coordinated CO which ultimately lead to its removal. Greater control over this methodology is achieved by trapping coordinatively unsaturated intermediates with easily displaceable ligands such as tetrahydrofuran (THF) or acetonitrile. Such intermediates are termed "lightly stabilized" species which may be further reacted at mild conditions with greater control over the kinetic pathways leading to products. Systematic cluster build-up also occurs when the precursor complexes contain *sigma*-bonded groups that may be oxidatively added to a lower-coordinated fragment (or to a lightly stabilized intermediate) in solution.

Greater understanding of these processes, of course, derives from appropriate kinetic studies (see Chapter 4). The patterns of associative and dissociative reactions that are recognized in the chemistry of monometal complexes are also seen for cluster complexes. One of the interesting new features of metal cluster chemistry is that associative reactions can occur by pathways in which the metal framework opens to accept an incoming ligand.

1.2.2. Ligand Transformations

Some of the same themes that have been delineated for the systematic synthesis of metal cluster compounds are also seen in the transformations of ligands already coordinated to one or more metal centers in the cluster complexes, as described in Chapter 5. Here, too, the activation of metal cluster complexes to permit milder reaction conditions and greater control of kinetic pathway and products is emphasized. Nucleophiles are seen to activate carbonyl cluster complexes as also achieved by one-electron reducing agents. Unsaturated metal cluster complexes play an important role in stoichiometric as well as in catalytic transformations. Certain bridging ligands are seen to play an internal "lightly stabilizing" role for coordination sites. Change in attachment ("hapticity") of ligands such as (μ, η^2-CO), μ, η^2-C(OR), or [μ-O=C(R)] are either observed or postulated in the reactions of the cluster complexes in which they are found. As mentioned earlier in relation to kinetic studies, the metal-metal bonds are also observed to play a role in cluster reactivity, that is, in cluster complexes containing strongly coordinated bridging ligands accompanied by labile metal-metal bonds.

1.2.3. Cluster Rearrangements

The lability of metal-metal bonds leading to cluster rearrangements is discussed in Chapter 6. Indeed, motion of the metal atoms also involves motion of the ligands, and this provides a different model for fluctionality than the more conventional interchange of ligands over a rigid metal cluster core. The various modes of cluster rearrangements and the important question of fragmentation reactions of cluster complexes are also discussed.

1.2.4. The Relation of Clusters to Catalysis

The oil shortages of the 1970s touched off a flurry of activity on the potential use of cluster complexes as catalysts. This work was prompted by analogy to conventional heterogeneous catalysts where it is known that for certain reactions, the so-called "demanding" methanation of CO, or the direct synthesis of ammonia from H_2 and N_2, several metal atoms are required to be in close proximity on the surface of a suitable support; complete dispersal of the supported metal catalyst is known to interrupt such catalytic reactions. The hope was that a well-defined metal cluster complex in solution would be able to carry out the same catalytic reactions with a greater degree of selectivity than conventional catalysts, where aggregation of the metal particles is not controlled. At the temperatures required for many of the demanding catalytic conversions, especially the synthesis of ethylene glycol from syngas ($2CO + 3H_2$ at around 210–250°C, 500–3400 atm.), the cluster complexes employed as the loaded form of the catalyst [$Rh_4(CO)_{12}$, or $Rh_6(CO)_{16}$] do not maintain their integrity. Still, as recorded in Chapter 7, there are now a variety of reactions known in which metal cluster complexes have been shown to be genuine homogeneous catalysts.[15]

Another important aspect of metal cluster chemistry is its relation to heterogeneous catalysis, an aspect which goes beyond the scope of the present volume. Much has been written and hypothesized about this relationship ever since the first connections were made between heterogeneous catalysis and organometallics by Burwell.[16] Of particular importance were analogies by the late Earl Muetterties between ligands bound to clusters and those on surfaces.[17] The relation between organometallic cluster chemistry and heterogeneous catalysis comes about in several ways. The existence of several metal atoms in a cluster provides potential structural and chemical analogs for multisite binding and catalysis of organic substrates or fragments on metal particles. Metal clusters also have been investigated as precursors to well-defined surface-supported metal catalysts.[18-20] Indeed, investigators of this area have coined an apt phrase to describe their activities, namely, "surface organometallic chemistry," hoping to develop molecular approaches to surface catalysis.[19,20] This area is well worth noting for current and future developments.

Beyond the attachment of well-defined cluster complexes to surfaces is the idea of converting such species into well-defined surface-supported crystallites (see the chapters "Supported Metal Catalysts Prepared from Molecular Clusters: Activities for Hydrogenolysis and Skeletal Isomerization of Hydrocarbons" by G. Maire, and "Supported Bimetallic Catalysts Derived from Molecular Metal Clusters" by L. Guczi in reference 18. Here we should mention the pioneering efforts of Primet, Basset, et al.[21] in drawing attention to the shifts in carbonyl absorptions of platinum complexes of increasing nuclearity (work of P. Chini and co-workers) to the similar shifts in absorptions of CO on supported platinum crystallites of varying size distribution. Soon thereafter, a pioneering study of M. Ichikawa appeared[22] in which well-defined molecular complexes (of platinum) were used to prepare surface-supported crystallites to achieve special effects in heterogeneous catalysis. These early efforts were soon joined by a growing number of investigators of a scope too large to encompass in this brief introduction. Suffice it to say that special catalytic effects obtained by crystallites derived from metal cluster precursors are thus far only short-lived (by industrial standards), where such constructions are unstable under the thermodynamic conditions of catalysis. Of course most catalysts can be said to be *meta*-stable, and the only question of importance is to determine exactly how long the prepared catalyst takes to deactivate (by various pathways). Conversely, where metal combinations are stable, there is no need to load preformed mixed-metal cluster complexes. The metal combinations will form under catalytic conditions even when they are loaded onto the support through separate complexes, as recently elegantly shown for Pt—Re mixed-metal catalysts by W. Sachtler and co-workers.[23]

Even if specific catalytic effects derived from metal cluster precursors are too short-lived to be of practical importance, research in this area offers advantages of a fundamental nature. Mixed-metal cluster complexes of well-defined geometry serve as important standards in the application of EXAFS to the study of supported metal catalysts. Additionally, a mixed-metal crystallite derived from a mixed-metal cluster may demonstrate an important specificity for the particular metal combination not attainable by any other means.

One such example may be cited in the interconversion of aromatic nitro complexes into isocyanides.[24] A high degree of specificity unattained in other preparations of mixed-metal catalysts was shown for Fe—Pd bimetallic particles derived from Fe—Pd mixed-metal complexes. Thus, if the combination is shown to be effective, even if a catalyst prepared by such means is not sufficiently long-lived, there may be other ways to effect the combination, that is, to deposit crystallites of one metal (e.g., Pd) on the oxide of the other (i.e., Fe_xO_y). The specificity of the mixed-metal combination may then be achieved at the interface of the crystallite (i.e., Pd) with that of the support (i.e., Fe_xO_y).

The general question of organometallic complexes (not necessarily metal cluster complexes) as catalyst precursors has recently been discussed by W. Keim.[25] True justice to the important interface between metal cluster complexes and heterogeneous catalysis cannot possibly be done in this introduction, the subject meriting a separate volume unto itself. We trust that active workers in the field will work towards that end, some of which is partially covered in references 16 through 19. An interested reader should also peruse the collected volume *Metal Clusters*.[26]

The present volume concludes with a general bibliography by M. I. Bruce of the large number of reviews of metal cluster chemistry. While some of the citations appear in one (or more) of the other chapters in this volume, it is believed this collection will be a useful cross-reference to researchers in the field.

References

1. F. A. Cotton, *Quarterly Reviews* (Chem. Soc., London), 1966, **20**, 389.
2. M. H. Chisholm, Ed., *Reactivity of Metal-Metal Bonds*, ACS Symposium Series 155, American Chemical Society, Washington, DC, 1981.
3. F. A. Cotton and R. A. Walton, *Multiple bonds between metal atoms.* New York: Wiley, 1982.
4. L. Mond, H. Hirtz and M. D. Coop, *J. Chem. Soc.*, 1910, **997**, 798.
5. J. Dewar and H. O. Jones, *Proc. R. Soc.* (London), 1905, **A76**, 558.
6. J. Dewar and H. O. Jones, *Proc. R. Soc.* (London), 1907, **A79**, 66. W. Hieber, *Z. Anorg. Chem.*, 1932, **204**, 165.
7. W. Hieber, *Adv. Organometal. Chem.*, 1970, **8**, 1.
8. S.-J. Hwu and J. D. Corbett, *J. Solid State Chem.*, 1986, **64**, 331.
9. H. M. Powell and R. V. G. Ewens, *J. Chem. Soc.* (London), 1939, 286.
10. L. F. Dahl, E. Ishishi and R. E. Rundle, *J. Chem. Phys.*, 1957, **26**, 1750.
11. C. H. Wei and L. F. Dahl, *J. Am. Chem. Soc.*, 1969, **91**, 1351.
12. E. H. Braye, L. F. Dahl, W. Hübel and D. L. Wampler, *J. Am. Chem. Soc.*, 1962, **84**, 4633.
13. K. H. Whitmire, *Coord. Chem. Rev. (B)*, 1988, **17**, 95.
14. P. Chini, G. Longoni and V. G. Albano, *Adv. Organometal. Chem.*, 1976, **14**, 285–341.
15. G. Süss-Fink, *Nachr. Chem. Tech. Lab.*, 1988, **36**, 1110–1113.
16. R. L. Burwell, Jr., in *Chem. and Eng. News*, Aug. 22, 1966, and *Catalysis Progress in Research*, F. Basolo and R. L. Burwell, Jr., Plenum Press, New York, 1973, p. 51.
17. E. L. Muetterties, *Bull. Soc. Chim. Belg.*, 1975, **84**, 959–986.
18. C. Gates, L. Guczi and H. Knözinger, Eds., *Metal Clusters in Catalysis*, Elsevier, Amsterdam, 1986.
19. J.-M. Basset, B. C. Gates, et al., *Surface Organometallic Chemistry: Molecular*

Approaches to Surface Catalysis, NATO ASI Series C, Vol. 231, Kluwer Academic Publ., Dordrecht, Boston & London, 1988.

20. H. H. Lamb, B. C. Gates and H. Knözinger, *Angew. Chem. Int. Ed. Engl.*, 1988, **27**, 1127–1144.

21. M. Primet, J. M. Basset, E. Garbowski and M. V. Mathieu, *J. Am. Chem. Soc.*, 1975, **97**, 3655.

22. M. Ichikawa, *Bull. Chem. Soc. Japan*, 1978, **51**, 2268.

23. S. M. Augustine and W. M. H. Sachtler, *J. Catal.*, 1989, **116**, 184.

24. P. Braunstein, R. Devenish, P. Gallezot, B. T. Heaton, C. J. Humphreys, J. Kervennal, Suzanne Mulley and M. Ries, *Angew. Chem. Int. Ed. Engl.*, 1988, **27**, 927.

25. W. Keim, *J. Molec. Catal.*, 1989, **52**, 19.

26. M. Moskovits, Ed., *Metal clusters*. New York: Wiley-Interscience, J. Wiley & Sons, 1986.

2

Structural and Bonding Aspects of Metal Cluster Chemistry

D. Michael P. Mingos and Andrew S. May

2.1. Introduction

In the early 1960s there were few examples of compounds with metal-metal bonds and the rare examples were frequently chance products of reactions aimed at synthesizing alternative mononuclear products.[1] Since those days more predictable synthetic routes to cluster compounds (reviewed in Chapter 3) have emerged as the result of the pioneering work of Chini and Lewis[2,3] and currently compounds with up to fifty metal atoms have been definitively characterized using single crystal X-ray crystallographic and spectroscopic techniques.[4] In addition synthetic routes to heterometallic cluster compounds have been developed by Stone, Vahrenkamp, and others.[5–7] A rudimentary understanding of the bonding in these compounds has also emerged from a combination of theoretical ideas developed from molecular orbital theory and chemical intuition.[8] The field has now reached an exciting point in its development where the sizes of the cluster compounds being characterized are sufficiently large for meaningful comparisons of physical and chemical properties to be made with both the bulk metal and metal surfaces. Earl Muetterties played a particularly important role in communicating and developing the importance of analogies between metals and molecular clusters.[9]

A metal cluster compound has been defined in terms of a group of two or more metal atoms held together by direct and substantial metal-metal bonding. This has proved to be a reasonable working definition although the phrase "direct and substantial metal-metal bonding" does leave a great deal of room for chemical interpretation and argument and does not form the basis of an objective criterion. The lengths of metal-metal bonds in molecular clusters vary over a substantial range even for compounds with the same formal metal-metal bond order. For example, with molybdenum, metal-metal bond lengths from 2.524 Å to 3.235 Å have been observed for cluster compounds which formally have a single bond order. The bond lengths at the extremes of this range vary by as much as 15% from the metal-metal distance observed in the bulk metal (2.80 Å).[10] Metal-metal bond lengths show such a large variation because frequently the metal-metal bond is the weakest bond in the molecule and therefore the potential energy surface associated with extension of the metal-metal bond is softer than those associated with the other bonds in the molecule. The metal-metal bond is therefore the most deformable bond in the structure and the small energy changes associated with a lengthening of the metal-metal bond can be compensated for by favorable bonding and nonbonding steric interactions between the ligands.[11] In addition the radial distribution functions for the d, s, and p valence orbitals of a transition metal atom are rather different and small changes in the relative contributions of these orbitals can cause large variations in the optimum metal-metal bond lengths.[12]

The occurrence of direct metal-metal bonding associated with the preceding definition of clusters can be problematical when the clusters are also connected by bridging ligands. The orbitals associated with metal-metal bonds generally have exactly the same symmetry characteristics as the linear combinations of the orbitals of the bridging ligands and therefore it is not possible to analyze the problem using either symmetry arguments or crude molecular orbital calculations.[13] Either very accurate calculations or spectroscopic measurements are required to delineate the relative contributions of direct and indirect metal-metal bonding effects. The latter are mediated by the bridging ligands connecting the metal atoms. The general conclusion of such calculations is that in those clusters with bridging ligands the direct metal-metal bonding is energetically not very significant.[14] Nonetheless, a formal metal-metal bond designation is retained because it maintains the connection with simplified bonding schemes based on the inert gas rule and it is useful for interpreting the magnetic and structural properties of a series of related cluster compounds. For example, in the following pairs of compounds the metal-metal bond separation consistently increases when the formal bond order is reduced from 1 to 0:

Compound	Formal Bond Order	Metal–metal Distance (Å)
$[Cr(C_5H_5)(\mu\text{–}SR)(NO)]_2$	1.0	2.95
$[Fe(C_5H_5)(\mu\text{–}SR)(CO)]_2$	0.0	3.39
$[Co(C_5H_5)(\mu\text{–}PR_2)]_2$	1.0	2.56
$[Fe(C_5H_5)(\mu\text{–}PR_2)]_2$	0.0	3.36

However, such comparisons are only valid for compounds with similar bridging ligands, because changes in the electronic and steric characteristics of the bridging ligands can create variations in the metal-metal bond lengths of a similar magnitude. For example, $[Fe(\mu\text{–}SR)(NO)_2]_2$ and $[Fe(\mu\text{-}I)(NO)_2]_2$ both have formal metal-metal bond orders of 1, but the metal-metal bond length in the former is 2.72 Å and in the latter 3.05 Å.[15,16] The size and the electronic effects of the bridging group clearly play an important role in influencing the length of the metal-metal bond being bridged.

Attempts to "view" the electron density associated with the metal-metal bond "directly" using highly accurate X-ray diffraction studies have not proved very successful and have not contributed significantly to the problem of deciding the relative weights of indirect and direct metal-metal bonding effects.[17]

An important general development in inorganic chemistry has been the recognition that multiple bonding is an important feature in the chemistry of the transition metals. In the transition metal series multiple bonding has been well established for the following metals: V, Cr, Mo, W, Re, Ru, Os, and Rh and a very complete account of this area of chemistry has been given in recent reviews and a book by Cotton and Walton.[18,19] For main group atoms the maximum formal bond order is limited to three because of the nodal characteristics of the p orbitals of these atoms, but for the transition metals formal bond orders of five can be achieved if the d orbitals are used for one σ, two π, and two δ bonds. Although there is some evidence for the formation of quintuple bonds for metal dimers in the gas phase the maximum bond order in molecular clusters is generally four because one of the d^δ orbitals is used in metal-ligand bonding.[19]

The assignment of a formal metal-metal bond order in a cluster rests on obtaining internal consistency from the available structural, spectroscopic, magnetic, and force constant data. For clusters of the earlier transition metals these multiple bonds are frequently observed in compounds without bridging ligands and the structural and spectroscopic data are completely consistent with the assignment of a formal bond order on the basis of the number of d electrons associated with each metal atom. For clusters of the later transition metals the multiple bonding generally occurs in compounds with bridging ligands and the extent of bonding is more difficult to delineate. In such compounds a formal bond order is generally assigned on the basis of the attainment of the inert gas configuration at the individual metal atoms. For example, in the dimers $[Fe(C_5H_5)(\mu\text{-}NO)]_2$ and $[Co(C_5H_5)(\mu\text{-}CO)]_2$ the formal metal-metal bond orders are two whereas in $[Co(C_5H_5)(\mu\text{-}NO)]_2$ and $[Ni(C_5H_5)(\mu\text{-}CO)]_2$ the formal bond orders are one. Bond orders of 1.5 are assigned to the compounds $[Co_2(C_5H_5)_2(CO)(NO)]$ and $[Co_2(C_5H_5)_2(CO)_2]^-$ because they have an intermediate number of valence electrons.[20] The bond length data for these compounds, summarized in Table 2.1, highlight the difficulty of establishing bond-order bond-length relationships for compounds that do not have identical bridging ligands. Fenske has noted that the dominant bonding interaction

Table 2.1 ▪ **Summary of Metal–Metal Bond Lengths in Some Metal–Cyclopentadienyl Dimers**

Compound	M—M (Å)	Formal Bond Order
$[Fe_2(NO)_2(\eta\text{-}C_5H_5)_2]$	2.326	2.0
$[Co_2(CO)_2(\eta\text{-}C_5Me_5)_2]$	2.338	2.0
$[Co_2(CO)(NO)(\eta\text{-}C_5H_5)_2]$	2.370	1.5
$[Co_2(CO)_2(\eta\text{-}C_5H_5)_2]$	2.372	1.5
$[Co_2(NO)_2(\eta\text{-}C_5H_5)_2]$	2.372	1.5
$[Ni_2(CO)_2(\eta\text{-}C_5H_5)_2]$	2.357	1.0
$[Ni_2(CO)_2(\eta\text{-}C_5H_4Me)_2]$	2.390	1.0

in these dimers occurs through the bridging ligands rather than through direct interactions between the metal atoms. For the carbonyls the lone pair metal interactions are particularly important, whereas for the bridging nitrosyl the lower lying π^* orbitals make a larger contribution. Since the latter interact with orbitals that are metal-metal antibonding the metal-metal distance is longer in those compounds with bridging nitrosyls. It is important to note that the synergic bonding interactions that occur for ligands in bridging positions influence the relative contributions of the bonding and antibonding metal-metal components [see (1) and (2) for example].[21]

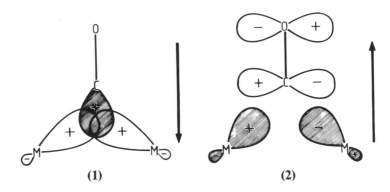

(1)   **(2)**

The application of the inert gas formalism to cluster compounds is only useful if the metal-ligand combination found in the cluster would have conformed to this formalism in a mononuclear complex. For example, the iridium dimer $[Ir_2Cl_2(COD)_2]$ has a geometry based on two square planar fragments linked by bridging halides and a long nonbonded Ir-Ir separation (>3.0 Å). In this complex the iridium atoms are described as 16-electron square planar moieties. In the related complex $[Ir_2(PPh_2)_2(CO)_2(PPh_3)_2]$ the geometries are tetrahedral about the metal atoms and the metals are linked by a short metal-metal bond length (2.55 Å). This complex is formulated with a double bond between the metal atoms and the inert gas rule is achieved at both metal centers.[22,23]

2.2. Survey of Important Classes of Transition Metal Cluster Compounds

If the elements with incompletely filled f shells are excluded then the majority of the remaining elements form molecular cluster compounds. For the purposes of this chapter, however, only the cluster compounds of the transition metal elements will be considered. For the transition elements in their bulk states the maximum binding energies occur approximately at the center of the transition series which corresponds to half-filling of the d and s valence bands. In molecular cluster compounds the ligands which surround the metal core attempt to emulate this bonding situation. Consequently cluster compounds of the earlier transition metal elements are generally associated with π-donor ligands which donate additional electrons to the metal bonding molecular orbitals, particularly if they occupy bridging positions. In contrast for cluster compounds of the later transition metals π-acceptor ligands are able to withdraw electron density from the cluster and thereby depopulate skeletal molecular orbitals which otherwise would have been metal-metal antibonding.

The metal's formal oxidation state is also important for the formation of stable molecular cluster compounds. In particular it is important for the metal to have a low formal oxidation state in order to maximize the metal-metal bonding effects. Therefore, the π-acid and π-donor character of the ligands has to be accompanied by their ability to stabilize low oxidation states.

Thermodynamic studies have indicated that the strengths of metal-metal bonds in molecular clusters follow those of the bulk metal and in particular are greater as a column of the transition series is descended.[24] Consequently, the range of cluster compounds and their stabilities generally increase for the heavier elements of a periodic group.

2.2.1. π-Donor Clusters

Cluster compounds of the earlier transition metals are associated with ligands such as O^{2-}, S^{2-}, Cl^-, Br^-, I^-, and OR^- and the metals are commonly in oxidation states of $+2$ and $+3$. Geometrically these clusters show a strong preference for triangular and octahedral metal skeletal geometries. $[Re_3Cl_9L_3]$ (**3**)[25] represents an example of a triangular metal cluster and $[Mo_6Cl_8L_6]^{4+}$ [26] and $[Nb_6Cl_{12}L_6]^{2+}$ [27] (**4**) and (**5**) provide important examples of octahedral metal clusters. In $[Mo_6Cl_8L_6]^{4+}$ the chloro-ligands are located on the faces of the metal octahedron and in $[Nb_6Cl_{12}L_6]^{2+}$ the chloro- ligands span the twelve edges of the octahedron. Electronically this structural difference is particularly important because a face-bridging halide ligand has five of its valence electrons involved in bonding. The number of valence electrons contributed by the other common π-donor ligands is summarized in Table 2.2. The ability of halide ligands to act as terminal, edge- and face-bridging ligands can result in the aggregation of clusters into more complex three-dimensional extended structures. Some examples of these extended structures are illustrated in Figure 2.1.[28] In these examples halide bridges are replacing the terminal ligands in the clusters $[Re_3Cl_9L_3]$, $[Mo_6Cl_8L_6]^{4+}$, and $[Nb_6Cl_{12}L_6]^{2+}$ in order to generate the extended structures.

Table 2.2 ▪ Electron-Donating Characteristics of Common Bridging Ligands in Metal Clusters

Edge-Bridging (μ_2)	
Two-electron donors:	O, S, Se
Three-electron donors:	SR, OR
	PR_2, AsR_2
	Cl, Br, I
Face-Bridging (μ_3)	
Four-electron donors:	O, S, Se
	PR, AsR
Five-electron donors:	Cl, Br, I

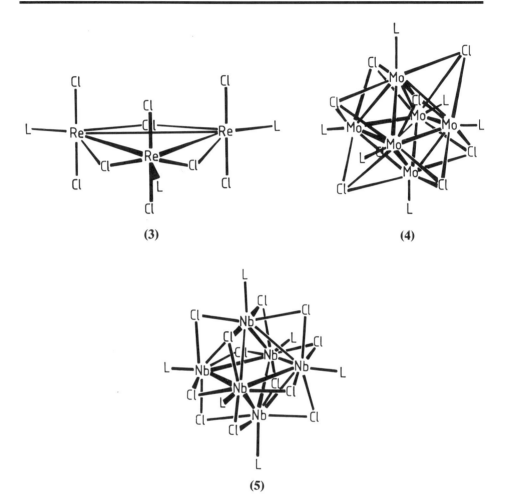

(3)   (4)

(5)

An alternative type of condensation process involving the metal skeleton is illustrated in Figure 2.2.[29] In these clusters the basic Mo_3X_3 triangular clusters are being linked in a columnar fashion to form oligomers based on face-sharing octahedra. In the limit the polymer $[Mo_3X_3]_n$ has an infinite chain of condensed octahedra.

Incomplete fragments of the $[Mo_6Cl_8L_6]^{4+}$ and $[Nb_6Cl_{12}L_6]^{2+}$ octahedral clusters have also been identified. For example, $[Mo_5Cl_{13}]^{2-}$ (**6**)[30] has a square-pyramidal arrangement of metal atoms and $[Mo_4(OPr^i)_8Br_4]$ (**7**)[31] and $[Mo_4I_{11}]^{2-}$ (**8**)[32] have "butterfly" geometries derived from the octahedron by the removal of two adjacent metal vertices. In contrast $[Mo_4(OPr^i)_8Cl_4]$ (**9**)[33] has a square-planar geometry corresponding to the removal of two *trans*- vertices from the octahedron.

The octahedral metal cluster unit has also been stabilized by S, Se, Te, and Sb ligands and Simon and Schäfer[34,35] have developed an extensive structural chemistry based on the condensation and the oligomerization of these cluster units. The

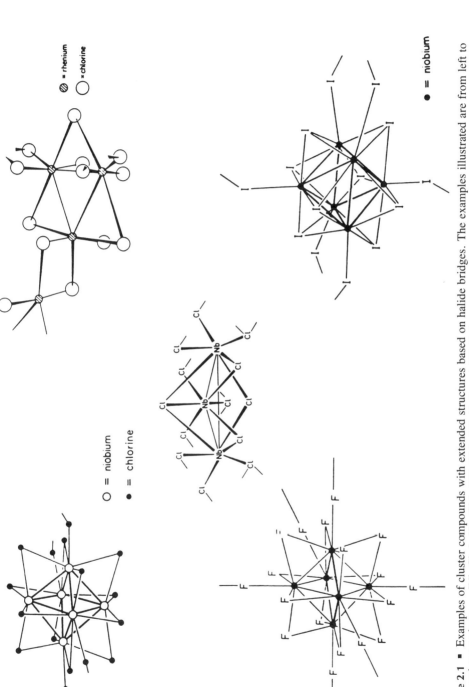

Figure 2.1 ▪ Examples of cluster compounds with extended structures based on halide bridges. The examples illustrated are from left to right and top to bottom: [Nb$_6$Cl$_{14}$], [Re$_3$Cl$_9$], [Nb$_3$Cl$_8$], [Nb$_6$F$_{15}$], and [Nb$_6$I$_{11}$].

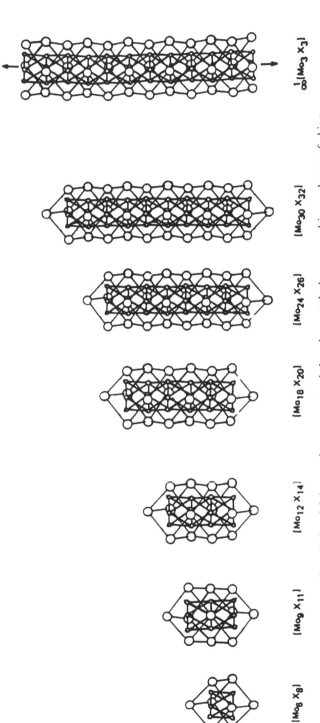

Figure 2.2 ■ Extended molybdenum cluster compounds based on octahedra arranged in a columnar fashion.

sulphido- ligand is a particularly important bridging ligand and has led to the isolation of many molybdenum and iron compounds with interesting solid state and biological properties. The Chevrel-Sergent compounds $[Mo_6S_8]M'$ ($M' = Pb^{2+}$, Cu^{2+}, etc.)[36] have a central octahedral fragment very similar to that described for $[Mo_6Cl_8]^{4+}$, but these units are linked in an infinite fashion through sulphide bridges to the counter cations M' (Figure 2.3). In contrast to $[Mo_6Cl_8]^{4+}$ these clusters do not have a closed shell diamagnetic ground state. The weak interactions between the paramagnetic cluster cations which are mediated by the bridging ligands and the counter cations lead to a band structure which supports metallic conduction. These compounds also display superconducting properties at low temperatures.

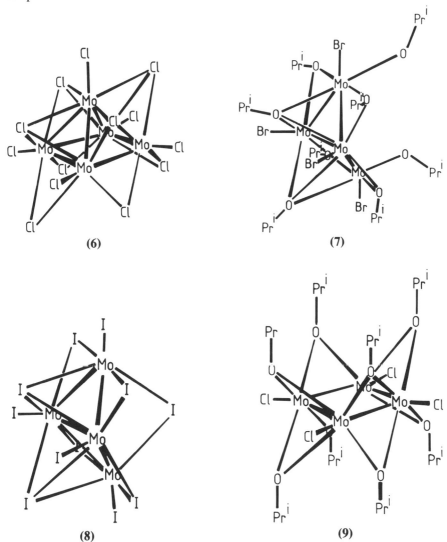

(6)   (7)

(8)   (9)

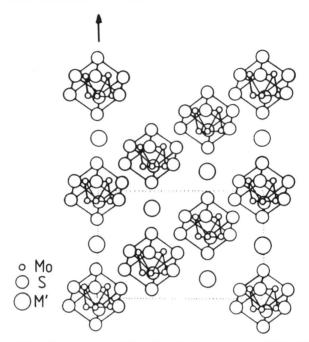

o Mo
◯ S
◯ M'

Figure 2.3 ▪ The structure of the Chevrel phase compound [Mo_6S_8]Pb.

The iron-sulphur proteins constitute a large and important group of biological materials which are responsible for hydrogen uptake, ATP formation, pyruvate metabolism, nitrogen fixation, and photosynthetic electron transport. The 4Fe and 8Fe ferrodoxins contain the Fe_4S_4 "cubane" cluster unit illustrated in Figure 2.4. This unit has been identified in both cases and the clusters show a D_{2d} distortion. In [$Fe_4S_4(SPh)_4$]$^{2-}$ this takes the form of two long and four short distances and in the reduced form, [$Fe_4S_4(SPh)_4$]$^{3-}$, the Fe_4 shows a more elongated core.[37,38]

The dimeric anions [$Fe_6Mo_2S_6(SR)_9$]$^{3-}$ [39,40] (R = Et, CH_2CH_2OH, and Ph) have two Fe_3Mo cubane clusters linked by SR bridges (see Figure 2.5). EXAFS studies have indicated that the molybdenum environment in these clusters is very similar to that present in the enzyme nitrogenase. The metal-metal bonding in these compounds is not thought to be particularly strong; for example, the iron molybdenum cluster has been described in terms of a $2Fe^{II}Fe^{III}Mo^{IV}$ model with strong antiferromagnetic coupling between the unpaired spins on the iron atoms.

Recently Fenske et al.[41,42] have synthesized some high nuclearity sulphido- and selenido- cluster compounds and the structures of some of the derivatives are illustrated in Figure 2.6. The highest nuclearity example is based on a central Ni_{10} pentagonal antiprism with bridging Se and Ni(PPh$_3$) groups leading to an overall stoichiometry of [$Ni_{34}Se_{22}(PPh_3)_{10}$].

In some of the lower nuclearity π-donor clusters multiple bonding between the metal atoms is observed. For example, the short Re—Re bond lengths in [Re_3Cl_{12}]$^{3-}$ have been interpreted in terms of double bonds between the metal atoms.[43] This proposal is consistent with more sophisticated molecular orbital cal-

Figure 2.4 ▪ The structure of the $[Fe_4S_4(SR)_4]^{2-}$ cluster.

culations and spectroscopic data. Interesting bond alternation effects have also been noted. For example, $[Mo_4Cl_8(PEt_3)_4]$ (**10**) has a rectangular geometry and the alternating bond pattern has been interpreted in terms of single and triple Mo—Mo bonds.[44] The compound can therefore be viewed as a condensation product of two quadruply bonded molybdenum dimers. Similarly $[Tc_6Cl_{12}]^{2-}$ can be described as the condensation product of three quadruply bonded units (**11**).[45,46]

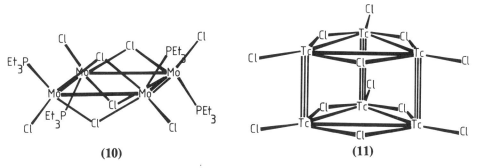

(**10**)   (**11**)

2.2.2. π-Acceptor Clusters

The great majority of compounds of this type occur for the later transition metals and the most effective and widely used ligand in this context is carbon monoxide. The dominant role of carbon monoxide as a ligand for stabilizing low oxidation state cluster compounds arises because it is a very flexible ligand which can occupy terminal, edge-bridging, or face-capping locations in a cluster. Furthermore, this ligand functions as a two-electron ligand in each of these bonding situations and

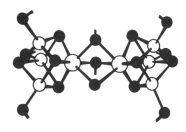

Figure 2.5 ▪ The molecular structure of $[Fe_6-Mo_2S_2(SR)_9]^{3-}$.

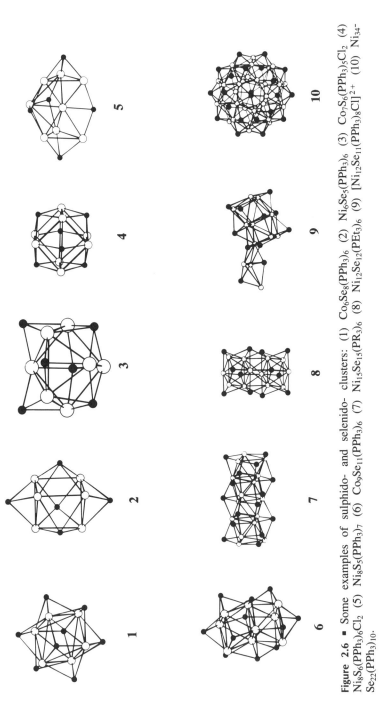

Figure 2.6 ▪ Some examples of sulphido- and selenido- clusters: (1) Co$_6$Se$_8$(PPh$_3$)$_6$ (2) Ni$_6$Se$_5$(PPh$_3$)$_6$ (3) Co$_7$S$_6$(PPh$_3$)$_5$Cl$_2$ (4) Ni$_8$S$_6$(PPh$_3$)$_6$Cl$_2$ (5) Ni$_8$S$_5$(PPh$_3$)$_7$ (6) Co$_9$Se$_{11}$(PPh$_3$)$_6$ (7) Ni$_{15}$Se$_{15}$(PR$_3$)$_6$ (8) Ni$_{12}$Se$_{12}$(PEt$_3$)$_6$ (9) [Ni$_{12}$Se$_{11}$(PPh$_3$)$_8$Cl]$^{2+}$ (10) Ni$_{34}$-Se$_{22}$(PPh$_3$)$_{10}$.

therefore terminal to bridging intramolecular exchange processes frequently have very low activation energies.[47] Furthermore, there are well-established routes for encouraging the aggregation of metal-carbonyl clusters based either on the elimination of carbon monoxide or by redox condensation processes. The other π-acceptor ligands which are capable of stabilizing cluster compounds are isocyanides, nitric oxide, phosphines, and polyenes (in particular cyclopentadienyl and benzene). Although H^- is not in itself a π-acceptor ligand there are many carbonyl and phosphine cluster compounds which also have H^- as a ligand and therefore these clusters will be considered together with the π-acid ligands.

2.2.3. Structural Aspects of π-Acceptor Clusters

Figure 2.7 provides a histogram based on the Cambridge Crystallographic Data File[48] illustrating the relative numbers of structurally determined cluster compounds as a function of cluster nuclearity. A log scale is required because of the predominance of low nuclearity examples and the limited number of compounds with more than seven metal atoms. At the time of writing the highest nuclearity example of a metal-carbonyl cluster whose structure has been unambiguously determined by single crystal X-ray studies has 42 metal atoms. The π-acceptor clusters can be neutral, cationic, or anionic and the most common structural entity is the metal triangle. Although the vast majority of cluster compounds adopt deltahedral geometries when the metal nuclearities are less than seven, that is, tetrahedra, trigonal bipyramids, and octahedra, for higher nuclearity clusters condensed clusters based on these components tend to predominate rather than the alternative spherical geometries, for example, dodecahedra, bicapped square antiprisms, and icosahedra. This behavior is rather different to that commonly associated with main group polyhedral molecules where the lower nuclearity examples are unstable because of "ring strain" effects. Presumably, the participation of the metal d orbitals reduces the "ring strain" effects and leads to a relative stabilization of triangular, octahedral, and tetrahedral fragments. For the higher nuclearity clusters with more than twelve metal atoms the condensation of tetrahedral and octahedral fragments leads to structures which bear a strong resemblance to fragments of face-centered cubic, hexagonal close-packed, and body-centered cubic lattices.

2.2.3.1. Clusters with Three Metal Atoms

Some examples of cluster compounds based on a triangle of metal atoms are summarized in Table 2.3. In agreement with an inert gas rule formulation the great majority of these compounds have a total of 48 valence electrons. The achievement of inert gas configurations at the individual metal atoms can be associated with a wide variety of ligand types and geometries. Although carbon monoxide predominates other π-acceptor and π-donor ligands are also observed. Even for very closely related compounds such as $[Fe_3(CO)_{12}]$ (**12**) and $[Ru_3(CO)_{12}]$ (**13**) the carbonyl ligands adopt different geometries, with the former having two carbonyls bridging one edge of the metal triangle and the latter no bridging carbonyls. NMR evidence suggests that these dramatic structural differences require only small changes in the total energies of the molecules.[49] Several research groups have tried to account for the polyhedral arrangements of carbonyls in these clusters.[50,51] The most satisfac-

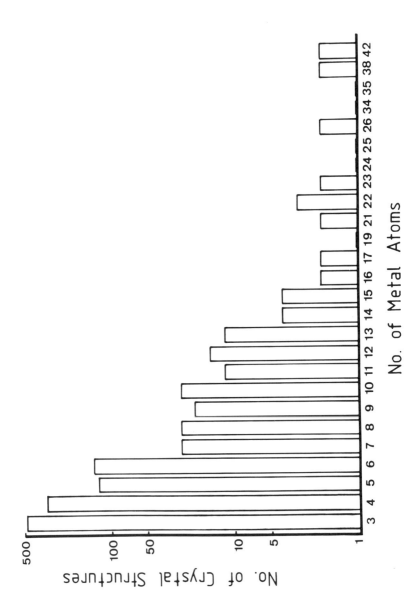

Figure 2.7 ▪ A histogram showing the number of crystal structures of metal cluster compounds as a function of nuclearity.

Table 2.3 ▪ Selected Examples of Clusters with Triangular Geometries

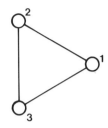

Compound	No. of Valence Electrons	Heteroatom Positions	Ref.
$[Co_3(CO)_{10}]^-$	48	—	1
$CrFe_2(CO)_{11}(PPh)$	48	—	2
$Fe_3(CO)_{12}$	48	—	3
$[Fe_3(CO)_{11}]^{2-}$	48	—	4
$MoNi_2(CO)_2(Cp)_3(PhC)$	48	—	5
$[Mo_3O(CO)_6(Cp)_3]^+$	48	—	6
$[Ni_3S_2(PEt_3)_6]^{2+}$	48	—	7
$Os_3(CO)_{12}$	48	—	8
$[Pd_3S_2(PMe_3)_6]^{2+}$	48	—	9
$Ru_3(CO)_{12}$	48	—	10
$[W_3(CO)_9(OEt)_3]^{3-}$	48	—	11
$Ni_3(CO)_2(Cp)_3$	49	—	12
$H_2Os_3(CO)_{10}$	46	—	13
$[Pt_3(CO)(Me_2PCH_2PMe_2)_4]^{2+}$	46	—	14
$Rh_3(CO)_5(PPh_2)_3$	46	—	15, 16
$Pd_3(SO_2)_2(t\text{-}BuNC)_5$	44	—	17
$Pt_3(CO)_3(P(C_6H_{11})_3)_3$	44	—	18
$FePt_2(CO)_5(P(OPh)_3)_3$	44	—	19
$Au_2Os(CO)_4(PPh_3)_2$	42	—	20
$Pt_3(t\text{-}BuNC)_6$	42	—	21
$[Pd_3(CO)(Ph_2PCH_2PPh_2)_3]^{2+}$	42	—	22

References

1. H. N. Adams, G. Fachinetti and J. Strähle, *Angew. Chem. Int. Ed. Engl.*, 1980, **19**, 404.
2. G. Huttner, G. Mohr and P. Friedrich, *Z. Naturforsch., Teil B*, 1978, **33**, 1254.
3. F. A. Cotton and J. M. Troup, *J. Am. Chem. Soc.*, 1974, **96**, 4155.
4. F. Y.-K. Lo, G. Longoni, P. Chini, L. D. Lower and L. F. Dahl, *J. Am. Chem. Soc.*, 1980, **102**, 7691.
5. H. Beurich, R. Blumhofer and H. Vahrenkamp, *Chem. Ber.*, 1982, **115**, 2409.
6. K. Schloter, U. Nagel and W. Beck, *Chem. Ber.*, 1980, **113**, 3775.
7. C. A. Ghilardi, S. Midollini and L. Sacconi, *Inorg. Chim. Acta*, 1978, **31**, L431.
8. M. R. Churchill and B. G. DeBoer, *Inorg. Chem.*, 1977, **16**, 878.
9. H. Werner, W. Bertleff and U. Schubert, *Inorg. Chim. Acta*, 1980, **43**, 199.
10. M. R. Churchill, F. J. Hollander and J. P. Hutchinson, *Inorg. Chem.*, 1977, **16**, 2655.
11. J. E. Ellis and G. L. Rochfort, *Organometallics*, 1982, **1**, 682.
12. L. R. Byers, V. A. Uchtman and L. F. Dahl, *J. Am. Chem. Soc.*, 1981, **103**, 1942.
13. A. G. Orpen, A. V. Rivera, E. G. Bryan, D. Pippard and G. M. Sheldrick, *J. Chem. Soc. Chem. Commun.*, 1978, 723.

(*continued*)

References (*continued*)

14. S. S. M. Ling, N. Hadj-Baghieri, L. Manojlovic-Muir and K. W. Muir, *Inorg. Chem.*, 1987, **26**, 231.
15. R. J. Haines, N. D. C. T. Steen and R. B. English, *J. Organomet. Chem.*, 1981, **209**, C34.
16. R. J. Haines, N. D. C. T. Steen and R. B. English, *J. Chem. Soc. Dalton Trans.*, 1984, 515.
17. S. Otsuka, Y. Tatsuno, M. Miki, T. Aoki, M. Matsumoto, H. Yoshioka and K. Nakatsu, *J. Chem. Soc. Chem. Commun.*, 1973, 445.
18. A. Albinati, G. Cartuan and A. Musco, *Inorg. Chim. Acta,* 1977, **22**, L31.
19. V. G. Albano and G. Ciani, *J. Organomet. Chem.*, 1974, **66**, 311.
20. B. F. G. Johnson, J. Lewis, P. R. Raithby and A. Sanders, *J. Organomet. Chem.*, 1984, **260**, C29.
21. M. Green, J. A. K. Howard, M. Murray, J. L. Spencer and F. G. A. Stone, *J. Chem. Soc. Dalton Trans.,* 1977, 1509.
22. L. Manojlovic-Muir, K. W. Muir, B. R. Lloyd and R. J. Puddephatt, *J. Chem. Soc. Chem. Commun.,* 1985, 536.

tory account appears to be that of Kepert,[52] who has represented the energy of the carbonyl shell in terms of competing attractive and repulsive pairwise potentials.

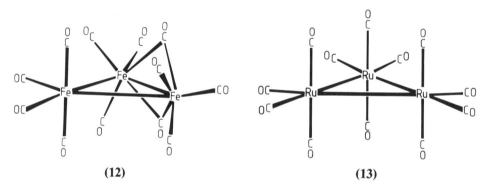

(12)   (13)

The noncarbonyl ligands in these clusters can either bridge the edges of the triangles or cap the triangular face. [$Mn_3(NO)_4(Cp)_4$] has nitrosyls edge and face bridging (**14**). Ligands which can contribute three orbitals for bonding, for example, CO, NO, S, PR, O, and RC, are capable of capping the triangle. Some examples of these compounds are illustrated in (**15**) and (**16**). In [HRh_3Cp_4] (**17**) the cyclopentadienyl ligand caps the face and donates electron density through its a_1 and e π-molecular orbitals.

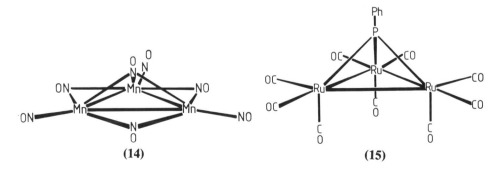

(14)   (15)

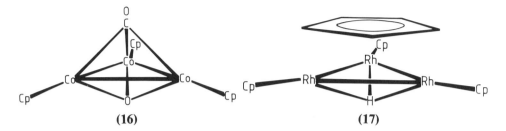

(16)   (17)

The problems which can arise from too great a reliance upon the inert gas formalism can be illustrated by reference to $[Ni_3S_2(PEt_3)_6]^{2+}$ and $[Pd_3S_2(PMe_3)_6]^{2+}$ (18) which both have 48 valence electrons. The metal-metal bond lengths are 2.90 Å in the nickel compound and range from 3.01 to 3.15 Å in the palladium compound and are ca 0.4 Å longer than the metal-metal distances in the bulk metals. Consequently, these compounds are better formulated as "aggregates" of three square-planar d^8 complexes linked through the common bridging sulphur ligands rather than clusters.

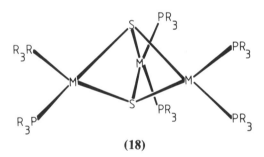

(18)

Both $[Ni_3(CO)_2(Cp)_3]$ and $[Co_3S_2(Cp)_3]^{53}$ provide examples of triangular clusters which have more than 48 valence electrons, that is, 49 and 50, respectively, but which retain significant metal-metal bonding. The additional electrons occupy metal-metal orbitals which are not sufficiently antibonding to result in the scission of a specific metal-metal bond. Dahl and his co-workers have examined in some detail the geometric and spectroscopic implications of these additional antibonding electrons and have been able to identify the symmetries of the relevant molecular orbitals. In the related 50-electron complex $[Fe_3S_2(CO)_9]$ one of the metal-metal bonds is considerably longer than the other bonds and a localized view of the bonding can be adopted. This type of cluster will be discussed in more detail later.

The ligand arrangement in $[H_2Os_3(CO)_{10}]$ (19) is very similar to that in $[Fe_3(CO)_{12}]$, but the cluster has only 46 rather than 48 electrons. In contrast $[H_3Re_3(CO)_{12}]$, which has a hydrido- ligand bridging each of the triangular edges, has the characteristic 48 valence electrons. These apparent anomalies result from the three-center two-electron nature of the metal-hydrogen-metal bonding interaction. This three-center bond can be formally written as a protonated metal-metal bond as follows:

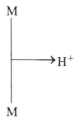

This formulation accounts for the lengthening of the metal-metal bond on protonation and provides useful circumstantial evidence for the presence of a bridging hydride in a metal cluster compound when only X-ray data is available. Furthermore, since the protonation involves the formation of a dative bond from an existing metal-metal bond then the total number of valence electrons is unaffected and identical to that for a related cluster with no bridging hydrides. $[H_3Re_3(CO)_{12}]$ is isoelectronic with $[Os_3(CO)_{12}]$ because each of the metal-metal bonds donates to a single proton.

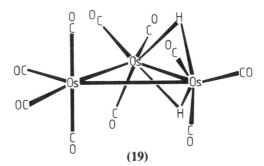

(19)

If two protons span the same edge, two dative bonds are required and this can only be achieved if the parent cluster is formally described with a double bond between the two metal atoms. Therefore, $[H_2Os_3(CO)_{10}]$ can be formulated in terms of a 46-electron triangular cluster with a double bond, $[Os_3(CO)_{10}]^{2-}$, and protonated twice at the double bond. It is significant that the hydrido- bridged Os—Os bond in $[H_2Os_3(CO)_{10}]$ is significantly shorter than the remaining Os—Os bonds in the molecule.

These ideas can be extended to triply and quadruply protonated metal-metal bonds and to those situations where the hydrido- ligand is face capping. The bonding to a face-capping hydrido- ligand is described in terms of a four-center two-electron bond and corresponds to a donation of an electron pair from a face localized orbital to the $1s$ orbital of the proton. Therefore, in general a cluster with face-capping hydrido- ligands has the same number of valence electrons as the parent unprotonated cluster. For example, $[(\mu_3\text{-}H)Rh_3(Cp)_4]$ has 48 valence electrons, characteristic of a metal triangle. Similarly the tetrahedral clusters $[H_4Co_4(Cp)_4]$

(20) and $[H_4Ru_4(CO)_{12}]$ both have 60 valence electrons, characteristic for this geometry, but in the first compound the hydrido- ligands are face capping and in the second example edge bridging. $[H_4Re_4(CO)_{12}]$ appears to be anomalous since although the metal skeleton is tetrahedral it has only 56 valence electrons. However, the bonding in the hypothetical anion $[Re_4(CO)_{12}]^{4-}$ can be adequately represented by face localized three-center two-electron metal-metal bonds.[54] Donation of electron density from these localized orbitals to protons localized on the faces gives a satisfactory account not only for the observed electron count but also for the location of the hydrido- ligands.

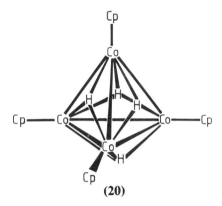

(20)

The platinum metals, which have a preference for 16-electron complexes in their low oxidation states, form planar triangular clusters with 42 valence electrons, for example $[Pt_3(\mu\text{-}CO)_3(PR_3)_3]$, $[Pt_3(\mu\text{-}SO_2)_3(PR_3)_3]$, and $[Pt_3(\mu\text{-}CNR)_3(CNR)_3]$. These clusters can be adequately described in terms of localized metal-metal bonds. There are in addition, however, platinum metal clusters which retain the triangular geometry and have 44 valence electrons. Examples of these clusters include $[Pt_3(CO)_3(PPh_3)_4]$, $[Pt_3Br(SO_2)_2(PCy_3)_3]^-$, and $[Pd_3(SO_2)_2(CNBu^t)_5]$. A molecular orbital description is more appropriate for such clusters because it allows the additional electron pair to be accommodated in a delocalized molecular orbital with either a_2' or a_2'' symmetry.[55] This molecular orbital is not strongly antibonding and therefore the clusters respond by a slight expansion of the metal-metal bond lengths. The situation is therefore somewhat analogous to that described previously for the cyclopentadienyl triangular clusters.

Linear three-atom metal clusters can invariably be described by a localized bonding description. There are many examples of metal carbonyl clusters of this type with 50 valence electrons, for example $[Mn_3(CO)_{14}]^-$. The angle about the central atom can deviate substantially from 180°. An example of such a compound is $[HOs_3(CO)_{10}(PEt_3)(CF_3CCHCF_3)]$ where the Os—Os—Os bond angle is 162.3°. In the extreme case, $[Os_3(CO)_{11}(C(CH_2)_2)]$, the Os—Os—Os bond angle is only 81.7° because the $C(CH_2)_2$ ligand joins the two ends of the chain together. For metal atoms which conform to the 16-electron rule a linear three-atom sequence is generally associated with 44 valence electrons. The square-planar co-

Table 2.4 ▪ **Examples of Clusters with Three-Atom Chains**

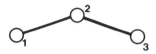

Compound	No. of Valence Electrons	Heteroatom Positions	Ref.
$[Mn_3(CO)_{14}]^-$	50	—	1
$HOs_3(CO)_{10}(PEt_3)(CF_3CCHCF_3)$	50	—	2
$Os_3(CO)_{11}(C(CH_2)_2)$	50	—	3
$Os_3(CO)_{10}(Cp)Cl$	50	—	4
$HOs_3(CO)_{10}(NC_5H_4CH=CH)$	50	—	5
$HOs_3(CO)_9(PMe_2Ph)(NC_5H_4CH=CH)$	50	—	5
$[Rh_3(PhCH_2NC)_{12}I_2]^{3+}$	50	—	6
$Ru_3(CO)_8(Cp)_2$	50	—	7
$Mn_2Pt(CO)_{10}(C_5H_5N)_2$	48	Pt(2)	8
$Co_2Pt(CO)_8(C_5H_5N)_2$	48	Pt(2)	8
$Fe_2Pt(CO)_6(NO)_2(NCPh)_2$	48	Pt(2)	9
$Mo_2Pt(CO)_6(Cp)_2(C_6H_{11}NC)(C_6H_{11}NHCOEt)$	46	Pt(2)	10
$[Ni_3(C_{12}H_{17})_2]^{2-}$	46	—	11
$[Pd_3(NCMe)_6(PPh_3)_2]^{2+}$	44	—	12
$Mn_3(CH_3C_5H_6)_4$	41	—	13, 14

References

1. R. Bau, S. W. Kirtley, T. N. Sorrell and S. Winarko, *J. Am. Chem. Soc.* 1974, **96**, 988.
2. Z. Dawoodi, M. J. Mays and P. R. Raithby, *J. Chem. Soc. Chem. Commun.*, 1979, 721.
3. B. F. G. Johnson, J. Lewis, P. R. Raithby and S. W. Swankey, *J. Organomet. Chem.*, 1982, **231**, C65.
4. M. A. Gallop, B. F. G. Johnson, J. Lewis and P. R. Raithby, *J. Chem. Soc. Chem. Commun.*, 1986, 706.
5. K. Burgess, H. D. Holden, B. F. G. Johnson, J. Lewis, M. B. Hursthouse, N. P. C. Walker, A. J. Deeming, P. J. Manning and R. Peters, *J. Chem. Soc. Dalton Trans.*, 1985, 85.
6. A. L. Balch and M. M. Olmstead, *J. Am. Chem. Soc.*, 1979, **101**, 3128.
7. N. Cook, L. E. Smart, P. Woodward and J. D. Cotton, *J. Chem. Soc. Dalton Trans.*, 1979, 1032.
8. D. Moras, J. Dehand and R. Weiss, *C. R. Acad. Sci., Ser. C*, 1968, **267**, 1471.
9. P. Braunstein, G. Predieri, F. J. Lahoz and A. Tiripicchio, *J. Organomet. Chem.*, 1985, **288**, C13.
10. P. Braunstein, E. Keller and H. Vahrenkamp, *J. Organomet. Chem.*, 1979, **165**, 233.
11. K. Jonas, C. Kruger and J. C. Sekutowski, *Angew. Chem. Int. Ed. Engl.*, 1979, **18**, 487.
12. A. L. Balch, J. R. Boehm, H. Hope and M. M. Olmstead, *J. Am. Chem. Soc.*, 1976, **98**, 7431.
13. D. R. Wilson, J.-Z. Liu and R. D. Ernst, *J. Am. Chem. Soc.*, 1982, **104**, 1120.
14. M. C. Bohm, R. D. Ernst, R. Gleiter and D. R. Wilson, *Inorg. Chem.*, 1983, **22**, 3815.

ordination environments about the individual metal atoms are clearly discernible in the structure of $[Pd_3(CNMe)_6(PPh_3)_2]^{2+}$.

In heterometallic clusters involving $AuPPh_3$ fragments it is not always possible to establish unambiguously whether Au—Au bonding is making a very significant contribution. For example, in $[Os(CO)_4(AuPPh_3)_2]$,[56] the Au—Au distance is 2.929 Å, which suggests that the bonding is best described in terms of the following canonical forms resulting in a fractional Au—Au bond order.

$$Au-PPh_3$$

$$/$$

$$Os \longleftrightarrow Os \quad Au-PPh_3$$

$$\backslash \qquad \qquad Au-PPh_3$$

$$Au-PPh_3$$

2.2.3.2. Four-Atom Clusters

Examples of tetrahedral metal clusters are summarized in Table 2.5. The assignment of two-center two-electron bonds along the six edges of the tetrahedron leads to a total electron count of 60 if the metal atoms conform to the inert gas rule. There are many examples of such clusters and only a few representative examples are summarized in the table. For metals that generally form 16-electron complexes the localized bonding description is no longer valid and molecular orbital calculations are required to demonstrate that the preferred electron count in such clusters is sensitive to the conformations of the ligands at the individual metal centers. The more stable structure is generally associated with 56 valence electrons and $[H_8Pt_4(PPr_2^iPh)_4]$ provides an example of such a cluster.

Some of the remaining anomalous electron counts in the table can be attributed to the occurrence of face-capping hydrides, for example $[H_4Re_4(CO)_{12}]$ and perhaps the platinum hydrides described in the table. For the latter neutron diffraction studies have not been completed and therefore it has not been possible to define unambiguously the locations of the hydride ligands. The incorporation of $AuPR_3$ fragments into the cluster also leads to departures from the predictions based on the inert gas rule because of the pronounced tendency of gold to form 14-electron complexes in its +1 oxidation state. $[AuPt_3(CO)_2(SO_2)(PCy_3)_4]^+$ and $[HAu_3Rh(CO)(PPh_3)_5]^+$ provide some illustrative examples of such heterometallic clusters.

The "butterfly" geometry resulting from the scission of one of the metal-metal bonds of the tetrahedron is commonly observed in cluster compounds and generally associated with a total of 62 valence electrons. These clusters do not always retain a small interplanar dihedral angle and there are some examples of planar butterfly clusters, for example $[Re_4(CO)_{16}]^{2-}$. The potential energy surface for the change in interplanar angle is soft and depends critically on the steric requirements of the ligand spanning the wingtip positions of the butterfly.

A localized description of the bonding in such clusters suggests a total valence electron count of 62, but if the bonding between the metal atoms and the ligand spanning the wingtip positions cannot be adequately described in a localized way then it is necessary to describe the metal atoms and the bridging atoms together as a polyhedron. For example, $[FeRu_3(CO)_{12}(PhCCPh)]$ has 60 valence electrons and the delocalized nature of the bonding can be emphasized by describing the cluster as a M_4C_2 octahedron rather than as a butterfly. This description gives a more satisfactory explanation of the electron count in the molecule.

The introduction of platinum or palladium into these clusters again introduces anomalies and generally such clusters are characterized by 58 valence electrons. $[Pt_4(CO)_5(PMe_2Ph)_4]$ and $[Mo_2Pt_2(CO)_6(PEt_3)_2(Cp)_2]$ provide typical examples of

Table 2.5 ▪ Selected Examples of Clusters with Tetrahedral Geometries

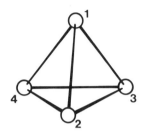

Compound	No. of Valence Electrons	Heteroatom Positions	Ref.
$H_4Co_4Cp_4$	60	—	1
$Co_2Rh_2(Cp^*)_2(CO)_7$	60	Rh(1,2)	2
$[Fe_4(CO)_{13}]^{2-}$	60	—	3
$Ni_4(t-BuNC)_4(PhCCPh)_3$	60	—	4
$H_3Ni_4(Cp)_4$	63	—	5, 6
$Pd_4(CO)_5(PPh_2Me)_4$	58	—	7
$AuPt_3(SO_2)_2Cl(P(C_6H_{11})_3)_3$	56	Au(1)	8
$Pt_4H_8(PPr_2^iPh)_4$	56	—	9
$H_4Re_4(CO)_{12}$	56	—	10
$[AuPt_3(CO)_2(SO_2)(P(C_6H_{11})_3)_4]^+$	54	Au(1)	8
$[HAu_3Rh(CO)(PPh_3)_5]^+$	54	Rh(1)	11
$H_2Pt_4(PBu_3^t)_4$	50	—	9
$[H_2Pt_4(PBu_3^t)_4]^{2+}$	48	—	12

References

1. G. Huttner and H. Lorenz, *Chem. Ber.*, 1975, **108**, 973.
2. P. Braunstein, H. Lehner, D. Matt, A. Tiripicchio and M. T. Camellini, *Nouv. J. Chim.*, 1985, **9**, 597.
3. G. Van Buskirk, C. B. Knobler and H. D. Kaesz, *Organometallics*, 1985, **4**, 149.
4. M. G. Thomas, E. L. Muetterties, R. O. Day and V. W. Day, *J. Am. Chem. Soc.*, 1976, **98**, 4645.
5. G. Huttner and H. Lorenz, *Chem. Ber.*, 1974, **107**, 996.
6. T. F. Koetzle, J. Muller, D. L. Tipton, D. W. Hart and R. Bau, *J. Am. Chem. Soc.*, 1979, **101**, 5631.
7. J. Dubrawski, J. C. Kriege-Simondsen and R. D. Feltham, *J. Am. Chem. Soc.*, 1980, **102**, 2089.
8. D. M. P. Mingos and R. W. M. Wardle, *J. Chem. Soc. Dalton*, 1986, 73.
9. P. W. Frost, J. A. K. Howard, J. L. Spencer, D. G. Turner and D. Gregson, *J. Chem. Soc. Chem. Commun.*, 1981, 1104.
10. R. D. Wilson and R. Bau, *J. Am. Chem. Soc.*, 1976, **98**, 4687.
11. P. D. Boyle, B. J. Johnson, A. Buehler, L. H. Pignolet, *Inorg. Chem.*, 1986, **25**, 5.
12. R. J. Goodfellow, E. M. Hamon, J. A. K. Howard, J. L. Spencer and D. G. Turner, *J. Chem. Soc. Chem. Commun.*, 1984, 1604.

such clusters. The energy difference between butterfly and tetrahedral geometries is small and the $[Pt_4(CO)_5(PR_3)_4]$ clusters rearrange rapidly on an NMR timescale through a tetrahedral geometry.

There are a small number of compounds that form square-planar clusters. Some examples of these compounds are listed in Table 2.7. This geometry may be

Table 2.6 ▪ Selected Examples of Clusters with Butterfly Geometries

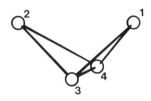

Compound	No. of Valence Electrons	Heteroatom Positions	Ref.
$Fe_4(CO)_{12}(NCPh)$	62	—	1
$Os_4S(CO)_{13}$	62	—	2
$Os_4(CO)_{12}(SC(Ph)CH)$	62	—	3
$[Re_4(CO)_{16}]^{2-}$	62	—	4
$[Ag_2Pt_2Cl_4(C_6F_5)_4]^{2-}$	60	*Pt*(1,2)	5
$FeRu_3(PhCCPh)(CO)_{12}$	60	—	6
$Cr_2Pt_2(CO)_6(PEt_3)_2(Cp)_2$	58	Cr(1,2)	7
$Mo_2Pt_2(CO)_6(PEt_3)_2(Cp)_2$	58	Mo(1,2)	7
$Pt_4(CO)_2(Ph_2PCH_2PPh_2)(Ph_2PCH_2P(O)Ph_2)$	58	—	8
$W_2Pt_2(CO)_6(PEt_3)_2(Cp)_2$	58	W(1,2)	7
$[H_7Pt_4(PB^t_3)_4]^+$	54	—	9

References

1. E. Keller and D. Wolters, *Chem. Ber.,* 1984, **117**, 1572.
2. R. D. Adams, I. T. Horvath, B. E. Segmüller and L. W. Yang, *Organometallics,* 1983, **2**, 1301.
3. R. D. Adams and Suning Wang, *Organometallics,* 1985, **4**, 1902.
4. M. R. Churchill and R. Bau, *Inorg. Chem.,* 1968, **7**, 2606.
5. R. Uson, J. Fornies, M. Tomas, F. A. Cotton and L. R. Falvello, *J. Am. Chem. Soc.,* 1984, **106**, 2482.
6. J. R. Fox, W. L. Gladfelter, G. L. Geoffroy, I. Tavanaiepour, S. Abdel-Mequid and V. W. Day, *Inorg. Chem.,* 1981, **20**, 3230.
7. R. Bender, P. Braunstein, J.-M. Jud and Y. Dusausoy, *Inorg. Chem.,* 1984, **23**, 4489.
8. A. A. Frew, R. H. Hill, L. Manojlovic-Muir, K. W. Muir and R. J. Puddephatt, *J. Chem. Soc. Chem. Commun.,* 1982, 198.
9. R. J. Goodfellow, E. M. Hamon, J. A. K. Howard, J. L. Spencer and D. G. Turner, *J. Chem. Soc. Chem. Commun.,* 1984, 1604.

formally derived from the butterfly geometry by breaking the "hinge" metal-metal bond. This implies a total of 64 valence electrons for clusters with this geometry where the metal atoms obey the inert gas rule. As in the previous case it is possible for the four metal atoms to be distorted from a planar arrangement by the presence of a bridging ligand. For example, in the compound $[Os_4S(CO)_{12}(CCHPh)]$ the sulphur bridge produces a fold in the metal square.

By breaking a further metal-metal bond it is possible to arrive at a chain of four metal atoms analogous to the chains found in the trinuclear case. Two examples of this type of compound are $[Os_4S_2(CO)_{12}(PMe_2Ph)]$[57] and $[Os_4S_2(CO)_{12}(t-BuNC)]$,[57] which have a bent chain of four osmium atoms bridged by two sulphur ligands. Both of these compounds have 66 valence electrons in agreement with the inert gas rule.

Table 2.7 ▪ Selected Examples of Clusters with Square-Planar Geometries

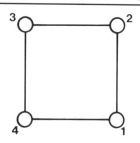

Compound	No. of Valence Electrons	Heteroatom Positions	Ref.
$Ag_2Au_2(PhCCPh)_4(PPh_3)_2$	64	Au(1,3)	1
$Co_2Fe_2(CO)_{11}(PPh)_2$	64	Co(1,2)	2
$Fe_4(CO)_{11}(PC_6H_4Me)_2(P(OMe)_3)$	64	—	3, 4
$Fe_3Rh(CO)_9(Cp^*)(PPh)_2$	64	—	5
$Pt_4(CH_3CO_2)_8$	64	—	6, 7
$Os_4S(CO)_{12}(CCHPh)$	64	—	8
$Fe_4(CO)_{11}(PC_6H_4Me)_2$	62	—	2, 9
$Fe_4(CO)_{10}(PC_6H_4Me)_2(P(OMe)_3)$	62	—	3, 4
$Fe_3Rh(CO)_8(Cp^*)(PPh_2)$	62	—	5
$Ru_4(CO)_{11}(PPh)_2$	62	—	10
$Ag_2Au_2(CH_2PPh_3)_4(ClO_4)_4$	56	Au(1,3)	11

References

1. O. M. Abu-Salah and C. B. Knobler, *J. Organomet. Chem.*, 1986, **302**, C10.
2. H. Vahrenkamp, E. J. Wucherer and D. Wolters, *Chem. Ber.*, 1983, **116**, 1219.
3. T. Jaeger, S. Aime and H. Vahrenkamp, *Organometallics*, 1986, **5**, 245.
4. H. Vahrenkamp and D. Wolters, *Organometallics*, 1982, **1**, 874.
5. H. H. Ohst and J. K. Kochi, *Organometallics*, 1986, **5**, 1359.
6. M. A. A. F. De C. T. Carrondo and A. C. Skapski, *Acta Cryst.*, 1978, **34**, 1857.
7. M. A. A. F. De C. T. Carrondo and A. C. Skapski, *Acta. Cryst.*, 1978, **34**, 3576.
8. R. D. Adams and Suning Wang, *Organometallics*, 1985, **4**, 1902.
9. H. Vahrenkamp and D. Wolters, *J. Organomet. Chem.*, 1982, **224**, C17.
10. J. S. Field, R. J. Haines and D. N. Smit, *J. Organomet. Chem.*, 1982, **224**, C49.
11. R. Uson, A. Laguna, M. Laguna, A. Uson, P. G. Jones and C. F. Erdbrügger, *Organometallics*, 1987, **6**, 1778.

2.2.3.3. Five-Atom Clusters

The great majority of trigonal bipyramidal clusters listed in Table 2.8 have 72 valence electrons. There is also a smaller second group that have 76 valence electrons. The additional four valence electrons have an interesting geometric effect and the bond lengths to the apical metal atoms are increased.

There is also a group of compounds, including $[Os_5C(CO)_{14}(CO_2Me)I]$,[58] $[NiRu_4(CO)_9(PPh_2)_2(CCPr)_2]$,[59] and $[Cu_5Ph_6]^-$,[60] which have a trigonal bipyramidal geometry with no bonding in the equatorial plane of the bipyramid. These clusters might be expected to have 78 electrons on the basis of the inert gas rule. Only $[Os_5C(CO)_{14}(CO_2Me)I]$ has this number of valence electrons. $[NiRu_4(CO)_9(PPh_2)_2(CCPr)_2]$ has 76 valence electrons due to the presence of

Table 2.8 ▪ Examples of Clusters with Trigonal Bipyramidal Geometries

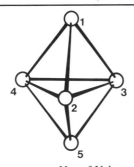

Compound	No. of Valence Electrons	Heteroatom Positions	Ref.
$AuCoRu_3(CO)_{13}(PPh_3)$	72	Au(1),Co(2)	1
$AuCo_3Fe(CO)_{12}(PPh_3)$	72	Au(1),Fe(5)	2
$AuCo_3Ru(CO)_{12}(PPh_3)$	72	Au(1),Ru(5)	3
$Au_2Ru_3S(CO)_8(PPh_3)_3$	72	Au(1,3)	4
$Au_2Ru_3S(CO)_9(PPh_3)_2$	72	Au(1,3)	5
$Au_2Ru_3(CO)_9(CCHBu^t)(PPh_3)_2$	72	Au(1,3)	6
$Co_2Pt_3(CO)_9(PEt_3)_3$	72	Co(2,3)	27
$[H_6Cu_3Ir_2(NCMe)_3(PMe_2Ph)_6]^{3+}$	72	Ir(1,5)	7
$[CuFe_4(CO)_{13}(PPh_3)]^-$	72	Cu(1)	8
$HCuRu_4(CO)_{12}(PMePh_2)$	72	Cu(1)	8
$Fe_3Bi_2(CO)_9$	52	Bi(1,5)	9
$[Fe_4Hg(CH_3)(CO)_{13}]^-$	72	Hg(1)	8
$Os_5(CO)_{16}$	72	—	11
$[HOs_5(CO)_{15}]^-$	72	—	12
$[Os_5(CO)_{15}I]^{2-}$	72	—	13
$H_2Os_5(CO)_{14}(C_5H_5N)$	72	—	14
$H_2Os_5(CO)_{14}(PEt_3)$	72	—	15
$H_2Os_5(CO)_{13}(PEt_3)(P(OMe)_3)$	72	—	15
$[Pb_5]^{2-}$	72	—	16
$[PtRh_4(CO)_{12}]^{2-}$	72	Pt( )	17
$[Sn_5]^{2-}$	72	—	16
$Co_5(CO)_{11}(PMe_2)_3$	76	—	18
$[FeRh_4(CO)_{15}]^{2-}$	76	Fe(1)	19
$[Ir_4Ru(CO)_{15}]^{2-}$	76	Ru(1)	20
$[Ni_5(CO)_{12}]^{2-}$	76	—	21
$[Ni_3Mo_2(CO)_{16}]^{2-}$	76	Mo(1,5)	10
$[Ni_3W_2(CO)_{16}]^{2-}$	76	W(1,5)	10
$HOs_5(CO)_{14}(py)$	76	—	22
$[Rh_5(CO)_{15}]^-$	76	—	23
$[Rh_5(CO)_{14}I]^{2-}$	76	—	24
$H_8Pt_5(PBu_2{}^tPh)_5$	68	—	25
$[H_2IrAu_4(PPh_3)_6]^+$	66	Ir(2)	26

References

1. M. I. Bruce and B. K. Nicholson, *Organometallics,* 1984, **3**, 101.

(continued)

References (*continued*)

2. J. W. Lauher and K. Wald, *J. Am. Chem. Soc.*, 1981, **103**, 7648.
3. P. Braunstein, J. Rose, A. Dedieu, Y. Dusausoy, J. P. Mangeot, A. Tiripicchio and M. Tiripicchio-Camellini, *J. Chem. Soc. Dalton Trans.*, 1986, 225.
4. L. J. Farrugia, M. J. Freeman, M. Green, A. G. Orpen, F. G. A. Stone and I. D. Salter, *J. Organomet. Chem.*, 1983, **249**, 273.
5. M. I. Bruce, O. B. Shawkataly and B. K. Nicholson, *J. Organomet. Chem.*, 1985, **286**, 427.
6. M. I. Bruce, E. Horn, O. B. Shawkataly and M. R. Snow, *J. Organomet. Chem.*, 1985, **280**, 289.
7. L. F. Rhodes, J. C. Huffman and K. G. Caulton, *J. Am. Chem. Soc.*, 1985, **107**, 1759.
8. C. P. Horwitz, E. M. Holt, C. P. Brock and D. F. Shriver, *J. Am. Chem. Soc.*, 1985, **107**, 8136.
9. M. R. Churchill, J. C. Fettinger and K. H. Whitmire, *J. Organomet. Chem.*, 1985, **284**, 13.
10. J. K. Ruff, R. P. White and L. F. Dahl, *J. Am. Chem. Soc.*, 1971, **93**, 2159.
11. C. R. Eady, B. F. G. Johnson, J. Lewis, B. E. Reichert and G. M. Sheldrick, *J. Chem. Soc. Chem. Commun.*, 1976, 271.
12. J. J. Guy and G. M. Sheldrick, *Acta Cryst.*, 1978, **B34**, 1722.
13. A. V. Rivera, M. Sheldrick and M. B. Hursthouse, *Acta Cryst.*, 1978, **B34**, 3376.
14. B. F. G. Johnson, W. J. H. Nelson, M. A. Pearsall, P. R. Raithby and M. McPartlin, unpublished results.
15. B. F. G. Johnson, J. Lewis, P. R. Raithby and M. J. Rosales, *J. Organomet. Chem.*, 1983, **259**, C9.
16. P. A. Edwards and J. D. Corbett, *Inorg. Chem.*, 1977, **16**, 903.
17. A. Fumagalli, S. Martinengo, P. Chini, A. Albinati and S. Bruckner, *Proc. A11 XIII Congr. Naz. Chim. Inorg.*, Camerino, Italy, 1980, Soc. Chim. Ital.
18. E. Keller and H. Vahrenkamp, *Chem. Ber.*, 1979, **112**, 2347.
19. A. Ceriotti, G. Longoni, M. Manassero, M. Sansoni, R. Della Pergola, B. T. Heaton and D. O. Smith, *J. Chem. Soc. Chem. Commun.*, 1982, 886.
20. A. Fumagalli, T. F. Koetzle and F. Takusagawa, *J. Organomet. Chem.*, 1981, **213**, 365.
21. G. Longoni, P. Chini, L. D. Lower and L. F. Dahl, *J. Am. Chem. Soc.*, 1975, **97**, 5034.
22. P. F. Jackson, B. F. G. Johnson, J. Lewis, W. J. H. Nelson and M. McPartlin, *J. Chem. Soc., Dalton Trans.*, 1982, 2099.
23. A. Fumagalli, T. F. Koetzle, F. Takusagawa, P. Chini, S. Martinengo and B. T. Heaton, *J. Am. Chem. Soc.*, 1980, **102**, 1740.
24. S. Martinengo, G. Ciani and A. Sironi, *J. Chem. Soc. Chem. Commun.*, 1983, 39.
25. D. Gregson, J. A. K. Howard, M. Murray and J. L. Spencer, *J. Chem. Soc. Chem. Commun.*, 1981, 716.
26. A. L. Casalnuovo, J. A. Casalnouvo, P. V. Nilsson and L. H. Pignolet, *Inorg. Chem.*, 1985, **24**, 2554.
27. J.-P. Barbier, P. Braunstein, J. Fischer and L. Ricard, *Inorg. Chim. Acta.*, 1978, **31**, L361.

nickel in the cluster framework, while $[Cu_5Ph_6]^-$ has only 62 electrons (if each phenyl group is considered to be a one electron donor). In both of these cases it is necessary to consider the bonding in terms of a delocalized molecular orbital treatment.

A final group of compounds which can be considered with the trigonal bipyramids are those clusters which consist of three triangles sharing a single edge, that is, trigonal bipyramids with an axial bond but no equatorial bonds. The compounds which fall into this group are $[AuFe_4(CO)_{13}(PEt_3)]^-$,[61] $[Pd_2Pt_3(PPh_3)_5(Bu^tCP)_3]$,[62] and $[Au_2Os_3(CO)_{10}(PEt_3)_2]$.[63]

With one exception (see Table 2.9), all of the known square-pyramidal clusters have 74 valence electrons. This number of valence electrons is consistent with the inert gas rule. However, the majority of these clusters also have a capping atom or ligand on the square face and so it is also possible to think of these clusters as octahedral if the donor atom is considered to be part of the cluster framework. Ligands known to occupy this capping position are C, N, S, PEt,

Table 2.9 ▪ **Examples of Clusters with Square-Pyramidal Geometries**

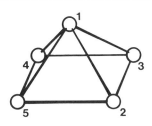

Compound	No. of Valence Electrons	Heteroatom Positions	Ref.
$[CoFe_4C(CO)_{14}]^-$	74	Co(2)	2
$Fe_5C(CO)_{15}$	74	—	3
$[Fe_5C(CO)_{14}]^{2-}$	74	—	4
$[Fe_5N(CO)_{14}]^-$	74	—	4
$HFe_5N(CO)_{14}$	74	—	5
$[Fe_5C(CO)_{13}(NO)]^-$	74	—	6
$[Fe_4RhC(CO)_{14}]^-$	74	Rh(2)	7
$Ni_2Ru_3(CO)_8(Cp)(PhCCPh)$	74	Ni(2,4)	8
$Os_5C(CO)_{15}$	74	—	9
$Os_5(CO)_{15}(POCH_3)$	74	—	10
$[Os_5C(CO)_{14}]^{2-}$	74	—	11
$Os_5S(CO)_{15}$	74	—	12
$Os_4PtS(CO)_{13}(PPh_3)$	74	Pt(2)	13
$Rh_2Ru_3(CO)_{13}(PEt_3)(PPh)$	74	Rh(2,3)	14
$Ru_5C(CO)_{15}$	74	—	15
$Ru_5C(CO)_{14}(PPh_3)$	74	—	15
$HRu_5C(CO)_{14}(SEt)$	74	—	16
$Ru_5C(CO)_{13}(PPh_3)_2$	74	—	15
$HRu_5C(CO)_{12}(PPh_3)(SEt)$	74	—	16
$Ru_5C(CO)_{13}(Ph_2P(CH_2)_4PPh_2)$	74	—	17
$H_3Ru_5C(CO)_{11}(PPh_2)(PMePh_2)$	74	—	18
$Ru_5(CO)_{15}(PPh)$	74	—	19
$Ru_5(CO)_{15}(PEt)$	74	—	19
$Ru_5(CO)_{13}(CCPh)(PPh_2)$	74	—	20
$Ru_5(CO)_{12}(PPh_3)(CCH_2Pr^i)$	74	—	21
$[Ru_5N(CO)_{14}]^-$	74	—	22
$HAu_2Ru_3(CO)_9(COMe)(PPh_3)_2$	72	Au(2,3)	23

References

1. E. Roland, K. Fischer and H. Vahrenkamp, *Angew. Chem. Int. Ed. Engl.,* 1983, **22**, 326.
2. J. A. Hriljae, P. N. Sweepston and D. F. Shriver, *Organometallics,* 1985, **4**, 158.
3. E. H. Braye, L. F. Dahl, W. Hubel and D. S. Wampter, *J. Am. Chem. Soc.,* 1962, **84**, 4633.
4. A. Gourdon and Y. Jeannin, *C.R. Hebd. Seances. Acad. Sci. Ser. B.,* 1982, **295**, 101.
5. M. Tachikawa, J. Stein, E. L. Muetterties, R. G. Teller, M. A. Beno, E. Gebert and J. M. Williams, *J. Am. Chem. Soc.* 1980, **102**, 6648.
6. A. Gourdon and Y. Jeannin, *J. Organomet. Chem.,* 1985, **282**, C39.
7. M. Tachikawa, A. C. Sievert, M. R. Thompson, C. S. Day, V. W. Day and E. L. Muetterties, *J. Am. Chem. Soc.,* 1980, **102**, 1725.

(continued)

References (*continued*)

8. A. Tiripicchio, M. Tiripicchio-Camellini and E. Sappa, *J. Chem. Soc. Dalton Trans.,* 1984, 627.
9. P. F. Jackson, B. F. G. Johnson, J. Lewis, J. N. Nicholls, M. McPartlin and W. J. H. Nelson, *J. Chem. Soc. Chem. Commun.,* 1980, 564.
10. J. M. Fernandez, B. F. G. Johnson, J. Lewis and P. R. Raithby, *Acta Cryst.,* 1979, **B35**, 1711.
11. B. F. G. Johnson, J. Lewis, W. J. H. Nelson, J. N. Nicholls, J. Puga, P. R. Raithby, M. J. Rosales, M. Schröder and M. D. Vargas, *J. Chem. Soc. Dalton Trans.,* 1983, 2447.
12. R. D. Adams, I. T. Horvath, B. E. Segmüller and L. W. Yang, *Organometallics,* 1983, **2**, 1301.
13. R. D. Adams, J. E. Babin, R. Mahtab and Sunning Wang, *Inorg. Chem.,* 1986, **25**, 4.
14. M. J. Mays, P. R. Raithby, P. L. Taylor and K. Henrick, *J. Chem. Soc. Dalton Trans.,* 1984, 959.
15. B. F. G. Johnson, J. Lewis, J. N. Nicholls, J. Puga, P. R. Raithby, M. J. Rosales, M. McPartlin and W. Clegg, *J. Chem. Soc. Dalton Trans.,* 1983, 277.
16. A. G. Cowie, B. F. G. Johnson, J. Lewis, J. N. Nicholls, P. R. Raithby and M. J. Rosales, *J. Chem. Soc. Dalton Trans.,* 1983, 2311.
17. J. Evans, B. P. Gracey, L. R. Gray and M. J. Webster, *J. Organomet. Chem.,* 1982, **240**, C61.
18. M. I. Bruce, B. W. Skelton, A. H. White and M. L. Williams, *J. Chem. Soc. Chem. Commun.,* 1985, 744.
19. K. Natarajan, L. Zsolnai and G. Huttner, *J. Organomet. Chem.,* 1981, **209**, 85.
20. S. A. MacLaughlin, N. J. Taylor and A. J. Carty, *Organometallics,* 1983, **2**, 1194.
21. K. Kwek, N. J. Taylor and A. J. Carty, *J. Am. Chem. Soc.,* 1984, **106**, 4636.
22. M. L. Blohm and W. L. Gladfelter, *Organometallics,* 1985, **4**, 45.
23. L. J. Farrugia, M. J. Freeman, M. Green, A. G. Orpen, F. G. A. Stone and I. D. Salter, *J. Organomet. Chem.,* 1983, **249**, 273.

and PPh. There are, in addition, two clusters that have an acetylene group coordinated to the square face of the cluster, that is, $[Ni_2Ru_3(CO)_8(Cp)(PhCCPh)]$ and $[Ru_5(CO)_{13}(CCPh)(PPh_2)]$. There is only one square-pyramidal cluster which has no capping ligand over the square face. This is $[HAu_2Ru_3(CO)_9(COMe)(PPh_3)_2]$. This compound is also unusual in that it is the only 72-electron square-pyramidal cluster. The presence of two $AuPPh_3$ groups is obviously an important contributing factor.

An alternative geometry adopted by 74 valence electron clusters is the edge-bridged tetrahedron (Table 2.10). Most of the compounds that adopt this geometry are osmium clusters although there are several heteronuclear clusters that have a gold atom bridging the edge of a tetrahedron. The two pentanuclear platinum clusters $[Pt_5(CO)_6(PPh_3)_4]$ and $[Pt_5(CO)_3(SO_2)_3(PPh_3)_4]$, which both have 70 valence electrons, are best described in terms of a delocalized bonding scheme.

The third common pentanuclear geometry is the bi-diminished pentagonal bipyramid. This geometry can be formally derived from the square pyramid by scission of one of the basal-apical metal-metal bonds. This geometry might be expected to require 76 valence electrons on the basis of the inert gas rule, and the majority of known clusters of this type do indeed conform to this rule as can be seen in Table 2.11. The only exceptions to this rule occur where the cluster includes $Au(PR_3)$ groups and the special case of the unique nickel cluster listed at the end of the table.

An alternative geometry for a 76 valence electron pentanuclear cluster is the bi-edge-bridged triangle. A list of the compounds known to adopt this arrangement of metal atoms is shown in Table 2.12. This geometry is rather less common than the bi-diminished pentagonal bipyramid, but in this case there are no interstitial atoms because of the flat raftlike geometry of the metal cluster atoms.

Table 2.10 ▪ Examples of Clusters with Edge-Bridged Tetrahedral Geometries

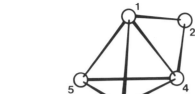

Compound	No. of Valence Electrons	Heteroatom Positions	Ref.
$H_2Os_5(CO)_{16}$	74	—	1
$[H_2Os_5(CO)_{15}I]^-$	74	—	2
$H_2Os_5(CO)_{15}(P(OMe)_3)$	74	—	2
$Os_5(CO)_{15}(CCHPh)$	74	—	3
$H_3Os_5(CO)_{14}(C_5H_4N)$	74	—	4
$HOs_5(CO)_{13}(PhNC_6H_4N)(PEt_3)$	74	—	5
$HOs_5(CO)_{13}(PhNC_6H_4N)$	74	—	6
$H_2AuNiOs_3(CO)_9(Cp)(PPh_3)$	72	Au(2),Ni(3)	7
$HAuOs_4(CO)_{13}(PEt_3)$	72	Au(2)	8
$H_3AuOs_4(CO)_{12}(PEt_3)$	72	Au(2)	8
$HOs_5(CO)_{13}(PhNC_6H_4N)$	72	—	9
$H_3AuRu_4(CO)_{12}(PPh_3)$	72	Au(2)	10
$Pt_5(CO)_6(PPh_3)_4$	70	—	11
$Pt_5(CO)_3(SO_2)_3(PPh_3)_4$	70	—	12
$[H_4Au_4Re(P(p\text{-}tol)_3)_2(PPh_3)_4]^-$	68	Re(1)	13

References

1. J. J. Guy and G. M. Sheldrick, *Acta Cryst.*, 1978, **B34**, 1725.
2. G. R. John, B. F. G. Johnson, J. Lewis, W. J. H. Nelson and M. McPartlin, *J. Organomet. Chem.*, 1979, **171**, C14.
3. J. G. Jeffrey, B. F. G. Johnson, J. Lewis, P. R. Raithby and D. A. Welch, *J. Chem. Soc. Chem. Commun.*, 1986, 318.
4. B. F. G. Johnson, W. J. H. Nelson, M. A. Pearsall, P. R. Raithby and M. McPartlin, unpublished results.
5. Z. Dawoodi, M. J. Mays and P. R. Raithby, *J. Chem. Soc. Chem. Commun.*, 1981, 801.
6. Z. Dawoodi, M. J. Mays and P. R. Raithby, *J. Chem. Soc. Chem. Commun.*, 1980, 712.
7. P. Braunstein, J. Rose, A. M. Manotti-Lanfredi, A. Tiripicchio and E. Sappa, *J. Chem. Soc. Dalton Trans.*, 1984, 1843.
8. B. F. G. Johnson, D. A. Kaner, J. Lewis, P. R. Raithby and M. J. Taylor, *Polyhedron*, 1982, **1**, 105.
9. Z. Dawoodi, M. J. Mays and P. R. Raithby, *J. Chem. Soc. Chem. Commun.*, 1980, 712.
10. J. Evans, A. C. Street and M. Webster, *Organometallics*, 1987, **6**, 794.
11. J. P. Barbier, R. Bender, P. Braunstein, J. Fischer and L. Ricard, *J. Chem. Res.*, 1978, **230**, 2910.
12. C. E. Briant, D. G. Evans and D. M. P. Mingos, *J. Chem. Soc. Chem. Commun.*, 1982, 1144.
13. B. D. Alexander, P. D. Boyle, B. J. Johnson, S. A. Casalnuovo, S. M. Johnson, A. M. Mueting and L. H. Pignolet, *Inorg. Chem.*, 1987, **26**, 2547.

Table 2.11 ■ Examples of Clusters with Bi-Diminished Pentagonal Bipyramid Geometries

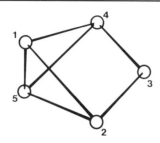

Compound	No. of Valence Electrons	Heteroatom Positions	Ref.
$[Fe_5C(CO)_{12}Br_2]^{2-}$	76	–	1
$Os_5C(CO)_{15}(Ph_2P(CH_2)_2PPh_2)$	76	–	2
$H_2Os_5C(CO)_{15}(CCPh)$	76	–	3
$[Os_5C(CO)_{15}I]^-$	76	–	4
$HOs_5C(CO)_{14}(CO_2Et)$	76	–	5
$HOs_5C(CO)_{14}(OP(OMe)_2)$	76	–	6
$Os_5(CO)_{13}(PhCCPh)_2$	76	–	7
$HOs_5C(CO)_{13}(OP(OMe)_2)(P(OMe)_3)$	76	–	8
$HOs_5C(CO)_{13}(OP(OMe)OP(OMe)_2)$	76	–	9
$Os_5C(CO)_{16}$	76	–	10
$Ru_5C(CO)_{16}$	76	–	11
$H_2Ru_5C(CO)_{15}$	76	–	11
$Ru_5C(CO)_{15}(NCMe)$	76	–	12
$HRu_5C(CO)_{13}(PPh_3)(SEt)$	76	–	13
$HAuFe_4C(CO)_{12}(PPh_3)$	74	Au(3)	14
$AuRu_4C(CO)_{12}(PEt_3)I$	74	Au(3)	15
$HAuRu_4C(CO)_{12}(PPh_3)$	74	Au(3)	15
$Ni_5(CO)_6((Me_3Si)_2C(H)PPCH(SiMe_3)_2)_2Cl$	71	–	16

References

1. J. S. Bradley, E. W. Hill, G. B. Ansell and M. A. Madrick, *Organometallics,* 1982, **1**, 1634.
2. B. F. G. Johnson, J. Lewis, P. R. Raithby, M. J. Rosales and D. A. Welch, *J. Chem. Soc. Dalton Trans.,* 1986, 453.
3. D. H. Farrar, G. R. John, B. F. G. Johnson, J. Lewis, P. R. Raithby and M. J. Rosales, *J. Chem. Soc. Chem. Commun.,* 1981, 886.
4. P. F. Jackson, B. F. G. Johnson, J. Lewis, J. N. Nicholls, M. McPartlin and W. J. H. Nelson, *J. Chem. Soc. Chem. Commun.,* 1980, 564.
5. B. F. G. Johnson, J. Lewis, W. J. H. Nelson, J. N. Nicholls, M. D. Vargas, D. Braga, K. Hendrick and M. McPartlin, *J. Chem. Soc. Dalton Trans.,* 1984, 1809.
6. J. M. Fernandez, B. F. G. Johnson, J. Lewis, P. R. Raithby and G. M. Sheldrick, *Acta Cryst.,* 1978, **B34**, 1994.
7. D. H. Farrar, G. R. John, B. F. G. Johnson, J. Lewis, P. R. Raithby and M. J. Rosales, *J. Chem. Soc. Chem. Commun.,* 1981, 886.
8. J. M. Fernandez, B. F. G. Johnson, J. Lewis and P. R. Raithby, *J. Chem. Soc. Dalton Trans.,* 1981, 2250.
9. A. G. Orpen and G. M. Sheldrick, *Acta Cryst.,* 1978, **B34**, 1992.
10. B. F. G. Johnson, J. Lewis, W. J. H. Nelson, J. N. Nicholls, J. Puga, P. R. Raithby, M. J. Rosales, M. J. Schröder and M. D. Vargas, *J. Chem. Soc. Dalton Trans.,* 1983, 2447.

(continued)

References (*continued*)

11. B. F. G. Johnson, *Phil. Trans. R. Soc. Lond.,* 1982, **A308**, 5.
12. B. F. G. Johnson, J. Lewis, J. N. Nicholls, J. Puga, P. R. Raithby, M. J. Rosales, M. McPartlin and W. Clegg, *J. Chem. Soc. Dalton Trans.,* 1983, 277.
13. A. G. Cowie, B. F. G. Johnson, J. Lewis, J. N. Nicholls, P. R. Raithby and M. J. Rosales, *J. Chem. Soc. Dalton Trans.,* 1983, 2311.
14. B. F. G. Johnson, D. A. Kaner, J. Lewis, P. R. Raithby and M. J. Rosales, *J. Organomet. Chem.,* 1982, **231**, C59.
15. A. G. Cowie, B. F. G. Johnson, J. Lewis and P. R. Raithby, *J. Chem. Soc. Chem. Commun.,* 1984, 1710.
16. M. M. Olmstead and P. P. Power, *J. Am. Chem. Soc.,* 1984, **106**, 1495.

$[H_2Au_2Os_3(CO)_{11}(PPh_3)_2]$ also has this structure although it has fewer valence electrons. It is interesting to note that the two gold atoms in this cluster are connected together rather than bridging separate edges of the osmium triangle.

The "bow-tie" group of clusters listed in Table 2.13 form an interesting group of pentanuclear clusters. The dihedral angle between the two triangular planes

Table 2.12 ▪ Examples of Clusters with Bi-Edge-Bridged Triangular Geometries

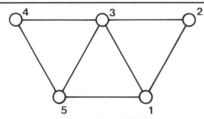

Compound	No. of Valence Electrons	Heteroatom Positions	Ref.
$Ni_2Ru_3(CO)_9(Cp)_2(PPh)$	76	Ni(2,4)	1
$Os_4PtS_2(CO)_{11}(PMe_2Ph_2)$	76	Pt(2)	2
$Ru_5(CO)_{14}(t-BuNC)_2$	76	—	3
$Ru_5(CO)_{14}(CCPh)(PPh_2)$	76	—	4
$Ru_5(CO)_{13}(CCPPh_2)(PPh_2)$	76	—	5
$HRu_5(CO)_{13}(HCCPPh_2)(PPh_2)$	76	—	6
$Ru_5(CO)_{12}(CCPh)(PhC—C—C—CPh)(PPh_2)$	76	—	7
$H_2Au_2Os_3(CO)_{11}(PPh_3)_2$	74	Au(4,5)	8

References

1. M. Lanfranchi, A. Tiripicchio, E. Sappa and A. J. Carty, *J. Chem. Soc. Dalton Trans.,* 1986, 2737.
2. R. D. Adams, I. T. Horvath and Suning Wang, *Inorg. Chem.,* 1986, **25**, 1617.
3. M. I. Bruce, J. G. Matisons, J. R. Rodgers and R. C. Wallis, *J. Chem. Soc. Chem. Commun.,* 1981, 1070.
4. S. A. MacLaughlin, N. J. Taylor and A. J. Carty, *Organometallics,* 1983, **2**, 1194.
5. M. I. Bruce, M. L. Williams, J. M. Patrick and A. H. White, *J. Chem. Soc. Dalton Trans.,* 1985, 1229.
6. M. I. Bruce, B. W. Skelton, A. H. White and M. L. Williams, *J. Chem. Soc. Chem. Commun.,* 1985, 744.
7. S. A. MacLaughlin, N. J. Taylor and A. J. Carty, *Organometallics,* 1984, **3**, 392.
8. J. A. K. Howard, L. Farrugia, C. Foster, F. G. A. Stone and P. Woodward, *Eur. Crystalogr. Meet.,* 1980, **6**, 73.

Table 2.13 ▪ **Examples of Clusters with Bow-Tie Geometries**

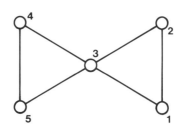

Compound	No. of Valence Electrons	Heteroatom Positions	Ref.
$Co_4Ge(CO)_{14}$	68	Ge(3)	1
$Fe_5(CO)_{13}(C_{11}H_{16}N_4)$	78	—	2
$Os_5(CO)_{19}$	78	—	3
$Os_5(CO)_{17}(HCCH)$	78	—	4
$Os_5(CO)_{16}(P(OMe)_3)_3$	78	—	3
$H_2Os_5S_2(CO)_{14}$	78	—	5
$[Fe_4Pt(CO)_{16}]^{2-}$	76	Pt(3)	6
$[Fe_4Pd(CO)_{16}]^{2-}$	76	Pd(3)	6
$CoCr_4S_4(Cp)_4(SBu^t)_2$	75	Co(3)	7
$PtRh_4(CO)_4(Cp)_4$	74	Pt(3)	8
$PtRh_4(CO)_4(Cp^*)_4$	74	Pt(3)	9
$MnCr_4S_4(Cp)_4(SBu^t)_2$	73	Mn(3)	10
$Cr_4MnS_4(Cp)_4(SBu^t)_2$	72	—	11

References

1. R. F. Gerlach, K. M. Mackay and B. M. Nicholson, *J. Chem. Soc. Dalton Trans.*, 1981, 80.
2. G. Fischer, G. Sedelmeier, H. Prinzbach, K. Knoll, G. Wilharm, G. Huttner and I. Jibril, *J. Organomet. Chem*, 1985, **297**, 307.
3. D. H. Farrar, B. F. G. Johnson, J. Lewis, P. R. Raithby and M. J. Rosales, *J. Chem. Soc. Dalton Trans.*, 1982, 2051.
4. B. F. G. Johnson, J. Lewis, P. R. Raithby and M. J. Rosales, *J. Chem. Soc. Dalton Trans.*, 1983, 2645.
5. R. D. Adams, I. T. Horvath and L. W. Yang, *Organometallics*, 1983, **2**, 1257.
6. G. Longoni, M. Manassero and M. Sansoni, *J. Am. Chem. Soc.*, 1980, **102**, 3242.
7. A. A. Pasynskii, I. L. Ermenko, G. Sh. Gasanov, O. G. Ellert, V. M. Novotortsev, V. T. Kalinnikov, Yu. T. Struchkov and V. E. Shklover, *Izv. Akad, Nauk. SSSR, Ser, Khim.* 1983, 1446.
8. M. Green, J. A. K. Howard, G. N. Pain and F. G. A. Stone, *J. Chem. Soc. Dalton Trans.*, 1982, 1327.
9. M. Green, J. A. K. Howard, R. M. Mills, G. A. Pain, F. G. A. Stone and P. Woodward, *J. Chem. Soc. Chem. Commun.*, 1981, 869.
10. I. L. Ermenko, A. A. Pasynskii, G. Sh. Gasanov, B. Orazsakhatov, Yu. T. Struchkov and J. E. Shklover, *J. Organomet. Chem.*, 1984, **275**, 183.
11. A. A. Pasynskii, I. L. Ermenko, B. Orazsakhatov, G. Sh. Gasanov, V. E. Shklover and Yu. T. Struchkov, *J. Organomet. Chem.*, 1984, **269**, 147.

varies from 0° to 90° depending on the properties of the metal and ligand atoms in the individual clusters. A localized bonding scheme based on the inert gas rule gives the expected total of 78 valence electrons for this particular geometry. The series of four osmium clusters $[Os_5(CO)_{19}]$, $[Os_5(CO)_{16}(P(OMe)_3)_3]$, $[Os_5(CO)_{17}(HCCH)]$, and $[H_2Os_5S_2(CO)_{14}]$ have interplanar angles of 21.2°, 24.8°, 34.5°, and 56.3°, respectively. The change in this angle is due entirely to differences in the interactions between the ligand groups around the central metal atom. This metal atom could be considered as a single metal atom surrounded by two Os—Os bidentate groups as well as other ligands. The two 76-electron compounds in the table are constrained to a dihedral angle close to 0° by the square-planar coordination of the central platinum or palladium atom. The clusters with 74 electrons are best described in terms of a delocalized bonding scheme while the three chromium clusters are perhaps also best described in this fashion.

As well as the clusters which fall conveniently into groups there are also a number of unique clusters. For example, $[H_2Os_3Pt_2C(CO)_{10}(PCy_3)_2]^{64}$ has an arrangement of metal atoms which can be described as an edge-bridged square of metal atoms. It has 74 rather than 76 electrons due to the 16-electron configuration of the two platinum atoms. $[Fe_5S_2(CO)_{13}(CS)]^{65}$ has a metal framework which consists of a square with a single metal atom attached to one corner, while $[Ru_5P(CO)_{16}(PPh_2)]^{66}$ consists of a metal triangle with a chain of two metals attached to one vertex. Two other triangles with extra atoms attached to separate vertices are $[Os_3W_2S_2(CO)_{14}(PPhMe_2)_2]^{67}$ and $[H_2Os_3Re_2(CO)_{20}]$.^{68} These clusters have 80 valence electrons in accordance with the inert gas rule. There are also some five-atom chains in compounds such as $[Ru_5(CO)_{15}(CCPPh_2)(PPh_2)]$,^{69} which occurs in two isomeric forms, $[Pt_2W_3(CO)_6(CR)_3(Cp)_3]^{70}$ and $[Pt_3W_2(CO)_4(CR)_2(Cp)_2(COD)_2]$.^{70}

2.2.3.4. Six-Atom Clusters

The classic six-atom cluster compounds are the 86-electron octahedral cluster compounds. These compounds have been especially important in the development of cluster chemistry. If one were to consider an octahedral cluster in terms of a localized bonding scheme based on the inert gas rule one would expect an octahedral cluster to have only 84 valence electrons. In fact it is evident from Table 2.14 that although 84-electron octahedral clusters are known, they are extremely rare. Among the very earliest octahedral clusters to be characterized were clusters which contained interstitial carbon atoms such as $[Ru_6C(CO)_{14}(C_6H_3Me_3)]$. Since this time clusters have been isolated which contain interstitial hydrogen atoms as well as more examples of octahedral carbido- clusters.

The copper clusters listed in Table 2.14 which have 84 electrons are the only cases where the bonding in these clusters can be considered in terms of a localized inert gas model. In these clusters containing d^{10} metals the metal-metal bonding is not very strong and the oxidation states at the individual metal atoms impose a strong influence on the total valence electron count. For example, all copper alkyl and aryl clusters retain a +1 metal oxidation state. In the case of $[Ni_6(Cp)_6]$ (90 electrons) and $[Ni_6(Cp)_6]^+$ (89 electrons) the extra electrons are presumably delocalized over the cluster in low-lying antibonding molecular orbitals. In $[Co_6C(CO)_{14}]^-$ the lone electron is believed to be localized predominantly on one

Table 2.14 ▪ Examples of Clusters with Octahedral Geometries

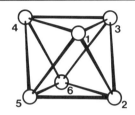

Compound	No. of Valence Electrons	Heteroatom Positions	Ref.
$Au_2Fe_4C(CO)_{12}(PEt_3)_2$	86	Au(1,2)	1
$Co_2Rh_4(CO)_{16}$	86	Co(Disordered)	2
$[Co_4Ni_2(CO)_{14}]^{2-}$	86	Ni(Disordered)	3
$Co_6(CO)_{16}$	86	—	4
$[HCo_6(CO)_{15}]^-$	86	—	5
$[Co_6(CO)_{15}]^{2-}$	86	—	4
$[Co_6(CO)_{14}]^{4-}$	86	—	6
$[Co_6C(CO)_{13}]^{2-}$	86	—	7
$[Fe_6C(CO)_{16}]^{2-}$	86	—	8
$Fe_6C(CO)_{11}(NO)_4$	86	—	9
$[Fe_6C(CO)_{15}(NO)]^-$	86	—	9
$[Fe_5MoC(CO)_{17}]^{2-}$	86	Mo(1)	10
$[Fe_5RhC(CO)_{16}]^-$	86	Rh(1)	10
$[Fe_2Rh_4(CO)_{16}]^{2-}$	86	Fe(1,6)	11
$[FeRh_5(CO)_{16}]^-$	86	Fe(1)	12
$Ir_6(CO)_{16}$	86	—	13
$[Ir_6(CO)_{15}]^{2-}$	86	—	14
$[Ir_6(CO)_{15}(COEt)]^-$	86	—	15
$[Ir_6(CO)_{15}(CO_2Me)]^-$	86	—	16
$Ir_6(CO)_{12}(P(OPh)_3)_4$	86	—	17
$Ir_6(CO)_{11}(P(OMe)_3)_5$	86	—	18
$[Ni_6(CO)_{12}]^{2-}$	86	—	19
$H_2Os_6(CO)_{18}$	86	—	20, 21
$[HOs_6(CO)_{18}]^-$	86	—	20
$[Os_6(CO)_{18}]^{2-}$	86	—	20
$Os_6(CO)_{16}(CMe)_2$	86	—	22
$[PtRh_5(CO)_{15}]^-$	86	Pt(1)	23
$[Re_6C(CO)_{19}]^{2-}$	86	—	24
$[H_2Re_6C(CO)_{18}]^{2-}$	86	—	25
$Rh_6(CO)_{16}$	86	—	26
$[Rh_6(CO)_{15}I]^-$	86	—	27
$[Rh_6(CO)_{15}(COEt)]^-$	86	—	28
$[Rh_6(CO)_{15}(CO_2Me)]^-$	86	—	28
$[Rh_6(CO)_{14}(C_3H_5)]^-$	86	—	29
$[Rh_6(CO)_{14}]^{4-}$	86	—	30
$Rh_6(CO)_{10}(C_7H_8)_3$	86	—	31
$Rh_6(CO)_{10}(Ph_2P(CH_2)PPh_2)_3$	86	—	32
$[Rh_6C(CO)_{13}]^{2-}$	86	—	33

(continued)

Table 2.14 *Continued* ▪ **Examples of Clusters with Octahedral Geometries**

Compound	No. of Valence Electrons	Heteroatom Positions	Ref.
$H_2Ru_6(CO)_{18}$	86	—	34
$[HRu_6(CO)_{18}]^-$	86	—	35
$[Ru_6(CO)_{18}]^{2-}$	86	—	36
$Ru_6(CO)_{10}(Ph_2PCH_2PPh_2)_3$	86	—	37
$Ru_6C(CO)_{17}$	86	—	38
$[Ru_6C(CO)_{16}]^{2-}$	86	—	39, 40
$Ru_6C(CO)_{16}(PPh_2Et)$	86	—	41
$Ru_6C(CO)_{16}(t\text{-}BuNC)$	86	—	42
$HRu_6C(CO)_{15}(NO)$	86	—	43
$Ru_6C(CO)_{15}(MeCH{=}CH{-}CH{=}CHMe)$	86	—	44
$Ru_6C(CO)_{14}(C_{14}H_{14})$	86	—	45
$Ru_6C(CO)_{14}(NO)_2$	86	—	46
$Ru_6C(CO)_{14}(C_6H_3Me_3)$	86	—	47
$Ru_6C(CO)_{11}(C_6H_6)_2$	86	—	48
$Cu_4Ir_2(PPh_3)_2(CCPh)_8$	90	Ir(1,6)	49
$Ni_6(Cp)_6$	90	—	50
$[Ni_6(Cp)_6]^+$	89	—	50
$Co_4Ge_2(CO)_{11}(Me)_2$	68	Ge(1,6)	51
$[Co_6C(CO)_{14}]^-$	87	—	52
$H_6Cu_6(PPh_3)_6$	84	—	53
$H_6Cu_6(P(C_6H_4Me)_3)_6$	84	—	54
$H_6Cu_6(P(NMe_2)_3)_6$	84	—	55
$Cu_6(C_6H_4NMe_2)_4(CCPh)_2$	84	—	56
$[Au_6C(P(C_6H_4Me)_3)_6]^{2+}$	80	—	57
$CoFe_4RhC(CO)_6$	86	Co(1),Rh(2)	58

References

1. B. F. G. Johnson, D. A. Kaner, J. Lewis, P. R. Raithby and M. J. Rosales, *J. Organomet. Chem.*, 1982, **231**, C59.
2. S. Martinengo, P. Chini, V. G. Albano, F. Cariati and T. Salvatori, *J. Organomet. Chem.*, 1973, **59**, 379.
3. V. G. Albano, G. Ciani and P. Chini, *J. Chem. Soc. Dalton Trans.*, 1974, 432.
4. V. G. Albano, P. Chini and V. J. Scatturin, *J. Chem. Soc. Chem. Commun.*, 1968, 163.
5. D. W. Hart, R. G. Teller, C. Y. Wei, R. Bau, G. Longoni, S. Campanella, P. Chini and T. F. Koetzle, *J. Am. Chem. Soc.*, 1981, **103**, 1458.
6. V. G. Albano, P. L. Bellon, P. Chini and V. Scatturin, *J. Organomet. Chem.*, 1969, **16**, 461.
7. V. G. Albano, D. Braga and S. Martinengo, *J. Chem. Soc. Dalton Trans.*, 1986, 981.
8. M. R. Churchill and J. Wormald, *J. Chem. Soc. Dalton Trans.*, 1974, 2410.
9. A. Gourdon and Y. Jeannin, *J. Organomet. Chem.*, 1985, **282**, C39.
10. M. Tachikawa, A. C. Sievert, M. R. Thompson, C. S. Day, V. W. Day and E. L. Muetterties, *J. Am. Chem. Soc.*, 1980, **102**, 1725.
11. A. Ceriotti, G. Longoni, M. Manassero, M. Sansoni, R. Della Pergola, B. T. Heaton and D. O. Smith, *J. Chem. Soc. Chem. Commun.*, 1982, 886.
12. Yu. L. Slovokhotov, Yu. T. Struchkov, V. E. Lopatin and S. A. Gubin, *J. Organomet. Chem.*, 1984, **266**, 139.
13. L. Garlaschelli, S. Martinengo, P. L. Bellon, F. Demartin, M. Manassero, M. Y. Chang, C.-Y. Wei and R. Bau, *J. Am. Chem. Soc.*, 1984, **106**, 6664.
14. F. Demartin, M. Manassero, L. Garlaschelli and S. Martinengo, *J. Chem. Soc. Chem. Commun.*, 1980, 903.

(*continued*)

References *(continued)*

15. F. Demartin, M. Manassero, L. Garlaschelli, C. Raimondi and S. Martinengo, *J. Organomet. Chem.,* 1983, **243**, C10.
16. L. Garlaschelli, M. C. Malatesta, S. Martinengo, F. Demartin, M. Manassero and M. Sansoni, *J. Chem. Soc. Dalton Trans.,* 1986, 777.
17. F. Demartin, M. Manassero, M. Sansoni, L. Garlaschelli, U. Sartorelli and F. Tagliabue, *J. Organomet. Chem.,* 1982, **234**, C39.
18. F. Demartin, M. Manassero, M. Sansoni, L. Garlaschelli, M. C. Malatesta and U. Sartorelli, *J. Organomet. Chem.,* 1983, **248**, C17.
19. J. C. Calabrese, L. F. Dahl, A. Cavalieri, P. Chini, G. Longoni and S. Martinengo, *J. Am. Chem. Soc.,* 1974, **96**, 2616.
20. M. McPartlin, C. R. Eady, B. F. G. Johnson and J. Lewis, *J. Chem. Soc. Chem. Commun.,* 1976, 883.
21. A. G. Orpen, *J. Organomet. Chem.,* 1978, **159**, C1.
22. C. R. Eady, J. M. Fernandez, B. F. G. Johnson, J. Lewis, P. R. Raithby and G. M. Sheldrick, *J. Chem. Soc. Chem. Commun.,* 1978, 421.
23. A. Fumagalli, S. Martinengo, P. Chini, A. Albinati, S. Bruckner and B. T. Heaton, *J. Chem. Soc. Chem. Commun.,* 1978, 195.
24. T. Beringhelli, G. Ciani, G. D'Alfonso, A. Sironi and M. Freni, *J. Chem. Soc. Chem. Commun.,* 1985, 978.
25. G. Ciani, G. D'Alfonso, M. Freni, P. Romiti and A. Sironi, *J. Organomet. Chem.,* 1983, **244**, C27.
26. E. R. Corey, L. F. Dahl and W. Beck, *J. Am. Chem. Soc.,* 1963, **85**, 1202.
27. V. G. Albano, P. L. Bellon and M. Sansoni, *J. Chem. Soc. (A),* 1971, 678.
28. P. Chini, A. Fumagalli, and S. Martinengo, *Gazz. Chim. Ital.,* 1972, **102**, 330.
29. G. Ciani, A. Sironi, P. Chini, A. Ceriotti and S. Martinengo, *J. Organomet. Chem.,* 1980, **192**, C39.
30. P. Chini and S. Martinengo, *J. Chem. Soc. Chem. Commun.,* 1969, 1092.
31. J. Antony, J. Jarvis and R. Whyman, *J. Chem. Soc. Chem. Commun.,* 1975, 563.
32. A. Ceriotti, G. Ciani, L. Garlaschelli, U. Sartorelli and A. Sironi, *J. Organomet. Chem.,* 1982, **229**, C9.
33. V. G. Albano, D. Braga and S. Martinengo, *J. Chem. Soc. Dalton Trans.,* 1981, 717.
34. M. R. Churchill and J. Wormald, *J. Am. Chem. Soc.,* 1971, **93**, 5670.
35. C. R. Eady, P. F. Jackson, B. F. G. Johnson, J. Lewis, M. C. Malatesta, M. McPartlin and W. J. H. Nelson, *J. Chem. Soc. Dalton Trans.,* 1980, 383.
36. P. F. Jackson, B. F. G. Johnson, J. Lewis, M. McPartlin and W. J. H. Nelson, *J. Chem. Soc. Chem. Commun.,* 1979, 735.
37. A. Ceriotti, G. Ciani, L. Garlaschelli, U. Sartorelli and A. Sironi, *J. Organomet. Chem.,* 1982, **229**, C9.
38. A. Sirigu, M. Bianchi and E. Benedetti, *J. Chem. Soc. Chem. Commun.,* 1969, 596.
39. B. F. G. Johnson, J. Lewis, S. W. Sankey, K. Wong, M. McPartlin and W. J. H. Nelson, *J. Organomet. Chem.,* 1980, **191**, C3.
40. G. B. Ansell and J. S. Bradley, *Acta Cryst.,* 1980, **B36**, 726.
41. S. C. Brown, J. Evans and M. Webster, *J. Chem. Soc. Dalton Trans.,* 1981, 2263.
42. R. D. Adams, P. Mathur and B. E. Segmüller, *Organometallics,* 1983, **2**, 1258.
43. B. F. G. Johnson, J. Lewis, W. J. H. Nelson, J. Puga, M. McPartlin and A. Sironi, *J. Organomet. Chem.,* 1983, **253**, C5.
44. P. F. Jackson, B. F. G. Johnson, J. Lewis, P. R. Raithby, G. J. Will, M. McPartlin and W. J. H. Nelson, *J. Chem. Soc. Chem. Commun.,* 1980, 1190.
45. G. B. Ansell and J. S. Bradley, *Acta Cryst.,* 1980, **B36**, 1930.
46. B. F. G. Johnson, J. Lewis, W. J. H. Nelson, J. Puga, P. R. Raithby, D. Braga, M. McPartlin and W. Clegg, *J. Organomet. Chem.,* 1983, **243**, C13.
47. R. Mason and W. R. Robinson, *J. Chem. Soc. Chem. Commun.,* 1968, 468.
48. M. P. Gomez-Sal, B. F. G. Johnson, J. Lewis, P. R. Raithby and A. H. Wright, *J. Chem. Soc. Chem. Commun.,* 1985, 1682.
49. M. R. Churchill and S. A. Bezman, *Inorg. Chem.,* 1974, **13**, 1418.
50. M. S. Paquette and L. F. Dahl, *J. Am. Chem. Soc.,* 1980, **102**, 6621.

(continued)

References (*continued*)

51. S. P. Foster, K. M. Mackay and B. K. Nicholson, *J. Chem. Soc. Chem. Commun.*, 1982, 1156.
52. V. G. Albano, P. Chini, G. Ciani, M. Sansoni and S. Martinengo, *J. Chem. Soc. Dalton Trans.*, 1980, 163.
53. M. R. Churchill, S. A. Bezman, J. A. Osborn and J. Wormald, *Inorg. Chem.*, 1972, **11**, 1818.
54. D. Ho and R. Bau, *Inorg. Chim. Acta,* 1984, **84**, 213.
55. T. H. Lemmen, K. Folting, J. C. Huffman and K. G. Caulton, *J. Am. Chem. Soc.*, 1985, **107**, 7774.
56. R. W. M. ten Hoedt, J. G. Noltes, G. van Koten and A. L. Spak, *J. Chem. Soc. Dalton Trans.*, 1978, 1800.
57. P. L. Bellon, M. Manassero and M. Sansoni, *J. Chem. Soc. Dalton Trans.*, 1973, 2423.
58. V. E. Leopatin, S. P. Gubin, N. M. Mikova, M. TS. Tsybenov, Yu. L. Slovokhotov and Yu. T. Struchkov, *J. Organomet. Chem.*, 1985, **292**, 275.

edge. The 76-electron octahedral gold cluster $[Au_6(PPh_3)_6]^{2+}$ has been reformulated as $[Au_6C(PPh_3)_6]^{2+}$ in 1989 by Schmidbaur. This cluster has only been isolated in small quantities and not fully characterized. The other 76-electron Au_6 clusters which have been isolated adopt a different geometry based on two edge-sharing tetrahedra.

The majority of 84-electron clusters that have been structurally characterized adopt a bicapped tetrahedral geometry. The compounds which adopt this geometry are summarized in Table 2.15. The examples include several heteronuclear clusters involving two or more Group Ib metal atoms. In these clusters the Group Ib metals occupy adjacent sites in the cluster framework rather than capping opposite faces of the central tetrahedron.

An alternative geometry adopted by several 86-electron clusters is the capped square pyramid. All of the clusters that adopt this geometry have 86 electrons and three of the clusters listed in Table 2.16 are heterometallic. This group of seven clusters includes examples that have no capping ligand over the square face, for example $[H_2Os_6(CO)_{18}]$, as well as clusters with μ_4-capping ligands, for example $[Os_6S(CO)_{17}]$. $[AuRu_5C(CO)_{13}(NO)(PEt_3)]$ is rather unusual in that it exists in two forms, one of which is the capped square pyramid while in the other form the $AuPEt_3$ group only bridges one basal-axial edge of the pyramid. The $AuPR_3$ group is a particularly flexible metal-containing fragment that can edge-bridge or face-cap with almost equal facility.

Another six-atom cluster geometry is the edge-sharing bi-tetrahedron, examples of which are listed in Table 2.17. The number of valence electrons for this geometry varies from 86 to 76. Only a small number of examples of this structure are known at present. The heterometallic cluster $[Hg_2Pd_4(CO)_4(PEt_3)_4Br_2]$ has a large separation between the two central palladium atoms which are believed to be nonbonded. In this case it is possible to rationalize this structure in terms of a square of 16-electron palladium atoms capped by two mercury atoms to give a total of 82 valence electrons. The two 76-electron gold clusters form an interesting contrast with the 76-electron octahedral gold cluster listed in Table 2.14. This clearly shows how ligand dependent the cluster geometry can be in particular cases.

The trigonal prismatic clusters listed in Table 2.18 are all 90-electron clusters except for the platinum cluster $[Pt_6(CO)_{12}]^{2-}$, which has only 86 valence electrons. This cluster is the first member of a series of columnar platinum cluster

Table 2.15 ▪ Examples of Clusters with Bicapped Tetrahedral Geometries

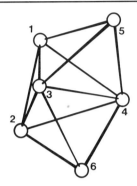

Compound	No. of Valence Electrons	Heteroatom Positions	Ref.
$H_2Ag_2Ru_4(CO)_{12}(PPh_3)_2$	84	Ag(1,5)	1
$H_2Ag_2Ru_4(CO)_{12}(Ph_2PCH_2PPh_2)$	84	Ag(1,5)	2
$H_2AgCuRu_4(CO)_{12}(PPh_3)_2$	84	Ag(5),Cu(1)	1
$Au_3Ru_3(CO)_8(C_{12}H_{15})(PPh_3)_3$	84	Au(1,3,5)	3
$Au_3Ru_3(CO)_9(COMe)(PPh_3)_3$	84	Au(3,5,6)	4
$HAu_2CoRu_3(CO)_{12}(PPh_3)_2$	84	Au(1,5),Co(2)	5
$H_2Cu_2Ru_4(CO)_{12}(PPh_3)_2$	84	Cu(1,5)	1
$Os_6(CO)_{18}$	84	—	6
$Os_6(CO)_{17}(PPh_3)$	84	—	7
$Os_6(CO)_{16}(PPh_3)_2$	84	—	7
$Os_6(CO)_{16}(t\text{–}BuNC)_2$	84	—	8
$Os_6(CO)_{16}(MeCCEt)$	84	—	9
$Ni_3Os_3(CO)_9(Cp)_3$	90	Ni(1,5,6)	10

References

1. M. J. Freeman, M. Green, A. G. Orpen, I. D. Salter and F. G. A. Stone, *J. Chem. Soc. Chem. Commun.*, 1983, 1332.
2. P. A. Bates, S. S. D. Brown, A. J. Dent, M. B. Hursthouse, G. F. M. Kitchen, A. G. Orpen, I. D. Salter and V. Sik, *J. Chem. Soc. Chem. Commun.*, 1986, 600.
3. M. I. Bruce, O. B. Shawkataly and B. K. Nicholson, *J. Organomet. Chem.*, 1984, **275**, 223.
4. L. W. Bateman, M. Green, K. A. Mead, R. M. Mills, I. D. Salter, F. G. A. Stone and P. Woodward, *J. Chem. Soc. Dalton Trans.*, 1983, 2599.
5. M. I. Bruce and B. K. Nicholson, *Organometallics*, 1984, **3**, 101.
6. R. Mason, K. M. Thomas and D. M. P. Mingos, *J. Am. Chem. Soc.*, 1973, **95**, 3800.
7. C. Coutour, D. H. Farrar, M. P. Gomez-Sal, B. F. G. Johnson, R. A. Kamarudin, J. Lewis and P. R. Raithby, *Acta Cryst.*, 1986, **C42**, 163.
8. A. G. Orpen and G. M. Sheldrick, *Acta Cryst.*, 1978, **B34**, 1989.
9. M. P. Gomez-Sal, B. F. G. Johnson, R. A. Kamarudin, J. Lewis and P. R. Raithby, *J. Chem. Soc. Chem. Commun.*, 1985, 1622.
10. E. Sappa, M. Lanfranchi, A. Tiripicchio and M.-T. Camellini, *J. Chem. Soc. Chem. Commun.*, 1981, 995.

Table 2.16 ▪ **Examples of Clusters with Capped Square-Pyramidal Geometries**

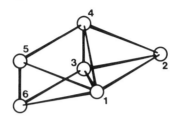

Compound	No. of Valence Electrons	Heteroatom Positions	Ref.
$AuRu_5C(CO)_{13}(NO)(PEt_3)$	86	Au(2)	1
$H_2Os_6(CO)_{18}$	86	—	2, 3
$Os_6(CO)_{17}(HCCEt)$	86	—	4
$Os_6(CO)_{17}S$	86	—	5
$Os_6(CO)_{16}(CPh)_2$	86	—	6
$Au_2Os_4(CO)_{13}(PEt_3)_2$	86	Au(5,6)	7
$H_2Au_2Ru_4(CO)_{12}(Ph_2PCH_2PPh_2)$	86	Au(5,6)	8
$Re_6P(CO)_{19}(PMe)(PMe_2)$	86	—	9

References

1. K. Henrick, B. F. G. Johnson, J. Lewis, J. Mace, M. McPartlin and J. Morris, *J. Chem. Soc. Chem. Commun.,* 1985, 1617.
2. M. McPartlin, C. R. Eady, B. F. G. Johnson and J. Lewis, *J. Chem. Soc. Chem. Commun.,* 1976, 883.
3. A. G. Orpen, *J. Organomet. Chem.,* 1978, **159**, C1.
4. M. P. Gomez-Sal, B. F. G. Johnson, R. A. Kamarudin, J. Lewis and P. R. Raithby, *J. Chem. Soc. Chem. Commun.,* 1985, 1622.
5. R. D. Adams, I. T. Horvath and P. Mathur, *Organometallics,* 1984, **3**, 623.
6. J. M. Fernandez, B. F. G. Johnson, J. Lewis and P. R. Raithby, *Acta Cryst.,* 1978, **B34**, 3086.
7. C. M. Hay, B. F. G. Johnson, J. Lewis, R. C. S. McQueen, P. R. Raithby, R. M. Sorrell and M. J. Taylor, *Organometallics,* 1985, **4**, 202.
8. P. A. Bates, S. S. D. Brown, A. J. Dent, M. B. Hursthouse, G. F. M. Kitchen, A. G. Orpen, I. D. Salter and V. Sik, *J. Chem. Soc. Chem. Commun.,* 1986, 600.
9. N. J. Taylor, *J. Chem. Soc. Chem. Commun.,* 1985, 478.

compounds $[Pt_3(CO)_6]_n^{2-}$ ($n = 2-6$) which have the platinum triangles stacked above each other. In the solid state the packing does not occur in a perfectly eclipsed fashion, leading to a slight helical twist in the cluster. In solution NMR studies have indicated that the triangles rotate relative to each other. All except one of the remaining clusters, $[Re_6(CO)_{18}(PMe)_3]$, have an interstitial carbon or nitrogen atom. The exception has three μ_4-PMe groups attached to the square faces of the cluster. None of the clusters in this group are heterometallic and all except the platinum cluster obey the inert gas rule.

The triangular raft clusters listed in Table 2.19 are a rather more diverse group of compounds although like the trigonal prisms they are also expected to have 90 electrons on the basis of the inert gas rule. The osmium clusters in Table 2.19 all obey this rule but the heterometallic clusters do not. In this latter group the central triangle in each cluster is made up of three d^8 or d^9 metals, each

Table 2.17 ▪ **Examples of Clusters with Edge-Sharing Bi-Tetrahedral Geometries**

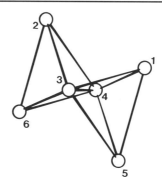

Compound	No. of Valence Electrons	Heteroatom Positions	Ref.
$H_2Os_6(CO)_{12}(CNMe_2)_2(SMe)_2$	86	—	1
$H_2Au_2Os_4(CO)_{12}(PPh_3)_2$	84	Au(1,5)	2
$Hg_2Pd_4(CO)_4(PEt_3)_4Br_2$	82	Hg(1,2)	3
$[H_4Au_5Re(PPh_3)_7]^{2+}$	78	Re(3)	4
$[Au_6(PPh_3)_6]^{2+}$	76	—	5,6
$Au_6(PPh_3)_4(Co(CO)_4)_2$	76	—	7

References

1. R. D. Adams and J. E. Babin, *Inorg. Chem.*, 1987, **26**, 980.
2. B. F. G. Johnson, D. A. Kaner, J. Lewis, P. R. Raithby and M. J. Taylor, *Polyhedron,* 1982, **1**, 105.
3. E. G. Mednikov, V. V. Bashilov, V. I. Sokolov, Yu. L. Slovokhotov and Yu. T. Struchkov, *Polyhedron*, 1983, **2**, 141.
4. P. D. Boyle, B. J. Johnson, A. Buehler and L. H. Pignolet, *Inorg. Chem.*, 1986, **25**, 5.
5. C. E. Briant, K. P. Hall, D. M. P. Mingos and A. C. Wheeler, *J. Chem. Soc. Dalton Trans.,* 1986, 687.
6. C. E. Briant, K. P. Hall and D. M. P. Mingos, *J. Organomet. Chem.*, 1983, **254**, C18.
7. J. W. A. Van der Velden, J. J. Bour, W. P. Bosman and J. H. Noordick, *Inorg. Chem.*, 1983, **22**, 1913.

of which has a 16-electron configuration. These clusters may therefore be considered analogous to the 42-electron triangles considered earlier with each edge of the triangle bridged by a metal atom with an 18-electron configuration to give a total of 84 valence electrons for the whole cluster. In $[Fe_3Pt_3(CO)_{15}]^{2-}$ and $[Fe_3Pt_3(CO)_{15}]^-$ the central Pt_3 unit can be considered as analogous to a 44-electron platinum triangle with the extra electrons (or electron) occupying a weakly antibonding molecular orbital. $[HRu_6(CO)_{18}(OCNMe_2)_2]$ has 92 valence electrons and it probably also has a pair of electrons occupying a similar orbital even though in this case the central triangle is considered to be nonbonded.

It is also of course possible to construct a six-atom raft in a rhombic rather than a triangular form. The compounds that adopt this geometry are listed in

Table 2.18 ▪ Examples of Clusters with Trigonal Prismatic Geometries

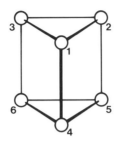

Compound	No. of Valence Electrons	Heteroatom Positions	Ref.
$[Co_6C(CO)_{15}]^{2-}$	90	—	1
$Co_6C(CO)_{12}S_2$	90	—	2
$[Co_6N(CO)_{15}]^-$	90	—	3
$Re_6(CO)_{18}(PMe)_3$	90	—	4
$[Rh_6C(CO)_{15}]^{2-}$	90	—	5
$[Rh_6N(CO)_{15}]^-$	90	—	6
$[Pt_6(CO)_{12}]^{2-}$	86	—	7

References

1. S. Martinengo, D. Strumolo, P. Chini, V. G. Albano and D. Braga, *J. Chem. Soc. Dalton Trans.*, 1985, 35.
2. G. Bor, U. K. Dietler, P. L. Stanghellini, G. Gervasio, R. Rosetti, G. Sbrignadello and G. A. Battiston, *J. Organomet. Chem.*, 1981, **213**, 277.
3. S. Martinengo, G. Ciani, A. Sironi, B. T. Heaton and J. Mason, *J. Am. Chem. Soc.*, 1979, **101**, 7095.
4. N. J. Taylor, *J. Chem. Soc. Chem. Commun.*, 1985, 478.
5. V. G. Albano, M. Sansoni, P. Chini and S. Martinengo, *J. Chem. Soc. Dalton Trans.*, 1973, 651.
6. R. Bonfichi, G. Ciani, A. Sironi and S. Martinengo, *J. Chem. Soc. Dalton Trans.*, 1983, 253.
7. J. C. Calabrese, L. F. Dahl, P. Chini, G. Longoni and S. Martinengo, *J. Am. Chem. Soc.*, 1974, **96**, 2614.

Table 2.20. Only two of these, $[HCuRu_5(CO)_8(PPh_3)]$ and $[Os_6(CO)_{19}]$, have the 90 valence electrons predicted from the inert gas rule. Three of the compounds listed have 92 valence electrons.

Table 2.21 provides examples of compounds that have a cluster framework based on an edge-bridged bi-diminished pentagonal bipyramid. It is possible to generate three different isomers by bridging alternative edges of the bi-diminished pentagonal bipyramid and examples of all three isomers are known.

There are also some six-atom clusters that do not have structures based on those given in Tables 2.14 through 2.21. For example, $[Au_2Os_4(CO)_{12}(PPh_2Me)_2]^{71}$ is a rare case of a diminished (nido) pentagonal bipyramid, the missing vertex being one from the equatorial plane. This cluster might be expected to have 86 valence electrons but because of the presence of the two $Au(PPh_2Me)$ groups it only has 82. $[Rh_6(CO)_9(Bu_2^tAs)_2(Bu^tAs)]^{72}$ has

Table 2.19 ▪ Examples of Clusters with Triangular Six-Atom-Raft Geometries

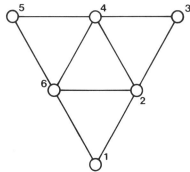

Compound	No. of Valence Electrons	Heteroatom Positions	Ref.
$Os_6(CO)_{20}(P(OMe)_3)$	90	—	1
$Os_6(CO)_{19}(P(OMe)_3)_2$	90	—	1
$Os_6(CO)_{19}O$	90	—	2
$Os_6O(CO)_{18}(PPh_3)$	90	—	1
$H_2Os_6(CO)_{18}(PPh)$	90	—	1
$Os_6(CO)_{17}(P(OMe)_3)_4$	90	—	3
$Os_6(CO)_{15}(P(OMe)_3)_6$	90	—	1
$[HRu_6(CO)_{18}(OCNMe_2)_2]^-$	92	—	4
$[Fe_3Pt_3(CO)_{15}]^{2-}$	86	Fe(1,3,5)	5
$[Fe_3Pt_3(CO)_{15}]^-$	85	Fe(1,3,5)	5
$[H_9Ag_3Rh_3(MeC(CH_2PPh_2)_3)_3]^{3+}$	84	Rh(1,3,5)	6
$Au_6(MeC_6H_4CS_2)_6$	84	—	7
$[Cu_3Fe_3(CO)_{12}]^{3-}$	84	Fe(1,3,5)	8
$H_9Cu_3Os_3(PMe_2Ph)_9$	84	Os(1,3,5)	9
$Ir_3Pt_3(CO)_6(Cp)_3$	84	Ir(1,3,5)	10

References

1. J. G. Jeffrey, Ph.D. thesis, Cambridge University, 1985.
2. R. J. Goudsmit, B. F. G. Johnson, J. Lewis, P. R. Raithby and K. H. Whitmire, *J. Chem. Soc. Chem. Commun.*, 1983, 246.
3. R. J. Goudsmit, B. F. G. Johnson, J. Lewis, P. R. Raithby and K. H. Whitmire, *J. Chem. Soc. Chem. Commun.*, 1982, 640.
4. N. M. Boag, C. B. Knobler and H. D. Kaesz, *Angew. Chem. Int. Ed. Engl.*, 1983, **22**, 249.
5. G. Longoni, M. Manassero and M. Sansoni, *J. Am. Chem. Soc.*, 1980, **102**, 7973.
6. F. Bachechi, J. Ott and L. M. Venanzi, *J. Am. Chem. Soc.*, 1985, **107**, 1760.
7. J. A. Schuerman, F. R. Fronczek and J. Selbin, *J. Am. Chem. Soc.*, 1986, **108**, 336.
8. G. Doyle, K. A. Eriksen and D. Van Engen, *J. Am. Chem. Soc.*, 1986, **108**, 445.
9. T. H. Lemmen, J. C. Huffman and K. G. Caulton, *Angew. Chem. Int. Ed. Engl.*, 1986, **25**, 262.
10. M. J. Freeman, A. D. Miles, M. Murray, A. G. Orpen and F. G. A. Stone, *Polyhedron*, 1984, **3**, 1093.

Table 2.20 ▪ Examples of Clusters with Rhombic Six-Atom-Raft Geometries

Compound	No. of Valence Electrons	Heteroatom Positions	Ref.
$HCuRu_5(CO)_8(PPh_3)$	90	Cu(1)	1
$Os_6S(CO)_{19}$	90	—	2
$[Co_6P(CO)_{16}]^-$	92	—	3
$Os_6(CO)_{20}(CCHPh)$	92	—	4
$H_6Cu_2Mn_4(CO)_{12}((EtO)_2POP(EtO)_2)_2$	92	Cu(1,4)	5
$[H_{16}Cu_2Re_4(PMe_2Ph)_8]^{2+}$	80	Cu(1,4)	6
$Au_4Fe_2(CO)_8(Ph_2PCH_2PPh_2)_2$	74	Fe(3,6)	7

References

1. J. Evans, A. C. Street and M. Webster, *J. Chem. Soc. Chem. Commun.*, 1987, 637.
2. R. D. Adams, I. T. Horvath and P. Mathur, *Organometallics*, 1984, **3**, 623.
3. G. Ciani and A. Sironi, *J. Organomet. Chem.*, 1983, **241**, 385.
4. J. G. Jeffrey, B. F. G. Johnson, J. Lewis, P. R. Raithby and D. A. Welch, *J. Chem. Soc. Chem. Commun.*, 1986, 318.
5. V. Riera, M. A. Ruiz, A. Tiripicchio and M. T. Camellini, *J. Chem. Soc. Chem. Commun.*, 1985, 1505.
6. L. F. Rhodes, J. C. Huffman and K. G. Caulton, *J. Am. Chem. Soc.*, 1983, **105**, 5137.
7. C. E. Briant, K. P. Hall and D. M. P. Mingos, *J. Chem. Soc. Chem. Commun.*, 1983, 843.

the metal atoms of its core arranged in the form of a pentagonal pyramid, and this also has 82 valence electrons.

$[H_2Rh_6(CO)_8(PBu^t_2)_4]^{73}$ and $[Au_6(PPh_2(CH_2)_3PPh_2)_4]^{2+}$ [74] are two examples of clusters that have a cluster core consisting of a bi-edge-bridged tetrahedron. Neither of these has the 88 valence electrons implied by the inert gas rule. The rhodium cluster has 84 valence electrons, while the gold cluster has only 80. $[Co_5Ge(CO)_{16}]^-$ [75] has a total of 92 valence electrons and has a metal atom framework that consists of a tetrahedron sharing a vertex with a triangle for which an electron count of 90 might be expected. The germanium atom occupies the shared vertex.

$[Co_6(C)_2S(CO)_{14}]^{76}$ and $[Au_6Se_2(PPh_3)_6]^{77}$ have an interesting geometry that can be considered as a bi-edge-bridged square. The cobalt cluster has the expected total of 92 valence electrons while the gold cluster has a total of 86 valence electrons corresponding to four 16-electron gold atoms in the square and two 14-electron gold groups bridging the edges.

$[H_2Os_6(CO)_{19}]^{78}$ and $[Os_6(CO)_{17}(C_5H_5N)_2]^{79}$ have a cluster core consisting of a trigonal bipyramid of osmium atoms with a further osmium atom attached to one of the equatorial positions, while $[HgCo_4Ru(CO)_{16}]^{80}$ has a cobalt atom

Table 2.21 ▪ Examples of Edge-Bridged Bi-Diminished Pentagonal Bipyramids

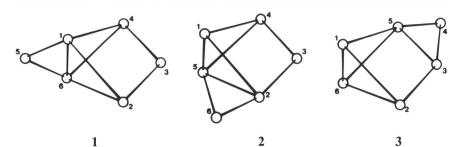

| | 1 | | 2 | | 3 |

Compound	No. of Valence Electrons	Heteroatom Positions	Ref.
Type 1			
$AuRu_5C(CO)_{15}(PPh_3)Cl$	88	Au(5)	1
$AuRu_5C(CO)_{14}(PPh_3)(MeCO)$	88	Au(5)	2
$AuRu_5C(CO)_{13}(PPh_3)(Cp)$	88	Au(5)	2
$AuRu_5C(CO)_{14}(PPh_3)Br$	86	Au(5)	1
$AuRu_5C(CO)_{13}(PPh_3)_2I$	86	Au(5)	3
$Au_2Ru_4C(CO)_{12}(PMe_2Ph)_2$	86	Au(3,5)	4
Type 2			
$Os_6S_2(CO)_{17}$	90	—	5
$Au_2Co_2Ru_2C(CO)_{12}(PPh_3)_2$	84		
Type 3			
$HRu_6C(CO)_{15}(SEt)_3$	92	—	6

References

1. B. F. G. Johnson, J. Lewis, J. N. Nicholls, J. Puga and K. H. Whitmire, *J. Chem. Soc. Dalton Trans.,* 1983, 787.
2. A. G. Cowie, B. F. G. Johnson, J. Lewis, J. N. Nicholls, P. R. Raithby and A. G. Swanson, *J. Chem. Soc. Chem. Commun.,* 1984, 637.
3. A. G. Cowie, B. F. G. Johnson, J. Lewis, J. N. Nicholls, P. R. Raithby, and M. J. Rosales, *J. Chem. Soc. Dalton Trans.,* 1983, 2311.
4. A. G. Cowie, B. F. G. Johnson, J. Lewis and P. R. Raithby, *J. Chem. Soc. Chem. Commun.,* 1984, 1710.
5. R. D. Adams, D. F. Foust and B. E. Segmüller, *Organometallics,* 1983, **2**, 308.
6. B. F. G. Johnson, J. Lewis, K. Wong and M. McPartlin, *J. Organomet. Chem.,* 1980, **185**, C17.

attached to the apical mercury atom of a trigonal bipyramid consisting of a triangle of cobalt atoms with mercury and ruthenium caps. All three have the 88 electrons necessary to satisfy the inert gas rule.

One isomer of $[H_2Os_6S_2(CO)_{17}]^{81}$ has a cluster core that consists of a butterfly of osmium atoms with a chain of two osmium atoms attached to one of the wingtip atoms. $[H_2Os_6S_2(CO)_{18}]^{81}$ is similar but the extra pair of electrons causes the breaking of a bond to give a cluster core that consists of a triangle with a chain of three atoms attached. The second isomer of $[H_2Os_6S_2(CO)_{17}]$ is a triangular raft-shaped cluster with one of the central bonds broken. $[Os_6S_2(CO)_{15}(HCNC_6H_5)_2]^{82}$

Table 2.22 ▪ Examples of Clusters with Capped Octahedral Geometries

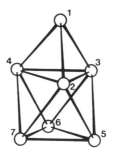

Compound	No. of Valence Electrons	Heteroatom Positions	Ref.
$AuRu_6C(CO)_{15}(NO)(PPh_3)$	98	Au(1)	1
$Ir_7(CO)_{12}(C_8H_{12})(C_8H_{11})(C_8H_{10})$	98	—	2
$[NiRh_6(CO)_{16}]^{2-}$	98	Ni(1)	3
$Os_7(CO)_{21}$	98	—	4
$Pd_7(CO)_7(PMe_3)_7$	98	—	5
$[Re_7C(CO)_{22}]^-$	98	—	6
$[Re_7C(CO)_{21}]^{3-}$	98	—	7
$[Rh_7(CO)_{16}]^{3-}$	98	—	9
$[Rh_7(CO)_{16}I]^{2-}$	100	—	8

References

1. B. F. G. Johnson, J. Lewis, W. J. H. Nelson, P. Puga, P. R. Raithby, D. Braga, M. McPartlin and W. Clegg, *J. Organomet. Chem.*, 1983, **243**, C13.
2. C. G. Pierpont, *Inorg. Chem.*, 1979, **18**, 2972.
3. A. Fumagalli, G. Longoni, P. Chini, A. Albinati and S. Bruckner, *J. Organomet. Chem.*, 1980, **202**, 329.
4. C. R. Eady, B. F. G. Johnson, J. Lewis, R. Mason, P. B. Hitchcock and K. M. Thomas, *J. Chem. Soc. Chem. Commun.*, 1977, 385.
5. R. Goddard, P. W. Jolly, C. Kruger, K. P. Schick and G. Wilke, *Organometallics*, 1982, **1**, 1709.
6. T. Beringhelli, G. D'Alfonso, M. De Angelis, G. Ciani and A. Sironi, *J. Organomet. Chem.*, 1987, **322**, C2.
7. G. Ciani, G. D'Alfonso, M. Freni, P. Romiti and A. Sironi, *J. Chem. Soc. Chem. Commun.*, 1982, 339.
8. V. G. Albano, G. Ciani, S. Martinengo, P. Chini and G. Giordano, *J. Organomet. Chem.*, 1975, **88**, 381.
9. V. G. Albano, P. L. Bellon and G. Ciani, *J. Chem. Soc. Chem. Commun.*, 1969, 1024.

is another cluster based on a butterfly but in this case the two extra metal atoms are each attached to one of the two "hinge" atoms of the butterfly. In $[Co_4Zn_2(CO)_{15}]^{83}$ a cobalt atom is attached to each of the zinc atoms which form the wingtips of a butterfly.

2.2.3.5. Seven-Atom Clusters

Seven-atom clusters as a group are much rarer than the smaller clusters discussed in the preceding sections. The only large group of seven-atom clusters with the same geometry are the capped octahedral clusters listed in Table 2.22. Altogether there are nine clusters with a capped octahedral geometry and all except one have 98 valence electrons. Only two of these clusters have the idealized C_{3v} symmetry and the rest, including the 100-electron cluster $[Rh_7(CO)_{16}I]^{2-}$, have an elongated bond in the capping tetrahedron. This has led to the suggestion that the 98-electron species are supersaturated. $[Rh_7(CO)_{16}I]^{2-}$ has the electron count expected for an edge-bridged octahedron and can be rationalized in terms of this geometry. Another edge-bridged octahedron is $[Au_2Fe_5C(CO)_{14}(PEt_3)_2]$, which has only 98 electrons because one of the $AuPEt_3$ groups is edge-bridging.

An alternative geometry that might be expected for 100-electron clusters is the edge-bridged capped square pyramid known for $[H_2Os_7(CO)_{21}]$.[84] This provides another possible way of edge-bridging an 86-electron cluster. An alternative geometry for 98-electron seven-vertex clusters is a square pyramid sharing a triangular face with a trigonal bipyramid. One of the two possible orientations for this structure is found for $[Os_7S(CO)_{19}]$.[85] In this case the trigonal bipyramid points towards the base of the square pyramid.

Another possible structure for 102-electron clusters is the square-capped trigonal prism found in $[Rh_7N(CO)_{15}]^{2-}$,[86] $[CoRh_6N(CO)_{15}]^{2-}$,[87] and $[IrRh_6N(CO)_{15}]^{2-}$.[87] The two heterometallic clusters differ in that the cobalt atom occupies a prism position while the iridium atom occupies the capping position.

There are two 96-electron tricapped-tetrahedral compounds for which crystallographic data is available, that is $[Au_3CoRu_3(CO)_{12}(PPh_3)_3]$[88] and $[HAu_3Ru_4(CO)_{12}(PPh_3)_3]$.[89] The $AuPPh_3$ groups occupy adjacent positions in the cluster polyhedron as was found in the similar six-vertex bicapped tetrahedral clusters.

$[Au_2Os_5C(CO)_{14}(PPh_3)_2]$[90] is a 98-electron cluster consisting of a square pyramid of osmium atoms with two $AuPPh_3$ bridging opposite basal-axial edges of the pyramid.

The 94-electron cluster $[Pt_7(Me_2C_6H_3NC)_{12}]$[91] has a central core of five platinum atoms in the shape of a trigonal bipyramid with two more platinum atoms bridging axial-equatorial edges so that they share a common equatorial atom.

The 96-electron cluster $[HgPt_6(Me_2C_6H_3NC)_{12}]$[92] consists of a mercury atom sandwiched between two Pt_3 triangles to give a pair of vertex-sharing tetrahedra. The only seven-vertex 102-electron cluster is $[H_2Os_7(CO)_{22}]$,[84] which consists of a trigonal bipyramid sharing a vertex with a triangle of metal atoms.

The clusters listed in Table 2.23 have a structure that consists of two butterfly-shaped fragments sharing a vertex. The four clusters that have 106 valence electrons, $[HgRu_6(CO)_{18}(CCBu^t)_4]$, $[HgRu_6(CO)_{20}(NO)_2]$, $[Fe_4HgRh_2(CO)_{14}(Cp)(COMe)]$, and $[Co_2Fe_4Hg(CO)_{14}(Cp)(COMe)]$, all have a mercury atom as the shared atom. The two other clusters, $[H_2AgOs_6(CO)_{20}]^-$ and $[H_2AuOs_6(CO)_{20}]^-$, adopt the same geometry but in both of these clusters there are only 102 valence electrons.

$[Au_7(PPh_3)_7]^+$ [93-95] is the only cluster that has a cluster core consisting of a pentagonal bipyramid of metal atoms.

The final seven-vertex cluster to be considered is a chain of seven metal atoms that is known for the compound $[Pt_3W_4(CO)_8(Cp)_4(CC_6H_4Me)_4]$,[96] which has a total of 102 valence electrons. A total of 114 electrons would be expected for a chain of atoms all of which obeyed the inert gas rule. In this case delocalized bonding through the bridging CC_6H_4Me groups may account for the electron deficiency.

Table 2.23 ▪ Vertex Sharing Butterfly Clusters

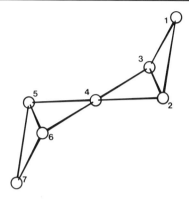

Compound	No. of Valence Electrons	Heteroatom Positions	Ref.
$Co_2Fe_4Hg(CO)_{14}(Cp)(COMe)$	106	Co(1,7),Hg(4)	1
$Fe_4HgRh_2(CO)_{14}(Cp)(COMe)$	106	Hg(4),Rh(2,6)	1
$HgRu_6(CO)_{18}(CCBu^t)_2$	106	Hg(4)	2
$HgRu_6(CO)_{20}(NO)_2$	106	Hg(4)	3
$[H_2AgOs_6(CO)_{20}]^-$	102	Ag(4)	4
$[H_2AuOs_6(CO)_{20}]^-$	102	Au(4)	5

References

1. L. J. Farrugia, *J. Chem. Soc. Chem. Commun.*, 1987, 147.
2. S. Ermer, K. King, K. I. Hardcastle, E. Rosenberg, A. M. M. Lanfredi, A. Tiripicchio and M. T. Camellini, *Inorg. Chem.*, 1983, **22**, 1339.
3. M. P. Gomez-Sal, B. F. G. Johnson, J. Lewis, P. R. Raithby and S. N. A. B. S. Mustaffa, *J. Organomet. Chem.*, 1984, **272**, C21.
4. M. Fajardo, M. P. Gomez-Sal, H. D. Holden, B. F. G. Johnson, J. Lewis, R. C. S. McQueen and P. R. Raithby, *J. Organomet. Chem.*, 1984, **267**, C25.
5. B. F. G. Johnson, D. A. Kaner, J. Lewis and P. R. Raithby, *J. Chem. Soc. Chem. Commun.*, 1981, 753.

2.2.3.6. Eight-Atom Clusters

Like the seven-atom clusters there are only a small number of compounds that fall into this group. The largest group of eight-atom clusters are the bicapped octahedra listed in Table 2.24. All except two of these are *para-* bicapped. The exceptions are $[Os_6Pt_2(CO)_{17}(C_8H_{12})_2]$ and $[Pd_8(CO)_8(PMe_3)_7]$, which are both *meta-* bicapped. All of these clusters have 110 electrons, which is in agreement with the total expected from the capping principle.[8]

Two alternative geometries for 110-electron clusters are known although there are many more possible structures that have not yet been realized. $[HOs_8(CO)_{22}]^{-}$[97] has a cluster framework that consists of a bicapped tetrahedron sharing an edge with another tetrahedron. This geometry is another example of the way in which larger clusters are derived from the condensation of triangles, tetrahedra, and octahedra. An identical structure is adopted by $[Os_6Pt_2(CO)_{16}(C_8H_{12})_2]$[98] although this cluster has only 108 valence electrons instead of 110. The metal framework in $[Au_2Ru_5WC(CO)_{17}(PEt_3)_2]$[99] and $[Cu_2Ru_6C(CO)_{16}(MeCN)_2]$[100]

Table 2.24 ▪ Examples of Clusters with Bicapped Octahedral Geometries

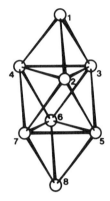 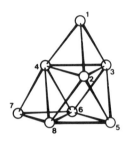

Compound	No. of Valence Electrons	Heteroatom Positions	Ref.
Para- bicapped			
$AuRe_7C(CO)_{21}(PPh_3)$	110	Au(1)	1
$Cu_2Ru_6(CO)_{18}(C_6H_4Me)_2$	110	Cu(1,8)	2
$[Os_8(CO)_{22}]^{2-}$	110	—	3
$[Re_8C(CO)_{24}]^{2-}$	110	—	4
Meta- bicapped			
$Os_6Pt_2(CO)_{17}(C_8H_{12})_2$	110	Pt(1,7)	5
$Pd_8(CO)_8(PMe_3)_7$	110	—	6

References

1. T. J. Henly, J. R. Shapley and A. L. Rheingold, *J. Organomet. Chem.*, 1986, **310**, 55.
2. J. S. Bradley, G. B. Ansell and M. A. Modrick, *Acta Cryst.*, 1984, **C40**, 365.
3. P. F. Jackson, B. F. G. Johnson, J. Lewis, and P. R. Raithby, *J. Chem. Soc. Chem. Commun.*, 1980, 60.
4. G. Ciani, G. D'Alfonso, M. Freni, P. Romiti and A. Sironi, *J. Chem. Soc. Chem. Commun.*, 1982, 705.
5. C. Couture, D. H. Farrar and R. J. Goudsmit, *Inorg. Chim. Acta*, 1984, **89**, L29.
6. M. Bachmann, I. Hawkins, M. B. Hursthouse and R. L. Short, *Polyhedron*, 1987, **6**, 1987.

consists of an octahedron sharing a face with a trigonal bipyramid. This arrangement can be considered as a bicapped octahedron.

Only three eight-vertex 112-electron clusters are known despite the multitude of possible geometries for this electron count. The geometry adopted by $[Os_8(CO)_{22}I]^{-97}$ is a bi-edge-bridged bicapped tetrahedron, while $[Ru_8S_2(CO)_{17}(C_6H_5Me)]^{101}$ has a structure consisting of two square pyramids sharing triangular faces with a tetrahedron. The two sulphur ligands cap the square faces of the square pyramids. The third 112-electron compound $[Pt_4W_4(CO)_8(CC_6H_4Me)_4(Cp)_4]$,[96] consists of a star-shaped ring of eight metal atoms with the tungsten atoms at the points of the star. The platinum-platinum vectors are considered to be too long to be bonding (2.954 Å), suggesting that the bonding in this system is extensively delocalized. A similar cluster $[Hg_4Mn_4(CO)_8(MeC_5H_4)_4]$,[102] does consist of a square of mercury atoms with bridging manganese atom along each edge, although this has 112 electrons rather than the 110 that might be expected.

The only known dodecahedral cluster is the 112-electron copper cluster $[H_8Cu_8(Ph_2P(CH_2)_3PPh_2)_4]$.[103] The copper +1 oxidation state is retained in this cluster and the total number of valence electrons falls below that predicted on the basis of the polyhedral electron skeletal electron pair approach. The situation is therefore analogous to that in $[H_6Cu_6(PPh_3)_6]$.

There are three different structures known for 114-electron clusters. The best known group is the three square-antiprismatic clusters $[Co_8C(CO)_{18}]^{2-}$,[104] $[Rh_8C(CO)_{19}]$,[105] and $[Ru_8P(CO)_{19}(CH_2C_6H_5)]$.[106] Two examples of square-antiprismatic clusters with more than 114 valence electrons are $[Ni_8C(CO)_{16}]^{2-}$[107] and $[Bi_8]^{2+}$,[108] both of which have 118.

An alternative 114-electron structure is the bicapped trigonal prism adopted by $[Cu_2Rh_6C(CO)_{15}(NCMe)_2]$.[109] In this structure the CuNCMe groups cap the triangular faces of the trigonal prism. Another geometry that might be expected to have 114 electrons is the bi-edge-bridged octahedron found for $[Au_2Ru_6C(CO)_{16}(PMePh_2)_2]$,[110] but in this compound the presence of the two gold atoms reduces the electron count to only 110 valence electrons instead of 114.

The 116 valence electron cluster $[Co_6Ni_2C_2(CO)_{16}]^{2-}$[111] has a cluster core that consists of two triangular prisms sharing a square face with a carbon atom at the center of each prism.

The only cubic cluster compound that has been crystallographically characterized is $[Ni_8(CO)_8(PPh)_6]$.[112] It has a terminal CO ligand attached to each nickel atom and a PPh ligand bridging each face of the cube. It has a total of 120 valence electrons. An alternative geometry for 120-electron clusters is the cuneane structure adopted by $[Co_8S_2(t\text{-}BuNC)_4(NO)_8]$.[113] This is also an electron precise, three-connected cluster.

$[Co_6Ge_2(CO)_{19}]$[114] consists of a square of cobalt atoms capped by two germanium atoms to which a further two cobalt atoms are attached.

$[Ir_8(CO)_{22}]^{2-}$[115] is an example of a dimeric cluster, better formulated as $[(Ir_4(CO)_{11})_2]^{2-}$ because it consists of two tetrahedral units linked together by a single metal-metal bond.

The gold cluster $[Au_8(PPh_3)_8]^{2+}$[116,117] has a nucleus that can be described as a capped-centered hexagonal chair, while $[Au_8(PPh_3)_7]^{2+}$[118] has a different core geometry based on a centered hexagonal chair with edge-bridging AuPPh$_3$ fragments.

2.2.3.7. Nine-Atom Clusters

A total of 21 nine-atom clusters have been structurally characterized, as summarized in Table 2.25 and illustrated in Figure 2.8. The cluster core of $[Co_9Si(CO)_{21}]^{2-}$ consists of a capped square antiprism of cobalt atoms with an interstitial silicon atom in the center of the square antiprism. $[Rh_9P(CO)_{21}]^{2-}$, $[Ni_9C(CO)_{17}]^{2-}$, and the "bare" metal clusters such as $[Sn_9]^{4-}$ and $[Ge_9]^{4-}$ also adopt this geometry.

$[Rh_9(CO)_{19}]^{3-}$ and $[PtRh_8(CO)_{19}]^{2-}$ consist of two octahedra of metal atoms sharing a triangular face. In the case of the heterometallic cluster the platinum atom occupies one of the vertices in the shared face.

$[Cu_5Fe_4(CO)_{16}]^{2-}$ has a unique large "square" planar array of atoms with

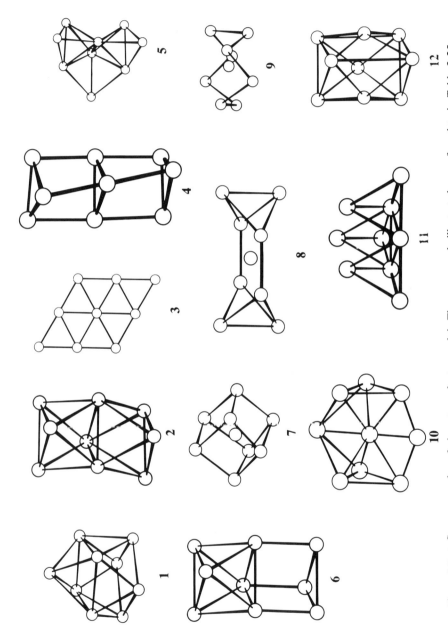

Figure 2.8 ▪ Some examples of nine-atom cluster nuclei. The compounds illustrated are referred to in Table 2.25.

Table 2.25 ▪ Nine-Vertex Clusters (See Figure 2.8)

Compound	No. of Valence Electrons	Structure (Fig. 2.8)	Ref.
$[Co_9Si(CO)_{21}]^{2-}$	129	1	1
$[Rh_9P(CO)_{21}]^{2-}$	130	1	2
$[Ni_9C(CO)_{17}]^{2-}$	130	1	3
$[Sn_9]^{4-}$	130	1	4
$[Ge_9]^{4-}$	130	1	5
$[Rh_9(CO)_{19}]^{3-}$	122	2	6
$[PtRh_8(CO)_{19}]^{2-}$	122	2	7
$[Cu_5Fe_4(CO)_{16}]^{3-}$	122	3	8
$[Pt_9(CO)_{18}]^{2-}$	128	4	9
$Os_9(CO)_{21}(CHC(Me)CH)^-$	120	5	10
$Os_9(CO)_{21}(CHC(Et)CH)^-$	120	5	10
$Au_2Os_7(CO)_{20}(PEt_3)_2$	122	—	11
$[Ni_9(CO)_{18}]^{2-}$	128	6	12
$[Au_9(PPh_3)_8]^+$	114	7	13
$[Au_9(PPh_3)_8]^{3+}$	112	8	
$[Au_9(P(C_6H_4OMe)_3)_8]^{3+}$	112	8, 9	14, 15
$[Au_9(P(C_6H_4Me)_3)_8]^{3+}$	112	9	16
$Au_9(P(C_6H_{11})_3)_5(SCN)_3$	112	10	17
$Ag_6Fe_3(CO)_{12}((Ph_3P)_3CH)$	120	11	18
$[Bi_9]^{5+}$	130	12	19
$[Ge_9]^{2-}$	128	12	5

References

1. V. M. Mackay, B. K. Nicholson, W. T. Robinson and A. W. Sims, *J. Chem. Soc. Chem. Commun.*, 1984, 1276.
2. J. L. Vidal, W. E. Walker, R. L. Pruett and R. C. Schoening, *Inorg. Chem.*, 1979, **18**, 129.
3. A. Ceriotti, G. Longoni, M. Manassero, M. Perego and M. Sansoni, *Inorg. Chem.*, 1985, **24**, 117.
4. J. D. Corbett and P. A. Edwards, *J. Am. Chem. Soc.*, 1977, **99**, 3313.
5. C. H. E. Belin, J. D. Corbett and A. Cisar, *J. Am. Chem. Soc.*, 1977, **99**, 7163.
6. S. Martinengo, A. Fumagalli, R. Bonfichi, G. Ciani and A. Sironi, *J. Chem. Soc. Chem. Commun.*, 1982, 825.
7. A. Fumagalli, S. Martinengo, G. Ciani and G. Marturano, *Inorg. Chem.*, 1986, **25**, 592.
8. G. Doyle, K. A. Eriksen and D. Van Engen, *J. Am. Chem. Soc.*, 1986, **108**, 445.
9. J. C. Calabrese, L. F. Dahl, P. Chini, G. Longoni and S. Martinengo, *J. Am. Chem. Soc.*, 1974, **96**, 2614.
10. B. F. G. Johnson, J. Lewis, W. J. H. Nelson, P. R. Raithby, M. D. Vargas, M. McPartlin and A. Sironi, *J. Chem. Soc. Chem. Commun.*, 1983, 1476.
11. S. R. Drake, B. F. G. Johnson, J. Lewis, M. McPartlin, K. Henrick and J. Morris, *J. Chem. Soc. Chem. Commun.*, 1986, 928.
12. R. A. Nagaki, L. D. Lower, G. Longoni, P. Chini and L. F. Dahl, *Organometallics*, 1986, **5**, 1764.

(*continued*)

References (*continued*)

13. J. G. M. Van der Linden, M. L. H. Paulissen and J. E. J. Schmitz, *J. Am. Chem. Soc.*, 1983, **105**, 1903.
14. K. P. Hall, B. R. C. Theobald, D. I. Gilmour, D. M. P. Mingos and A. J. Welch, *J. Chem. Soc. Chem. Commun.*, 1982, 528.
15. C. E. Briant, K. P. Hall and D. M. P. Mingos, *J. Chem. Soc. Chem. Commun.*, 1984, 290.
16. P. L. Bellon, F. Cariati, M. Manassero, L. Naldini and M. Sansoni, *J. Chem. Soc. Chem. Commun.*, 1971, 1423.
17. M. K. Cooper, G. R. Dennis, K. Hendrick and M. McPartlin, *Inorg. Chim. Acta*, 1980, **45**, L151.
18. C. E. Briant, R. G. Smith and D. M. P. Mingos, *J. Chem. Soc. Chem. Commun.*, 1984, 586.
19. R. M. Friedman and J. D. Corbett, *Inorg. Chem.*, 1973, **12**, 1134.

four iron atoms defining the corners of the square and copper atoms at the center of each edge and in the center of the cluster.

2.2.3.8. Ten-Atom Clusters

The most aesthetically pleasing ten-atom clusters among those listed in Table 2.26 and illustrated in Figure 2.9 are the series of clusters that have as their central unit a tetra-capped octahedron of metal atoms in the shape of a large tetrahedron. Several examples of this type of cluster are known, including $[H_4Os_{10}(CO)_{24}]^{2-}$, $[Os_{10}C(CO)_{24}]^{2-}$, $[HOs_{10}C(CO)_{24}]^{-}$, $[Os_{10}C(CO)_{23}(P(OMe)_3)I_2]$, $[Os_{10}C(CO)_{21}(P(OMe)_3)_4]$, $[Os_{10}C(CO)_{23}(NO)]^{-}$, $[Os_{10}C(CO)_{22}(NO)I]^{2-}$, $[Cu_6Fe_4(CO)_{16}]^{2-}$, and $[Hg_6Rh_4(PMe_3)_{12}]$. There are several clusters derived from this unit where one of the bonds to a capping atom is broken by a bridging ligand, such as $[Os_{10}C(CO)_{24}(NO)]^{-}$, $[Os_{10}C(CO)_{24}I]^{-}$, and $[Os_{10}C(CO)_{24}I_2]$. The two heterometallic clusters with only 132 electrons are based on 84-electron octahedra rather than the 86-electron octahedra of the osmium clusters and consequently have two fewer valence electrons in total.

The structure adopted by $[Os_{10}S_2(CO)_{23}]$ is rather different. The cluster core is based on two octahedra sharing an edge. In this description the two sulphur atoms are considered to be part of the octahedra. The remaining osmium atoms cap the cluster so that the apical vertices of the two octahedra are bonded together. Another significant group of clusters are the bicapped square antiprisms adopted by the rhodium clusters $[Rh_{10}S(CO)_{22}]^{2-}$, $[Rh_{10}P(CO)_{22}]^{3-}$, and $[Rh_{10}As(CO)_{22}]^{3-}$, all of which have 142 valence electrons. $[Ru_{10}C_2(CO)_{24}]^{2-}$ has a structure based on two octahedra sharing an edge. $[Au_2Os_8(CO)_{22}(PPh_3)_2]$ has a similar structure but in this case the two gold atoms (*trans* to the shared bond in one of the octahedra) are not considered to be bonded together.

$[Co_3Ni_7C_2(CO)_{15}]^{3-}$ has a structure consisting of two capped octahedra sharing a rhombic face. The cluster core of $[Ni_{10}C_2(CO)_{16}]^{2-}$ can be thought of as two square-capped trigonal prisms sharing a common square face so that the two caps are *trans*- to each other. The two palladium clusters $[Pd_{10}(CO)_{14}(PBu_3)_4]$ and $[Pd_{10}(CO)_{12}(PBu_3)_6]$ have a cluster core consisting of an octahedron of palladium atoms with the remaining four metal atoms edge-bridging. $[Fe_4Pt_6(CO)_{22}]^{2-}$ has an unusual core structure consisting of a bi-edge-bridged tetrahedron of platinum atoms with an iron atom bridging each of the four bonds connecting the bridging atoms to the tetrahedron.

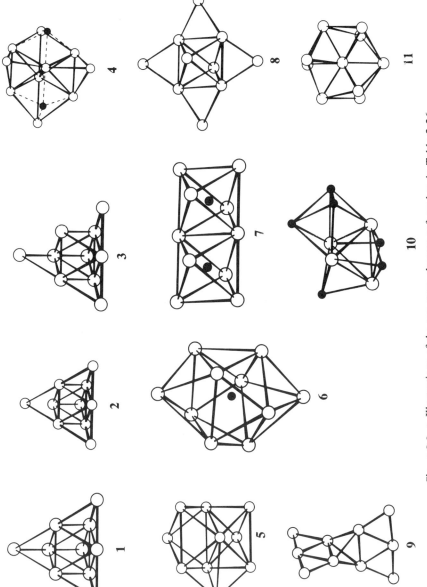

Figure 2.9 ▪ Illustrations of the ten-atom clusters referred to in Table 2.26.

Table 2.26 ▪ Ten-Vertex Clusters (See Figure 2.9)

Compound	No. of Valence Electrons	Structure (Fig. 2.9)	Ref.
$[H_4Os_{10}(CO)_{24}]^{2-}$	134	1	1
$[Os_{10}C(CO)_{24}]^{2-}$	134	1	2
$[HOs_{10}C(CO)_{24}]^-$	134	1	3
$Os_{10}C(CO)_{23}(POMe)_3)I_2$	134	1	4
$Os_{10}C(CO)_{21}(P(OMe)_3)_4$	134	1	4
$[Os_{10}C(CO)_{23}(NO)]^-$	134	1	5
$[Os_{10}C(CO)_{22}(NO)I]^{2-}$	134	1	4
$[Cu_6Fe_4(CO)_{16}]^{2-}$	132	1	6
$Hg_6Rh_4(PMe_3)_{12}$	132	1	7
$[Os_{10}C(CO)_{24}(NO)]^-$	134	1	5
$[Os_{10}C(CO)_{22}I]^-$	134	2	4
$Os_{10}C(CO)_{24}I_2$	134	3	4
$Os_{10}S_2(CO)_{23}$	134	4	8
$[Rh_{10}(CO)_{21}]^{2-}$	134	5	9
$[Rh_{10}S(CO)_{22}]^{2-}$	142	6	10
$[Rh_{10}P(CO)_{22}]^-$	142	6	11
$[Rh_{10}As(CO)_{22}]^{2-}$	142	6	12
$[Ru_{10}C_2(CO)_{24}]^{2-}$	138	7	13
$Au_2Os_8(CO)_{22}(PPh_3)_2$	134	7	14
$[Co_3Ni_7C_2(CO)_{15}]^{3-}$	138	5	15
$[Ni_{10}C_2(CO)_{16}]^{2-}$	138	5	16
$Pd_{10}(CO)_{14}(PBu_3)_4$	136	8	17
$Pd_{10}(CO)_{12}(PBu_3)_6$	136	8	18
$[Fe_4Pt_6(CO)_{22}]^{2-}$	138	9	19
$Au_2Ir_8(CO)_{20}(PhPPPh)(PEt_3)_2$	144	—	20
$Co_4As_6(PPh_3)_4$	134	10	21
$[Au_{10}(PPh(C_6H_5)_2)_6Cl_3]^+$	124	11	22

References

1. B. F. G. Johnson, J. Lewis, W. J. H. Nelson, M. D. Vargas, D. Braga and M. McPartlin, *J. Chem. Soc. Chem. Commun.*, 1983, 241.
2. P. F. Jackson, B. F. G. Johnson, J. Lewis, W. J. H. Nelson and M. McPartlin, *J. Chem. Soc. Dalton Trans.*, 1982, 2099.
3. P. F. Jackson, B. F. G. Johnson, J. Lewis, M. McPartlin and W. J. H. Nelson, *J. Chem. Soc. Chem. Commun.*, 1982, 48.
4. R. J. Goudsmit, B. F. G. Johnson, J. Lewis, W. J. H. Nelson, M. D. Vargas, D. Braga, M. McPartlin and A. Sironi, *J. Chem. Soc. Dalton Trans.*, 1985, 1795.
5. D. Braga, K. Henrick, B. F. G. Johnson, J. Lewis, M. McPartlin, W. J. H. Nelson and J. Puga, *J. Organomet. Chem.*, 1984, **266**, 173.
6. G. Doyle, K. A. Eriksen and D. Van Engen, *J. Am. Chem. Soc.*, 1985, **107**, 7914.
7. R. A. Jones, F. M. Real, G. Wilkinson, A. M. R. Galas and M. B. Hursthouse, *J. Chem. Soc. Dalton Trans.*, 1981, 126.

(continued)

References (*continued*)

8. J. P. Attard, B. F. G. Johnson, J. Lewis, J. M. Mace, M. McPartlin and A. Sironi, *J. Chem. Soc. Chem. Commun.*, 1984, 595.
9. S. Martinengo, G. Ciani and A. Sironi, *J. Chem. Soc. Chem. Commun.*, 1986, 1282.
10. G. Ciani, L. Garlaschelli, A. Sironi and S. Martinengo, *J. Chem. Soc. Chem. Commun.*, 1981, 536.
11. J. L. Vidal, W. E. Walker and R. C. Schoening, *Inorg. Chem.*, 1981, **20**, 238.
12. J. L. Vidal, *Inorg. Chem.*, 1981, **20**, 243.
13. C. M. Hayward, J. R. Shapley, M. R. Churchill, C. Bueno and M. R. Rheingold, *J. Am. Chem. Soc.*, 1982, **104**, 7347.
14. B. F. G. Johnson, J. Lewis, W. J. H. Nelson, P. R. Raithby and M. D. Vargas, *J. Chem. Soc. Chem. Commun.*, 1983, 608.
15. G. Longoni, A. Ceriotti, R. Della Pergola, M. Manassero, M. Perego, G. Piro and M. Sansoni, *Philos. Trans. R. Soc. London, Ser. A*, 1982, **308**, 47.
16. A. Ceriotti, G. Longoni, M. Manassero, N. Masciocchi, L. Resconi, and M. Sansoni, *J. Chem. Soc. Chem. Commun.*, 1985, 181.
17. E. G. Mednikov, N. K. Eremenko, Yu. L. Slovokhotov, Yu. T. Struchkov, and S. P. Gubin, *J. Organomet. Chem.*, 1983, **258**, 247.
18. E. G. Mednikov, N. K. Eremenko, S. P. Gubin, Yu. L. Slovokhotov and Yu. T. Struchkov, *J. Organomet. Chem.*, 1982, **239**, 401.
19. G. Longoni, M. Manassero and M. Sansoni, *J. Am. Chem. Soc.*, 1980, **102**, 7973.
20. J. N. Nicholls, P. R. Raithby and M. D. Vargas, *J. Chem. Soc. Chem. Commun.*, 1986, in press.
21. D. Fenske and J. Hachgenei, *Angew. Chem. Int. Ed. Engl.*, 1986, **25**, 175.
22. C. E. Briant, K. P. Hall, A. C. Wheeler and D. M. P. Mingos, *J. Chem. Soc. Chem. Commun.*, 1984, 248.

$[Co_4As_6(PR_3)_4]$ has a cluster core consisting of a tricapped tetrahedron sharing a face with an octahedron.

The gold cluster $[Au_{10}(PPh(C_6H_5)_2)_6Cl_3]^+$ has a C_{3v} cluster geometry based on three trigonal bipyramids sharing a common vertex.

2.2.3.9. Larger Clusters

There are a group of three clusters, $[AuOs_{10}C(CO)_{24}PPh_3]^-$, $[AuOs_{10}C(CO)_{24}Br]^-$, and $[CuOs_{10}C(CO)_{24}MeCN]^-$, which are based on the Os_{10} core with the addition of heteroatoms. In the first case the gold atom bridges two of the atoms of the Os_{10} unit, one of which is an apical osmium atom. In the latter two clusters the heteroatom is connected to another nonapical osmium atom. The structures of these and other 11-atom clusters are illustrated in Figure 2.10.

$[Rh_{11}(CO)_{23}]^{3-}$ and $[Pt_2Rh_9(CO)_{22}]^{3-}$ have a similar metal cluster core consisting of three face-sharing octahedra. In the platinum/rhodium cluster the platinum atoms occupy the highest connectivity sites. $[PtRh_{10}N(CO)_{21}]^{3-}$ has a complex cluster core made up of a tricapped trigonal prism with two further capping atoms linking two of the prism caps. The platinum atom also occupies the highest connectivity vertex in this cluster.

$[Os_{11}C(CO)_{27}]^{2-}$ has a complex metal framework that can be described as a bi-end-capped trigonal prism sharing a square face with a bicapped square pyramid. In contrast, $[Co_{11}C_2(CO)_{22}]^{3-}$ has a square antiprism sharing a square face with a square-face-capped trigonal prism.

The Au_{11} clusters such as $[Au_{11}(PPh_3)_7(SCN)_3]$ all have a centered trirhombohedron, which may be derived from the icosahedron by replacing one triangular face with a single vertex, as the core of the cluster.

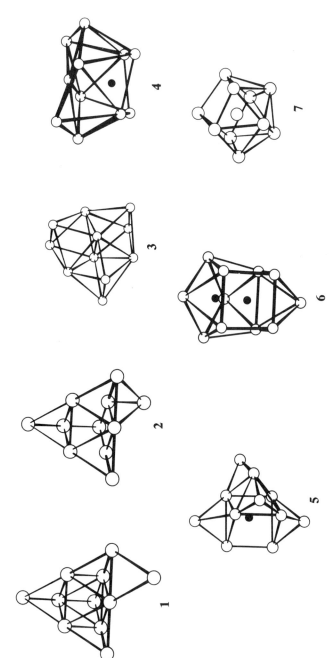

Figure 2.10 ▪ Examples of the 11-vertex cluster compounds referred to in Table 2.27.

Table 2.27 ▪ Clusters with More than Ten Vertices

Compound	No. of Valence Electrons	Structure (Fig. 2)	Ref.
11 atoms			
$[AuOs_{10}C(CO)_{24}(PPh_3)]^-$	146	10.1	1
$[AuOs_{10}C(CO)_{24}(Br)]^-$	145	10.1	2
$[CuOs_{10}C(CO)_{24}(NCMe)]^-$	146	10.2	1
$[Rh_{11}(CO)_{23}]^{3-}$	148	10.3	3
$[Pt_2Rh_9(CO)_{22}]^{3-}$	148	10.3	4
$[PtRh_{10}N(CO)_{21}]^{3-}$	150	10.4	5
$[Os_{11}C(CO)_{27}]^{2-}$	148	10.5	6
$[Co_{11}C_2(CO)_{22}]^{3-}$	154	10.6	7
$Au_{11}(PPh_3)_7(SCN)_3$	138	10.7	8
$Au_{11}(P(FC_6H_4)_3)_7I_3$	138	10.7	9
$Au_{11}(P(ClC_6H_4)_3)_7I_3$	138	10.7	10
$[Au_{11}(PPh_3)_7(CNPr^i)_2I]^{2+}$	138	10.7	11
$Au_{11}(PPh_3)_7I_3$	138	10.7	12
$[Au_{11}(Ph_2P(CH_2)_3PPh_2)_5]^{3+}$	138	10.7	13
12 atoms			
$Rh_{12}C_2(CO)_{25}$	166	11.1	14
$[Rh_{12}C_2(CO)_{24}]^{2-}$	166	11.2	15
$[Rh_{12}C_2(CO)_{23}]^{3-}$	167	11.2	16
$[Rh_{12}C_2(CO)_{23}]^{4-}$	168	11.2	17
$[HRh_{12}N_2(CO)_{23}]^{3-}$	166	11.3	18
$[Ni_{12}(CO)_{21}]^{4-}$	166	11.4	19
$[HNi_{12}(CO)_{21}]^{3-}$	166	11.4	20
$[H_2Ni_{12}(CO)_{21}]^{2-}$	166	11.4	20
$[Ni_9As_3(CO)_{15}Ph_3]^{2-}$	170	11.5	21
$[Ni_{10}As_2(CO)_{18}Me_2]^{2-}$	170	11.5	21
$[Os_{11}CuC(CO)_{27}(MeCN)]^-$	160	11.6	6
$[HFe_6Pd_6(CO)_{24}]^{3-}$	160	11.7	22
$Os_9Hg_3(CO)_3$	154	11.8	23
$[Co_3Ni_9C(CO)_{20}]^{3-}$	164	11.9	24
$Re_8In_4(CO)_{32}$	172	11.10	25
$[Rh_{12}(CO)_{30}]^{2-}$	170	11.11	26
$[H_2Rh_{12}(CO)_{25}]$	160	11.12	27
$[Ir_{12}(CO)_{26}]^{2-}$	162	11.12	28
13 atoms			
$[Ru_{12}TlC_2(CO)_{32}]^-$	162	12.1	29
$[Co_{13}C_2(CO)_{24}]^{4-}$	177	12.2	30
$[Co_{13}C_2(CO)_{24}]^{3-}$	176	12.2	31
$[HRh_{13}(CO)_{24}]^{4-}$	170	12.3	32
$[H_2Rh_{13}(CO)_{24}]^{3-}$	170	12.3	33
$[H_3Rh_{13}(CO)_{24}]^{2-}$	170	12.3	34
$[PtRh_{12}(CO)_{24}]^{4-}$	170	12.3	35
$[Pt_2Rh_{11}(CO)_{24}]^{3-}$	170	12.4	35
$[Rh_{12}Sb(CO)_{27}]^{3-}$	170	12.5	35
$[Au_{13}Cl_2(PMePh_2)_{10}]^{3+}$	162	12.5	36
$[Au_{13}(Ph_2PCH_2PPh_2)_6]^{4+}$	162	12.5	37

(continued)

Table 2.27 *Continued* ▪ Clusters with More than Ten Vertices

Compound	No. of Valence Electrons	Structure (Fig. 2)	Ref.
$[AgRh_{12}C_2(CO)_{30}]^{3-}$	186	12.6	38
14 atoms			
$[Rh_{14}(CO)_{26}]^{2-}$	180	13.1	39
$[Rh_{14}(CO)_{25}]^{4-}$	180	13.1	40
$[HRh_{14}(CO)_{25}]^{3-}$	180	13.1	41
$[Rh_{14}C_2(CO)_{33}]^{2-}$	220	13.2	42
15 atoms			
$[Rh_{15}(CO)_{27}]^{3-}$	192	14.1	43
$[Rh_{15}(CO)_{30}]^{2-}$	197	14.2	44
$[Rh_{15}C_2(CO)_{28}]^{-}$	200	14.3	45
$[Pt_{15}(CO)_{30}]^{2-}$	212	14.4	46
16 atoms			
$[Ni_{16}(C_2)_2(CO)_{23}]^{4-}$	216	15.1	47
$Fe_{10}Tl_6(CO)_{36}]^{6-}$	236	15.2	48
17 atoms			
$[Rh_{17}(CO)_{30}]^{3-}$	216	16.1	49
$[Rh_{17}S_2(CO)_{32}]^{3-}$	232	16.2	50
19 atoms			
$[Pt_{19}(CO)_{22}]^{4-}$	238	17	51
21 atoms			
$[AuOs_{20}C_2(CO)_{48}]^{2-}$	277	18	2
$[HgOs_{20}C_2(CO)_{48}]^{2-}$	278	18	2
22 atoms			
$[Rh_{22}(CO)_{37}]^{4-}$	276	19.1	52
$[Rh_{22}(CO)_{35}H_x]^{5-}$	$272+x$	19.2	53
$[Rh_{22}(CO)_{35}H_{x+1}]^{4-}$	$272+x$	19.2	53
23 atoms			
$[Pd_{23}(CO)_{22}(PEt_3)_{10}]$	294	20.1	54
$[Pd_{23}(CO)_{20}(PEt_3)_8]$	286	20.2	55
24 atoms			
$[Pt_{24}(CO)_{30}]^{2-}$	302	21	56
25 atoms			
$[Ag_{12}Au_{13}Cl_6(PPh_3)_{12}]^{m+}$	$305-m$	22	57
26 atoms			
$[Pt_{26}(CO)_{32}]^{2-}$	326	23.1	59
$[Pt_{26}(CO)_{30}]^{2-}$	322	23.2	59
34 atoms			
$[HNi_{34}C_4(CO)_{38}]^{5-}$	434	24.1	60
35 atoms			
$[Ni_{35}C_4(CO)_{39}]^{6-}$	448	25.1	60

(continued)

Table 2.27 *Continued* ▪ **Clusters with More than Ten Vertices**

Compound	No. of Valence Electrons	Structure (Fig. 2)	Ref.
38 atoms			
$Pd_{38}(CO)_{28}(PEt_3)_{12}$	460	26.1	61
$[HNi_{38}C_6(CO)_{42}]^{5-}$	494	26.2	62
42 atoms			
$[HNi_{38}Pt_6(CO)_{48}]^{5-}$	542	27	63
$[H_2Ni_{38}Pt_6(CO)_{48}]^{4-}$	542	27	63

References

1. D. Braga, K. Henrick, B. F. G. Johnson, J. Lewis, M. McPartlin, W. J. H. Nelson and M. D. Vargas, *J. Chem. Soc. Chem. Commun.*, 1986, 975.
2. S. R. Drake, B. F. G. Johnson, J. Lewis, M. McPartlin, K. Henrick and J. Morris, *J. Chem. Soc. Chem. Commun.*, 1986, 928.
3. A. Fumagalli, S. Martinengo, G. Ciani and A. Sironi, *J. Chem. Soc. Chem. Commun.*, 1983, 453.
4. A. Fumagalli, S. Martinengo and G. Ciani, *J. Organomet. Chem.*, 1984, **273**, C46.
5. S. Martinengo, G. Ciani and A. Sironi, *J. Am. Chem. Soc.*, 1982, **104**, 328.
6. D. Braga, K. Henrick, B. F. G. Johnson, J. Lewis, M. McPartlin, W. J. H. Nelson, A. Sironi and M. D. Vargas, *J. Chem. Soc. Chem. Commun.*, 1983, 1131.
7. V. G. Albano, D. Braga, G. Ciani and S. Martinengo, *J. Organomet. Chem.*, 1981, **213**, 293.
8. M. McPartlin, R. Mason and L. Malatesta, *J. Chem. Soc. Chem. Commun.*, 1969, 334.
9. P. Bellon, M. Manassero and M. Sansoni, *J. Chem. Soc. Dalton Trans.*, 1972, 1481.
10. V. G. Albano, P. Bellon, M. Manassero, and M. Sansoni, *J. Chem. Soc. Chem. Commun.*, 1970, 1210.
11. W. Bos, R. P. F. Kanters, C. J. Van Halen, W. P. Bosman, H. Behm, J. M. M. Smits, P. T. Beurskens, J. J. Bour and L. H. Pignolet, *J. Organomet. Chem.*, 1986, **307**, 385.
12. J. M. M. Smits, P. T. Beurskens, J. W. A. Van der Velden and J. J. Bour, *J. Cryst. Spectrosc.*, 1983, **13**, 373.
13. J. M. M. Smits, J. J. Bour, F. A. Vollenbroek and P. T. Beurskens, *J. Cryst. Spectrosc.*, 1983, **13**, 365.
14. V. G. Albano, P. Chini, S. Martinengo, M. Sansoni and D. Strumolo, *J. Chem. Soc. Dalton Trans.*, 1978, 459.
15. V. G. Albano, D. Braga, P. Chini, D. Strumolo and S. Martinengo, *J. Chem. Soc. Dalton Trans.*, 1983, 249.
16. V. G. Albano, D. Braga, S. Martinengo, C. Seregni and D. Strumolo, *J. Organomet. Chem.*, 1983, **252**, C93.
17. V. G. Albano, D. Braga, D. Strumolo, C. Seregni and S. Martinengo, *J. Chem. Soc. Dalton Trans.*, 1985, 1309.
18. S. Martinengo, G. Ciani and A. Sironi, *J. Chem. Soc. Chem. Commun.*, 1986, 1742.
19. P. Chini, G. Longoni, M. Manassero and M. Sansoni, *Abstr. Eighth Meet. Ital. Assoc. Crystallogr.*, Ferrara, Commun., 1977, **34**.
20. R. W. Broach, L. F. Dahl, G. Longoni, P. Chini, A. J. Schultz and J. M. Williams, *Adv. Chem. Ser.*, 1978, **167**, 93.
21. D. F. Rieck, R. A. Montag, T. S. McKechnie and L. F. Dahl, *J. Am. Chem. Soc.*, 1986, **108**, 1330.
22. G. Longoni, M. Manassero and M. Sansoni, *J. Am. Chem. Soc.*, 1980, **102**, 3242.
23. M. Fajardo, H. D. Holden, B. F. G. Johnson, J. Lewis and P. R. Raithby, *J. Chem. Soc. Chem. Commun.*, 1984, 24.
24. A. Ceriotti, R. Della Pergola, G. Longoni, M. Manassero and M. Sansoni, *J. Chem. Soc. Dalton Trans.*, 1984, 1181.
25. H. J. Haupt and H. Preut, *Acta Cryst.*, 1979, **B35**, 1205.
26. V. G. Albano and P. L. Bellon, *J. Organomet. Chem.*, 1969, **19**, 405.

(*continued*)

References (*continued*)

27. G. Ciani, A. Sironi and S. Martinengo, *J. Chem. Soc. Chem. Commun.*, 1985, 1757.
28. R. Della Pergola, F. Demartin, L. Garlaschelli, M. Manassero, S. Martinengo and M. Sansoni, *Inorg. Chem.*, 1987, **26**, 3487.
29. G. B. Ansell, M. A. Modrick and J. S. Bradley, *Acta Cryst.*, 1984, **C40**, 1315.
30. V. G. Albano, D. Braga, P. Chini, G. Ciani and S. Martinengo, *J. Chem. Soc. Dalton Trans.*, 1982, 645.
31. V. G. Albano, D. Braga, A. Fumagalli and S. Martinengo, *J. Chem. Soc. Dalton Trans.*, 1985, 1137.
32. G. Ciani, A. Sironi and S. Martinengo, *J. Chem. Soc. Dalton Trans.*, 1981, 519.
33. V. G. Albano, G. Ciani, S. Martinengo and A. Sironi, *J. Chem. Soc. Dalton Trans.*, 1979, 978.
34. V. G. Albano, W. M. Anker, A. Ceriotti, P. Chini, G. Ciani and S. Martinengo, *J. Chem. Soc. Chem. Commun.*, 1975, 859.
35. A. Fumagalli, S. Martinengo and G. Ciani, *J. Chem. Soc. Chem. Commun.*, 1983, 1381.
36. C. E. Briant, B. R. C. Theobald, J. W. White, L. K. Bell and D. M. P. Mingos, *J. Chem. Soc. Chem. Commun.*, 1981, 201.
37. J. W. A. Van der Velden, F. A. Vollenbroek, J. J. Bour, P. T. Beurskens, J. M. M. Smits and W. P. Bosman, *Rec. J. R. Neth. Chem. Soc.*, 1981, **100**, 148.
38. B. T. Heaton, L. Strona, S. Martinengo, D. Strumolo, V. G. Albano and D. Braga, *J. Chem. Soc. Dalton Trans.*, 1983, 2175.
39. S. Martinengo, G. Ciani and A. Sironi, *J. Chem. Soc. Chem. Commun.*, 1980, 1140.
40. G. Ciani, A. Sironi and S. Martinengo, *J. Chem. Soc. Dalton Trans.*, 1982, 1099.
41. G. Ciani, A. Sironi and S. Martinengo, *J. Organomet. Chem.*, 1980, **192**, C42.
42. S. Martinengo, D. Strumolo, P. Chini, V. G. Albano and D. Braga, *J. Chem. Soc. Dalton Trans.*, 1984, 1837.
43. S. Martinengo, G. Ciani, A. Sironi and P. Chini, *J. Am. Chem. Soc.*, 1978, **100**, 7096.
44. J. L. Vidal, L. A. Kapicak and J. M. Troup, *J. Organomet. Chem.*, 1981, **215**, C11.
45. V. G. Albano, M. Sansoni, P. Chini, S. Martinengo and D. Strumolo, *J. Chem. Soc. Dalton Trans.*, 1976, 970.
46. J. C. Calabrese, L. F. Dahl, P. Chini, G. Longoni and S. Martinengo, *J. Am. Chem. Soc.*, 1974, **96**, 2614.
47. A. Ceriotti, G. Longoni, M. Manassero, N. Masciocchi, G. Piro, L. Resconi and M. Sansoni, *J. Chem. Soc. Chem. Commun.*, 1985, 1402.
48. K. H. Whitmire, R. R. Ryan, H. J. Wasserman, T. A. Albright and Sung-Kwon Kang, *J. Am. Chem. Soc.*, 1986, **108**, 6831.
49. G. Ciani, A. Magni, A. Sironi and S. Martinengo, *J. Chem. Soc. Chem. Commun.*, 1981, 1280.
50. J. L. Vidal, R. A. Fiato, L. A. Cosby and R. L. Pruett, *Inorg. Chem.*, 1978, **17**, 2574.
51. D. M. Washecheck, E. J. Wucherer, L. F. Dahl, A. Ceriotti, G. Longoni, M. Manassero, M. Sansoni and P. Chini, *J. Am. Chem. Soc.*, 1979, **101**, 6110.
52. S. Martinengo, G. Ciani and A. Sironi, *J. Am. Chem. Soc.*, 1980, **102**, 7564.
53. J. L. Vidal, R. C. Schoening and J. M. Troup, *Inorg. Chem.*, 1981, **20**, 227.
54. E. G. Mednikov, N. K. Eremenko, Yu. L. Slovokhotov and Yu. T. Struchkov, *J. Organomet. Chem.*, 1986, **301**, C35.
55. Yu.T. Struchkov, personal communication.
56. R. A. Montag, A. Ceriotti and L. F. Dahl, *J. Am. Chem. Soc.*, in press.
57. B. K. Teo and K. Keating, *J. Am. Chem. Soc.*, 1984, **106**, 2224.
58. C. M. T. Hayward, J. R. Shapley, M. R. Churchill, C. Bueno and A. L. Rheingold, *J. Am. Chem. Soc.*, 1982, **104**, 7347.
59. D. M. Washecheck, Ph.D. thesis, University of Wisconsin—Madison, 1980.
60. A. Ceriotti, A. Fait, G. Longoni, G. Piro, L. Resconi, F. Demartin, M. Manassero, N. Masciocchi, and M. Sansoni, *J. Am. Chem. Soc.*, 1986, **108**, 5370.
61. E. G. Mednikov, N. K. Eremenko, Yu. L. Slovokhotov and Yu. T. Struchkov, *J. Chem. Soc. Chem. Commun.*, 1987, 218.
62. A. Ceriotti, A. Fait, G. Longoni and G. Piro, *J. Am. Chem. Soc.*, 1986, **108**, 8091.
63. A. Ceriotti, F. Demartin, G. Longoni, M. Manassero, M. Marchionna, G. Piva and M. Sansoni, *Angew. Chem. Int. Ed. Engl.*, 1985, **24**, 697.

$[Rh_{12}C_2(CO)_{24}]^{2-}$, $[Rh_{12}C_2(CO)_{23}]^{3-}$, and $[Rh_{12}C_2(CO)_{23}]^{4-}$ all have the metal atoms of the cluster core arranged in the form of a pair of square face-sharing square antiprisms as shown in Figure 2.11. $[Rh_{12}C_2(CO)_{25}]$ has a very irregular cluster core that could be envisaged as a distorted tetracapped cube or alternatively as a 4:5:3 stack. The structure of $[HRh_{12}N_2(CO)_{23}]^{3-}$ is not related to either of these structures. It is also an irregular structure that could be described as a distorted triangle-capped square antiprism sharing a square face with a square-capped trigonal prism so that the two capping atoms are bonded together.

$[Ni_{12}(CO)_{21}]^{4-}$, $[HNi_{12}(CO)_{21}]^{3-}$, and $[H_2Ni_{12}(CO)_{21}]^{2-}$ have similar cluster cores consisting of a pair of octahedra sharing a face with all of the shared edges bridged by a further nickel atom. The two nickel/arsenic clusters $[Ni_9As_3(CO)_{15}Ph_3]^{2-}$ and $[Ni_{10}As_2(CO)_{18}Me_2]^{2-}$ both have an icosahedral central unit if the arsenic atoms are considered to be part of the cluster cage.

$[Os_{11}CuC(CO)_{27}(MeCN)]^-$ has a central unit that rather surprisingly is unrelated to the Os_{10} clusters. The cluster core in this structure consists of a bi-triangular-face-capped trigonal prism sharing a square face with a bicapped square pyramid. The copper atom caps one of the remaining faces of the square pyramid so that it has a close interaction with one of the prism-capping atoms.

The clusters $[Os_9(CO)_{21}(CHC(R)CH)]^-$ (R = Me, Et) have a central core of metal atoms which consists of a square-based pyramid sharing two *cis*-faces with two trigonal bipyramids. In contrast, the osmium compound $[Os_3(CO)_{10}HO_2COs_6(CO)_{17}]^-$ as its formula suggests is an aggregate of two smaller clusters held together by ligands. The cluster core of $[Ni_9(CO)_{18}]^{2-}$ is made up of a trigonal prism sharing a face with an octahedron of nickel atoms. This geometry is therefore different from that noted previously for $[Pt_9(CO)_{18}]^{2-}$ and based on a stack of eclipsed triangles.

The 112-electron nine-vertex gold clusters form an interesting group because three different arrangements of metal atoms are encountered. In $[Au_9(PPh_3)_8]^{3+}$ and $[Au_9(P(C_6H_4Me)_3)_8]^{3+}$ the cluster core is based on two trigonal bipyramids sharing an equatorial vertex with the apical vertices bonded together. $[Au_9(P(C_6H_4OMe)_3)_8]^{3+}$ also adopts this structure, but a second isomer exists which has a centered crown of gold atoms. In $[Au_9(P(Cy)_3)_5(SCN)_3]$ the cluster consists of two butterfly units bonded together at the wingtips to form a ring with another gold atom in the center of the ring. The potential energy surface connecting these alternative structures is very soft, and the arrangement observed in the solid state depends on the packing forces as well as electronic effects. $[Au_9(PPh_3)_8]^+$ can be described either as a bicapped, centered chair or, alternatively, as a flattened cube.

$[Ag_6Fe_3(CO)_{12}((Ph_3P)_3CH)]$ has a core made up of a triangular raft of silver and iron atoms with iron atoms at the vertices of the triangle. Capping each of the outer triangles of the raft is a further silver atom. All three capping silver atoms are on the same side of the raft.

The bare metal clusters $[Ge_9]^{2-}$ and $[Bi_9]^{5+}$ both adopt the tricapped trigonal prism as their cluster geometry although the first has 128 valence electrons while the second has 130.

The only example of a cluster that has a hexacapped octahedron as the central unit is $[H_3Fe_6Pd_6(CO)_{24}]^{3-}$. The two uncapped faces of the octahedron are *trans*

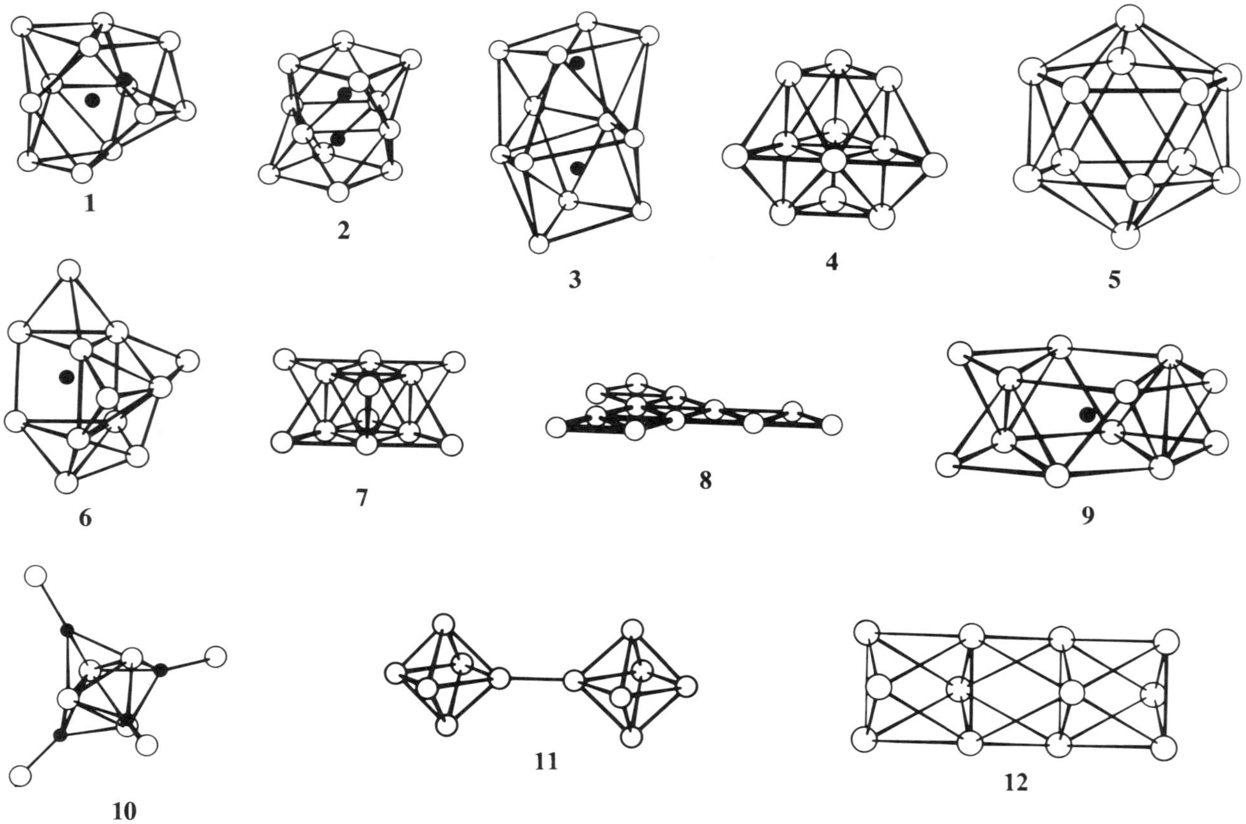

Figure 2.11 ■ The 12-vertex clusters referred to in Table 2.27.

to each other so that the cluster approximates to two close packed layers. Another unique cluster is $[Hg_3Os_9(CO)_{33}]$, which has a planar, propeller-shaped structure based on a triangle of mercury atoms.

$[Co_3Ni_9C(CO)_{20}]^{3-}$ has a cluster geometry based on a square antiprism capped on four of the triangular faces. The core of $[Re_8In_4(CO)_{32}]$ is best described as a tetrahedron of rhenium atoms with an $InRe(CO)_5$ unit bridging each face of the tetrahedron.

$[Rh_{12}(CO)_{30}]^{2-}$ is a dimeric cluster consisting of two octahedral $[Rh_6(CO)_{15}]^-$ units linked by a metal-metal bond. The final Rh_{12} cluster, $[H_2Rh_{12}(CO)_{25}]$, consists of a stack of three face-sharing octahedra of rhodium atoms. This cluster core is also found in $[Ir_{12}(CO)_{26}]^{2-}$ but the iridium cluster has two more electrons than the rhodium cluster, presumably because of the hydride ligands in the rhodium cluster.

$[Ru_{12}TlC_2(CO)_{32}]^-$ is another dimeric cluster that consists of two octahedral Ru_6 units held together by a thallium ion that achieves a square-planar configuration with respect to the metal atoms of the two octahedra as shown in Figure 2.12.

$[Co_{13}C_2(CO)_{24}]^{4-}$ and $[Co_{13}C_2(CO)_{24}]^{3-}$ both have similar structures that are best described in terms of a 4:5:4 stack of metal atoms. The rhodium clusters $[HRh_{13}(CO)_{24}]^{4-}$, $[H_2Rh_{13}(CO)_{24}]^{3-}$, and $[H_3Rh_{13}(CO)_{24}]^{2-}$ have a much more regular cluster core in which the metal atoms are arranged in the form of a centered anticuboctahedron, while $[PtRh_{12}(CO)_{24}]^{4-}$ is an anticuboctahedron of rhodium atoms with a platinum atom in the center. This arrangement of metal atoms can be considered as a fragment of a hexagonal close-packed lattice. $[Pt_2Rh_{11}(CO)_{24}]^{3-}$ has a centered tetracapped cube as its core with one of the platinum atoms occupying the central position. $[Rh_{12}Sb(CO)_{27}]^{3-}$ has an icosahedral cluster core with a central antimony atom and $[AgRh_{12}C_2(CO)_{30}]^{3-}$ represents a sandwich cluster of two Rh_6 trigonal prisms joined together by an octahedrally coordinated silver atom.

$[Rh_{14}(CO)_{26}]^{2-}$, $[Rh_{14}(CO)_{25}]^{4-}$, and $[HRh_{14}(CO)_{25}]^{3-}$ all have similar cluster frameworks that consist of a centered pentacapped cube of metal atoms. This arrangement of metal atoms, shown in Figure 2.13, approximates to a fragment of a body-centered cubic lattice. $[Rh_{14}C_2(CO)_{33}]^{3-}$ is another example of a cluster that can be considered to be dimeric in nature, although in this case three of the ligands bridge the bond connecting the two units together. The cluster core consists of two trigonal prisms of rhodium atoms each of which has a capping atom on one triangular face. The two capping atoms are bonded together to generate the 14-atom cluster.

The metal core of $[Rh_{15}(CO)_{27}]^{3-}$ shown in Figure 2.14 consists of a distorted centered anticuboctahedron of rhodium atoms with capping rhodium atoms on two of the square faces of the anticuboctahedron. In contrast, $[Rh_{15}(CO)_{30}]^{2-}$ has a cluster core that is best described as a body-centered cube of rhodium atoms with capping rhodium atoms on six of the square faces. The geometry of the metal atom cluster in $[Rh_{15}C_2(CO)_{28}]^-$ is different again. In this case, it can most simply be described as a centered bicapped pentagonal prism of metal atoms with two further metal atoms capping square faces of the prism. $[Pt_{15}(CO)_{30}]^{3-}$ consists of a stack of five nearly eclipsed Pt_3 rings.

$[Ni_{16}(C_2)_2(CO)_{23}]^{2-}$ has a complex cluster core with a large cavity that has enough space to contain two dicarbide units. It can be thought of as a 4: 6: 4 stack

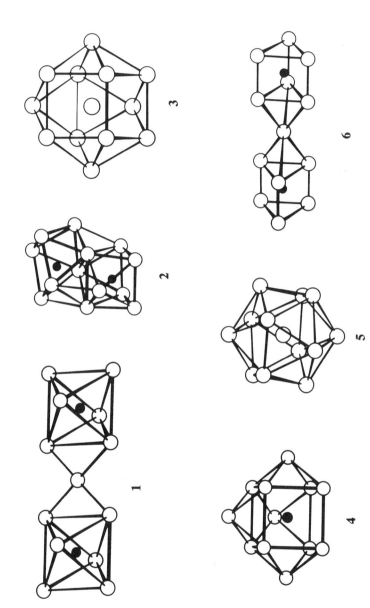

Figure 2.12 ▪ Illustrations of the 13-atom clusters from Table 2.27.

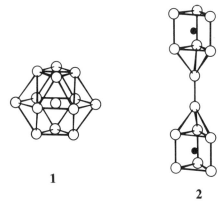

Figure 2.13 ▪ The two Rh_{14} cluster metal frameworks referred to in Table 2.27.

of atoms arranged as six trigonal prisms sharing square faces with a further two atoms capping two of the square faces.

The structure of $[Fe_{10}Tl_6(CO)_{36}]^{6-}$ is extremely complex. It is based upon two Fe_2Tl_3 trigonal bipyramids that have a further iron atom attached to two of the thallium atoms of each bipyramid while the other thallium atoms share two iron atoms with an equivalent thallium in the other bipyramid. The structures of these 16-atom clusters are shown in Figure 2.15.

$[Rh_{17}(CO)_{30}]^{3-}$ has a cluster unit based on the Rh_{13} anticuboctahedron. Four of the square faces of this unit have capping rhodium atoms over them to give the total of 17 metal atoms. The core of $[Rh_{17}S_2(CO)_{32}]^{3-}$ can be considered to be made up of three square antiprisms sharing square faces with a sulphur atom in the center of the outer antiprisms and a metal atom in the middle of the central one. Figure 2.16 illustrates the structures of these clusters.

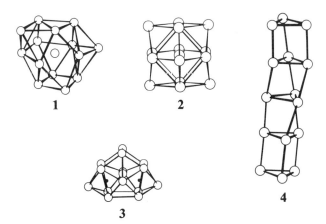

Figure 2.14 ▪ The four different 15-atom cluster cores.

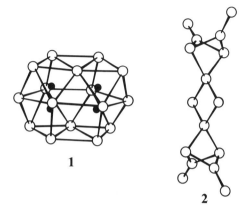

1

2

Figure 2.15 ▪ Illustrations of the 16-vertex cluster cores referred to in Table 2.27.

In contrast to the smaller platinum clusters $[Pt_{19}(CO)_{22}]^{4-}$ (Figure 2.17) has a structure that is based on two interpenetrating centered bicapped pentagonal prisms. One ring of five metal atoms and the two central atoms are shared by the two pentagonal prisms.

The two clusters $[AuOs_{20}C_2(CO)_{48}]^{2-}$ and $[HgOs_{20}C_2(CO)_{48}]^{2-}$ have an identical geometry (Figure 2.18) that can be described as two tricapped octahedra joined together through a ring of three atoms (one of which is the heteroatom) so that two twisted face-sharing trigonal prisms are formed between the tricapped octahedra.

The structure of $[Rh_{22}(CO)_{37}]^{4-}$ can be thought of as a centered anticuboctahedron with a cap on each square face and a triangle of atoms on top. The result is a 3: 6: 7: 6 stack of rhodium atoms as shown in Figure 2.19.

The cluster cores of $[H_xRh_{22}(CO)_{35}]^{5-}$ and $[H_{(x+1)}Rh_{22}(CO)_{35}]^{4-}$ consist of two distorted body-centered cubes sharing a square face. Six of the remaining square faces are capped so that the caps all lie approximately in one plane. This arrangement of metal atoms, shown in Figure 2.19, is clearly a fragment of a body-centered cubic lattice.

The two palladium clusters $[Pd_{23}(CO)_{22}(PEt_3)_{10}]$ and $[Pd_{23}(CO)_{20}(PEt_3)_8]$

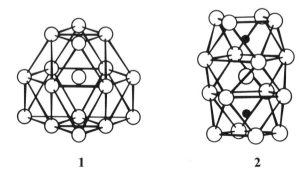

1   **2**

Figure 2.16 ▪ The two examples of Rh_{17} cluster metal frameworks.

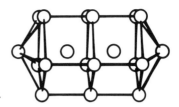

Figure 2.17 ■ The Pt_{19} cluster core geometry.

shown in Figure 2.20 both have different structures due to the different electron counts of 294 and 286, respectively. The former has a cluster nucleus consisting of a 19-atom octahedron of palladium atoms with a further 4 palladium atoms bridging the central atoms on 4 of the 6 faces of the octahedron. The latter cluster has a nucleus that consists of a centered cube capped on each face and on 8 of the 12 edges.

$[Ag_{12}Au_{13}Cl_6(PPh_3)_{12}]^{m+}$ has a structure that is similar to that of $[Pt_{19}(CO)_{22}]^{4-}$ (Figure 2.22). It consists of three interpenetrating icosahedra in a line so that the pentagonal rings are staggered rather than eclipsed as in the platinum cluster.

$[Pt_{26}(CO)_{32}]^{2-}$, which is illustrated in Figure 2.23, has a cluster core that approximates to a fragment of a hexagonal close-packed lattice with a 7: 12: 7 stack of metal atoms.

The two carbide clusters $[HNi_{34}C_4(CO)_{38}]^{5-}$ and $[Ni_{35}C_4(CO)_{39}]^{6-}$, shown in Figures 2.24 and 2.25, respectively, have closely related structures. The extra metal atom in the higher nuclearity cluster caps one of the surface bonds of the smaller cluster.

The largest clusters known at present are $[H_2Ni_{38}Pt_6(CO)_{48}]^{4-}$ and $[HNi_{38}Pt_6(CO)_{48}]^{5-}$, which have the aesthetically beautiful 42-atom octahedron shown in Figure 2.27 as the core of the cluster. The platinum atoms form an inner octahedron at the center of the cluster. $[Pd_{38}(CO)_{28}(PEt_3)_{12}]$ has a similar structure derived from that of the larger cluster by the removal of six vertices as shown in Figure 2.26. The other cluster shown in Figure 2.26, $[HNi_{38}C_6(CO)_{42}]^{5-}$, has a rather more complicated structure which is not obviously related to any of the other large nickel clusters.

2.2.4. Summary

The previous sections have indicated a diverse and at times bewildering array of three-dimensional structural possibilities for metal cluster compounds. The pattern

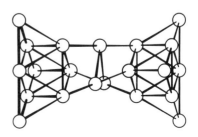

Figure 2.18 ■ The $Os_{20}M$ (M = Au, Hg) cluster core referred to in Table 2.27.

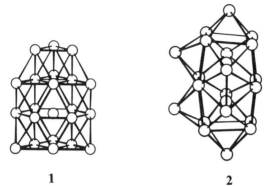

1   2

Figure 2.19 ▪ The two Rh$_{22}$ cluster cores.

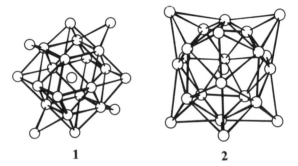

1   2

Figure 2.20 ▪ The alternative Pd$_{23}$ cluster nuclei.

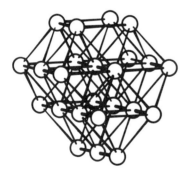

Figure 2.21 ▪ The cluster framework of the Pt$_{24}$ cluster.

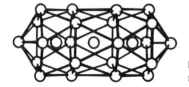

Figure 2.22 ▪ An illustration of the Ag$_{12}$Au$_{13}$ cluster nucleus.

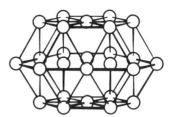

Figure 2.23 ■ The cluster core of $[Pt_{26}(CO)_{32}]^{2-}$

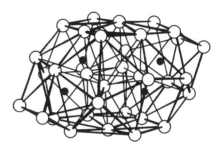

Figure 2.24 ■ The nucleus of the $[HNi_{34}C_4(CO)_{38}]^{5-}$ cluster.

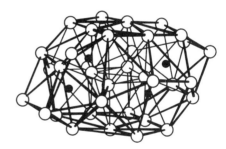

Figure 2.25 ■ The cluster core of $[Ni_{35}C_4(CO)_{39}]^{6-}$

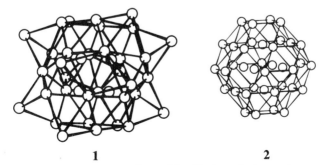

1   2

Figure 2.26 ■ Illustrations of the 38-atom cluster cores.

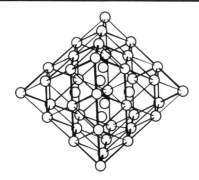

Figure 2.27 ▪ The $Ni_{38}Pt_6$ cluster nucleus.

is richer and has more dimensions than that which has been established for the borane and hydrocarbon polyhedral molecules, because the constituent metal atoms do not always have the same tendency to conform to the inert gas rule. Furthermore, the greater diversity in the electronic and steric requirements of the ligands associated with the metal cluster introduces new degrees of freedom not available in main group chemistry. The hydrocarbons $[C_nH_n]$ and the boranes $[B_nH_n]$ can form related derivatives where the hydrogens are replaced by other organic radicals or by halides, but these modifications generally do not have dramatic structural consequences. In contrast, the carbonyl ligands in $[M_n(CO)_m]$ can be replaced by phosphines with a wide range of Tolman cone angles,[119] cyclic polyenes, nitrosyls, main group atoms (e.g., P, S, Te), and radicals (e.g., PR, PR_2, SR). The following interesting differences between main group and transition metal polyhedral molecules can be identified.

The transition metals have a greater facility for forming low nuclearity clusters based on triangles, tetrahedra, octahedra, and prisms. Analogues of these polyhedral molecules are known in main group chemistry, for example, C_3H_6—cyclopropane, B_4Cl_4—tetrahedral, $B_6H_6^{2-}$—octahedral, C_6Me_6—hexamethyl prismane, but they tend to be highly reactive because of the strain energies associated with the 60° and 90° intracage bond angles. The availability of d orbitals for the transition metals reduces and perhaps even completely removes the strain energies associated with these low nuclearity polyhedra.

The boranes $B_nH_n^{2-}$ ($n = 6$–12) adopt deltahedral geometries and the hydrocarbons, C_nH_n three-connected polyhedra. For both elements it is possible to form large cages that do not have interstitial atoms. The most spectacular example is of course dodecahedrane, $C_{20}H_{20}$. Analogues of some of these structures are known for the transition metals, but for the higher nuclearity examples they are either associated with an interstitial atom or require main group atoms as part of the cage. For example, $[Rh_{12}Sb(CO)_{27}]^{3-}$ has an icosahedral metal cage geometry closely related to that observed for the borane $[B_{12}H_{12}]^{2-}$, but in the former example the cage is stabilized by the interstitial Sb atom. Similarly, although $[Ni_9(AsPh)_3(CO)_{15}]^{2-}$ and $[Ni_{10}(AsMe)_2(CO)_{17}]^{2-}$ have a Ni-As icosahedral cage geometry the corresponding homometallic $[Ni_{12}(CO)_{26}]^{2-}$ cluster is not known. The interstitial atoms clearly play an important role in the stabilization of high nuclearity metal clusters by strengthening the cluster radial bonding, and the structural survey given earlier has provided numerous examples of such cluster compounds.

The metal carbonyl clusters form a greater variety of "condensed ' cluster compounds derived from smaller moieties by sharing of vertices, edges, and faces. These condensation processes of course result in a significant increase in the cluster connectivities of the metal atoms at the points of intersection of the polyhedra involved in the condensation process. Since the metal atoms are able to sustain close-packed arrangements more readily than main group atoms, this assists the formation of condensed clusters. The permutation of these polyhedra and the alternative condensation processes involving vertex, edge, and face sharing leads to the tremendous range of possible cluster types.

For high nuclearity clusters these condensation processes lead to close-packed arrangements that can be frequently related to fragments of the bulk metal structures. For example, $[H_5Rh_{13}(CO)_{25}]$ has a centered anticuboctahedral arrangement that can be derived from hexagonal close-packing. The three layers have an ABA arrangement and the interstitial rhodium has a coordination number of twelve. $[Rh_{17}(CO)_{30}]^{3-}$ has a related structure based on an anticuboctahedron with four additional metal atoms capping the square faces.

2.3. Polyhedral Skeletal Electron Pair Approach[120]

The survey of structural data given in the previous sections has indicated that there is not a simple relationship between the number of valence electrons and the structure of the cluster. The pattern is more complex because transition metals do not all conform to the noble gas rule. For the later transition metals there is a pronounced tendency to form 16- and 14-electron complexes rather than 18-electron complexes. For example, Ni, Pd, Pt, Rh, and Ir form a wide range of square-planar, d^8, 16-electron complexes and Cu, Ag, Au, and Hg form many linear, d^{10}, 14-electron complexes. Therefore in order to interpret the structures of cluster compounds it is necessary to relate the total number of valence electrons to the topological aspects of the metal polyhedron and the valency requirements of the individual metal atoms. At the beginning of the 1970s, as a result of molecular orbital calculations that had been completed on individual polyhedral molecules, a set of structural generalizations for main group and transition metal polyhedral molecules emerged.[120-130] The historical development of these generalizations has been discussed in some detail elsewhere[131] and will not be repeated here. In this chapter these generalizations will be summarized in terms of specific rules that are applicable to the majority of cluster compounds where the individual metal atoms conform to the noble gas rule. In a subsequent section exceptions to the rules will be described in a systematic fashion.

2.3.1. Rules
Rule 1: Ring cluster compounds are characterized by $16m$ valence electrons where m is the number of cluster metal atoms.

In a two-dimensional ring compound it is possible to describe the bonding in terms of a localized bonding model as long as the constituent metal-containing fragments are capable of contributing at least two orbitals for skeletal bonding. The formation of such localized bonds and the attainment of the 18-electron configuration at each metal atom leads to a total of $16m$ valence electrons for ring compounds. Examples of triangular cluster compounds with 48 valence electrons

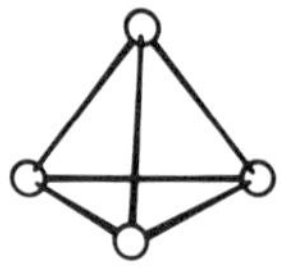

Tetrahedron, 60 valence electrons
$Co_4(CO)_{12}$, $Rh_4(CO)_{12}$

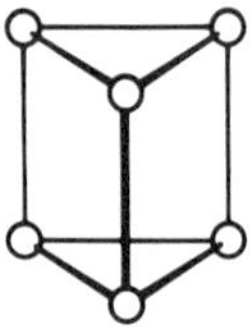

Trigonal prism, 90 electrons
$[Rh_6C(CO)_{15}]^{2-}$—central
carbido- donates four electrons

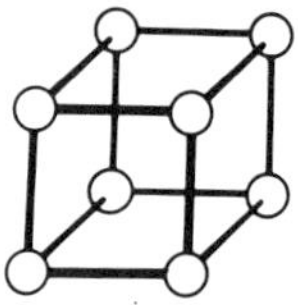

Cube, 120 valence electrons
$Ni_8(PPh)_6(CO)_8$—PPh ligands
bridge faces and are four electron
donors.

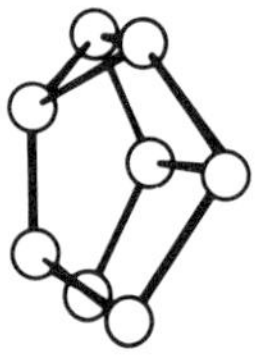

"Cuneane," 120 valence electrons
$[Co_8S_2(NBu^t)_4(NO)_8]$—NBu^t and
S act as bridging ligands and
donate four electrons.

Figure 2.28 ▪ Some three-connected polyhedra.

and square cluster compounds with 64 valence electrons are summarized in Tables 2.3 and 2.7. The introduction of metal atoms that do not conform to the 18-electron rule and multiple bonding between the metal atoms leads to exceptions to this generalization that will be discussed in Section 2.4 of this chapter.

Rule 2: Three connected polyhedral molecules are characterized by a total of 15m valence electrons

The formation of localized two-center two-electron bonds between each of the metal atoms in these three-dimensional polyhedral molecules requires each metal atom fragment to contribute three orbitals for skeletal bonding. Within the terminology of the isolobal analogy[132-135] this corresponds to each of the metal-containing fragments being isolobal with either CH or BH. Fragments that satisfy this requirement include $Ni(\eta—C_5H_5)$, $Fe(CO)_3$, $Co(PR_3)_3$, and $Rh(B_z)$ (B_z = polypyrazolylborate). Examples of clusters that conform to this generalization are summarized in Figure 2.28, together with the electron-donating characteristics of the terminal and bridging ligands. Molecular orbital calculations have indicated that the interstitial atoms effectively contribute all of their valence electrons to the total valence electron count,[136-140] because they interact strongly with symmetry matching radial and tangential skeletal molecular orbitals. Further examples of three connected clusters with 15m valence electrons are summarized in Tables 2.5 and 2.18. If the metal-containing fragment contributes less than three orbitals for skeletal bonding, then it is no longer possible to form localized bonds along the edges of the polyhedron. For example, PtL_2 and AuL fragments generally contribute only two and one valence orbitals for skeletal bonding respectively and it is necessary to discuss the bonding in terms of multicentered bonding schemes. These exceptions are discussed in more detail below.

Octahedron, 86 valence electrons
$Rh_6(CO)_{16}$

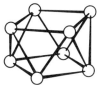

Square antiprism, 114 valence electrons
$[Co_8C(CO)_{18}]^{2-}$

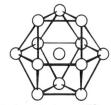

Anticuboctahedron, 170 valence electrons
$[Rh_{13}(CO)_{24}H_3]^{2-}$
Interstitial rhodium donates nine electrons

Figure 2.29 ▪ Four-connected polyhedra.

Rule 3: Four-connected polyhedral molecules are characterized by a total of $14m + 2$ valence electrons as long as the metal atoms lie approximately on a single spherical surface.

Metal carbonyl fragments generally utilize only three orbitals for skeletal bonding and therefore it is no longer possible to describe the bonding in four-connected clusters in terms of localized edge bonds. It has been shown that the skeletal bonding molecular orbitals are most satisfactorily explained in terms of a free electron spherical model.[141-145] A spherical arrangement of m atoms which are highly connected is characterized by one radial and m tangential bonding molecular orbitals. Occupation of these orbitals, the metal-carbonyl bonding M.O's and the nonbonding orbitals localized predominantly on the metal leads to a characteristic valence electron count of $14m + 2$.

Some examples of four-connected polyhedral molecules that conform to this generalization are illustrated in Figure 2.29. The octahedral geometry has been noted with either an interstitial atom, for example $[Ru_6C(CO)_{17}]$, or without, for example $[Rh_6(CO)_{16}]$. Additional examples of octahedral clusters with 86 valence electrons are summarized in Table 2.14. The square antiprismatic geometry is found in $[Co_8C(CO)_{18}]^{2-}$ and the anticuboctahedral geometry in $[H_3Rh_{13}(CO)_{24}]^{2-}$. In the latter example the interstitial rhodium atom contributes a total of nine valence electrons.

Rule 4: *Closo-*, *Nido-*, and *Arachno-* deltahedral clusters are characterized by $14m + 2$, $14m + 4$, and $14m + 6$ valence electrons, respectively.

Molecular orbital calculations on specific examples of deltahedral cluster compounds have demonstrated that in high connectivity situations the bonding is best described in terms of a spherical electron density model.[141,142] In common with the

Trigonal bipyramid, 72 electrons
$[Os_5(CO)_{15}]^{2-}$

Octahedron, 86 electrons
$Rh_6(CO)_{16}$

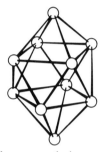

Bicapped square antiprism,
142 valence electrons—$[Rh_{10}S(CO)_{22}]^{2-}$

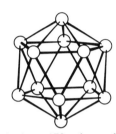

Icosahedron, 170 valence electrons
$[Rh_{12}Sb(CO)_{27}]^{3-}$

Figure 2.30 ▪ Illustrations of some deltahedra.

conclusions derived for four-connected molecules, deltahedral clusters are characterized by $m+1$ bonding skeletal molecular orbitals and a total of $14m+2$ valence electrons. Some examples of deltahedral transition metal cluster compounds are illustrated in Figure 2.30. These structures closely resemble those established for the borane anions, $B_nH_n^{2-}$ ($n = 5$–12); however, for the transition metal carbonyl clusters examples of pentagonal bipyramidal, dodecahedral, and tricapped trigonal prismatic clusters have not been structurally characterized. In the higher nuclearity clusters illustrated in the figure, for example the bicapped square antiprism and the icosahedron, the size of the cavity is sufficiently large to accommodate rather large main group atoms such as S and Sb.

In borane chemistry the structure formed by the removal of a vertex of a *closo*- deltahedral cluster is described as *nido*- and that formed by the removal of two vertices as *arachno*-. The series of ions $BmHm^{2-}$, $Bm - 1Hm - 1^{4-}$, and $Bm - 2Hm - 2^{6-}$ are structurally related because they are all characterized by $m + 1$ bonding skeletal bonding molecular orbitals.[144] It follows that for a series of boranes with the same number of boron atoms (m) the *closo*-, *nido*-, and *arachno*- structural variants are characterized by $4m+2$, $4m+4$, and $4m+6$ valence electrons. Corresponding series of transition metal carbonyl clusters with $14m+2$ (*closo*-), $14m+4$ (*nido*-), and $14m+6$ (*arachno*-) valence electrons are well established. Such a series based on the octahedron is illustrated in Figure 2.31. The butterfly geometry requires the loss of two adjacent vertices, but there is an alternative geometry based on the loss of *trans*- vertices and leading to a square-planar metal geometry.

The clusters $[Ru_4(CO)_{11}(\mu\text{-PR})_2L]$ provide examples of these *arachno*-

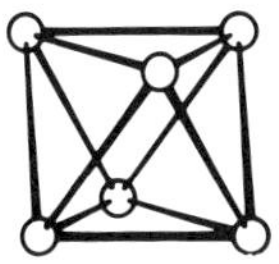

closo-
octahedron, 86 valence electrons
Rh$_6$(CO)$_{16}$

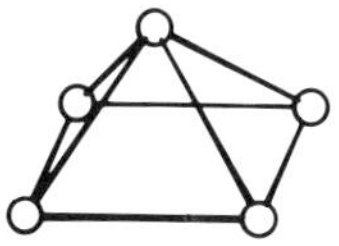

nido-
square pyramid, 74 valence electrons
Os$_5$C(CO)$_{15}$

arachno-
butterfly, 62 valence electrons
[Os$_4$N(CO)$_{12}$]$^-$

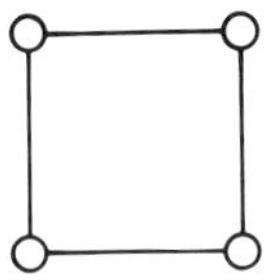

arachno-
square, 62 electrons
Fe$_4$(CO)$_{11}$(PPh)$_2$

Figure 2.31 ▪ The derivation of *nido-* and *arachno-* structures from the *closo-* octahedron.

octahedra and are characterized by 62 valence electrons. Since it is also possible to generate square-planar metal geometries with 64 valence electrons (i.e., ring cluster compounds with $16m$ valence electrons), there are related series of compounds with similar skeletal geometries but different electron counts. Such compounds with μ_4-capping main group atoms have been studied in some detail by Vahrenkamp, Haines, and their co-workers.[146-147] A detailed theoretical analysis has been developed by Halet and Saillard.[148] Examples of these alternatives are summarized below:

62 electrons	64 electrons
Fe$_4$(CO)$_{10}$(P(OMe)$_3$)(PC$_6$H$_4$Me)$_2$	Fe$_4$(CO)$_{11}$(P(OMe)$_3$)(PC$_6$H$_4$Me)$_2$
Fe$_3$Rh(CO)$_8$(Cp*)(PPh)$_2$	[Fe$_3$Rh(CO)$_8$(Cp*)(PPh)$_2$]$^{2-}$
[Fe$_3$Rh(CO)$_9$(Cp*)(PPh)$_2$]$^{2+}$	Fe$_3$Rh(CO)$_9$(Cp*)(PPh)$_2$
Fe$_4$(CO)$_{11}$(PPh)$_2$	Co$_2$Fe$_2$(CO)$_{11}$(PPh)$_2$

In some instances it has proved possible to move from one class to the other by either electrochemical or chemical means.

A second series of *closo-*, *nido-*, and *arachno-* structures based on the bicapped square antiprism is illustrated in Figure 2.32. The *arachno-* cluster [Ni$_8$C(CO)$_{16}$]$^{2-}$ with 118 valence electrons has been derived from the parent molecule by the removal of two *trans-* vertices. It is structurally identical to a four-connected square antiprism which is associated with $14m+2$ valence electrons, for example [Co$_8$C(CO)$_{18}$]$^{2-}$ with 114 valence electrons. Therefore, the alternative classifications of the square antiprism as either a four-connected polyhedron or an *arachno-*deltahedron lead to alternative electron counts and the possibility of some interesting electrochemical transformations.

Rule 5: The total electron count for a condensed polyhedron is equal to the sum of the characteristic electron counts for the parent polyhedra (A) and

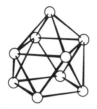

closo-	*nido-*	*arachno-*
Bicapped square antiprism	Capped square antiprism	Square antiprism
142 valence electrons	130 valence electrons	118 valence electrons
$[Rh_{10}S(CO)_{22}]^{2-}$	$[Ni_9C(CO)_{17}]^{2-}$	$[Ni_8C(CO)_{16}]^{2-}$
$14m + 2$	$14m + 4$	$14m + 6$

Figure 2.32 ▪ The derivation of some *nido-* and *arachno-* cluster cores from the bicapped square antiprism.

(*B*) minus the electron count of the atom, pair of atoms, or face of atoms common to both polyhedra.[149-150]

The characteristic electron counts are:

18 for a common vertex

34 for a common edge

48 (50) for a common triangle

62 (64) for a common square

Many transition metal carbonyl cluster compounds have condensed structures based on vertex-, edge-, and face-sharing polyhedra and this rule defines how the closed shell requirements of such molecules can be estimated. The general features of this rule are summarized in schematic fashion in Figure 2.33.

For a pair of clusters sharing a common vertex the total electron count is the sum of those of the constituent polyhedra minus 18 for the common vertex. Some examples of this type of condensation process are illustrated in Figure 2.34. In the first example the 78-electron bow-tie clusters are generated by the condensation of two triangles. In the second example a triangle and a trigonal bipyramid share a common vertex to generate a seven-atom cluster with a total of 102 valence electrons. The simultaneous condensation of two polyhedra through two nonadjacent vertices has been observed; for example, the 76 valence electron bi-diminished pentagonal bipyramids listed in Table 2.11 can be derived from the condensation of a "butterfly" (62 valence electrons) and a chain of three atoms ($+50$ valence electrons) through the two wingtip positions ($-2 \times 18 = 76$ valence electrons). There are also many examples of vertex-sharing clusters where the common atom is a metal which does not usually conform to the 18-electron rule (e.g., Cu, Ag, Au, Hg, Pd, and Pt). The closed shell requirements for such clusters will be discussed in a subsequent section. Some examples of edge-sharing condensed polyhedra are illustrated in Figure 2.35. In each case the observed electron count corresponds to the sum of those for the constituent polyhedra minus 34. If one of the constituent polyhedra is a triangle then the condensation is equivalent to edge-bridging of the parent polyhedron by a single metal atom and is associated with an increment in the electron count of 14 (i.e., $+48 - 34 = 14$). Successive addition of such edge-

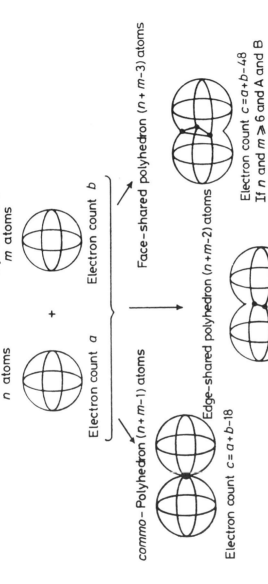

Figure 2.33 ■ Summary of the electron counting rules for condensed polyhedra derived by vertex-, edge-, and face-sharing of simple polyhedral species.

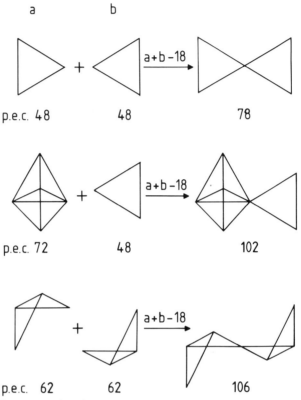

Figure 2.34 ▪ Some examples of vertex sharing between polyhedra. Examples of "bow-tie" compounds are listed in Table 2.13 while the vertex-sharing butterflies are listed in Table 2.23. An example of the 102 valence electron cluster is $[H_2Os_7(CO)_{22}]$.

bridging metal atoms leads to raft-type clusters, for example $[Os_6(CO)_{21}]$ with 90 valence electrons.[151]

In Figure 2.36 examples of clusters based on the condensation of two polyhedra sharing a common triangular face are illustrated. With one or two exceptions the observed electron count conforms to the rule $A + B - 48$, where 48 is the characteristic electron count for a metal triangle. If one of the polyhedra is a tetrahedron, the net result of condensation corresponds to capping of the parent polyhedron and an increment of the total electron count by 12. This corresponds to an alternative statement of the capping principle,[152] which states that a capped polyhedron and the parent polyhedron have an identical number of bonding skeletal molecular orbitals.

Figure 2.37 provides a nice illustration of the way in which rules 4 and 5 can be combined to provide an account of the structures of a wide range of osmium cluster compounds synthesized by the Lewis, Johnson group and characterized by McPartlin and Raithby.[153,154] The first row illustrates the *closo-*, *nido-*, and *arachno-* structures derived from the octahedron and subsequent rows illustrate the

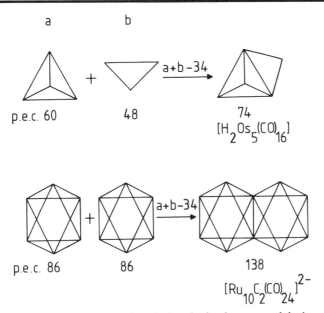

Figure 2.35 ▪ Some examples of edge sharing between polyhedra.

effect of successive capping of these structures on triangular faces. Each horizontal or vertical transition in the matrix corresponds to a change in the total number of valence electrons of 12. Figure 2.38 illustrates how edge bridging and face capping can be combined successively to build up larger condensed clusters and account for their closed shell requirements.

There are some columnar clusters where the simple electron counting rule developed earlier does not give an accurate description because the assumption that each of the metal fragments has three nonbonding d orbitals is no longer valid. A detailed molecular orbital analysis has shown that such clusters are characterized by $14m + 2 - 6(n_z - 2) + 2[(n_z - 2)/2]$ valence electrons.[158] In particular, the following series of rhodium clusters based on a column of octahedra-sharing faces conforms to this generalization.

		n_z*	Valence Electrons
$[Rh_6(CO)_{16}]$	octahedron	2	86
$[Rh_9(CO)_{19}]^{3-}$	confacial bioctahedron	3	122
$[Rh_{12}(CO)_{25}]$	three face-sharing octahedra	4	160

* n_z = number of layers in structure.

The structures of these clusters are illustrated in Figure 2.39.1–3. The structure shown in Figure 2.39.4 is derived from the confacial bioctahedron by the introduction of an additional capping atom and is electronically related to the latter by the capping principle, that is, it has a total of $122 + 12 = 134$ valence electrons.

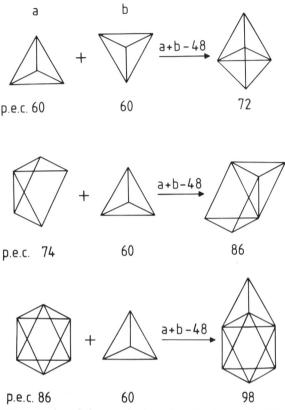

Figure 2.36 ▪ Some examples of clusters sharing triangular faces. The trigonal bipyramids are listed in Table 2.8 while the capped square pyramids are listed in Table 2.16 and the capped octahedra are given in Table 2.22.

The condensation of polyhedra through square faces is not such a common aggregation process but some examples are illustrated in Figure 2.40. The fact that a square-planar arrangement of atoms can be associated with 62 or 64 electrons leads to an extra degree of freedom for such clusters. In general if the bonding in the parent polyhedron is not adequately described by a localized bonding model then the electron count for the condensed polyhedron is obtained by subtracting 62 for the common square face, for example (1)–(2) in Figure 2.40. In contrast, if a localized description is apt then 64 is subtracted for the common square face. It is also possible to condense a pair of polyhedra through a pair of adjacent triangular faces, for example (3) in Figure 2.40. The observed electron count is equal to the sum of the polyhedral electron counts of the component polyhedra minus that characteristic for the common butterfly, that is, 62.[142,150] The polyhedral electron count, p.e.c., is defined as the total valence electron count.

Rule 6: If a transition metal atom occupying a vertex position is replaced by a main group atom then the polyhedral electron count is reduced by 10.

Isolobal, main group, and transition metal fragments are separated by 10

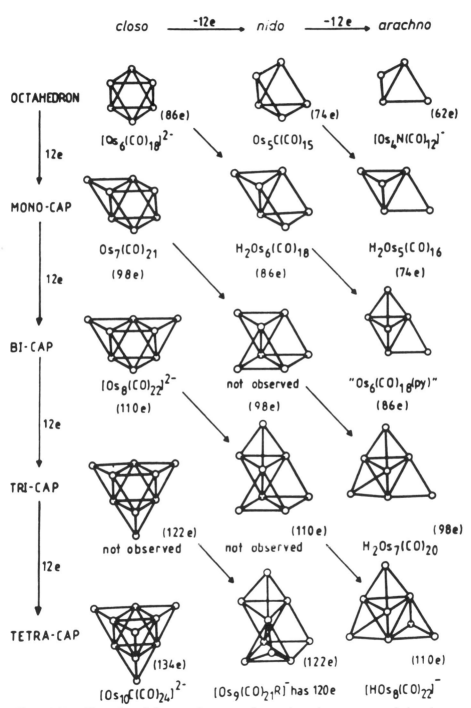

	closo	$\xrightarrow{-12e}$	nido	$\xrightarrow{-12e}$	arachno

OCTAHEDRON

(86e)   (74e)   (62e)

$[Os_6(CO)_{18}]^{2-}$ $Os_5C(CO)_{15}$ $[Os_4N(CO)_{12}]^-$

12e

MONO-CAP

$Os_7(CO)_{21}$ $H_2Os_6(CO)_{18}$ $H_2Os_5(CO)_{16}$

(98e)   (86e)   (74e)

12e

BI-CAP

$[Os_8(CO)_{22}]^{2-}$ not observed   "$Os_6(CO)_{18}(py)$"

(110e)   (98e)   (86e)

12e

TRI-CAP

(122e)   (110e)   (98e)

not observed   not observed $H_2Os_7(CO)_{20}$

12e

TETRA-CAP

(134e)   (122e)   (110e)

$[Os_{10}C(CO)_{24}]^{2-}$ $[Os_9(CO)_{21}R]^-$ has 120e $[HOs_8(CO)_{22}]^-$

Figure 2.37 ▪ Examples of the growth patterns for osmium cluster compounds based on capping of the octahedron and its *nido-* and *arachno-* derivatives.

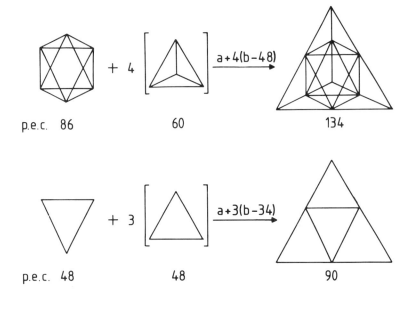

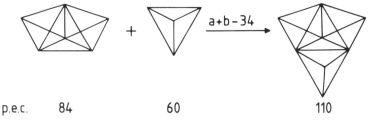

Figure 2.38 ▪ Three examples of multiple capping and edge sharing. Examples of the 134 valence electron tetracapped octahedron are given in Table 2.26 while the 90 valence electron triangular rafts are listed in Table 2.19. An example of the 110 valence electron cluster is $[HOs_8(CO)_{22}]^-$.

valence electrons corresponding at least formally to the occupation of the additional d shell. Some typical examples of this relationship are summarized:

$Os(CO)_3$	$14e^-$	—	B–H	$4e^-$
$Os(CO)_4$	$16e^-$	—	CH_2	$6e^-$
$Mn(CO)_5$	$17e^-$	—	CH_3	$7e^-$

Therefore, the polyhedral geometry is maintained if the metal carbonyl fragment is replaced by an isolobal fragment with the same number of electrons in the frontier orbitals.

Some examples of three-connected and deltahedral mixed main group

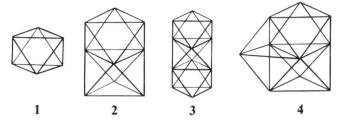

Figure 2.39 ▪ Clusters formed from face-sharing octahedra.

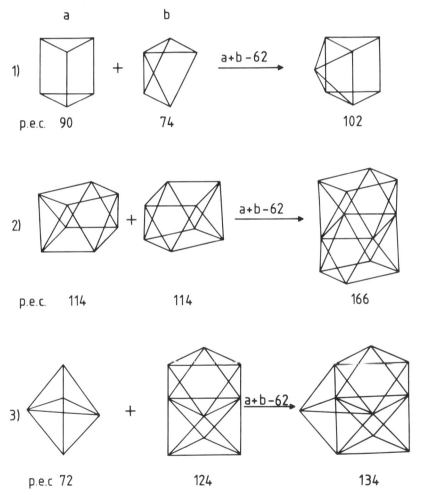

Figure 2.40 ▪ Some examples of clusters derived from square-face-sharing polyhedra. An example of the 102 valence electron capped trigonal prism is $[Rh_7N(CO)_{15}]^{2-}$ $[Rh_{12}C_2(CO)_{24}]^{2-}$ is an example of the 166 valence electron cluster.

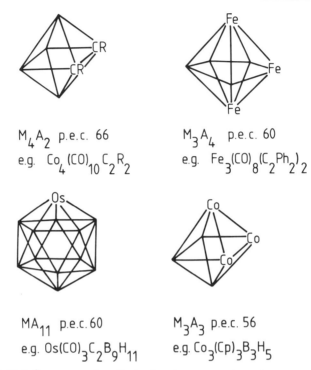

M_4A_2 p.e.c. 66

e.g. $Co_4(CO)_{10}C_2R_2$

M_3A_4 p.e.c. 60

e.g. $Fe_3(CO)_8(C_2Ph_2)_2$

MA_{11} p.e.c. 60

e.g. $Os(CO)_3C_2B_9H_{11}$

M_3A_3 p.e.c. 56

e.g. $Co_3(Cp)_3B_3H_5$

Figure 2.41 ▪ Some examples of mixed main group and transition metal clusters.

transition metal cluster compounds are illustrated in Figure 2.41. In Figure 2.42 some examples of condensed mixed-metal clusters are shown. All examples illustrated in these figures obey the electron counting rule summarized in rule 6.

Rule 7: High nuclearity clusters where radial bonding predominates are characterized by a total of $12m_s + \Delta_i$ valence electrons where m_s is the number of surface metal atoms and Δ_i is the electron count characteristic of the central atom or cluster lying at the center of the cluster.[156,157]

Examples of clusters that conform to this generalization are summarized in Table 2.28. For such high nuclearity clusters the energy differences between alternative hexagonal, cubic, body-centered cubic, and five-fold symmetry packing arrangements are small and examples of all these structural types are observed. This generalization emphasizes that the closed shell requirements of such clusters are defined primarily by the bonding requirements of the central interstitial cluster moiety. The interstitial moieties given in Table 2.28 have been recognized to date

Given the extreme complexity of these systems the agreement between observed and calculated electron counts for these clusters is remarkably good even for the highest nuclearity examples. Some of the compounds in the table have not been completely characterized because of the problems associated with defining light atom positions in structures where heavy atoms predominate, and the generalizations provide a method for estimating either the number of ligands or the charge on the cluster.[157]

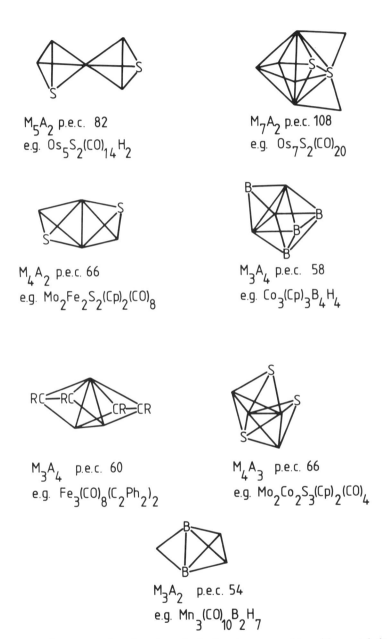

M_5A_2 p.e.c. 82
e.g. $Os_5S_2(CO)_{14}H_2$

M_7A_2 p.e.c. 108
e.g. $Os_7S_2(CO)_{20}$

M_4A_2 p.e.c. 66
e.g. $Mo_2Fe_2S_2(Cp)_2(CO)_8$

M_3A_4 p.e.c. 58
e.g. $Co_3(Cp)_3B_4H_4$

M_3A_4 p.e.c. 60
e.g. $Fe_3(CO)_8(C_2Ph_2)_2$

M_4A_3 p.e.c. 66
e.g. $Mo_2Co_2S_3(Cp)_2(CO)_4$

M_3A_2 p.e.c. 54
e.g. $Mn_3(CO)_{10}B_2H_7$

Figure 2.42 ▪ Some examples of condensed mixed main group and transition metal clusters.

Table 2.28

Interstitial Moiety	Characteristic Electron Count	Example
Single atom	18	$[Au_{13}Cl_2(PMe_2Ph)_{10}]^{3+}$
Dimer	34	$[Pt_{19}(CO)_{22}]^{4-}$
Linear trimer	50	$[Ag_{12}Au_{13}Cl_6(PPh_3)_{12}]^{m+}$
Triangle	48(50)	$[Pt_{26}(CO)_{32}]^{2-}$
Tetrahedron	60	$[Ni_{38}Pt_6(CO)_y]^{6-}$
Octahedron	86	$[Ni_{38}Pt_6(CO)_{48}H_{6-n}]^{n-}$
Edge-sharing bioctahedron	138	$[Pt_{52}(CO)_x]^{n-}$

There are a number of rhodium cluster compounds with a single interstitial atom, for example $[Rh_{14}(CO)_{25}]^{4-}$, $[Rh_{14}(CO)_{26}]^{2-}$, $[Rh_{15}(CO)_{27}]^{3-}$, and $[Rh_{17}(CO)_{30}]^{3-}$, which have $12m_s + 24$ rather than $12m_s + 18$ valence electrons. A molecular orbital analysis has indicated that in these clusters there are three low-lying $F_{0\pm1}^{\pi}$ tangential molecular orbitals in addition to the radial molecular orbitals which can accommodate the additional six electrons.[158]

$[Au_9(PPh_3)_8]^+$ has a centered cubic arrangement of metal atoms that can be related to the body-centered cubic lattice since the central metal atom has a coordination number of eight. The cluster $[Rh_{15}(CO)_{30}]^{3-}$ also has a geometry related to body-centered cubic packing with the additional six metal atoms capping the faces of the central cube. The structure does show a distortion from this ideal and the structure can also be described as a centered rhombohedron with the metal atoms lying approximately on a spherical surface. $[Rh_{14}(CO)_{25}]^{4-}$, $[Rh_{14}(CO)_{26}]^{2-}$, and $[Rh_{15}(CO)_{27}]^{3-}$ have structures that are intermediate between body-centered cubic and hexagonal close-packed.

The clusters $[Pt_{24}(CO)_{30}]^{2-}$, $[Pt_{38}(CO)_{44}]^{2-}$, and $[H_{6-n}Ni_{38}Pt_6(CO)_{48}]^{n-}$ have structures based on face-centered cubic packing and can be derived from a central octahedral moiety capped with additional metal atoms in such a way as to maintain cubic close packing. Since these are not infinite structures the packing does not have to follow a strict ABAB or ABCABC sequence and there are examples of alternative packing arrangements. For example, $[Rh_{22}(CO)_{37}]^{4-}$ has a BABC arrangement whereby the bottom three layers represent a fragment of hcp and the top three layers cubic close-packing.

Molecular clusters can also adopt structures with five-fold symmetry and $[Pt_{19}(CO)_{22}]^{4-}$, $[Au_{13}Cl_2(PMe_2Ph)_{10}]^{3+}$, and $[Ag_{12}Au_{13}Cl_6(PPh_3)_{12}]^{m+}$ provide examples of such compounds.

2.3.2. Theoretical Justification of the Rules

Although in the previous section the electron counting rules have been stated baldly and their applications emphasized they do represent the culmination of many empirical observations and they have been underpinned by molecular orbital analyses. These theoretical analyses have been summarized in a recent review and will not be developed in great detail here.[131] The Tensor Surface Harmonic Theory has proved particularly useful for interpreting these structural generalizations.[140-14] This methodology, which is based on a free electron particle on a sphere model was originally developed by Stone[142] to account for the closed shell requirements of deltahedral clusters and was subsequently extended to *nido-* and *arachno-* deltahedra by Stone and Alderton.[144] Johnston and Mingos[140,141] have accounted for the closed shell requirements of three- and four-connected polyhedral molecules using this methodology. The electron counting rule for condensed clusters has been justified by Mingos[150] and independently by Stone.[145] The application of the Tensor Surface Harmonic Theory to high nuclearity clusters has been discussed by Mingos[149] and Mingos and Lin Zhenyang.[155] The rules for the replacement of transition metals by main group atoms is based on the isolobal analogy which has been developed particularly by Hoffmann and co-workers.[134]

This approach has been emphasized because it provides a consistent scheme for a whole range of main group and transition metal polyhedral molecules. There are in the literature, however, alternative schemes to account for the bonding in such clusters. Of particular interest are Teo's Topological Electron Counting Model[159,160] and King's graph theory derived model.[161-164]

2.3.3. Free Electron Cluster Bonding Models

The spherical nature of many cluster molecules suggested as early as 1949[131] that their bonding may be described in terms of a particle on a sphere quantum mechanical approach. The cluster molecular orbitals in these approximate models were described by the quantum numbers L and M, by analogy with those for the angular parts of the wavefunctions for the Schrödinger solution of the hydrogen atom. The quantum numbers L and M define the number of angular nodes with $M = L, L - 1, \cdots - L$. In this simplified approach the $2L + 1$ components of each manifold were taken to be degenerate with their energies given by the following expression:

$$E_L = \frac{\hbar^2 L}{(L + 1)} 8\pi^2 \mu a^2 \tag{2.1}$$

where a = radius of the sphere. The actual geometry of the cluster was then introduced as a perturbation, which breaks the degeneracy of the L manifold.

These spherical models can adequately describe the bonding in those clusters that have atoms which contribute only s orbitals for skeletal bonding, for example hydrogen atom clusters. For clusters where the s, p, and d valence orbital interactions are important the results do not accurately reflect those obtained from conventional molecular orbital analyses. In such clusters, the atoms possess, in addition to the nodeless (σ-type) atomic orbitals, orbitals that are singly (π) and doubly (δ) noded with respect to the radial vector passing from the atom to the origin of the cluster (Figure 2.43).

The cluster molecular orbitals derived from the π and δ atomic orbitals have nodes between the atoms which define their bonding and antibonding character as well as nodes passing through the atoms. Therefore a simple node count does not provide an accurate estimate of the energy of the molecular orbital. A more sophisticated particle on a sphere model which overcomes these deficiencies has been developed by Stone and described is as the Tensor Surface Harmonic Theory.[140-145]

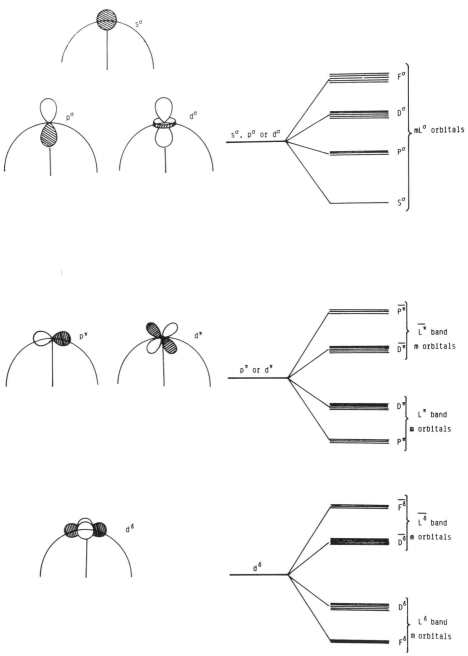

Figure 2.43 ▪ Designation of the nodal characteristics of *s*, *p*, and *d* atomic orbitals on the surface of a spherical cluster. The nodal places are referenced to the radius vector of the cluster.

According to this model the cluster atoms are also constrained to lie on the surface of a single sphere of unit radius with each atom position being described by the polar angular coordinates (θ_i, φ_i). The angular parts of the wavefunctions are evaluated using the Schrödinger equation for a particle on a sphere as stated earlier (the radial parts can be ignored if the cluster vertices all lie on the sphere):

$$\nabla^2 \Psi = -L(L+1)\Psi \tag{2.2}$$

$$\nabla^2 = (\sin \theta)^{-1}(\partial/\partial\theta) \sin \theta(\partial/\partial\theta) + (\sin^2 \theta)^{-1}(\partial^2/\partial\phi^2) \tag{2.3}$$

Stone's method differs from the earlier free electron models in that the values of the general spherical harmonics $S_{L,M}(\theta, \varphi)$ at the cluster atom position (θ_i, φ_i) are used as the coefficients (c_i) in an LCAO expansion of the atomic orbitals to yield the cluster molecular orbitals, $\Psi_{L,M}$:

$$\Psi_{L,M} = N\sum_i c_i\rho_i = N\sum_i S_{L,M}(\theta_i, \varphi_i)\rho_i \tag{2.4}$$

The Stone approach also differs from those given previously in taking into account the nodes inherent in the π and δ orbitals by utilizing vector and tensor surface harmonics. The earlier approaches had utilized only the scalar surface harmonics. The vector surface harmonics are the gradients of the scalar spherical harmonics. The mathematical aspects of this approach are beyond the scope of this chapter, but the important conclusions will be briefly summarized here.

The radial L^σ molecular orbitals give rise to energy levels that increase with the number of angular nodes: $S^\sigma < P^\sigma < D^\sigma$ etc. For deltahedral clusters with m atoms, m of these wavefunctions are generated in an Aufbau fashion (Figure 2.44). The S^σ molecular orbital is the most strongly bonding because all the radial atomic wavefunctions are in-phase and there are consequently no angular nodes. The P^σ functions are singly noded and for all three-dimensional polyhedra there are three components to the P^σ manifold and for polyhedra with more than 6 atoms they are bonding, although less strongly bonding than S^σ. The D^σ functions that are doubly noded are antibonding for all clusters with fewer than 12 metal atoms.

In gold cluster compounds the radial interactions resulting from s-p hybrid orbitals of the AuPR$_3$ fragments are dominant and the radial bonding model developed previously is pertinent. For example, $[Au_{13}Cl_2(PR_3)_{10}]^{3+}$ has four bonding skeletal molecular orbitals shown in Figure 2.44 and derived from S^σ and P^σ. They have the same symmetry as the $6s$ and $6p$ valence orbitals of the central atom and consequently they give rise to four strongly bonding molecular orbitals $S^\sigma + \lambda 6s$ and $P^\sigma + \lambda' 6p$. The central gold atom also has a filled $5d$ shell and consequently spherical gold cluster compounds of this type are characterized by $12m_s + 18$ valence electrons, where m_s is the number of surface gold Au—L fragments, each of which is characterized by a filled $5d$ shell and a two-electron Au—P σ-bond. The structures of these cluster compounds are discussed in more detail in Section 2.4.1.1.

For m cluster atoms that have two tangential p_π or d_π hybrid orbitals which participate strongly in bonding, the Stone Tensor Surface Harmonic analysis sug-

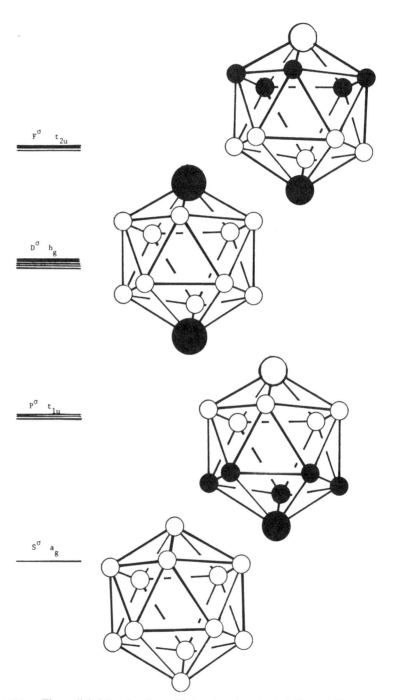

F^σ t_{2u}

D^σ h_g

P^σ t_{1u}

S^σ a_g

Figure 2.44 ▪ The radial L^σ molecular orbitals of an icosahedral cluster. The manner in which the energies vary with the number of nodes is particularly noteworthy.

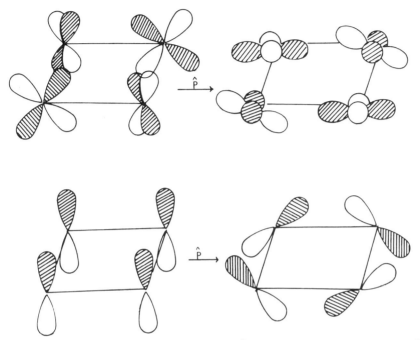

Figure 2.45 ▪ The parity transformation operation $\hat{P}$ has the effect of changing a tangential bonding molecular orbital into an equally antibonding tangential molecular orbital.

gests that the resultant molecular orbitals for deltahedral clusters are paired such that there are mL and $m\overline{L^\pi}$ antibonding sets, where m is the number of vertex atoms in the cluster (Figure 2.43). The bonding orbitals can be geometrically converted into the corresponding antibonding $\overline{L^\pi}$ by a rotation of each p_π orbital by $90°$ in the same sense (Figure 2.45). The L^π (t_{1u} and t_{2g}) and $\overline{L^\pi}$ (t_{1g} and t_{2u}) molecular orbitals for an octahedral cluster are illustrated in Figure 2.46. The local rotation which is described as a parity operation interconverts t_{1u} (P^π) into t_{1g} ($\overline{P^\pi}$) and t_{2g} (D^π) into t_{2u} ($\overline{D^\pi}$). It is noteworthy that P^π has only one nodal plane which coincides with the internal nodes of the individual p orbitals, whereas t_{1g} ($\overline{P^\pi}$) has two nodal planes located between the atoms and an additional pair of nodal planes passing through the atoms. Similarly D^π (t_{2g}) has only two inherent nodal planes and $\overline{D^\pi}$ (t_{2u}) has one inherent nodal plane and two additional nodal planes passing between the atoms and contributing to its antibonding character. The parity operation has the effect of increasing the number of genuine nodal planes by two and decreasing the number of inherent nodal planes by one. This emphasizes why it is not possible to analyze the bonding in such clusters by a simple nodal count based on scalar surface harmonic functions. If the inherent nodes are ignored it is clear that t_{1u} (P^π) and t_{2g} (D^π) are bonding and t_{1g} ($\overline{P^\pi}$) and t_{2u} ($\overline{D^\pi}$) are antibonding. The P^π molecular orbitals always have the same symmetry transformation properties as the P^σ and they mix extensively. This mixing, which is represented schematically in Figure 2.47, results in one set of strongly bonding $P^{\sigma/\pi}$ and one set of antibonding $P^{\pi/\sigma}$ molecular orbitals.

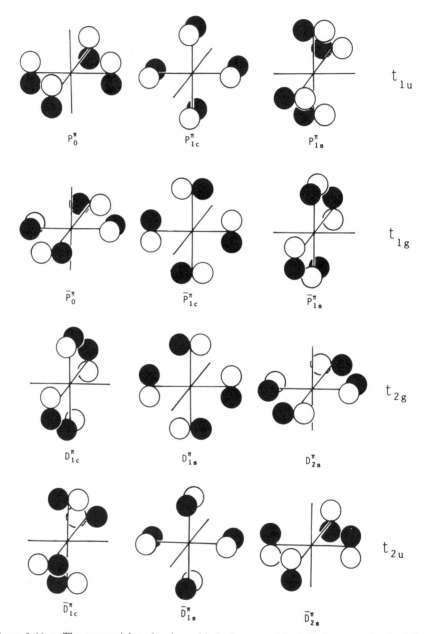

Figure 2.46 ▪ The tangential molecular orbitals for an octahedral cluster molecule. The parity operation has the effect of increasing the number of genuine nodal planes by two and decreasing the number of inherent nodal planes by one.

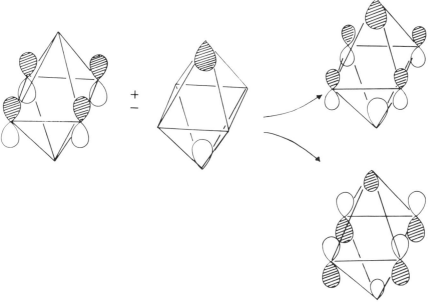

Figure 2.47 ▪ The mixing between radial and tangential molecular orbitals with the same symmetry transformation properties.

It follows from the analysis developed previously for deltahedral and four-connected clusters where σ and π interactions are significant that they are characterized by $(m + 1)$ skeletal bonding molecular orbitals:

$$S^\sigma \quad P^{\sigma/\pi} \quad \text{and} \quad (m - 3)L^\pi$$

and $(2m - 1)$ unavailable antibonding molecular orbitals comprised of

$$(m - 4)L^\sigma \quad P^{\pi/\sigma} \quad \text{and} \quad m\overline{L^\pi}$$

These molecular orbitals are described as unavailable because they are skeletal antibonding and hybridized towards the center of the cage and therefore cannot be used either for skeletal bonding or for bonding to ligands located on the outside of the cage. These molecular orbital patterns are represented schematically for deltahedral, four-connected, and three-connected clusters in Figure 2.48.

This analysis is immediately applicable to main group four-connected and deltahedral clusters which are characterized by a total of $4m + 2$ valence electrons, that is, $(m + 1)$ skeletal bonding molecular orbitals and m exo-polyhedral M-H bonds or lone pairs. The boron hydrides $B_mH_m^{2-}$ provide the most extensive series of deltahedral molecules of this type. The 'naked' metal clusters provide examples of clusters which conform to this generalization and have m exo-cage lone pairs. Three-connected clusters, for example C_mH_m, are characterized by $3m/2$ skeletal molecular orbitals (Figure 2.48).

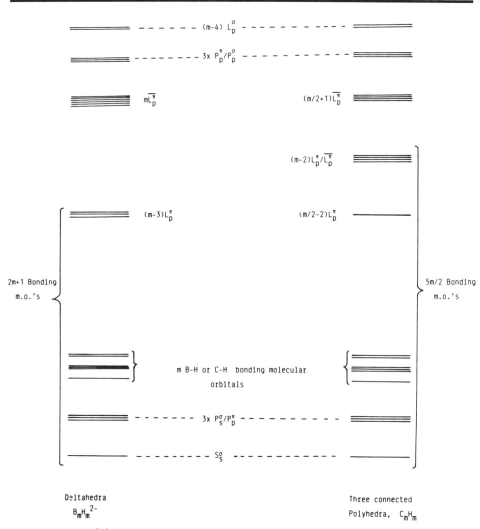

Figure 2.48 ▪ Schematic representation of the molecular orbital patterns for deltahedral and three-connected main group clusters such as BmHm^{2-} and CmHm.

Group Theoretical Implications of Parity Transformation

The irreducible representations spanned by the L^π and $\overline{L^\pi}$ molecular orbitals of a cluster can be derived from the L^σ functions by the following group theoretical direct product rule:

$$\Gamma_{\pi+\bar{\pi}} = \Gamma_\sigma \otimes \Gamma_{xyz} - \Gamma_\sigma \qquad (2.5$$

For the octahedron by standard group theoretical methods:

$$\Gamma_\sigma = a_{1g}(S^\sigma) + t_{1u}(P^\sigma) + e_g(D^\sigma) \tag{2.6}$$

In the octahedral point group $\Gamma_{xyz} = t_{1u}$ and therefore

$$\Gamma_{\pi+\bar{\pi}} = \Gamma_\sigma \otimes t_{1u} - \Gamma_\sigma = t_{1u} + t_{2g} + t_{1g} + t_{2u} \tag{2.7}$$

The L^π and $\overline{L^\pi}$ components are related by the parity operation, $\hat{P}$ (Figure 2.45). This operator has the effect of rotating all the p_π orbitals by $90°$ in the same sense and corresponds to the irreducible representation Γ_u^o. This operator is symmetric to all proper rotations and asymmetric to improper rotations and reflections of the point group. In the octahedral point group Γ_u^o corresponds to the a_{1u} irreducible representation, leading to the following relationships:

$$P^\pi(t_{1u}) - \hat{P}(a_{1u}) \rightarrow \overline{P^\pi}(t_{1g}) \tag{2.8}$$

$$D^\pi(t_{2g}) - \hat{P}(a_{1u}) \rightarrow \overline{D^\pi}(t_{2u}) \tag{2.9}$$

which underlines the fundamental paired nature of the tangential molecular orbitals.

The group theoretical methodology can also be used to account for some interesting exceptions to the $(m + 1)$ skeletal electron pair rule for deltahedra. These occur when the parity operation generates self-conjugate representations, that is

$$\Gamma_\pi \otimes \Gamma_u^o = \Gamma_{\bar{\pi}} = \Gamma_\pi \tag{2.10}$$

For example, in the tetrahedron the radial in-pointing atomic orbitals give rise to the following representations:

$$\Gamma_\sigma = a_1(S^\sigma) + t_2(P^\sigma) \tag{2.11}$$

In the T_d point group $\Gamma_{xyz} = t_2$ so the tangential p_π atomic orbitals give rise to the following representations:

$$\Gamma_{\pi+\bar{\pi}} = [\Gamma_\sigma \otimes t_2] - \Gamma_\sigma = t_1 + t_2 + e \tag{2.12}$$

Since Γ_u^o, the parity operation, transforms as a_2 the following relationships are relevant:

$$P^\pi(t_2) - \hat{P}(a_2) \rightarrow \overline{P^\pi}(t_1) \tag{2.13}$$

$$e - \hat{P}(a_2) \rightarrow e \tag{2.14}$$

The e representation is therefore described as "self-conjugate" and must correspond to a nonbonding set of tangential molecular orbitals with equal L^π and $\overline{L^\pi}$ character. A tetrahedral cluster can therefore have alternative electron counts depending on whether the nonbonding e set is utilized or not, that is, $(m + 2)$ (six electron pairs) if the e set is fully occupied and m (four electron pairs) if not. The $(m + 1)$ electron pair situation is unfavorable because it would lead to a diradical situation analogous to that found in cyclo-butadiene. B_4Cl_4 and $C_4Bu_4^t$ provide examples of tetrahedral clusters with four and six skeletal electron pairs respectively.

More generally it can be shown that deltahedra with a single vertex atom on a polar axis of order three or more, that is, belonging to the point groups C_{nv} ($n \geq 3$), T, or T_d, are characterized by a nonbonding e set, and therefore can be associated with either m or $m+2$ skeletal electron pairs. These polar deltahedra are always characterized by $3p+1$ atoms in total ($p = 1, 2 \cdots$), because the polar axis must pass through the unique atom and an external triangular face. It also follows from this economical group theoretical principle that $nido$- polyhedra with a single square face and a unique atom on the principal axis have a total of $4p+1$ atoms and also have a nonbonding self-conjugate set of e orbitals. Square-pyramidal $B_5H_5^{4-}$ and capped-square-antiprismatic $B_9H_9^{4-}$ provide specific examples of such $nido$-polyhedra with $(m+2)$ skeletal electron pairs. Similarly the $nido$-clusters $B_5H_5^{4-}$ and $B_{11}H_{11}^{4-}$ have an open pentagonal face, a total of $5p+1$ atoms, and $(m+2)$ skeletal electron pairs.

Transition Metal Deltahedral and Four-Connected Clusters

Wade[124] recognized that the bonding patterns in deltahedral transition metal clusters were related to those described previously for main group polyhedral molecules. In particular he noted the structural and electronic relationships between $[Ru_6H_2(CO)_{18}]$ (octahedral with a total of 86 valence electrons) and $[Fe_5C(CO)_{15}]$ (square pyramidal with a total of 74 valence electrons) and $B_6H_6^{2-}$ (octahedral with 26 valence electrons) and B_5H_9 (square pyramidal with a total of 24 valence electrons). He argued that this relationship arose because both $M(CO)_3$ and B—H fragments contributed three orbitals for skeletal bonding and generated a similar pattern of bonding and antibonding skeletal molecular orbitals, that is, $(m + 1)$ bonding and $(2m - 1)$ antibonding for the deltahedra. Therefore, the relationship could be summarized as follows:

Molecule	ML and BH Bonding	Nonbonding t_{2g}	Skeletal	Total
$B6H6^{2-}$	12		14	26
$[Ru_6H_2(CO)_{18}]$	36	36	14	86

Semiempirical molecular orbital calculations by Hoffmann, Mingos, and co-workers[133] provided a firmer theoretical foundation for these ideas and led to the basis of isolobal relationships between main group and transition metal fragments. A very readable and detailed account of these isolobal relationships is given in Hoffmann's Nobel Prize Lecture.[134]

The relationships between isostructural borane and metal clusters has also been highlighted by calculations on bare clusters completed by Mingos.[129] In particular the calculations indicated that both classes of cluster are characterized by the presence of $(2m-1)$ strongly antibonding and inaccessible cluster molecular orbitals. These orbitals are described as inaccessible by virtue of their high energies

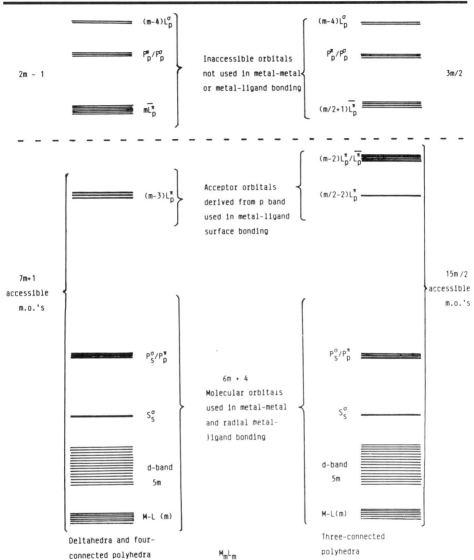

Figure 2.49 ▪ Schematic representations of the molecular orbital patterns for deltahedral, four-connected, and three-connected carbonyl cluster molecules. The molecular orbitals are generally occupied up to the dotted line shown. Above this line the molecular orbitals are described as inaccessible and bear a strong relationship to the related molecular orbitals of borane and hydrocarbon clusters illustrated in Figure 2.48.

and inwardly hybridized character (Figure 2.49). For both deltahedral boranes and metal clusters these inaccessible orbitals have a high proportion of p orbital character and in Stone's Tensor Surface Harmonic Theory can be associated with $(m-4)L^{\sigma}$ radial orbitals, three $P^{\pi/\sigma}$ and $m\,\overline{L^{\pi}}$ molecular orbitals. The ordering of atomic energy levels $nd > (n+1)s > (n+1)p$ for transition metal atoms ensures that these orbitals have a high proportion of p character and that the metal-ligand and metal-metal bonding occurs primarily through the d and s orbitals. It follows that isostructural deltahedral main group and transition metal molecules differ by a total of $10m$ valence electrons corresponding to the filling of the additional d shell molecular orbitals. The octahedral and square-pyramidal molecules described earlier provide specific illustrations of this generalization.

This generalization also holds for other classes of isostructural main group and transition metal cluster molecules, for example three-connected molecules, ring compounds, and capped polyhedra. The analogy does begin to show deficiencies, however, when the metal $nd - (n + 1)p$ promotion energies become large, for example for platinum and gold, and in condensed cylindrical clusters where the d_δ orbitals begin to make a significant contribution. These orbitals also influence the spectrum of molecular orbitals in halide clusters of the earlier transition metals. These exceptions to the simple generalizations have been discussed in some detail elsewhere.

2.4. Exceptions to the Rules

It is clear that the rules in Section 2.3.1 do not cover all of the examples of cluster molecules given in Section 2.2. It is necessary to define the fundamental reasons for the exceptions and to propose alternative generalizations.

2.4.1. Fragments That Do Not Generally Conform to the Noble Gas Rule

The successful application of the rules requires that each metal atom attain the noble gas configuration by forming metal-metal and metal-ligand bonds. There are, however, many metals that have a preference for forming 16-electron (square-planar) and 14-electron (linear) complexes. These preferences carry over to cluster chemistry and are reflected in the closed shell requirements for their cluster compounds.

2.4.1.1. Platinum Cluster Compounds

Platinum, palladium, and to a lesser extent rhodium and iridium form a wide range of square-planar (16-electron) complexes, because of the large $d \rightarrow p$ promotion energies for these metal atoms. In cluster compounds of these metals the molecular orbitals derived from the p_z orbital perpendicular to the metal-ligand plane are high lying and unavailable for bonding. This leads to a reduction in the number of bonding skeletal molecular orbitals. Molecular orbital calculations and symmetry based arguments have suggested the following closed shell requirements for platinum cluster compounds:[165,166]

Polyhedral Geometry	Calculated Closed Shell Requirement	Example
Triangle	42	$[Pt_3(\mu\text{-}SO_2)_3(PPh_3)_3]$
Tetrahedron	56	$[H_8Pt_4(PPr_2^iPh)_4]$
Butterfly	58	$[Pt_4(CO)_5(PMe_2Ph)_4]$
Trigonal Bipyramid	68	$[H_8Pt_5(PBu_2{}^tPh)_5]$

Except for the triangle the preferred electron count for platinum clusters is four electrons fewer than those predicted on the basis of the polyhedral skeletal electron pair approach.

In the series Ni, Pd, and Pt the preference for the noble gas rule diminishes and leads to some interesting differences. Nickel forms the 60-electron tetrahedral cluster $[Ni_4(CO)_6(P(CH_2CH_2CN)_3)_4]$ in agreement with the rules, platinum forms the tetrahedral and butterfly clusters $[H_8Pt_4(PBu_2{}^tPh)_5]$ (56 valence electrons) and $[Pt_4(CO)_5(PMe_2Ph)_4]$ (58 valence electrons) which clearly show the noncontribution of one of the atomic p orbitals, and palladium shows intermediate behavior forming a 60 valence electron tetrahedral cluster $[Pd_4(CO)_6(PPh_3)_4]$ and a 58 valence electron butterfly cluster $[Pd_4(CO)_5(PPh_3)_4]$. The relative stabilities of the palladium clusters are very similar and they can be interconverted by varying the CO pressure.

Platinum also forms a series of condensed clusters, whose structures can be rationalized using a modified form of the condensation rules which takes into account the 16-electron preferences of this metal. These condensed clusters and the way in which their closed shell requirements are rationalized are summarized in Figure 2.50.[167]

In gold clusters the filled d^{10} shell of the gold atoms makes little contribution to metal-metal bonding and the bonding is dominated by radial bonding interactions involving the outer AuL (L $=$ PPh_3 or Cl) fragments.[168-172] These radial interactions lead to multicentered bonding and the number of available skeletal molecular orbitals depends on the nuclearity of the cluster and the cluster topology. In the $[Au_6(PR_3)_6]^{2+}$ there are two bonding skeletal molecular orbitals (S^σ and P_x^σ) and the preferred cluster geometry is based on two tetrahedra sharing an edge. The octahedral $[Au_6(P(C_6H_4Me)_3)_6]^{2+}$ cluster has recently been shown to be a carbido- cluster. The $[Au_7(PPh_3)_7]^+$ cluster has three skeletal bonding molecular orbitals (S^σ, P_x^σ, P_y^σ) and a pentagonal bipyramidal geometry. The higher nuclearity gold cluster compounds generally have an interstitial atom and the peripheral atoms adopt either a toroidal or spherical topology. The toroidal clusters have three (S^σ, P_x^σ, P_y^σ) skeletal molecular orbitals which are stabilized by overlap with the $6s$, $6p_x$, and $6p_y$ orbitals of the central atom. $[Au_9(PPh_3)_8]^{3+}$, $[Au_8(PPh_3)_7]^{2+}$, and $[Au_{10}Cl_3(PCy_2Ph)_6]^+$ provide examples of such clusters which have geometries based on a centered chair of gold atoms with additional edge-bridging metal atoms. $[Au_9(P(p\text{-}OMeC_6H_4)_3)_8](BF_4)_3$ has an alternative geometry that can be described as a centered crown. The spherical clusters have four skeletal molecular orbitals (S^σ, P_x^σ, P_y^σ, P_z^σ,) that are stabilized by overlap with the $6s$ and $6p$ valence orbitals of the central gold atom. Examples of such clusters include $[Au_9(PPh_3)_8]^+$—a centered cube, $[Au_{13}Cl_2(PMe_2Ph)_{10}]^{3+}$—a centered icosahedron, and $[Au_{11}I_3(PPh_3)_7]$—a centered trirhombohedron derived from an icosahedron by the replacement of a triangle of metal atoms by a single atom.

Recently a large number of mixed metal compounds containing the $AuPPh_3$ fragment have been characterized. In these compounds compact structures based on face-sharing tetrahedra are frequently observed with the $AuPPh_3$ fragment capping the least hindered triangular faces. However, in some compounds the $AuPPh_3$ fragment bridges an edge rather than a face.

As just noted for an $AuPPh_3$ fragment the orbitals with a predominance of d orbital character are filled and the bonding capabilities of the fragment

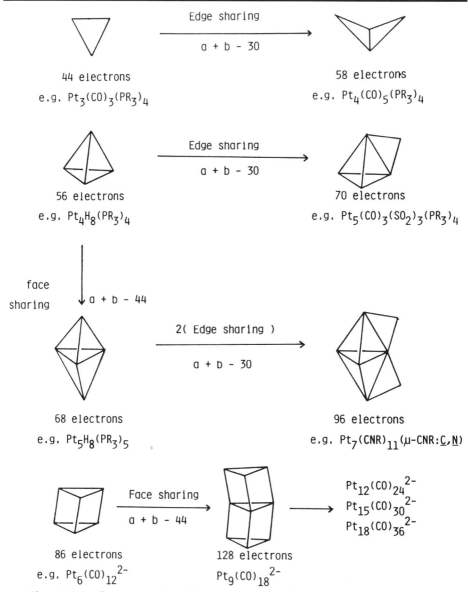

Figure 2.50 ▪ Some examples of the cluster condensation rules for platinum clusters.

are determined primarily by a $hy(s - z)$ hybrid orbital. The higher lying p_x and p_y orbitals remain essentially nonbonding. According to the condensation rules (rule 5) the introduction of a face-capping group leads to an increment in the electron count of 12 and an edge-bridging group an increment of 14. Since $AuPR_3^+$ presents one empty orbital only for skeletal bonding the increment in electron count is 12 whether it bonds to a face or an edge. Consequently, heterometallic gold clusters generally conform to the rules if they cap triangular faces, but represent exceptions if they bridge edges. For example, $[AuCoRu_3(CO)_{13}PPh_3]$, $[Au_2Ru_3S(CO)_8(PPh_3)_3]$, and $[H_6Cu_3Ir_2(NCMe)_3(PMe_2Ph)_6]^{3+}$ have trigonal bipyramidal geometries and have the 72 valence electrons $(14m + 2)$ predicted from rule 4 (see also Tables 2.15 and 2.16 for some examples of capped trigonal and square-pyramidal clusters). In contrast the edge-bridged tetrahedral cluster $[HAuOs_4(CO)_{13}(PEt_3)]$ has 72 valence electrons rather than the 74 predicted from rule 5. More complex examples of these apparent exceptions to the rules are found in Tables 2.11 and 2.12.[173]

2.4.2. Ligand Combinations

The adherence to the noble gas rule even in a mononuclear complex depends critically on the ligands coordinated to it. Thus small σ-donor ligands such as H and good π-acceptor ligands such as CO are generally present in such complexes, whereas weak σ-donors and π-donors such as Cl^- and O^{2-} result in compounds where the noble gas rule does not provide a useful unifying principle. Cyclic-polyenes and tertiary phosphines tend to be ambivalent and when present in combination with hydrides and π-acceptors do lead to complexes that conform to the rule, but when present by themselves or in combination with weak σ- and π-donors do not always form 18-electron complexes. These trends are carried over to cluster compounds. For example, clusters with halides, sulphides, phosphines, and cyclopentadienyl frequently represent exceptions to the polyhedral skeletal electron pair rules summarized earlier.

The following taken from the tables in Section 2.2 represent typical examples of exceptions resulting from ligand effects:

Compound	Valence Electrons	Cluster Geometry
$H_3Ni_4(Cp)_3$	58	Tetrahedral
Ni_6Cp_6	90	Octahedral
$[Fe_6S_8(PEt_3)_6]^{2+}$	96	Octahedral
$[Fe_4S_4(SR)_4]^{2-}$	54	Tetrahedral

In the clusters of first row transition metals with halide and sulphide ligands the metal-metal bonding is frequently not very strong and their magnetic properties are better interpreted in terms of antiferromagnetic coupling effects rather than a molecular cluster model. Furthermore, the variable electron configurations associated with these complexes lead to a rich and reversible electrochemistry. For clusters involving stronger π-donor ligands and heavier transition metals distinct closed shell requirements, albeit different from those which apply to π-acceptor clusters, begin to appear again. These closed shell requirements for *closo-*, *nido-*, and *arachno-* clusters derived from the octahedron have been discussed in some detail elsewhere.[174]

2.4.3. Topological Factors

The theoretical justification for the $14m + 2$ rule for four-connected and deltahedral clusters depends on the assumption that the polyhedral skeleton approximates to a spherical shell. In this idealized situation there is a good separation between bonding and antibonding tangential skeletal molecular orbitals and a clear definition of the closed shell requirements. There are situations, however, where the deviations from spherical symmetry are sufficiently large to permit the occurrence of orbitals in the nonbonding region and alternative closed shell possibilities. The group theoretical aspects of this problem have been discussed in some detail elsewhere[175-177] and only the primary conclusions will be presented here.

(a) **Polar deltahedral** clusters with C_{3v} or T_d symmetry are characterized by either $14m$ or $14m + 4$ valence electrons, where $m = 3p + 1$, $p = 1, 2, \cdots$.

Polar deltahedra are defined as having only one cluster atom on each principal axis. Examples of polar deltahedral clusters include the tetrahedron ($m = 4$, $p = 1$) and the capped octahedron ($m = 7$, $p = 2$). It follows that a tetrahedron can be associated with either 56 ($14m$) or 60 ($14m + 4$) valence electrons, for example $[H_4Re_4(CO)_{12}]$ and $[H_4Ru_4(CO)_{12}]$, and a capped octahedron with either 98 or 102 valence electrons, for example $[Os_7(CO)_{21}]$ has 98 valence electrons.

(b) **Bipolar deltahedral** clusters can be associated with $14m - 2$, $14m + 2$, and $14m + 6$ valence electrons. Bipolar deltahedral clusters have two metal atoms along each principal rotation axis and typical examples include the trigonal and pentagonal bipyramids and the bicapped square antiprism. Examples of this behavior include $[Os_5(CO)_{16}]$ (72 valence electrons, $14m + 2$) and $[Ni_5(CO)_{12}]^{2-}$ (76 valence electrons, $14m + 6$), both of which have trigonal bipyramidal skeletal geometries.

(c) **Nonpolar deltahedral** clusters can accommodate $14m$, $14m + 2$, and $14m + 6$ valence electrons. Nonpolar deltahedral clusters have no atoms lying on the principal symmetry axis and include the trigonal dodecahedron and the tricapped trigonal prism. Although examples of these exceptions have been documented for main group molecules and metallocarboranes there are no examples of this type in metal carbonyl cluster chemistry. The following series of deltahedral clusters serves to illustrate these possibilities:

Cluster	Skeletal Electron Pairs
B_8Cl_8	8
$Co_4Cp_4B_4H_4$	8
$B_8H_8^{2-}$	9
$Ni_4Cp_4B_4H_4$	10

2.4.4. Highly Condensed Clusters

The capping principle[152] states that when a polyhedron is capped by $M(CO)_3$ or related fragments then the total number of skeletal molecular orbitals remains unchanged. However, when many capping atoms are present additional orbitals are introduced into the nonbonding region which can accommodate additional electrons.[176] For example, the octahedron $[Os_6(CO)_{18}]^{2-}$, the monocapped octahedron $[Os_7(CO)_{21}]$, the bicapped octahedron $[Os_8(CO)_{22}]^{2-}$, and the tetra-capped octahedron $[Os_{10}C(CO)_{24}]^{2-}$ all have seven skeletal electron pairs but the related tetracapped octahedron $[Pd_{10}(CO)_{12}(PBu_3)_6]$ and hexacapped octahedron $[HFe_6Pd_6(CO)_{23}]^{2-}$ have eight skeletal electron pairs. Similarly although the square antiprism $[Co_8C(CO)_{18}]^{2-}$ is characterized by nine skeletal electron pairs the related tetracapped derivative $[Co_3Ni_9C(CO)_{20}]^{3-}$ has ten skeletal electron pairs.

Similarly the raft clusters formed by the edge sharing of triangular clusters represent two-dimensional analogues of the capping process and the number of skeletal electron pairs associated with the parent triangle (3) is retained. For example, $[Os_3(CO)_{12}]$ and the planar raft cluster $[Os_6(CO)_{21}]$ both have three skeletal bonding molecular orbitals. The latter has an additional low lying skeletal molecular orbital of a_2' symmetry and is susceptible to electrochemical reduction.[178] Johnson, Jeffrey, and Lewis[179] have demonstrated that the related cluster $[Os_6(CO)_{17}(P(OMe)_3)_4]$ does indeed undergo reversible two-electron reductions. A more detailed theoretical analysis of these capping processes is presented elsewhere.

2.4.5. Delocalized versus Localized Bonding

A classical view of metal-metal bonding suggests that the addition of an electron pair to a localized metal-metal bond should lead to its rupture, for example,

$$Mn_2(CO)_{10} + 2e^- \rightleftharpoons 2Mn(CO)_5^-$$

This behavior is reproduced in many clusters where the bonding can be described in localized terms and some illustrative examples are given:

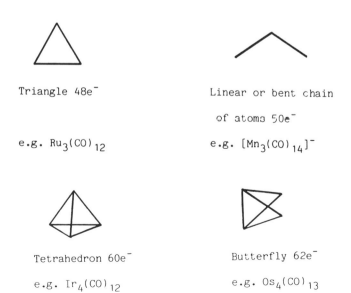

Triangle 48e⁻   Linear or bent chain

of atoms 50e⁻

e.g. $Ru_3(CO)_{12}$ e.g. $[Mn_3(CO)_{14}]^-$

Tetrahedron 60e⁻   Butterfly 62e⁻

e.g. $Ir_4(CO)_{12}$ e.g. $Os_4(CO)_{13}$

$66e^-$ $68e^-$

e.g. $[Fe_4S_4Cp_4]^{2+}$ e.g. $[Fe_4S_4Cp_4]$

In these clusters the antibonding electron density is being localized in specific bonding regions and the structures distort in a way which transforms these antibonding interactions into nonbonding ones. Formally this process can be represented as:

$$M—M + 2e^- \rightarrow M:^- + :M^- \tag{2.15}$$

An alternative mode of reducing the antibonding character in clusters where the bonding is of a more delocalized nature is a simultaneous expansion of all metal-metal bonds. For example, $[Co_3Cp_3S_2]$ has 50 valence electrons and is isoelectronic with $[Fe_3(CO)_9S_2]$.[180,181] The latter adopts a classical localized structure with one long and two short Fe—Fe bonds, but the former adopts a nonclassical structure with an equilateral but expanded triangle of metal atoms.

Similarly in platinum chemistry the common triangular cluster which is consistent with the attainment of the 16-electron rule has 42 valence electrons, for example $[Pt_3(CO)_3(PCy_3)_3]$. There are "classical" 44-electron linear clusters—$[Pt_3(CNR)_6(PR_3)_2]^{2+}$, and also "nonclassical" triangular clusters—$[Pt_3(CO)_3(PPh_3)_4]$ and $[Pt_3(SO_2)Cl(PPh_3)_3]^-$.[55]

2.5. Closing Remarks

The structures of transition metal cluster compounds cannot be uniformly interpreted on the basis of the total number of valence electrons in the molecule. Nonetheless for those clusters based on metal-ligand combinations which conform to the noble gas rule the polyhedral skeletal electron pair approach gives a very satisfactory account of their closed shell requirements. For other metal-ligand combinations it is necessary to utilize the results of more detailed molecular orbital and symmetry arguments.

References

1. E. W. Abel and F. G. A. Stone, *Q. Rev. Chem. Soc.*, 1969, **23**, 325.
2. P. Chini, *J. Organometal. Chem.*, 1981, **200**, 37.
3. B. F. G. Johnson and J. Lewis, *Adv. Inorg. Chem. Radiochem.*, 1981, **24**, 225.
4. M. D. Vargas and J. N. Nicholls, *Adv. Inorg. Chem. Radiochem.*, 1987, **30**.
5. F. G. A. Stone, *Angew. Chem. Int. Ed. Engl.*, 1984, **23**, 89.
6. H. Vahrenkamp, *Adv. Organometal. Chem.*, 1983, **22**, 169.

7. W. L. Gladfelter and G. L. Geoffroy, *Adv. Organometal. Chem.*, 1980, **18**, 207.
8. D. M. P. Mingos, *Acc. Chem. Res.*, 1984, **17**, 311.
9. E. L. Muetterties, *J. Organometal. Chem.*, 1980, **200**, 177.
10. L. Pauling, *The nature of the chemical bond*, 3rd Ed., Cornell University Press, 1980, p. 440 for metallic radii.
11. C. P. Horwitz, E. M. Holt and D. F. Shriver, *Inorg. Chem.*, 1984, **23**, 2491.
12. D. M. P. Mingos, *Adv. Organometal. Chem.*, 1977, **15**, 1.
13. R. Mason and D. M. P. Mingos, *J. Organometal. Chem.*, 1973, **50**, 53.
14. R. A. Kok and M. B. Hall, *J. Am. Chem. Soc.*, 1983, **105**, 676.
15. M. A. Bush and G. A. Sim, *J. Chem. Soc.* (*A*), 1970, 611.
16. L. F. Dahl, E. R. De Gil and R. D. Feltham, *J. Am. Chem. Soc.*, 1969, **91**, 1653.
17. K. Angerwood, K. H. Claus, R. Goddard and C. Krüger, *Angew. Chem. Int. Ed. Engl.*, 1985, **24**, 237 and references therein.
18. F. A. Cotton and R. A. Walton, *Struct. Bond.*, 1985, **62**, 1.
19. F. A. Cotton and R. A. Walton, *Multiple bonds between metal atoms*. New York: J. Wiley and Sons, 1982.
20. A. R. Pinhas and R. Hoffmann, *Inorg. Chem.*, 1979, **18**, 654.
21. K. A. Schugart and R. F. Fenske, *J. Am. Chem. Soc.*, 1986, **108**, 5094, 5100.
22. R. Mason, I. Sotofte, S. D. Robinson and M. F. Uttley, *J. Organometal. Chem.*, 1972, **46**, C61.
23. R. H. Sommerville and R. Hoffmann, *J. Am. Chem. Soc.*, 1976, **98**, 2240.
24. J. A. Connor, *Transition metal clusters*, edited by B. F. G. Johnson. New York: J. Wiley and Sons, 1981, p. 345.
25. J. A. Bertrand, F. A. Cotton and W. A. Dollase, *Inorg. Chem.*, 1963, **2**, 1166.
26. P. A. Vaughan, *Proc. Natl. Acad. Sci. U.S.A.*, 1950, **36**, 461.
27. A. Simon, H. G. Schnering, H. Wohrle and H. Schäfer, *Z. Anorg. Allg. Chem.*, 1965, **339**, 155.
28. R. E. McCarley, *Proc. Natl. Acad. Sci. U.S.A.*, 1982, **308**, 141.
29. M. Patel, M. Chevrel, M. Sergent, D. Decroux and C. R. Fischer, *R. Acad. Sci. Ser. C.*, 1979, **288**, 429.
30. K. Jodden, H. G. Schnering and H. Schäfer, *Angew. Chem. Int. Ed. Engl.*, 1975, **14**, 570.
31. M. H. Chisholm, R. J. Errington, K. Folting and J. R. Huffman, *J. Am. Chem. Soc.*, 1982, **104**, 2025.
32. S. Stensvad, B. J. Helland, M. W. Bakich, R. A. Jacobson and R. E. McCarley, *J. Am. Chem. Soc.*, 1978, **100**, 6527.
33. R. N. McGinnis, T. R. Ryan and R. E. McCarley, *J. Am. Chem. Soc.*, 1978, **100**, 7900.
34. A. Simon, *Angew. Chem. Int. Ed. Engl.*, 1981, **20**, 1.
35. H. Schäfer and H. G. Schnering, *Angew. Chem.*, 1964, **76**, 833.
36. R. Chevrel, P. Gougeon, M. Potel and M. J. Sergent, *Solid State Chem.*, 1985, **57**, 25.
37. R. H. Holm, *Acc. Chem. Res.*, 1977, **10**, 427.
38. R. H. Holm and J. A. Ibers, *Science*, 1980, **209**, 223.
39. G. Christou and C. D. Garner, *J. Chem. Soc. Dalton Trans.*, 1980, 2354, 2363.
40. R. H. Holm, *Chem. Soc. Rev.*, 1980, **10**, 455.
41. D. Fenske, J. Hachgenei and J. Ohmer, *Angew. Chem. Int. Ed. Engl.*, 1985, **24**, 706.
42. D. Fenske, J. Ohmer and J. Hachgenei, *Angew. Chem. Int. Ed. Engl.*, 1985, **24**, 993.
43. F. A. Cotton and T. E. Haas, *Inorg. Chem.*, 1964, **3**, 10.
45. R. A. Wheeler and R. Hoffmann, *Angew. Chem. Int. Ed. Engl.*, 1986, **25**, 822.

46. S. V. Kryuchov, A. F. Kuzina and V. I. Spitsyn, *Dobl. Akad. Nauk. SSSR*, 1982, **266**, 127.
47. F. A. Cotton, L. Kruczynski, B. L. Shapiro and L. F. Johnson, *J. Am. Chem. Soc.*, 1972, **94**, 6191.
48. Cambridge Crystalographic data base.
49. J. Evans, *Adv. Organometal. Chem.*, 1977, **16**, 319.
50. R. E. Benfield and B. F. G. Johnson, *J. Chem. Soc. Dalton Trans.*, 1978, 1554.
51. R. E. Benfield and B. F. G. Johnson, in *Transition metal clusters*, edited by B. F. G. Johnson. New York: J. Wiley and Sons, 1981, p. 471.
52. B. W. Clare, M. C. Favas, D. L. Kepert and A. S. May, *Advances in Dynamic Stereochemistry*, 1985, **1**, 1.
53. P. D. Frisch and L. F. Dahl, *J. Am. Chem. Soc.*, 1972, **94**, 5082.
54. R. Hoffmann, B. E. R. Schilling, R. Bau, H. D. Kaesz and D. M. P. Mingos, *J. Am. Chem. Soc.*, 1978, **100**, 6088.
55. D. I. Gilmour and D. M. P. Mingos, *J. Organometal. Chem.*, 1986, **302**, 127.
56. B. F. G. Johnson, J. Lewis, P. R. Raithby and A. Sanders, *J. Organometal. Chem.*, 1986, **260**, C29.
57. R. D. Adams, I. T. Horvath and K. Natarajan, *Organometallics*, **3**, 1540.
58. B. F. G. Johnson, J. Lewis, W. J. H. Nelson, J. N. Nicholls, M. D. Vargas, D. Braga, K. Henrick and M. McPartlin, *J. Chem. Soc. Dalton Trans.*, 1984, 1809.
59. M. Lanfranchi, A. Tiripicchio, E. Sappa, S. A. MacLaughlin and A. J. Carty, *J. Chem. Soc. Chem. Commun.*, 1983, 1332.
60. P. G. Edwards, R. W. Gellert, M. W. Marks, and R. Bau, *J. Am. Chem. Soc.*, 1982, **104**, 2072.
61. C. P. Horwitz, E. M. Holt, C. P. Brock and D. F. Shriver, *J. Am. Chem. Soc.*, 1985, **107**, 8136.
62. S. I. Al-Resayes, P. B. Hitchcock, J. F. Nixon and D. M. P. Mingos, *J. Chem. Soc. Chem. Commun.*, 1985, 365.
63. K. Burgess, B. F. G. Johnson, D. A. Kaner, J. Lewis, P. R. Raithby and S. N. A. B. Mustaffa, *J. Chem. Soc. Chem. Commun.*, 1983, 455.
64. L. J. Farrugia, A. D. Miles and F. G. A. Stone, *J. Chem. Soc. Dalton Trans.*, 1985, 2437.
65. P. V. Broadhurst, B. F. G. Johnson, J. Lewis and P. R. Raithby, *J. Am. Chem. Soc.*, 1981, **103**, 3198.
66. S. A. MacLaughlin, N. J. Taylor and A. J. Carty, *Inorg. Chem.*, 1983, **22**, 1409.
67. R. D. Adams, I. T. Horvath and P. Mathur, *J. Am. Chem. Soc.*, 1984, **106**, 6296.
68. M. R. Churchill and F. J. Hollander, *Inorg. Chem.*, 1978, **17**, 3546.
69. M. I. Bruce and M. L. Williams, *J. Organomet. Chem.*, 1985, **282**, C11.
70. M. R. Awang, G. A. Carriedo, J. A. K. Howard, K. A. Mead, I. Moore, C. M. Nunn and F. G. A. Stone, *J. Chem. Soc. Chem. Commun.*, 1983, 964.
71. C. M. Hay, B. F. G. Johnson, J. Lewis, R. C. S. McQueen, P. R. Raithby, R. M. Sorrell and M. J. Taylor, *Organometallics*, 1985, **4**, 202.
72. R. A. Jones and B. R. Whittlesey, *J. Am. Chem. Soc.*, 1985, **107**, 1078.
73. A. M. Arif, D. E. Heaton and R. A. Jones, *J. Chem. Soc. Chem. Commun.*, 1986, 1506.
74. J. W. A. Van der Velden, J. J. Bour, J. J. Steggerda, P. T. Beurskens, M. Roseboom and J. H. Noordik, *Inorg. Chem.*, 1982, **21**, 4321.
75. R. A. Croft, D. N. Duffy and B. K. Nicholson, *J. Chem. Soc. Dalton Trans.*, 1982, 1023.
76. G. Gervasio, R. Rosetti, P. L. Stanghellini and G. Bor, *Inorg. Chem.*, 1984, **23**, 2073.
77. C. Lensch, P. G. Jones and G. M. Sheldrick, *Z. Naturforsch.*, *Teil B*, 1982, **37**, 944.

78. B. F. G. Johnson, R. Khattar, J. Lewis, G. L. Powell and M. McPartlin, *J. Chem. Soc. Chem. Commun.*, 1986, 507.
79. B. F. G. Johnson, J. Lewis, M. McPartlin, M. A. Pearsall and A. Sironi, *J. Chem. Soc. Chem. Commun.*, 1984, 1089.
80. P. Braunstein, J. Rosé, A. Tiripicchio and M. Tiripicchio-Camellini, *J. Chem. Soc. Chem. Commun.*, 1984, 391.
81. R. D. Adams, I. T. Horvath, P. Mathur and B. E. Segmüller, *Organometallics*, 1983, **2**, 996.
82. R. D. Adams, Z. Dawoodi, D. F. Foust and B. E. Segmüller, *J. Am. Chem. Soc.*, 1983, **105**, 831.
83. J. M. Burtlich, S. E. Hayes and J. T. Lemley, *Organometallics*, 1985, **4**, 167.
84. B. F. G. Johnson, J. Lewis, M. McPartlin, J. Morris, G. L. Powell, P. R. Raithby and M. D. Vargas, *J. Chem. Soc. Chem. Commun.*, 1986, 430.
85. R. D. Adams, D. F. Foust and P. Mathur, *Organometallics*, 1983, **2**, 990.
86. S. Martinengo, G. Ciani and A. Sironi, *J. Chem. Soc. Chem. Commun.*, 1984, 1577.
87. S. Martinengo, G. Ciani and A. Sironi, *J. Chem. Soc. Chem. Commun.*, 1984, 1578.
88. M. I. Bruce and B. K. Nicholson, *Organometallics*, 1984, **3**, 101.
89. J. A. K. Howard, I. D. Salter and F. G. A. Stone, *Polyhedron*, 1984, **3**, 567.
90. B. F. G. Johnson, J. Lewis, W. J. H. Nelson, J. N. Nicholls, J. Puga, P. R. Raithby, M. J. Rosales, M. J. Schröder and M. D. Vargas, *J. Chem. Soc. Dalton Trans.*, 1983, 2447.
91. Y. Yamamoto, K. Aoki and H. Yamazaki, *Organometallics*, 1983, **2**, 1377.
92. Y. Yamamoto, H. Yamazaki and T. Sakuri, *J. Am. Chem. Soc.*, 1982, **104**, 2329.
93. J. W. A. Van der Velden, P. T. Beurskens, J. J. Bour, W. P. Bosman, J. H. Noordik, M. Kolenbrander and J. A. K. M. Buskes, *Inorg. Chem.*, 1984, **23**, 497.
94. K. P. Hall, D. I. Gilmour and D. M. P. Mingos, *J. Organomet. Chem.*, **268**, 275.
95. C. E. Briant, K. P. Hall and D. M. P. Mingos, *J. Chem. Soc. Chem. Commun.*, 1984, 248.
96. G. P. Elliot, J. A. K. Howard, C. M. Nunn and F. G. A. Stone, *J. Chem. Soc. Chem. Commun.*, 1986, 431.
97. B. F. G. Johnson, J. Lewis, W. J. H. Nelson, M. D. Vargas, D. Braga, K. Henrick and M. McPartlin, *J. Chem. Soc. Dalton Trans.*, 1984, 2151.
98. E. Sappa, M. Lanfranchi, A. Tiripicchio and M. T. Camellini, *J. Chem. Soc. Chem. Commun.*, 1981, 995.
99. S. R. Bunkhall, H. D. Holden, B. F. G. Johnson, J. Lewis, G. N. Pain, P. R. Raithby and M. J. Taylor, *J. Chem. Soc. Chem. Commun.*, 1984, 25.
100. J. S. Bradley, R. L. Pruett, E. Hill, G. B. Ansell, M. E. Leonowicz and M. A. Modrick, *Organometallics*, 1982, **1**, 748.
101. R. D. Adams, J. E. Babin and M. Tasi, *Inorg. Chem.*, 1986, **25**, 4460.
102. W. Gade and E. Weiss, *Angew. Chem. Int. Ed. Engl.*, 1981, **20**, 803.
103. T. H. Lemmen, K. Folting, J. C. Huffman and K. G. Caulton, *J. Am. Chem. Soc.*, 1985, **107**, 7774.
104. V. G. Albano, P. Chini, S. Martinengo, M. Sansoni, D. Strumolo and G. Ciani, *J. Chem. Soc. Dalton Trans.*, 1978, 463.
105. V. G. Albano, M. Sansoni, P. Chini, S. Martinengo and D. Strumolo, *J. Chem. Soc. Dalton Trans.*, 1975, 305.
106. L. M. Bullock, J. S. Field, R. J. Haines, E. Minshall, D. M. Smit and G. M. Sheldrick, *J. Organomet. Chem.*, 1986, **310**, C47.
107. A. Ceriotti, G. Longoni, M. Manassero, M. Perego and M. Sansoni, *Inorg. Chem.*, 1985, **24**, 117.
108. B. Krebs, M. Hucke and C. S. Brendel, *Angew. Chem. Int. Ed. Engl.*, 1982, **21**,

445.

109. V. G. Albano, D. Braga, S. Martinengo, P. Chini, M. Sansoni and D. Strumolo, *J. Chem. Soc. Dalton Trans.*, 1980, 52.

110. S. R. Bunkhall, H. D. Holden, B. F. G. Johnson, J. Lewis, G. N. Pain, P. R. Raithby and M. J. Taylor, *J. Chem. Soc. Chem. Commun.*, 1984, 25.

111. A. Arrigoni, A. Ceriotti, R. Della Pergola, G. Longoni, M. Manassero, N. Masciocchi and M. Sansoni, *Angew. Chem. Int. Ed. Engl.*, 1984, **23**, 322.

112. L. D. Lower and L. F. Dahl, *J. Am. Chem. Soc.*, 1976, **98**, 5046.

113. C. T. W. Chu, Ph.D. thesis, University of Wisconsin (Madison), 1977.

114. S. P. Foster, K. M. Mackay and B. K. Nicholson, *Inorg. Chem.*, 1985, **24**, 909.

115. F. Demartin, M. Manassero, M. Sansoni, L. Garlaschelli, C. Raimondi, S. Martinengo and F. Canzani, *J. Chem. Soc. Chem. Commun.*, 1981, 528.

116. M. Manassero, L. Naldini and M. Sansoni, *J. Chem. Soc. Chem. Commun.*, 1979, 385.

117. F. A. Vollenbroek, W. P. Bosman, J. J. Bour, J. H. Noordik and P. T. Beurskens, *J. Chem. Soc. Chem. Commun.*, 1979, 387.

118. J. W. A. Van der Velden, J. J. Bour, W. P. Bosman and J. H. Noordik, *J. Chem. Soc. Chem. Commun.*, 1981, 1218.

119. C. A. Tolman, *Chem. Rev.*, 1977, **77**, 313.

120. H. C. Longuet-Higgins and M. de V. Roberts, *Proc. Roy. Soc.*, 1955, **A230**, 110.

121. R. Hoffmann and W. N. Lipscomb, *J. Chem. Phys.*, 1962, **36**, 2179.

122. R. E. Williams, *Inorg. Chem.*, 1971, **10**, 210.

123. R. E. Williams, *Adv. Inorg. Chem. Radiochem.*, 1976, **18**, 67.

124. K. Wade, *J. Chem. Soc. Chem. Commun.*, 1971, 792.

125. K. Wade, *Adv. Inorg. Chem. Radiochem.*, 1976, **18**, 1.

126. R. W. Rudolph and W. R. Pretzer, *Inorg. Chem.*, 1972, **11**, 1974.

127. R. W. Rudolph, *Acc. Chem. Res.*, 1976, **9**, 446.

128. D. M. P. Mingos, *Nature Phys. Sci.*, 1972, **236**, 99.

129. D. M. P. Mingos, *J. Chem. Soc. Dalton Trans.*, 1974, 133.

130. R. Mason, K. M. Thomas and D. M. P. Mingos, *J. Am. Chem. Soc.*, 1973, **95**, 3802.

131. D. M. P. Mingos and R. L. Johnston, *Struct. Bond.*, 1987, **68**, 29, gives a historical account of bonding models for clusters.

132. M. Elian and R. Hoffmann, *Inorg. Chem.*, 1975, **14**, 1058.

133. M. Elian, M. M. L. Chen, D. M. P. Mingos and R. Hoffmann, *Inorg. Chem.*, 1976, **15**, 1148.

134. R. Hoffmann, *Angew. Chem. Int. Ed. Engl.*, 1982, **21**, 711.

135. R. Hoffmann, *Science*, 1981, **211**, 995.

136. D. M. P. Mingos, *J. Chem. Soc. Dalton Trans.*, 1976, 1163.

137. S. Harris and J. S. Bradley, *Organometallics*, 1984, **3**, 1086.

138. S. D. Wijeyesckera and R. Hoffmann, *Organometallics*, 1984, **3**, 949.

139. J.-F. Halet, D. G. Evans and D. M. P. Mingos, *J. Am. Chem. Soc.*, 1988, **110**, 87.

140. R. L. Johnston and D. M. P. Mingos, *J. Organometal. Chem.*, 1985, **280**, 407.

141. R. L. Johnston and D. M. P. Mingos, *J. Organometal. Chem.*, 1985, **280**, 419.

142. A. J. Stone, *Mol. Phys.*, 1980, **41**, 1339.

143. A. J. Stone, *Inorg. Chem.*, 1981, **20**, 563.

144. A. J. Stone and A. J. Alderton, *Inorg. Chem.*, 1982, **21**, 2297.

145. A. J. Stone, *Polyhedron*, 1984, **3**, 2051.

146. H. Vahrenkamp and D. Wolters, *J. Organomet. Chem.*, 1982, **224**, C17.

147. J. S. Field, R. J. Haines and D. N. Smit, *J. Organomet. Chem.*, 1982, **224**, C49.

148. J. F. Halet, R. Hoffmann and J.-Y. Saillard, *Inorg. Chem.*, 1985, **24**, 1695.

149. D. M. P. Mingos, *J. Chem. Soc. Chem. Commun.*, 1983, 706.

150. D. M. P. Mingos, *Acc. Chem. Res.*, 1984, **17**, 311.

151. D. G. Evans and D. M. P. Mingos, *Organometallics*, 1983, **2**, 435.
152. D. M. P. Mingos and M. I. Forsyth, *J. Chem. Soc. Dalton Trans.*, 1977, 610.
153. M. McPartlin, *Polyhedron*, 1984, **3**, 1279.
154. M. McPartlin and D. M. P. Mingos, *Polyhedron*, 1984, **3**, 1279.
155. D. M. P. Mingos and Z. Lin, *J. Chem. Soc. Dalton Trans.*, 1988, 1657.
156. D. M. P. Mingos, *J. Chem. Soc. Chem. Commun.*, 1985, 1352.
157. D. M. P. Mingos, *Chem. Soc. Rev.*, 1986, **15**, 31.
158. Z. Lin and D. M. P. Mingos, *J. Organometal. Chem.*, **339**, 367; **341**, 523.
159. B. K. Teo, *Inorg. Chem.*, 1984, **23**, 1251.
160. B. K. Teo, G. Longoni and F. R. Ching, *Inorg. Chem.*, 1984, **23**, 1258.
161. R. B. King and D. H. Rouvray, *J. Am. Chem. Soc.*, 1977, **99**, 7834.
162. R. B. King, *Inorg. Chim. Acta.*, 1981, **49**, 237; 1982, **57**, 79.
163. R. B. King, *Inorg. Chim. Acta.*, 1986, **99**, 109, 119, 125.
164. R. B. King, *Polyhedron*, 1982, **1**, 132.
165. D. G. Evans and D. M. P. Mingos, *J. Organometal. Chem.*, 1982, **240**, 321.
166. D. G. Evans, *J. Organometal. Chem.*, 1988, **397**, 352.
167. D. G. Evans and D. M. P. Mingos, *J. Organometal. Chem.*, 1983, **251**, C13.
168. D. G. Evans and D. M. P. Mingos, *J. Organometal. Chem.*, 1982, **232**, 171.
169. D. M. P. Mingos, *Phil. Trans. R. Soc. Lond.*, 1982, **A308**, 75.
170. D. M. P. Mingos and K. P. Hall, *Prog. Inorg. Chem.*, 1984, **32**, 239.
171. D. M. P. Mingos, K. P. Hall and D. I. Gilmour, *J. Organometal. Chem.*, 1984, **268**, 275.
172. D. G. Evans and D. M. P. Mingos, *J. Organometal. Chem.*, 1985, **295**, 389.
173. D. M. P. Mingos, *Polyhedron*, 1984, **3**, 1289.
174. R. L. Johnston and D. M. P. Mingos, *Inorg Chem.*, 1986, **25**, 1661.
175. R. L. Johnston and D. M. P. Mingos, *J. Chem. Soc. Dalton Trans.*, 1987, 647.
176. R. L. Johnston and D. M. P. Mingos, *J. Chem. Soc. Dalton Trans.*, 1987, 1445.
177. P. W. Fowler, *Polyhedron*, 1985, **4**, 2051.
178. D. M. P. Mingos, *Phil. Trans. R. Soc. Lond.*, 1982, **A308**, 14.
179. J. G. Jeffrey, Ph.D. thesis, Cambridge University, 1985.
180. a) P. D. Frisch and L. F. Dahl, *J. Am. Chem. Soc.*, 1972, **94**, 5082. b) N. Kamijo and T. Watanabe, *Acta Cryst.*, 1979, **B35**, 2537.
181. C.-H. Wei and L. F. Dahl, *Inorg. Chem.*, 1965, **4**, 493.

Systematics of the Synthesis of Transition Metal Carbonyl Clusters

Richard D. Adams

3.1. Introduction

Very few reviews have been published that focus on the methodology of cluster synthesis.[1-4] In this chapter, the types of reactions that have been useful in preparing cluster complexes in a rational and systematic way will be discussed, although these reactions may not always be the most efficient routes to a particular complex. When it is possible, we will try to rationalize the reactions in terms of the known chemistry of mononuclear metal complexes, but it must be recognized that the detailed mechanisms have not been established in most cases.

It is generally accepted that the bonds between transition metal atoms involve d or d-hybrid orbitals, and the isolobal analogy is useful in visualizing the form of the orbitals involved in the bonding.[6] To permit an adequate orbital overlap for bond formation, it is necessary that the metal atoms exist in low oxidation states.[7] Formally, metal-metal bonds can be divided into two categories that differ depending on the source of the bonding electrons. These are the homopolar metal-metal bond, equation (3.1), and the heteropolar metal-metal bond, equation (3.2). The latter may be represented by a resonance structure that contains a significant degree of charge separation.

$$L_nM\cdot \quad + \quad \cdot ML_n \longrightarrow L_nM\text{-}ML_n \qquad (3.1)$$
$$\mathbf{A}$$

$$L_nM: \quad + \quad M'L_n \longrightarrow L_nM\rightarrow ML_n \longleftrightarrow \overset{+}{L_nM}\text{-}\overset{-}{ML_n} \qquad (3.2)$$
$$\mathbf{B}$$

Dimanganese decacarbonyl (**1**) is probably the most illustrative example of a compound with a homopolar covalent metal-metal bond, A. In fact, it was the determination of the structure of this compound that provided the first convincing evidence for the existence of a metal-metal bond in a molecular complex.[8] In (1) the two 17-electron $Mn(CO)_5$ halves of the molecule are held together by a single unsupported (lacking bridging ligands) Mn—Mn bond.

(1)   (2)

Recently, Pomeroy and co-workers have characterized a number of heteronuclear complexes that contain unsupported heteropolar metal-metal bonds, B.[9-13] An illustrative example of a compound of this type is (2) $OsW(CO)_9[PMe_3]$, which was made by the displacement of a THF ligand from $W(CO)_5$ (THF) by the complex $Os(CO)_4[PMe_3]$.[9] The Os → W bond (3.0756(5) Å) in this compound is formed by the donation of two electrons from the 18-electron osmium atom to an empty orbital on the tungsten atom of the 16-electron $W(CO)_5$ grouping.

If a metal atom contains less than 18 electrons in the presence of a metal-metal single bond, then multiple metal-metal bonding may occur in order to raise the count to 18. The compounds (3) $[Cp^*Co(CO)_2]_2$[14,15] and (4) $[CpMo(CO)_2]_2$[16] are examples of compounds that contain metal-metal double and triple bonds, respectively. The unsaturation in these bonds makes them readily susceptible to addition reactions, and these and related compounds have been found to be useful reagents for the synthesis of higher nuclearity clusters. As implied by the preceding examples, electron deficiency in the valence shell of a transition metal atom is a condition that frequently leads to the formation of metal-metal bonds.

(3)   (4)

In much of the synthetic methodology that is described in this chapter, ligand eliminations that result in the loss of electrons in the valence shell of the metal atom play a central role in the cluster syntheses. Ligand elimination can be achieved by a variety of processes: (1) dissociative ligand elimination, (2) ligand displacement (i.e., substitution), and (3) reactions which lead to the formation and elimination of small molecules. Our distinction between dissociative ligand elimination and ligand displacement will correspond loosely to the mechanistic differences between dissociative and associative ligand substitution reactions.[17] Multiply bonded compounds such as (3) and (4) and coordinatively unsaturated compounds such as the various stable 16-electron complexes that exist for the elements Rh, Ir, Pd, and Pt [e.g., (5) $Pt(PPh_3)_2Cl_2$ or (6) $Ir(CO)(PPh_3)_2Cl$] possess an inherent electron deficiency that can often be utilized for cluster synthesis without the requirement of a ligand elimination.

$$
\begin{array}{cc}
PPh_3 & PPh_3 \\
| & | \\
Cl-Pt-Cl & Cl-Ir-CO \\
| & | \\
PPh_3 & PPh_3 \\
(5) & (6)
\end{array}
$$

Species that possess 17-electron configurations may be generated in the course of certain reactions.[18,19] Such species may be expected to couple by the formation of a metal-metal bond, equation (3.1). The coupling may be very rapid and the equilibrium may lie so far on the side of the metal-metal bonded product that the mononuclear intermediates might not be observed directly. Bridging ligands derived from elements of the main groups have been found to play an important role both in the synthesis and in the stabilization of metal clusters.[2,20]

3.2. Ligand Dissociation

The elimination of a CO ligand from a metal complex is one of the most general methods for the preparation of carbonyl clusters. The elimination of CO by dissociative processes is accomplished by three principal methods: (1) photolysis; (2) pyrolysis; and (3) chemically induced elimination. Binary metal carbonyls are ideal reagents and are known for most of the transition elements.

3.2.1. Photolysis

Although pyrolysis is more widely utilized than photolysis for promoting cluster-forming reactions, photolytic reactions are considered first since it is believed these reactions provide a better framework for understanding the cluster-forming processes.

In the presence of UV irradiation, metal carbonyl compounds readily undergo sequential expulsion of CO ligands to yield electron-deficient or solvent-coordinated species, equation (3.3).

These species may combine with an unactivated 18-electron complex to form a donor-acceptor metal-metal bond. The formation of the dinuclear compounds (7) $M_2(CO)_9$, M = Fe, Ru, Os may proceed in this fashion, equation (3.4).[21,22] An intermediate such as C similar to (2) may be traversed although the final products, (7), possess structures that have bridging carbonyl ligands. The isolation of the compounds (7) is facilitated by conditions that promote their precipitation from solution. Under other conditions further decarbonylation occurs and trinuclear clusters are obtained, equation (3.5). Under UV irradiation $CpRh(CO)_2$ loses CO to form dinuclear and trinuclear clusters, equation (3.6).[25,26] The unusual mixed-metal cluster $Os_2Cr(CO)_{11}(PMe_3)_2$ was made by the irradiation of $OsCr(CO)_9(PMe_3)$, equation (3.7).[25] The form of the chromium group that was eliminated was not reported.

$$M(CO)_x \xrightarrow{\text{h}v} \text{"}M(CO)_{x-1}\text{"} + CO \qquad (3.3)$$

$$M(CO)_5 + \text{"}M(CO)_4\text{"} \longrightarrow (OC)_5M \longrightarrow M(CO)_4 \longrightarrow M_2(CO)_9 \quad (3.4)$$
$$M = Fe, Ru, Os \qquad\qquad\qquad C \qquad\qquad\qquad (7)$$

$$3\ M(CO)_5 \xrightarrow{\text{h}v} M_3(CO)_{12} + 3\ CO \qquad (3.5)$$
$$M = Fe, Ru, Os$$

$$CpRh(CO)_2 \xrightarrow[-CO]{\text{h}v} Cp_2Rh_2(CO)_3 + Cp_2Rh_3(CO)_3 \qquad (3.6)$$

$$2\ (Me_3P)(OC)_4Os \longrightarrow Cr(CO)_5 \xrightarrow[-\text{"Cr"}]{\text{h}v} \qquad (3.7)$$

$$Co(CO)_4^- + Fe(CO)_5 \xrightarrow{\text{h}v} [FeCo(CO)_8]^- + CO \qquad (3.8)$$

Several heteronuclear monoanions, for example $[FeCo(CO)_9]^-$ and $[MnMo(CO)_{10}]^-$, have been prepared by this procedure, equation (3.8).[26] Higher nuclearity products are obtained when elements from the second and third rows are employed. For example, the reaction of $Co(CO)_4^-$ with $Os_3(CO)_{12}$ yields the monoanion (8) $[CoOs_3(CO)_{13}]^-$, Scheme 3.1.[27] It was proposed that the formation of (8) occurred by a series of decarbonylation steps, through which the cluster became increasingly condensed. The proposed intermediates D and E were not observed in this reaction, but each loss of a CO ligand is accompanied by the formation of one metal-metal bond.

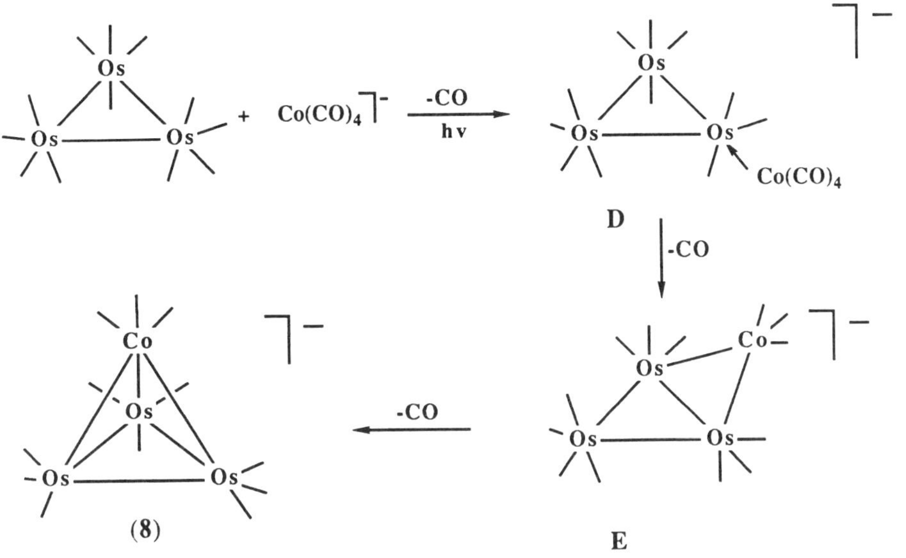

Scheme 3.1

3.2.2. Pyrolysis

Thermally induced elimination of ligands is the most convenient method to perform in the laboratory, but it suffers from a lack of ability to control the extent of ligand elimination. In unfavorable cases, all of the ligands are lost and bulk metal results, equations (3.9)[28] and (3.10).[29] This difficulty is more commonly encountered among the elements of the first transition series than with those of the second or third series. By controlling the temperature it is possible in certain cases to obtain selected cluster products, equations (3.11),[29,30] (3.12),[30,31] (3.13),[29,32] and (3.14).[33] However, in others, for example $Os_3(CO)_{12}$, equation (3.15),[29] a variety of clusters is obtained.

$$Ni(CO)_4 \xrightarrow{60°C} Ni^0 + 4\,CO \qquad (3.9)$$

$$Re_2(CO)_{10} \xrightarrow{130\text{-}170°C} Re^0 \qquad (3.10)$$

$$3\,Ru(CO)_5 \xrightarrow[-3\,CO]{50°C} Ru_3(CO)_{12} \xrightarrow{150°C} \underset{5\%}{Ru_6(C)(CO)_{17}} \xrightarrow{180°C} Ru^0 \quad (3.11)$$

$$3\,Fe_2(CO)_9 \xrightarrow{70°C} 3\,Fe(CO)_5 + \underset{10\%}{Fe_3(CO)_{12}} \longrightarrow Fe^0 \quad (3.12)$$

$$Co_2(CO)_8 \xrightarrow[-4\,CO]{50°C} Co_4(CO)_{12} \xrightarrow{63\text{-}100°C} Co_6(CO)_{16} \xrightarrow{120°C} dec. \quad (3.13)$$

$$2 \ [CpFe(CO)_2]_2 \xrightarrow{140°C} Cp_4Fe_4(CO)_4 + 4 \ CO \qquad (3.14)$$

$$Os_3(CO)_{12} \xrightarrow{210°C} \underset{80\%}{Os_6(CO)_{18}} + \underset{7\%}{Os_5(CO)_{16}} + \underset{10\%}{Os_7(CO)_{21}} + \underset{2\%}{Os_8(CO)_{23}} \qquad (3.15)$$

The mechanisms of the cluster growth processes in these reactions are not well understood. Some reactions might occur by the condensation of two unsaturated species. A kinetic study of the formation of $Co_4(CO)_{12}$ showed an inverse second order dependence on CO concentration, and it was proposed that $Co_2(CO)_8$ loses two moles of CO to yield $Co_2(CO)_6$, equation (3.16).[32] Two moles of $Co_2(CO)_6$ could then couple to form $Co_4(CO)_{12}$, equation (3.17). The unsaturated heteronuclear compound $CoRh(CO)_7$ was prepared recently and was shown to undergo a facile coupling to yield $Co_2Rh_2(CO)_{12}$, equation (3.18).[34] However, a distinction between the mechanisms a and b was not made. An unsaturated species like $CoRh(CO)_6$ could contain triple bond character between the metal atoms.

$$Co_2(CO)_8 \underset{+CO}{\overset{-CO}{\rightleftharpoons}} Co_2(CO)_7 \underset{+CO}{\overset{-CO}{\rightleftharpoons}} Co_2(CO)_6 \qquad (3.16)$$

$$2 \ Co_2(CO)_6 \longrightarrow Co_4(CO)_{12} \qquad (3.17)$$

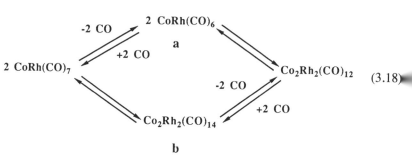

$$(3.18)$$

Johnson and Lewis have proposed cluster formation schemes based on the ejection of 18-electron complexes from small clusters followed by the condensation of the unsaturated fragments [see Scheme 3.2 proposed for the formation of high nuclearity carbonyl clusters of osmium by utilizing $Os(CO)_5$ eliminations].[35]

Attempts to prepare heteronuclear metal carbonyl clusters by pyrolytic decarbonylations have had only limited success,[36] equations (3.19)[37] and (3.20).[38] Heteronuclear clusters are prepared more efficiently by ligand displacement reactions vide infra.

$$Fe_2(CO)_9 + CpCo(CO)_2 \xrightarrow{60°C} CpFe_2Co(CO)_9 + 2 \ CO \qquad (3.19)$$

$$[CpNiCO]_2 + CpCo(CO)_2 \xrightarrow{68°C} Cp_3Ni_2Co(CO)_2 + 2 \ CO \qquad (3.20)$$

$$Os_3(CO)_{12} \rightleftharpoons "Os_2(CO)_7" + Os(CO)_5$$

$$2 \ "Os_2(CO)_7" \rightleftharpoons Os_4(CO)_{14}$$

$$Os_4(CO)_{14} \rightleftharpoons "Os_3(CO)_9" + Os(CO)_5$$

$$2 \ "Os_3(CO)_9" \rightleftharpoons Os_6(CO)_{18}$$

$$"Os_2(CO)_7" + "Os_3(CO)_9" \rightleftharpoons Os_5(CO)_{16}$$

Scheme 3.2

The stepwise loss and addition of CO ligands with the accompanying formation and cleavage of metal-metal bonds has been invoked to explain the opening and closing of a variety of clusters, Scheme 3.3.[39,40] Note that for each loss of a CO ligand one metal-metal bond is formed.

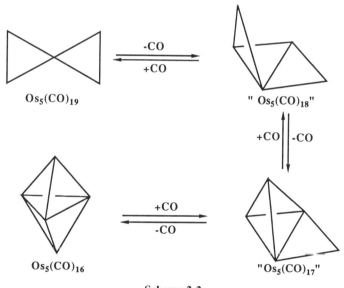

$$Os_5(CO)_{19}$$

$$" Os_5(CO)_{18}"$$

$$Os_5(CO)_{16}$$

$$"Os_5(CO)_{17}"$$

Scheme 3.3

The expulsion of other types of ligands can also be useful in the synthesis of clusters. Alkenes (ethylene, COD, and COT),[41] tertiary phosphines, and alkyl isocyanides can be eliminated from certain Group VIII metal complexes to yield cluster complexes, equations (3.21),[42] (3.22),[43] (3.23),[44] and (3.24).[47]

$$7 \ Ni(CNBu^t)_4 + 9 \ Ni(COD)_2 \longrightarrow 4 \ Ni_4(CNBu^t)_7 + 18 \ COD \quad (3.21)$$

$$3 \text{ Pt(COD)}_2 + 6 \text{ CNBu}^t \longrightarrow \qquad + 6 \text{ COD} \quad (3.22)$$

$$\text{Pt(PR}_3)_4 + \text{Fe}_2(\text{CO})_9 \longrightarrow \qquad + \text{CO} + 2 \text{ PR}_3 \quad (3.23)$$

$$(3.24)$$

$$\text{CpMn(CO)}_2\text{CS} + \text{Pt(PMe}_2\text{Ph})_2\text{C}_2\text{H}_4 \longrightarrow \qquad + \text{C}_2\text{H}_2$$

3.2.3. Chemically Induced Ligand Elimination

The reaction of trimethylamine oxide, Me_3NO, with a metal carbonyl compound is a very effective method of removing a selected number of carbonyl ligands, equation (3.25).[46,47] The reaction proceeds under very mild conditions and is stoichiometric. Best results are achieved when these reactions are performed in solvents that can function as weakly donating ligands that can stabilize the decarbonylated intermediates. Subsequent reactions of these complexes proceed by the displacement of these weakly donating ligands. Accordingly, most reactions of this type will be described in the following section on ligand displacements, vide infra.

$$M(CO)_x + n \text{ Me}_3NO \longrightarrow M(CO)_{x\text{-}n}(\text{sol})_n + n \text{ CO}_2 + n \text{ NMe}_3 \quad (3.25)$$

$$\text{sol} = \text{MeCN}$$

There have been very few reports of cluster syntheses that utilize Me_3NO in very poorly donating solvents, but one illustrative example is the reaction of $CpRh(CO)_2$ with Me_3NO in C_6H_6 solvent, equation (3.26).[48]

The heterotetranuclear cluster, $Rh_2Fe_2(CO)_8\{\mu\text{-Ph}_2PC(CH_2)PPh_2\}_2$, was made by the treatment of the heterodinuclear compound $RhFe(CO)_5\{\mu\text{-}Ph_2PC(CH_2)PPh_2\}$ with $Me_3NO\cdot2H_2O$ in toluene solvent at 298 K, equation (3.27).[49] Although it was not a problem in this reaction, complications can arise from the use of the hydrated form of Me_3NO due to reactions with the H_2O.[50]

(3.26)

$$CpRh(CO)_2 \ + \ 1 \ Me_3NO \ \xrightarrow{353K} \ Cp_2Rh_2(CO)_3 \ + \ Cp_3Rh_3(CO)_3 \ + \ Cp_4Rh_4(CO)_2$$

$$10\text{-}25\% \qquad\qquad 30\text{-}60\% \qquad\qquad 5\%$$

$$RhFe(CO)_5\{\mu\text{-}Ph_2PC(CH_2)PPh_2\} \ + \ 2 \ (Me_3NO \cdot 2 \ H_2O)$$

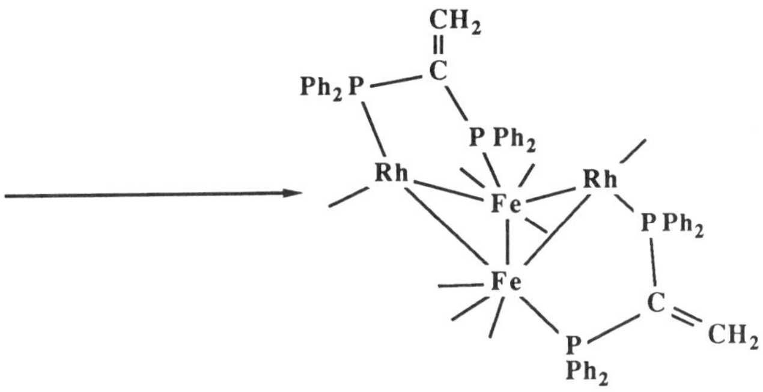

(3.27)

50%

Metal carbonyls will react with hydroxide ion to convert a CO ligand into CO_2 and yield a hydridometal carbonyl anion, equation (3.28).[51] The nucleophilic anions can condense to form larger clusters under forcing conditions, equation (3.29).[52]

$$Os_3(CO)_{12} \ \xrightarrow{+ \ OH^-} \ [Os_3(CO)_{11}(-\overset{O}{\underset{\underset{H}{O}}{\overset{\|}{C}}})]^- \ \xrightarrow{- \ CO_2} \ [HOs_3(CO)_{11}]^- \quad (3.28)$$

(3.29)

$$Os_3(CO)_{12} \ + \ OH^- \ \xrightarrow[48 \ hrs.]{373K} \ [H_3Os_4(CO)_{12}]^- \ + \ [HOs_6(CO)_{18}]^- \ + \ \text{minor products}$$

$$45\% \qquad\qquad 18\%$$

3.3. Ligand Displacement and Redox Condensation Reactions

These reactions are divided into three categories: (1) displacement of anionic ligands, (2) displacement of CO, and (3) displacement of weakly coordinated ligands. It has been assumed that these reactions are basically of an associative, nucleophilic substitution-like character. Redox condensation reactions, defined as reactions between coordinatively saturated species in different oxidation states,[3,53,54] are included in this section although there is evidence that some reactions of this type occur by electron transfer processes.[55] Electron transfer processes have been shown to promote CO ligand substitution reactions.[56]

3.3.1. Displacement of Anionic Ligands

Halides, X^-, are the most common and easily displaced anionic ligands. When a halide ligand is displaced from a metal complex by an anionic metal complex, a metal-metal bond is usually formed. Some of the earliest of these reactions described the preparation of dinuclear complexes containing heteronuclear metal-metal bonds, equations (3.30)[57] and (3.31).[58] Although good yields of heterodimetallic compounds can be obtained by the anion-halide displacement method, it has recently been shown that many of these compounds can also be conveniently prepared by metal-metal exchange reactions employing homonuclear dimetallic compounds.[19]

$$CpMo(CO)_3^- + CpW(CO)_3I \longrightarrow \underset{65\%}{Cp(CO)_3Mo\text{-}W(CO)_3Cp} + I^- \quad (3.30)$$

$$Mn(CO)_5^- + CpFe(CO)_2I \longrightarrow \underset{40\%}{(CO)_5Mn\text{-}Fe(CO)_2Cp} + I^- \quad (3.31)$$

Braunstein and co-workers have prepared a variety of heteronuclear clusters containing platinum and palladium from reactions between metal carbonyl anions and platinum or palladium halide complexes, equations (3.32),[59] (3.33),[60] and (3.34).[61] This has also led to the synthesis of some unusual high nuclearity mixed-metal carbonyl clusters, equations (3.35),[62] (3.36),[62] (3.37),[63] and (3.38).[64] Additional examples are listed in Table 3.1.

$$2\ Co(CO)_4^- + \text{trans-}Pdpy_2Cl_2 \longrightarrow (CO)_4Co-\underset{\underset{py}{|}}{\overset{\overset{py}{|}}{Pd}}-Co(CO)_4 + 2\ Cl^- \quad (3.32)$$

$$2\ CpMo(CO)_3^- + 2\ \text{cis-}Pt(PR_3)_2Cl_2 \longrightarrow \quad + 4\ Cl^- \quad (3.33)$$

$$2\ Co(CO)_4^- + Pt(PPh_3)_2Cl_2 \longrightarrow \quad + 4\ Cl^- \quad (3.34)$$

$$Fe(CO)_4{}^{2-} \ + \ CuBr \ \longrightarrow \quad u_3Fe_3(CO)_{12}{}^{3-} \quad + \ 3 \ Br^- \quad (3.35)$$

$$u_3Fe_3(CO)_{12}{}^{3-}$$

$$Cu_3Fe_3(CO)_{12}{}^{3-} \ + \ Cu(CO)Cl \longrightarrow \quad Cu_5Fe_4(CO)_{16}{}^{3-} \quad\quad (3.36)$$

$$Cu_5Fe_4(CO)_{16}{}^{3-}$$

$$7 \ [Ni_6(CO)_{12}]^{2-} \ + \ 6 \ PtCl_2 \ \longrightarrow \ [Ni_{38}Pt_6(CO)_{48}]^{6-} + \ 2 \ Ni^{2+} \ + \ 2 \ Ni(CO)_4 \ + \ 28 \ CO \tag{3.37}$$

$$+ \ [ML_nCl]_2 \ \longrightarrow \quad\quad (3.38)$$

$$ML_n = Rh(CO)_2, Rh(COD), Rh(CO)PPh_3, Ir(COD), PdC_3H_5, PtC_4H_7, etc.$$

Au(PR$_3$)X, X = halide or nitrate, compounds have been found to react with a variety of metal carbonyl anions to yield transition metal–gold complexes, equations (3.39)[65] and (3.40).[66] Occasionally, unreactive halide complexes such as Au(PR$_3$)Cl can be activated by the use of coreagents such as Ag[BF$_4$] or Tl[PF$_6$], equation (3.41).[67]

$$Co(CO)_4{}^- \ + \ Au(PPh_3)Cl \ \longrightarrow \ \underset{60\%}{Co(CO)_4Au(PPh_3)} \ + \ Cl^- \quad (3.39)$$

$$[FeCo_3(CO)_{12}]^- \ + \ Au(PPh_3)NO_3 \ \longrightarrow \ FeCo_3(CO)_{12}Au \ (PPh_3) \quad (3.40)$$

$$Fe_4(CO)_{12}(C)^{2-} + Au(PPh_3)Cl \xrightarrow[- TlCl]{+ Tl(PF_6)} \left[\text{Fe} \underset{\substack{| \\ Fe}}{\overset{\substack{PPh_3 \\ | \\ Au}}{\diagdown\diagup}} C \diagdown Fe \right]^{-} \quad (3.41)$$

3.3.2. Displacement of CO

The displacement of CO in an uncharged complex by a metal carbonyl anion is another effective method of increasing the metal nuclearity of a complex in a systematic and controllable fashion. The anion may be mononuclear, equation (3.42), M = Mn, Re; M' = Cr, Mo, W,[68] and equation (3.43),[69] or polynuclear and involve the displacement of several CO ligands and the formation of several metal-metal bonds, equations (3.44),[70] (3.45),[71] and (3.46).[54,72] These are classic redox reactions. Additional examples are listed in Table 3.1.

$$M(CO)_5^- + M'(CO)_6 \xrightarrow{433K} [(CO)_5M \longrightarrow M'(CO)_5]^- + CO \quad (3.42)$$
$$M = Mn,Re \qquad M' = Cr,Mo,W$$

$$Rh(CO)_4^- + Rh_4(CO)_{12} \longrightarrow [Rh_5(CO)_{15}]^- + CO \quad (3.43)$$

$$[Fe_3(CO)_{11}]^{2-} + Fe(CO)_5 \longrightarrow [Fe_4(CO)_{13}]^{2-} + 3 CO \quad (3.44)$$

$$[Ru_3(CO)_{11}]^{2-} + Ru_3(CO)_{12} \longrightarrow [Ru_6(CO)_{18}]^{2-} + 5 CO \quad (3.45)$$

$$[Rh_5(CO)_{15}]^- + Rh(CO)_4^- \longrightarrow [Rh_6(CO)_{15}]^{2-} + 4 CO \quad (3.46)$$

3.3.3. Displacement of Weakly Coordinated Ligands

THF, NCMe, COD, py, acetone, and many alkenes are the most common examples of weakly coordinated ligands. Complexes containing these ligands are frequently prepared from a carbonyl precursor by application of one of the methods discussed in Section 3.2, equation (3.25) in a reaction that precedes the cluster synthesis reaction, equations (3.47)–(3.49). Complexes containing weakly coordinated ligands are said to be "lightly stabilized."[73] There are two principal reasons for adopting this stepwise procedure: (1) one is able to control the stoichiometry of the cluster-forming reaction better; and (2) the cluster-forming reaction can be performed under milder conditions which may be more suitable to product formation and isolation. This is illustrated by the reactions (3.50)[8] and (3.51),[74] which show that the weakly coordinated ligand can be displaced even by simple uncharged 18-electron metal complexes. The metal-metal bond that is formed can

Table 3.1 • Representative Examples of Cluster Enlargements Through Redox Condensation Reactions

Reagents	Product	Ref.
1) $[Rh_6(CO)_{15}]^{2-} + Rh(CO)_4^-$	$[Rh_7(CO)_{16}]^{3-}$	1
2) $[Rh_6(CO)_{15}]^{2-} + Ni(CO)_4$	$[Rh_6Ni(CO)_{16}]^{2-}$	2
3) $Co(CO)_4^- + M_3(CO)_{12}$ (M=Fe, Ru)	$[M_3Co(CO)_{13}]^-$	3
4) $Co(CO)_4^- + RuCo_2(CO)_{11}$	$[RuCo_3(CO)_{12}]^-$	4
5) $Re(CO)_5^- + Ru_3(CO)_{12}$	$[Ru_3Re(CO)_{16}]^-$	5
6) $Mn(CO)_5^- + [CpNi(CO)]_2$	$[Ni_2Mn(CO)_5Cp_2]^-$	6
7) $[M_2(CO)_{10}]^{2-} + 3Ni(CO)_4$ (M=Cr, Mo, W)	$[M_2Ni_3(CO)_{16}]^{2-}$	7
8) $3[Fe_3(CO)_{11}]^{2-} + 2K_2[MCl_4]$ (M=Pd, Pt)	$[Fe_4M(CO)_{16}]^{2-}$	8
9) $[Pt_3(CO)_6]^{2-} + 3Fe(CO)_5$	$[Fe_3Pt_3(CO)_{15}]^{2-}$	9
10) $[Ni_6(CO)_{12}]^{2-} + M(CO)_6$ (M=Cr, Mo,W)	$[Ni_6M(CO)_{17}]^{2-}$	10
11) $[Rh_6(CO)_{15}(N)]^- + M(CO)_4^-$ (M=Co, Rh, Ir)	$[Rh_6M(CO)_{15}(N)]^{2-}$	11
12) $[Fe_4(CO)_{12}(C)]^{2-} + Co_2(CO)_8$	$[CoFe_4(CO)_{14}(C)]^-$	12
13) $2[Co_6(CO)_{15}(C)]^{2-} + Co_4(CO)_{12}$	$2[Co_8(CO)_{18}(C)]^{2-}$	13
14) $[Fe_4(CO)_{12}(C)]^{2-} + M(CO)_3L_3$ (M=Cr, W)	$[Fe_4M(CO)_{15}(C)]^{2-}$	14
15) $[Fe_4(CO)_{12}(C)]^{2-} + [Rh(CO)_2Cl]_2$	$[Fe_4Rh(CO)_{14}(C)]^-$	14
16) $[Fe_5(CO)_{14}(C)]^{2-} + [Rh(CO)_2Cl]_2$	$[Fe_5Rh(CO)_{16}(C)]^-$	14
17) $[Fe_5(CO)_{14}(C)]^{2-} + Ni(COD)_2$	$[Fe_5Ni(CO)_{14}(COD)(C)]^-$	14
18) $[Fe_5(CO)_{14}(C)]^{2-} + Pd(C_3H_5)_2Cl_2$	$Fe_5Pd(CO)_{16}(C)$	14
19) $[Fe_3(CO)_9(CCO)]^{2-} + M(CO)_3(NCR)_3$ (M=Cr, W)	$[Fe_3M(CO)_{13}(C)]^{2-}$	15
20) $[Fe_3(CO)_9(CCO)]^{2-} + Cr(CO)_3(NCMe)_3$	$[Fe_3Cr_2(CO)_{13}(C)]^{2-}$	15
21) $[Fe_3(CO)_9(CCO)]^{2-} + Rh(CO)_2(py)Cl$	$[RhFe_3(CO)_{12}(C)]^{2-}$	15
22) $[Fe_3(CO)_9(CCO)]^{2-} + [Rh(CO)_2Cl]_2$	$[Rh_3Fe_3(CO)_{15}(C)]^-$	15

1. S. Martinengo and P. Chini, *Gazz. Chim. Ital.,* 1972, **102**, 344.
2. A. Fumagalli, G. Longoni, P. Chini, A. Albinati and S. Bruckner, *J. Organomet. Chem.,* 1980, **202**, 329.
3. P. C. Steinhardt, W. L. Gladfelter, A. D. Harley, J. R. Fox and G. L. Geoffroy, *Inorg. Chem.,* 1980, **19**, 332.
4. E. Roland, W. Bernhardt and H. Vahrenkamp, *Chem. Ber.,* 1986, **119**, 2566.
5. J. Knight and M. J. Mays, *J. Chem. Soc. Dalton Trans.,* 1972, 1022.
6. A. T. T. Hsieh and J. Knight, *J. Organomet. Chem.,* 1971, **26**, 125.
7. J. K. Ruff, R. P. White, Jr. and L. F. Dahl, *J. Am. Chem. Soc.,* 1971, **93**, 2159.
8. G. Longoni, M. Manassero and M. Sansoni, *J. Am. Chem. Soc.* 1980, **102**, 3242.
9. G. Longoni, M. Manassero and M. Sansoni, *J. Am. Chem. Soc.,* 1980, **102**, 7973.
10. T. L. Hall and J. K. Ruff, *Inorg. Chem.,* 1981, **20**, 4444.
11. S. Martinengo, G. Ciani and A. Sironi, *J. Chem. Soc. Chem. Commun.,* 1984, 1577.
12. J. A. Hriljac, P. N. Swepston and D. F. Shriver, *Organometallics,* 1985, **4**, 158.
13. P. Chini, G. Longoni and V. G. Albano, *Adv. Organomet. Chem.,* 1976, **14**, 285.
14. M. Tachikawa, R. L. Geerts and E. L. Muetterties, *J. Organomet. Chem.,* 1981, **213**, 11.
15. J. A. Hriljac, E. M. Holt and D. F. Shriver, *Inorg. Chem.,* 1987, **26**, 2943.

be viewed as a donor-acceptor bond, B. A CO ligand shift has also occurred in the formation of the product of reaction (3.51). When more than one ligand can be displaced, more metal-metal bonds can be made, equations (3.52)[13] and (3.53).[75] Lightly stabilized complexes have been used for the enlargement of high nuclearity clusters, equations (3.54) and (3.55).[54] A variety of heteronuclear clusters containing encapsulated carbido ligands have been made by capping the square pyramid of metal atoms in $[Fe_5(C)(CO)_{14}]^{2-}$ with fragments from lightly stabilized metal complexes, equation (3.56).[77] Additional examples are listed in Table 3.1.

$$CpMn(CO)_3 \xrightarrow[\text{THF}]{h\nu} CpMn(CO)_2(THF) \qquad (3.47)$$

$$Cr(CO)_6 \xrightarrow[\text{NCMe}]{\Delta} Cr(CO)_3(NCMe)_3 \qquad (3.48)$$

$$Os_3(CO)_{12} \xrightarrow[\text{NCMe}]{Me_3NO} Os_3(CO)_{11}(NCMe) \xrightarrow[\text{NCMe}]{Me_3NO} Os_3(CO)_{10}(NCMe)_2 \qquad (3.49)$$

(3.50)

$$W(CO)_5THF + Os(CO)_4PMe_3 \xrightarrow[\text{-THF}]{298K} \underset{\mathbf{2}}{\overset{}{\text{—}W\leftarrow Os\text{—}PMe_3}} \xrightarrow{333K} decomp.$$

$$CpMn(CO)_2THF + Cp^*Rh(CO)_2 \xrightarrow[\text{-THF}]{298K} \underset{Cp}{Mn}\rightleftarrows \underset{Cp^*}{Rh} \qquad (3.51)$$

$$Os_3(CO)_{10}(C_8H_{14})_2 + M(CO)_2 \longrightarrow \begin{matrix} Os \\ Os \quad M(CO) \\ Os \end{matrix} \qquad (3.52)$$

$$M = Os(CO)_3 \text{ or } IrCp^*$$

$$3\ Pt(C_2H_4)_3 + 3\ Cp^*Ir(CO)_2 \xrightarrow{273K} \begin{matrix} Cp^* \\ Ir\text{—}CO \\ Pt\text{———}Pt \\ OC \quad Cp^* \\ Ir\text{—}Pt\text{—}Ir \\ Cp^* \quad C \\ O \end{matrix} \qquad (3.53)$$

$$[Rh_{13}(CO)_{24}H]^{4-} + [Rh(CO)_2(NCMe)_2]^+ \xrightarrow{298K} [Rh_{14}(CO)_{25}H]^{3-} + CO \quad (3.54)$$

$$[Rh_{14}(CO)_{25}]^{4-} + [Rh(CO)_2(NCMe)_2]^+ \xrightarrow{298K} [Rh_{15}(CO)_{27}]^{3-} \quad (3.55)$$

$$\left[\text{Fe cluster}\right]^{2-} + M(CO)_3L_3 \longrightarrow \left[\text{Fe cluster}-M\right]^{2-} \qquad (3.56)$$

$$M = Cr, Mo, W$$

$H_2Os(CO)_4$ has been found to add readily to the lightly stabilized clusters $Os_3(CO)_{11}(NCMe)$, equation (3.57), and $Os_5(CO)_{15}(NCMe)$, equation (3.58), to yield open clusters that can be closed by subsequent thermal decarbonylation.[78]

$$Os_3(CO)_{10}(NCMe) \xrightarrow{\ H_2Os(CO)_4\ } \qquad (3.57)$$

$$(3.58)$$

$$Os_5(CO)_{15}(NCMe) \xrightarrow[298K]{H_2Os(CO)_4} \underset{Os_6(CO)_{19}(H)_2}{\quad} \xrightarrow[383K]{-CO} \underset{Os_6(CO)_{18}(H)_2}{\quad}$$

$$(3.59)$$

$$Os_3(CO)_{11}(NCMe)_2 \xrightarrow{HRe(CO)_5} \underset{}{\overset{HRe(CO)_5}{\underset{+NCMe}{\rightleftharpoons}}}$$

The reaction of $Os_3(CO)_{10}(NCMe)_2$ with two equivalents of $HRe(CO)_5$ appears to occur in a stepwise fashion, equation (3.59).[79] The proposed intermediate $Os_3Re(CO)_{15}(NCMe)(H)$ was obtained from the reverse reaction by heating $Os_3Re_2(CO)_{20}(H)_2$ in acetonitrile. The cleavage of the M—H bond resembles that of an oxidative-addition reaction. There have been a few examples of analogous reactions involving other types of metal-ligand bonds, equation (3.60).[80]

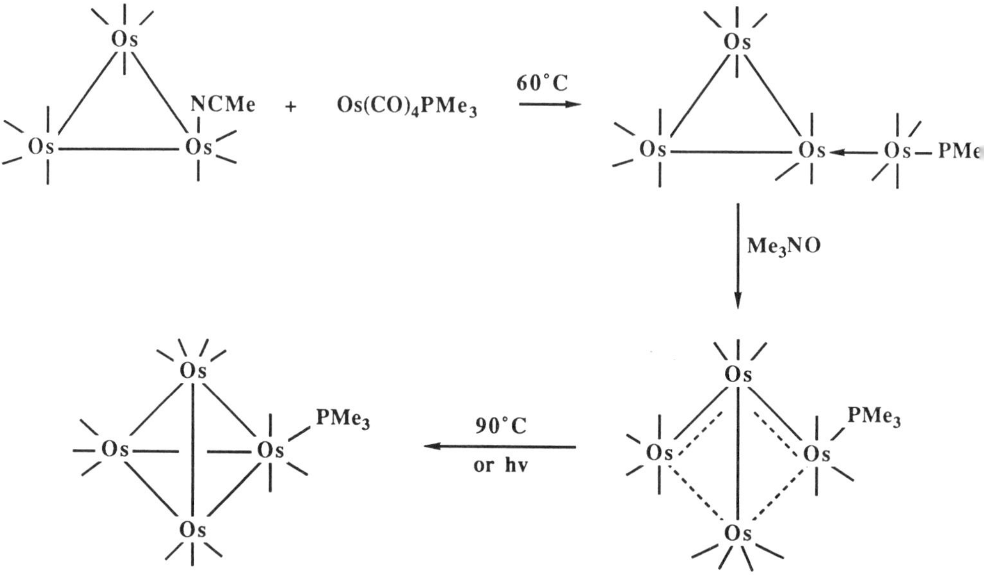

Scheme 3.4

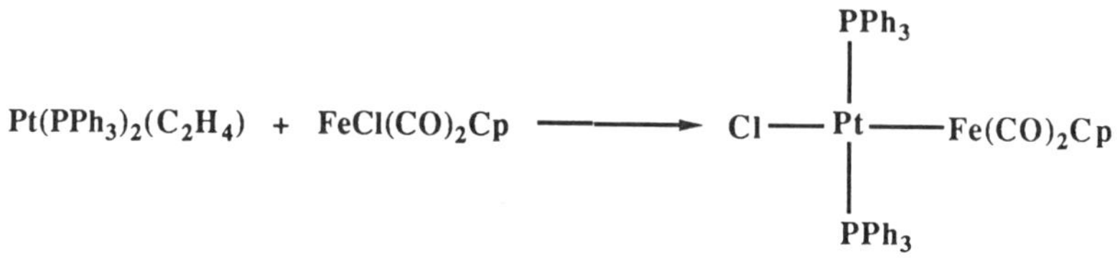

$$Pt(PPh_3)_2(C_2H_4) + FeCl(CO)_2Cp \longrightarrow Cl-Pt-Fe(CO)_2Cp \qquad (3.60)$$

with PPh₃ ligands above and below the Pt.

Higher nuclearity clusters have also been obtained from reactions in which both of the reagents contain weakly coordinated ligands, equation (3.61).[81]

$$Os_6(CO)_{17}(NCMe) + 2\ Pt(COD)_2 \xrightarrow{298K} Os_6(CO)_{17}(PtCOD)_2$$

$$-CO \Big\updownarrow +CO \qquad (3.61)$$

$$Os_6(CO)_{16}(NCMe)_2 + 2\ Pt(COD)_2 \longrightarrow Os_6(CO)_{16}(PtCOD)_2$$

Pomeroy and co-workers have coupled this method with the ligand elimination procedures (i.e., Me₃NO and irradiation) mentioned previously to assemble and condense the tetraosmium clusters $Os_4(CO)_{15}PMe_3$, $Os_4(CO)_{14}PMe_3$, and $Os_4(CO)_{13}PMe_3$ in a truly elegant fashion, see Scheme 3.4.[82]

3.4. Formation and Elimination of Small Molecules

In reactions of this type, two ligands, one from each complex, are combined to produce a stable small molecule which is expelled. A metal-metal bond is formed between the metal atoms in order to bring their valence electron counts up to 18. The simplest example of such a reaction is that of the formation and expulsion of H₂ in the reaction between two metal hydride complexes, equation (3.62).[83]

Norton has studied the nature of the elimination of H_2 from $H_2Os(CO)_4$ and found that it occurs by a bimolecular process, equation (3.63),[84] that is preceded by the decarbonylation of one of the $H_2Os(CO)_4$ molecules.

$$2\ HCo(CO)_4 \longrightarrow Co_2(CO)_8\ +\ H_2 \tag{3.62}$$

$$\tag{3.63}$$

$$H_2Os(CO)_4 \xrightarrow{-CO} H_2Os(CO)_3 \xrightarrow[-H_2]{+H_2Os(CO)_4} H_2Os_2(CO)_7 \xrightarrow{+CO} \overset{|\ /}{\underset{H\ /\,|}{-Os}} \overset{|\ /}{\underset{/\,|}{-Os}-}\!\!{_H}$$

Metal-alkyl complexes react with metal-hydride complexes to yield alkanes or aldehydes. These are accompanied by the formation of products containing metal-metal bonds. The metal-containing product obtained from the aldehyde elimination reaction is ligand deficient and may engage in further reactions. In some cases, the reaction path can be changed simply by changing the reaction solvent, equations (3.64) and (3.65).[85] The alkane-forming reaction is believed to occur by an initial loss of CO from the alkyl complex and is followed by the oxidative addition of the metal hydride complex to give an intermediate such as F. Reductive elimination of alkane is then followed by a readdition of CO. The aldehyde-forming reaction is initiated by a CO insertion reaction, followed by the oxidative addition of the metal hydride complex to yield an intermediate, such as G, and then reductive elimination of the aldehyde. There are some cases, however, where alkane elimination is believed to occur from the inserted intermediate, G.[86] $Os(CO)_4(H)Me$ appears to be one of these. The unimolecular reductive elimination of methane from $Os(CO)_4(H)Me$ is much slower than that from binuclear intermediates due to the formation of the high energy fragment $Os(CO)_4$. Thus, $Os(CO)_4(H)Me$ is transformed into polynuclear osmium complexes, equation (3.66).[84]

$$\tag{3.64}$$

$$MeOC_6H_4CH_2Mn(CO)_5\ +\ HMn(CO)_5 \xrightarrow{C_6H_6} MeOC_6H_4Me\ +\ Mn_2(CO)_{10}$$

$$\tag{3.65}$$

$$MeC_6H_4CH_2Mn(CO)_5\ +\ HMn(CO)_5 \xrightarrow{NCMe} MeOC_6H_4CH_2\overset{\displaystyle O}{\overset{\|}{C}}\!\!{_{\diagdown\,H}}\ +\ Mn_2(CO)_9(NCMe)$$

$$(CO)_{n-1}\!\!\overset{\displaystyle R}{\underset{H}{\overset{/}{M}}}\!\!- M(CO)_n \qquad\qquad (CO)_{n-1}\!\!\overset{\displaystyle \overset{O}{\diagdown}C-R}{\underset{H}{\overset{/}{M}}}\!\!- M(CO)_n$$

$$(\mathbf{F}) \qquad\qquad\qquad\qquad (\mathbf{G})$$

These reactions have been shown to be very effective for the preparation of heteronuclear multimetallic compounds [e.g., equations (3.67)–(3.68), M = Mn, R = Me; M = Re, R = Et] in MeCN solution.[86] The acetonitrile ligands are easily displaced from these products by CO or by reaction with an additional equivalent of the metal hydride.

$$\tag{3.66}$$

$$2\ Os(CO)_4HMe \xrightarrow{-MeH} \overset{|\ /}{\underset{H\ /\,|}{-Os}}\overset{|\ /}{\underset{/\,|}{-Os-}}\!\!{_{Me}} \xrightarrow[-MeH]{+Os(CO)_4(H)Me} \overset{|\ /}{\underset{Me\ /\,|}{-Os}}\overset{|\ /}{\underset{/\,|}{-Os}}\overset{|\ /}{\underset{Me\ /\,|}{-Os-}}$$

$$RM(CO)_5 + HM' \xrightarrow{+ \ NCMe} MM'(CO)_4(NCMe) + R\text{-}C\overset{O}{\underset{H}{\diagdown}} \quad (3.67)$$

$$M = Mn,Re \quad M' = Re(CO)_5, CpW(CO)_3$$

$$RM(CO)_5 + H_2Os(CO)_4 \longrightarrow Os(CO)_4[M(CO)_4(NCMe)]_2 + 2\ R\text{-}C\overset{O}{\underset{H}{\diagdown}} \quad (3.68)$$

$$M = Mn,Re$$

$$M(CO)_3Cp(H) + (PPh_3)AuCl \xrightarrow{298 \ K} (PPh_3)Au\text{-}M(CO)_3Cp(H) + HCl \quad (3.69)$$

Although the vast majority of these reactions have involved the formation and elimination of H_2, alkanes, and aldehydes, there have been a limited number of other types [e.g., equation (3.69), M = Cr, Mo, W].[87]

3.5. Bridge-Assisted Reactions

Bridging ligands can be formed by either of four basic processes: 1) ligand displacement induced by a ligand of a second metal complex; 2) displacement of a ligand substituent; 3) oxidative addition of a reactive ligand to a metal complex; and 4) the use of polydentate ligands. The most effective bridging ligands E are derived from the heavier members of the main groups, (e.g., GeR_2, SnR_2, GeR, SnR, PR_2, AsR_2, SR, SeR, Cl, Br, and I).

3.5.1. Ligand Displacement Induced by a Ligand in a Second Metal Complex

A bridging ligand can be formed by employing a lone pair of electrons on the ligand of one complex to displace a ligand and form a donor-acceptor bond to the metal atom of a second complex, equation (3.70). Further ligand elimination can lead to the formation of a metal-metal bond.

$$\underset{|}{\overset{E:}{L_nM}} + M'L_n \xrightarrow[(a)]{-L} L_nM\overset{E}{\diagdown}M'L_{n-1} \xrightarrow[(b)]{-L} L_{n-1}M\overset{E}{\diagup}\!\diagdown M'L_{n-1} \quad (3.70)$$

Some new heterodinuclear complexes have been made by taking advantage of the donor and bridging capacity of ER_2 groups E = P, As, equations $(3.71)^{88,89}$–$(3.72).^{90}$

$$2\ [(CO)_5Cr\ddot{P}(Bu^t)_2]^- + [Rh(COD)Cl]_2 \xrightarrow{-2\ Cl^-} 2 \quad \overset{Bu^t \quad Bu^t}{\underset{(CO)_5Cr\text{——}Rh\ COD}{\overset{P}{\diagup\!\diagdown}}} \quad (3.71)$$

$$Fe(CO)_5 + Me_2AsML_n \xrightarrow{-CO} \overset{Me \quad Me}{\underset{(CO)_4Fe\text{——}ML_n}{\overset{As}{\diagup\!\diagdown}}} \quad (3.72)$$

$$Cp*_2Th(PPh_2)_2 + Pt(COD)_2 \xrightarrow[\text{-2 COD}]{\text{+ PMe}_3} \quad \text{(3.73)}$$

By using two bridging PPh_2 groups, the first complex to contain a metal-metal bond between an actinide element and a transition metal has been made, equation (3.73).[91]

This approach has been used successfully for the preparation of higher nuclearity clusters, equation (3.74).[92] The intermediate, H, formed simply by the substitution of a carbonyl ligand by the arsenic atom of the $Me_2AsM(CO)_3Cp$ molecule, has been characterized. No metal-metal bond is formed in H; however, in the final steps three metal-metal bonds are formed and the $AsMe_2$ ligand is separated from the metal atom to which it was originally attached. By using this methodology, the first cluster, $FeCoMoW(CO)_7Cp_2(\mu_3\text{-S})(\mu\text{-AsMe}_2)$, containing four different metal atoms, was made.[93]

$$\text{(3.74)}$$

Clusters that possess bridging ligands with a lone pair of electrons can be enlarged by bridged-assisted addition reactions. Triply bridging ligands, such as P, As, S, Se, and Te, are known to engage in these reactions. The reactions of $Os_3(CO)_9(\mu_3\text{-S})_2$, with tungsten carbonyls, demonstrate this, equations (3.75)[94] and (3.76).[95] The reaction of $Os_3(CO)_9(\mu_3\text{-S})_2$ with $W(CO)_6$ terminates with the loss of one CO ligand and the coordination of a $W(CO)_5$ grouping to one of the triply bridging sulfido ligands. In the reaction with $W(CO)_5PMe_2Ph$, two CO ligands are eliminated and a $W(CO)_3PMe_2Ph$ group is incorporated into the cluster.

Some clusters can form higher nuclearity products by self-condensation reactions, equation (3.77),[96] or by the addition of lightly stabilized clusters, equations (3.78)–(3.79).[97] In some cases, the bridging capacity of the ligands is expanded, that is, triply bridging sulfur to quadruply bridging sulfur, equations (3.75) and

(3.77)–(3.79). A series of sulfido-ruthenium carbonyl clusters was obtained from $Ru_3(CO)_9(\mu_3\text{-}S)_2$ through the sequential addition of mononuclear ruthenium carbonyl fragments derived from $Ru(CO)_5$, Scheme 3.5.[98]

$$+ \ W(CO)_6 \quad \xrightarrow[-CO]{h\nu} \quad \tag{3.75}$$

$$+ \ W(CO)_5PMe_2Ph \quad \xrightarrow[-2\ CO]{h\nu} \quad \tag{3.76}$$

$$2\ Os_3(CO)_{10}(\mu_3\text{-}S) \quad \xrightarrow[-3\ CO]{h\nu} \quad \tag{3.77}$$

$$Os_6(CO)_{17}(\mu_4\text{-}S)_2$$

$$\tag{3.78}$$

$$Os_3(CO)_{10}(\mu_3\text{-}S) + Os_3(CO)_{10}(NCMe)_2 \quad \longrightarrow \quad \xrightarrow{-2\ CO}$$

$$Os_4(CO)_{12}(\mu_3\text{-}S)_2 + Os_3(CO)_{10}(NCMe)_2 \quad \longrightarrow \quad \tag{3.79}$$

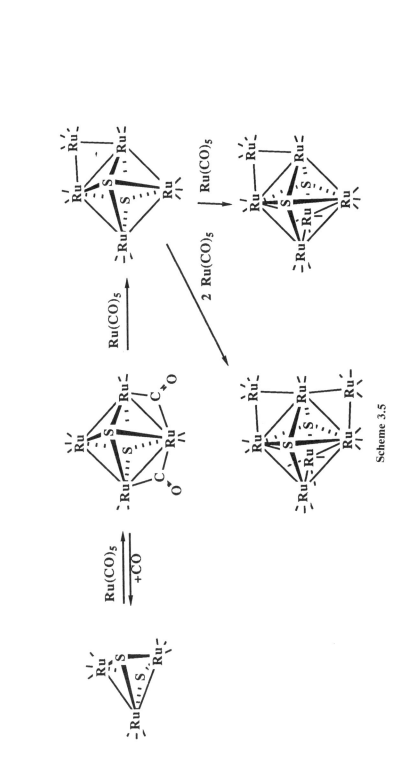

Scheme 3.5

An elegant example of metal aggregation about a sulfur site was reported by Darensbourg, equation (3.80), M = Cr, Mo, W.[99] The reaction proceeds in two steps. Three $M(CO)_5$ groups are assembled about a single sulfur atom in the anion, $[M(CO)_5]_3(\mu_3\text{-}S)^{2-}$, which contains no metal-metal bonds. Subsequent elimination of three moles of CO leads to $[M(CO)_4]_3(\mu_3\text{-}S)^{2-}$, which contains three metal-metal bonds. This step is reversible. Intermediates formed by the loss of one and two moles of CO that contain one and two metal-metal bonds were anticipated, but were not observed. It is possible to add still another $M(CO)_5$ grouping to the lone pair of electrons on the sulfur atom in $[M(CO)_4]_3(\mu_3\text{-}S)]^{2-}$.

(3.80)

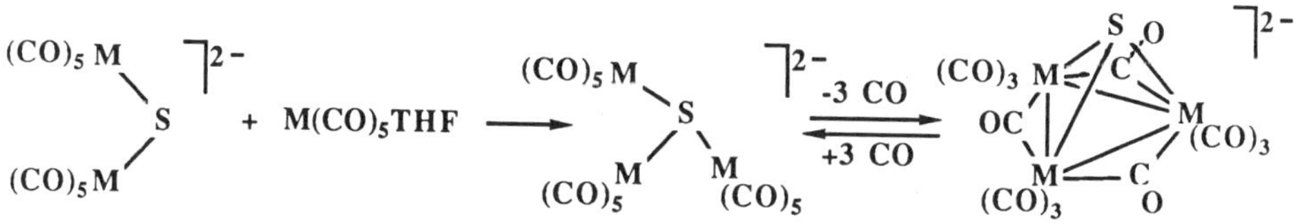

M = Cr,Mo,W

This technique has found considerable applicability in the preparation of heteronuclear clusters, equations (3.76), (3.81),[100] (3.82),[101] and (3.83).[102] The repositioning of the bridging sulfido ligand is a notable feature of reaction (3.81). In reactions (3.82) and (3.83), the sulfur-sulfur bond in the S_2^{2-} ligand was cleaved. Anionic clusters, such as $[Fe_2(CO)_6(S_2)]^{2-}$, can be enlarged in bridged-assisted reactions that involve halide displacement steps, equation (3.84), ML_n = (diphos) $NiCl_2$, $(PPh_3)_2PtCl_2$, $CpCoI_2$.[103] Although there are very few characterized examples of metal carbonyl cluster compounds containing bridging oxo ligands, a recent report has shown that this ligand can also promote cluster synthesis by expanding its bridging capacity, equation (3.85).[104]

(3.81)

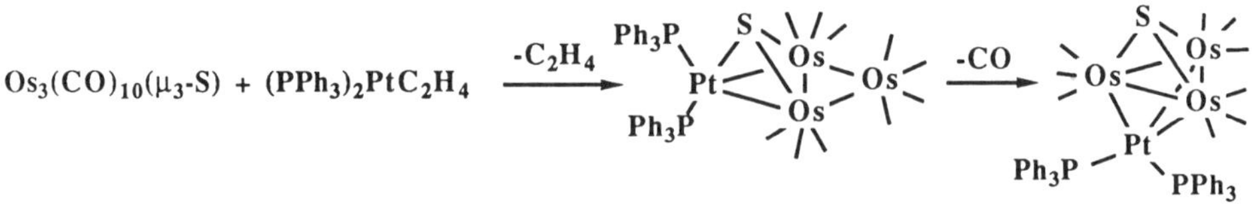

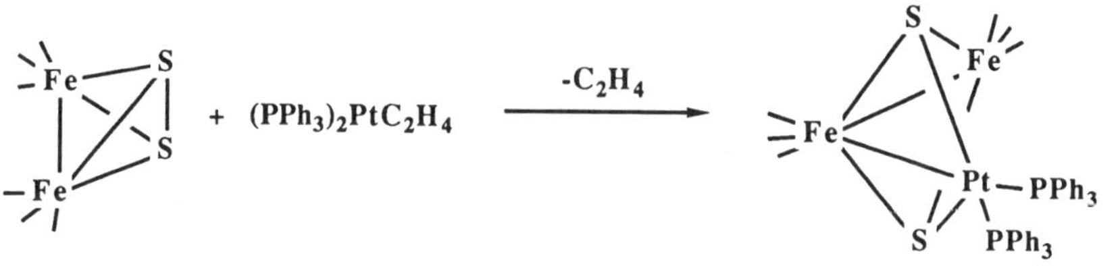

$Os_3(CO)_{10}(\mu_3\text{-}S)$ + $(PPh_3)_2PtC_2H_4$

(3.82)

$$\text{(3.83)}$$

$$\text{(3.84)}$$

$$\text{(3.85)}$$

$[Fe_3(CO)_9(\mu_3\text{-}O)]^{2-}$ + $[Mn(CO)_3(NCMe)_3]^+$ $\longrightarrow$

Bridging ligands with a potential to adopt bonding modes in which they contain a free pair of electrons also appear to be able to promote cluster formation. For example, the conversion of a triply bridging phosphinidene ligand to an edge-bridged intermediate results formally in the formation of a lone pair of electrons on the phosphorus atom, equation (3.86). It is believed that this process is involved in the condensation of the compound $Os_3(CO)_9(\mu_3\text{-}PR)(\mu\text{-}H)_2$ with the compounds $M_3(CO)_{12}$, M = Ru, and Os to yield the hexanuclear and pentanuclear compounds, $M_3Os_3(CO)_{17}(\mu\text{-}PR)$ and $M_2Os_3(CO)_{15}(\mu_4\text{-}PR)$.[105]

Recently, it has been shown that the bridging dialkylaminocarbyne ligand can also promote the capture of metal-containing groups. The reaction of (9) $Ru_3(CO)_{10}(\mu\text{-}CNMe_2)(\mu\text{-}H)$ with $Ru(CO)_5$ leads to the formation of $Ru_4(CO)_{12}(\mu_4\text{-}\eta^2\text{—}CNMe_2)(\mu\text{-}H)$, equation (3.87), which contains the first example of a quadruply bridging dialkylaminocarbyne ligand.[106] The structure of the product suggests that the addition step may have involved the carbon-nitrogen "double bond" of the aminocarbyne ligand in (9).

$$\text{(3.86)}$$

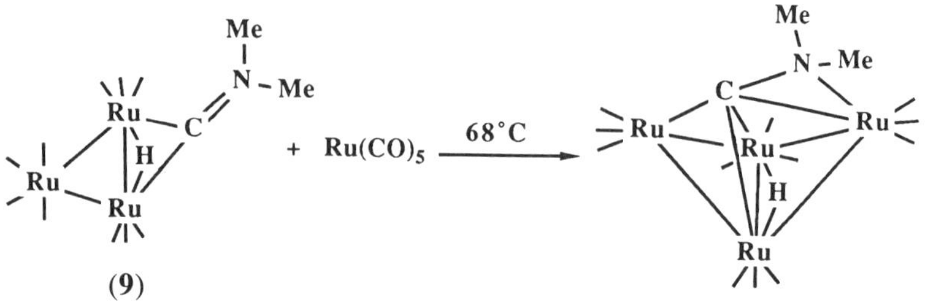

$$(3.87)$$

(9)

It is well known that the oxygen atoms of carbonyl ligands can serve as coordination sites for metal complexes.[107] Thus, it is possible that M—O interactions such as these might precede and assist in the incorporation of unsaturated metal carbonyl fragments into clusters. This is strongly indicated in the reaction of (10) $Ru_4Mo_2(CO)_{13}(\mu_4-\eta^2-CO)(\mu_4-S)Cp_2$ with $Ru(CO)_5$ to give (11) $Ru_5Mo_2(CO)_{14}(\mu_4-\eta^2-CO)_2(\mu_4-S)Cp_2$, shown schematically in equation (3.88).[108] Compound (10) contains a square-pyramidal cluster of three ruthenium and two molybdenum atoms. A fourth ruthenium atom bridges an Ru—Ru edge of the cluster. The molybdenum atom at the apical site contains one terminal carbonyl ligand. Upon addition of the ruthenium-containing group to the unbridged Ru—Ru edge of the square pyramid to form (11), the terminal carbonyl ligand is converted to a second quadruply bridging carbonyl ligand with its oxygen atom bonded to the added ruthenium atom. The incoming ruthenium-containing group probably interacted with the oxygen atom of the terminal carbonyl ligand before the formation of the metal-metal bonds to the cluster, and may have helped to direct the group to the observed bonding site.

Ligands with uncoordinated π-bonds, such as coordinated acetylides, are capable of capturing metal carbonyl groups to form cluster complexes, equations (3.89)[109] and (3.90).[110]

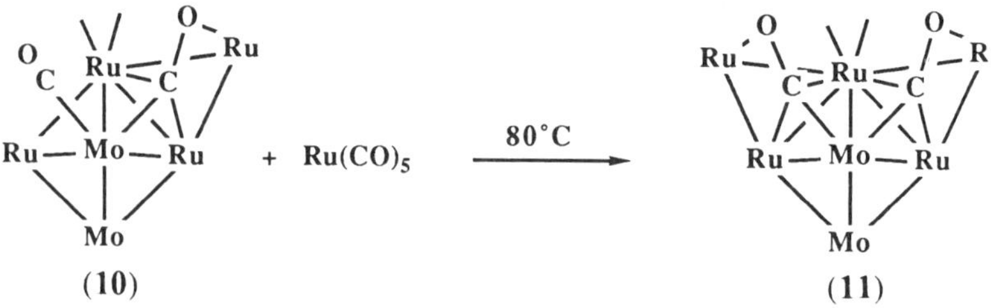

$$(3.88)$$

(10)   (11)

$$(3.89)$$

$$CpM(CO)_2-C\equiv CPh + RuCo_2(CO)_{11} \longrightarrow$$
$$M = Fe,Ru$$

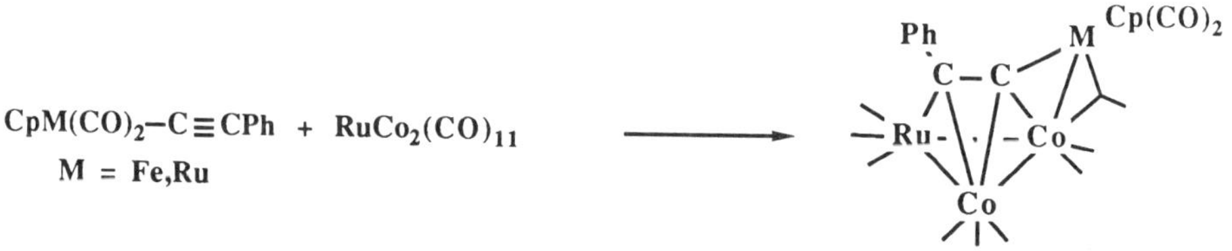

(3.90)

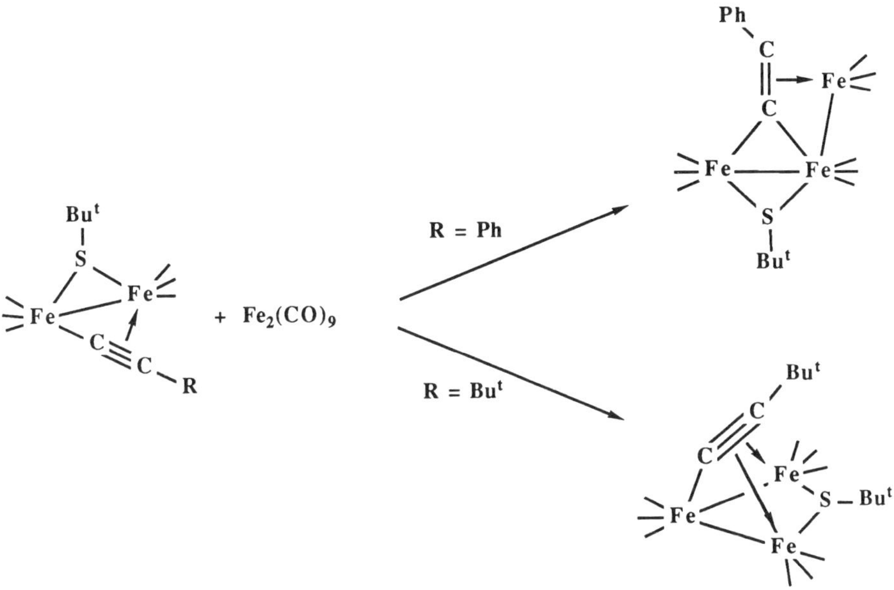

(3.91)

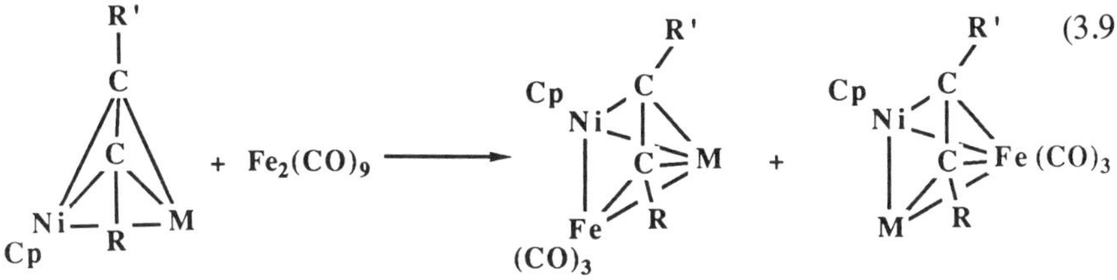

M = Mo(CO)$_2$Cp   M = Co(CO)$_3$,NiCp

Ligands without free electron pairs can also promote cluster formation. For example, bridging alkyne ligands can readily expand their bridging capacity, equation (3.91).[111]

Shriver has shown that the ketenylidene ligand in $[Fe_3(CO)_9(\mu\text{-CCO})]^{2-}$ is an excellent precursor to the bridging carbido ligand. He has used this reagent to prepare a variety of new heteronuclear cluster complexes, equation (3.92).[112] Additional examples of this reaction are listed in Table 3.1. Similarly, the cyanate ligand in $[Ru_4(CO)_{13}(NCO)]^-$ is decarbonylated upon heating to yield the nitrido cluster $[Ru_4(CO)_{12}(\mu_4\text{-N})]^-$. The latter can be enlarged by a sequence of redox condensation reactions, Scheme 3.6.[113]

(3.92)

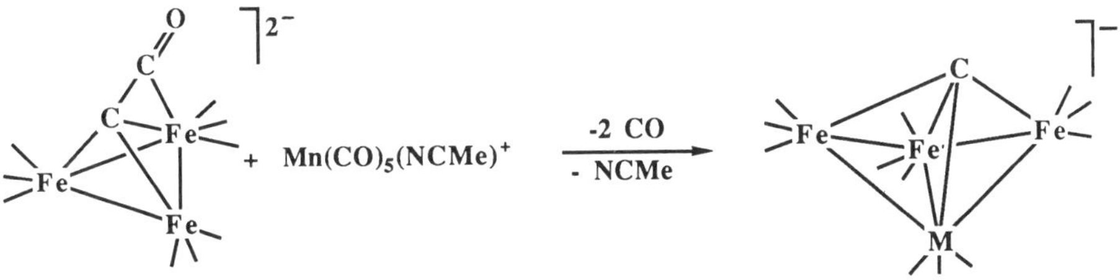

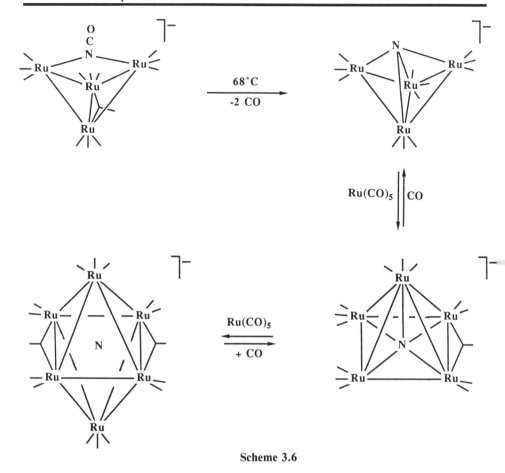

Scheme 3.6

3.5.2. Displacement of a Ligand Substituent

The nucleophilic displacement of substituents from a small molecule ER_aX_b can lead to the aggregation of metal atoms about E and subsequently to the formation of metal-metal bonds. Some of the first reactions of this general type were performed by Markó, who made the triply bridged alkylidyne and arsenic compounds $Co_3(CO)_9(\mu_3-CR)$, equation (3.93),[114] and $Co_3(CO)_9(\mu_3-As)$, equation (3.94).[115] Halide displacement from certain gem-dihalo compounds has led to ER_2 bridged complexes, equation (3.95).[116]

$$3\ Co(CO)_4^- + RCCl_3 \longrightarrow$$

(3.93)

$$3\ Co(CO)_4^- + AsCl_3 \longrightarrow$$ (3.94)

(3.95)

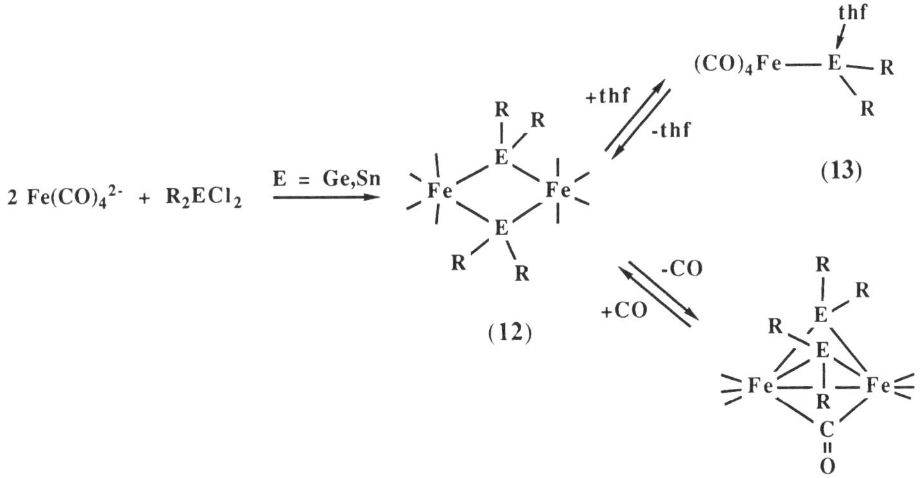

$$2\ Fe(CO)_4^{2-} + R_2ECl_2 \xrightarrow{\ E = Ge,Sn\ }$$

(12)

(13)

(14)

Curiously, the M—E bonds in the compounds (12) are relatively weak and can be reversibly cleaved by donors as weak as THF to yield "germylene" and "stannylene" adducts, (13). Decarbonylation of the compounds (12) yields the heptacarbonyl complex, (14), that has a metal-metal bond. For E = Ge, Sn, and Pb, compounds containing M—E bonds are also made efficiently by reactions of uncharged metal carbonyl compounds with compounds containing E—H bonds, vide infra.

Halide displacement from coordinated halophosphines and arsines can lead to cluster complexes in good yields, equations (3.96),[117] (3.97),[118] (3.98),[119] and (3.99).[120]

(3.96)

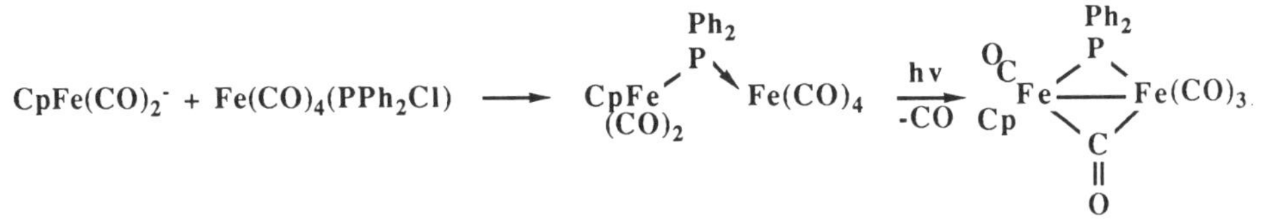

$$CpFe(CO)_2^- + Fe(CO)_4(PPh_2Cl) \longrightarrow$$

(3.97)

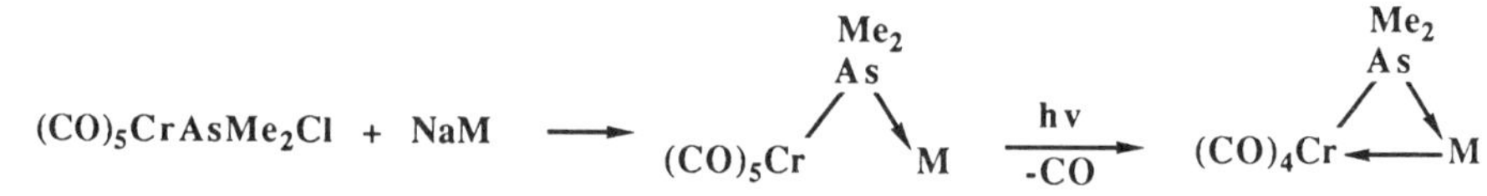

$$(CO)_5CrAsMe_2Cl + NaM \longrightarrow (CO)_5Cr\overset{Me_2}{\underset{}{As}}M \xrightarrow[-CO]{h\nu} (CO)_4Cr\overset{Me_2}{\underset{}{As}}M$$

M = CpMo(CO)₃, CpW(CO)₃, Mn(CO)₅, Re(CO)₅ and Co(CO)₄

(3.98)

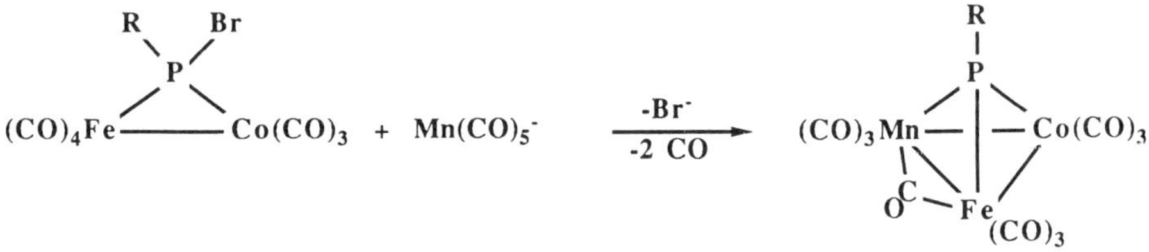

$$(CO)_4Fe\overset{R\quad Br}{\underset{}{P}}Co(CO)_3 + Mn(CO)_5^- \xrightarrow[-2\,CO]{-Br^-} (CO)_3Mn\overset{R}{\underset{}{P}}Co(CO)_3$$

(3.99)

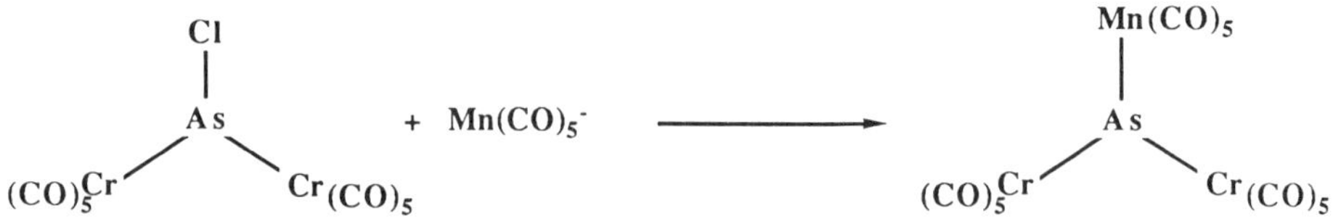

$$(CO)_5^{Cr}\overset{Cl}{\underset{As}{}}Cr(CO)_5 + Mn(CO)_5^- \longrightarrow (CO)_5^{Cr}\overset{Mn(CO)_5}{\underset{As}{}}Cr(CO)_5$$

(3.100)

$$[\text{structure}] + Co(CO)_4^- \xrightarrow[-6\,CO]{-Cl} [Co_6(CO)_{15}(\mu_6\text{-C})]^{2-}$$

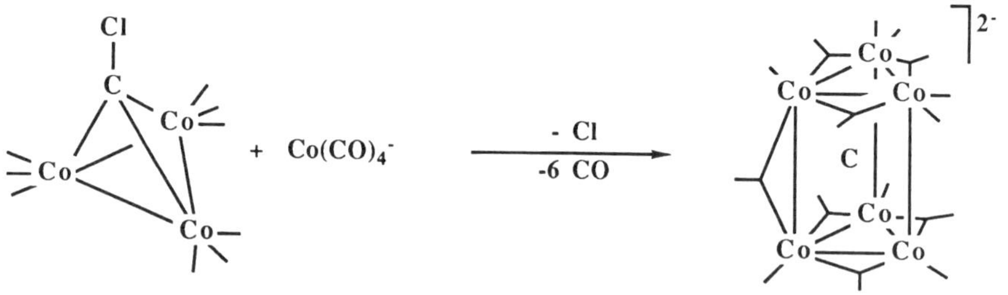

The addition of three moles of Co(CO)₄⁻ to Co₃(CO)₉(μ_3-CCl) yields [Co₆(CO)₁₅(μ_6-C)]²⁻, equation (3.100).[121] In this reaction, the first addition probably involves the displacement of Cl⁻ at the μ_3-CCl group to yield a tetra-cobalt intermediate (not observed). Addition of the two remaining cobalt carbonyl groups probably proceeds via redox condensation type reactions, vide supra.

3.5.3. Oxidative Addition of a Ligand

Unsaturated metal carbonyl fragments can be inserted into reactive E—X bonds. The reaction can be viewed alternatively as an oxidative addition. Facile ligand eliminations invariably follow the first step and yield condensed products. One of the simplest examples of these reactions is the reaction of $Fe(CO)_4(PRCl_2)$ with $Fe_2(CO)_9$, the latter serving as a source of $Fe(CO)_4$, equation (3.101).[122] The diiron product (**15**) is believed to have been formed by the insertion of a $Fe(CO)_4$ group into one P—Cl bond of the $Fe(CO)_4(PRCl_2)$ complex. The loss of two CO ligands will precede the formation of the Fe—Fe bond and the conversion of the Cl ligand from a terminal to a bridge bonding mode. In the reducing environment that is provided by the zero-valent metal carbonyl reagent "reductive dehalogenation" frequently occurs by redox processes (3.101b). Final addition of a $Fe(CO)_4$ group to the electron-rich phosphorus atom yields the stable triiron cluster, (3.101c). Interestingly, the yield of the compound $Co_3(CO)_9(\mu_3\text{-As})$ is much higher by the reductive dehalogenation reaction (3.102)[111] than by the displacement reaction (3.94). Mixed-metal clusters have been prepared from complexes containing co-ordinated halophosphines, equation (3.103).[123-127]

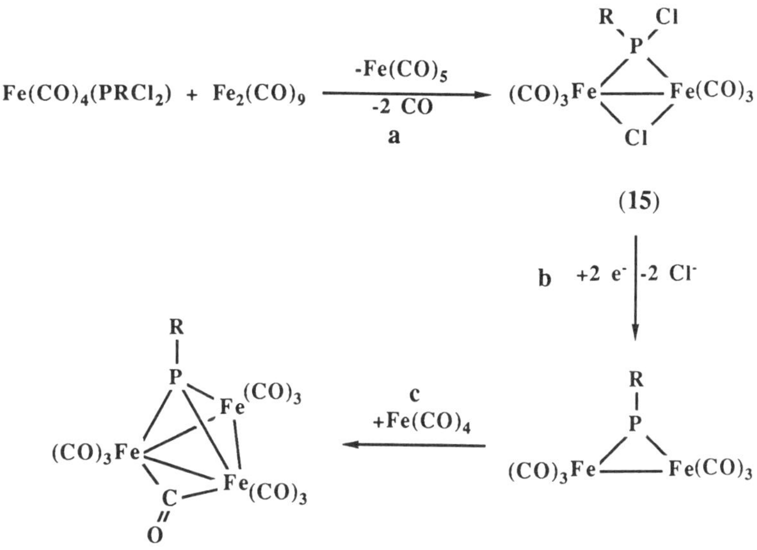

$$\text{Fe(CO)}_4\text{(PRCl}_2\text{)} + \text{Fe}_2\text{(CO)}_9 \xrightarrow[\substack{-2\ CO \\ a}]{-\text{Fe(CO)}_5}$$

(15)

b   +2 e⁻ | -2 Cl⁻   (3.101)

c   +Fe(CO)₄

Oxidative addition of an E—H bond has proven to be an effective method for preparing polynuclear metal complexes with bridging E groups. The heavier elements of Groups IV and V have been among the most extensively studied, equations (3.104),[127] (3.105),[128] and (3.106).[129]

$$\text{AsI}_3 + \text{Co}_2\text{(CO)}_8 \longrightarrow \text{Co}_3\text{(CO)}_9\text{(}\mu_3\text{-As)} + 3\ \text{I}^- \qquad (3.102)$$

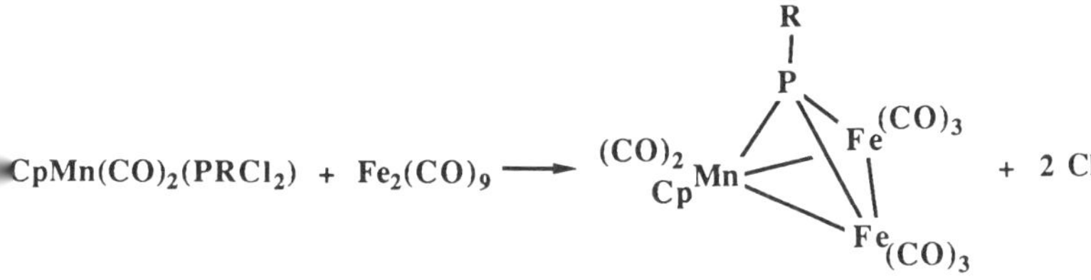

$$\text{CpMn(CO)}_2\text{(PRCl}_2\text{)} + \text{Fe}_2\text{(CO)}_9 \longrightarrow \qquad + 2\ \text{Cl}^- \qquad (3.103)$$

$$3\ Fe(CO)_5\ +\ 2\ PhPH_2\quad\xrightarrow[\substack{-2\ H_2\\-6\ CO}]{h\nu}\quad (3.104)$$

$$(3.105)$$

$$3/2\ Co_2(CO)_8\ +\ PhGeH_3\quad\xrightarrow[-3/2\ H_2]{-CO}\quad\xrightarrow{-2\ CO}$$

$$Co_2(CO)_8\ +\ Fe(CO)_5\ +\ PhSH\quad\xrightarrow{-C_6H_6}\quad (3.106)$$

From reaction (3.106), it is apparent that the cleavage of E—R bonds can also play a role in the formation of bridging ligands. By using metal complexes containing coordinated primary and secondary phosphine and arsine ligands, it is possible to exercise greater control over the reaction and thus prepare more eso-teric complexes, equations (3.107),[127] (3.108),[130] and (3.109).[131] R_2PH ligands can be deprotonated with alkyllithium reagents to yield negatively charged MPR_2 complexes that can be used in synthesis through displacement reactions.[88,89,127]

$$2\ Fe(CO)_4(PR_2H)\quad\xrightarrow[\substack{-2\ CO\\-H_2}]{h\nu}\quad (3.107)$$

$$Cr(CO)_5(PRH_2)\ +\ Fe_3(CO)_{12}\quad\xrightarrow{-H_2}\quad (3.108)$$

$$(3.109)$$

$$+\ Co(CO)_3(C_3H_5)\quad\xrightarrow{-C_3H_6}$$

There are only a few known examples of metal complexes that contain thiol (SH) ligands, and very few of these have been used in cluster synthesis. One example of a reaction of this type is shown in equation (3.110).[132] The thiol group in $CpW(CO)_3SH$ reacts with the lightly stabilized osmium cluster complex $Os_3(CO)_{11}(NCMe)$ by an S-H oxidative addition to yield the sulfur-bridged "open" cluster (16) $Os_3(CO)_{10}(\mu_3-S)W(CO)_3Cp$. At 110°C, (16) loses two moles of CO and three W—Os bonds are made to yield the condensed cluster (17) $Os_3W(CO)_{11}Cp(\mu-H)(\mu_3-S)$. To compensate for the formation of the one additional W—Os bond, one Os—Os bond was cleaved. As a result, compound (17) is electron precise.

$$(3.110)$$

$CpW(CO)_3SH + Os_3(CO)_{11}(NCMe)$

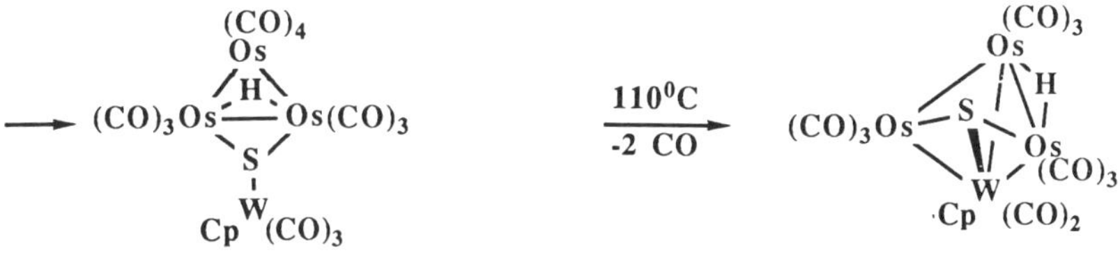

(16)   (17)

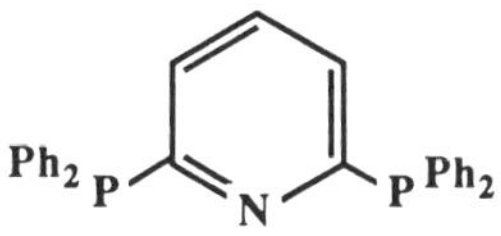

(18) 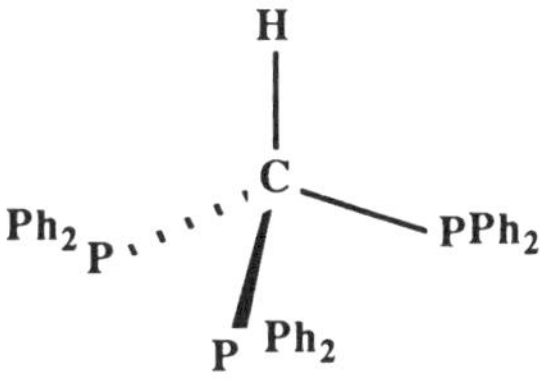   (19)

3.5.4. Polydentate Bridging Ligands

Chelating polydentate phosphine and related ligands have been used to assemble groups of metal atoms in the form of coordination complexes. Two-dimensional ligands such as (18) 2,6-bis(diphenylphosphino)pyridine tend to arrange the metal atoms in chains, equation (3.111).[133] Three-dimensional ligands such as (19) 1,1,1-tris(diphenylphosphino)methane have shown an ability to assemble clusters, equation (3.112).[134,135] Phosphine substituted cyclopentadienyl ligands have been shown to be very useful in the preparation of stable heterobimetallic complexes, equation (3.113).[136]

18 + $[Rh(CO)_2Cl]_2$ $\longrightarrow$

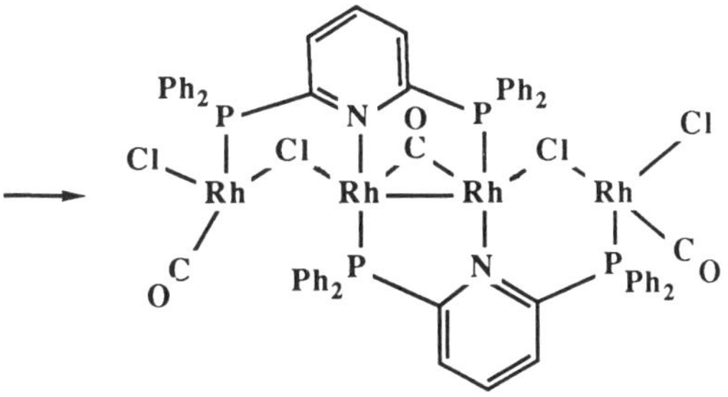

$$(3.111)$$

$$19 \quad + \quad 3 \ Ni(CO)_4 \quad \longrightarrow \quad$$

(3.112)

(3.113)

Dithiocarboxylate ligands have been shown to promote the assembly of planar gold clusters by serving as chelates that bridge pairs of metal atoms in an alternating sequence on opposite sides of the square cluster, $Au_4(S_2CMe)_4$,[137] and the raft cluster, $Au_6(S_2C\text{-}o\text{-tolyl})_6$,[138] equation (3.114).

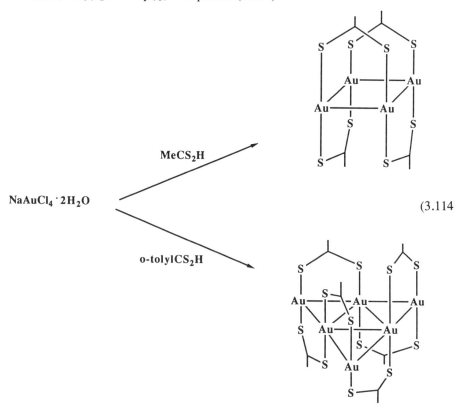

NaAuCl$_4$·2H$_2$O

MeCS$_2$H

o-tolylCS$_2$H

(3.114

3.6. Reactions of Unsaturated Compounds

In this section, we will consider the formation of higher nuclearity metal complexes from unsaturated compounds that contain multiple metal-metal bonds [e.g., (3) and (4)], multiple metal-carbon bonds [e.g., (20) $Cr(CO)_5[C(Ph)OMe]$ and (21) $CpW(CO)_2(\equiv C-tol)]$ or electron-deficient complexes [e.g., (5) and (6)]. It must be recognized, however, that other important features in their chemistry, such as the formation of bridging ligands, may also occur. This section begins with a discussion of unsaturated compounds such as those of Rh, Ir, or Pd and Pt that tend to form stable 16-electron and sometimes stable 14-electron mononuclear metal complexes. In general, these complexes exhibit no significant tendency to oligomerize, and can be utilized to make polynuclear metal complexes by substituting one or more of their ligands with metal-containing groups [e.g., equations (3.32)–(3.34)]. However, there are a few interesting rhodium complexes, $[Rh(PR_3)_2H]_n$, where $n = 2$ (22) and 3 (23), R = OR, NR_2, F and $[Rh(P_2)H]_n$, where $n = 2$, $P_2 = (i\text{-PrO})_2P(CH_2)_2P(O\text{-}i\text{-Pr})_2$ and $n = 4$ (24), $P_2 = (MeO)_2P(CH_2)_2-P(OMe)_2]^{139-142}$ that do exhibit a tendency to oligomerize. In the fragment $Rh(PR_3)_2H$, the metal atom contains only 14 valence electrons. In the polynuclear species (22),[140] (23),[141] and (24),[142] the metal atoms have 16-electron configurations, and their Rh—Rh distances are short enough to formulate the existence of hydrogen bridged metal-metal bonds. The steric bulk of the phosphine ligands appears to play an important role in determining the extent of the cluster assembly and can be used to adjust the equilibria between the different species.[142]

Platinum and palladium complexes containing sterically bulky phosphine ligands exist as stable 14-electron species that have only two ligands [e.g., PtL_2; L = PBu^t_3, PBu^t_2Ph, $P(c\text{-}C_6H_{11})_3]$.[143] With less bulky ligands these complexes form cyclotrimers [e.g., (25),[144] (26),[145] (27)[146]] in which the metal atoms achieve 16-electron configurations.

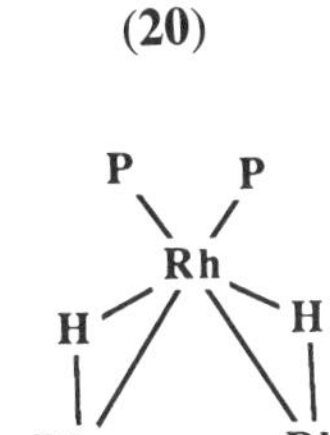

(20)

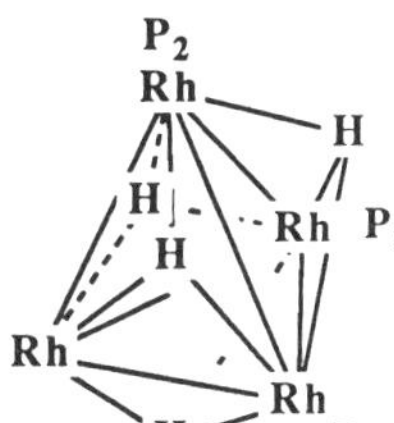

(21)

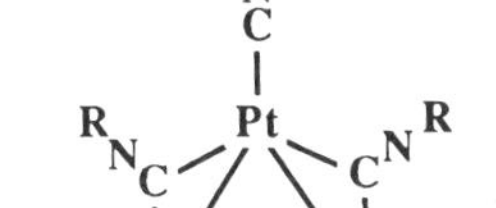

(22)

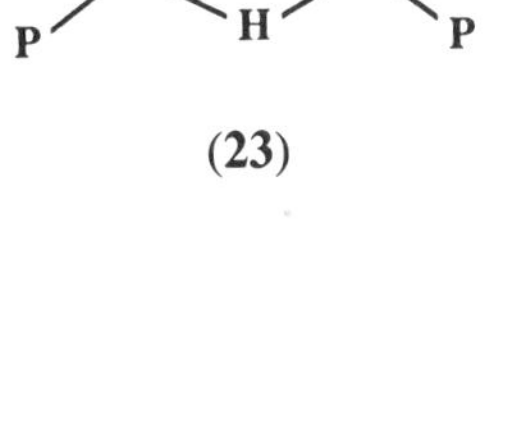

(23)

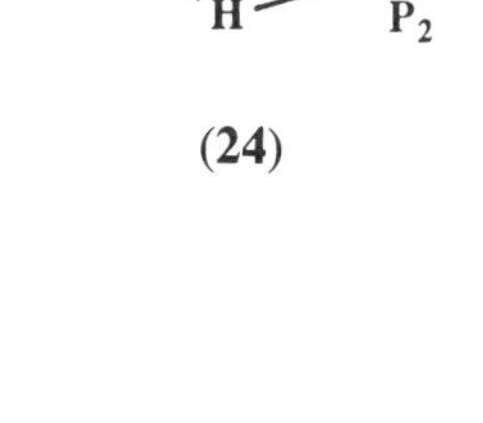

(24)

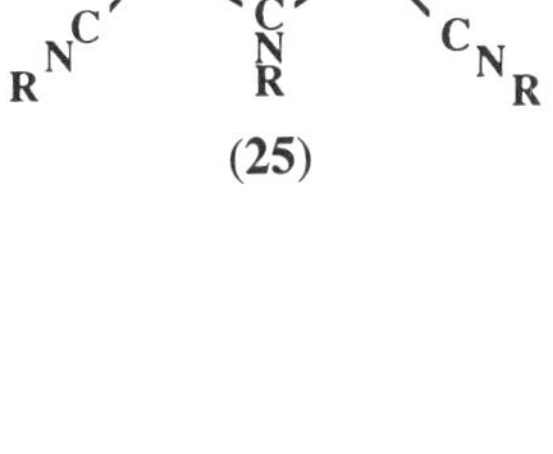

(25)

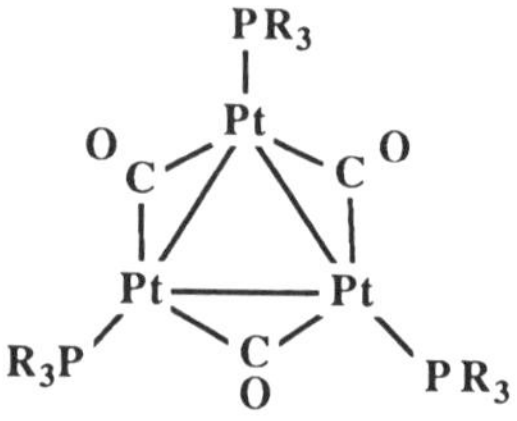

(26) 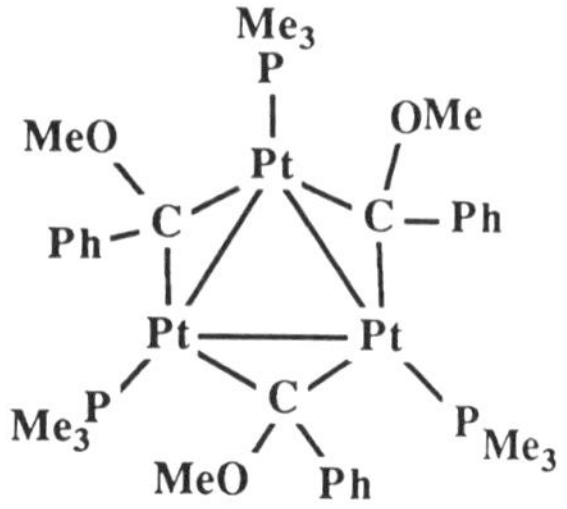   (27)

A spontaneous trimerization mechanism for these 14-electron species has been suggested in at least one case.[146]

It is well known that molecules with metal-metal multiple bonds exhibit high reactivity to ligand addition reactions.[147] In general, compounds containing metal-metal multiple bonds do not spontaneously oligomerize. However, there are several reported examples where metal-containing groupings have been added across the metal-metal bond to yield heteronuclear metal complexes, equations (3.115),[148] (3.116),[149] and (3.117).[150] To date, cluster syntheses utilizing compounds that have metal-metal triple bonds have not been highly successful, and in all cases where success has been achieved, bridging ligands have also been involved [e.g., equations (3.118)[151,152] and (3.119)].[153] In fact, in the absence of bridging ligands, some clusters containing the [CpMo(CO)₂]₂ group spontaneously break apart, equation (3.120).[154]

(3.115)

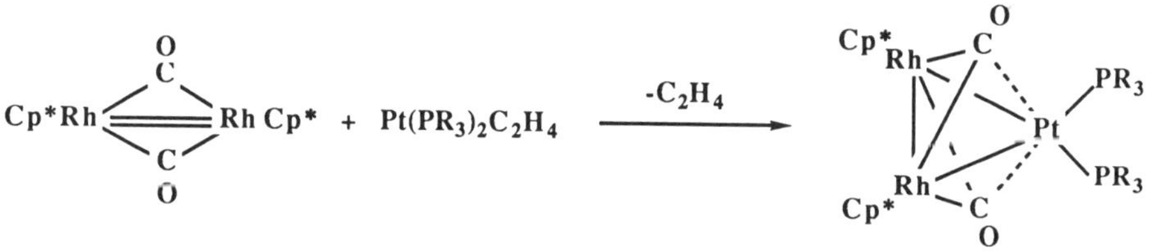

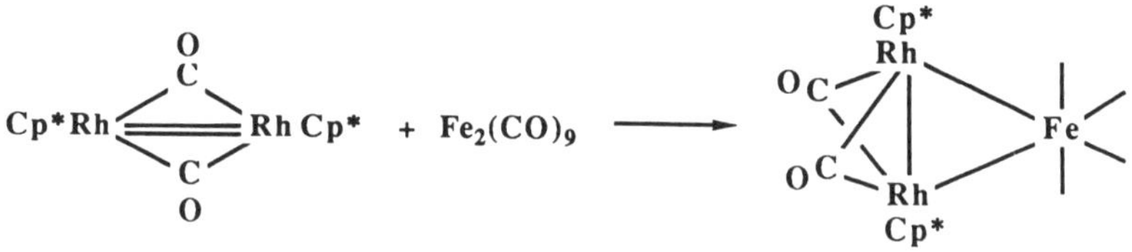

(3.116)

(3.117)

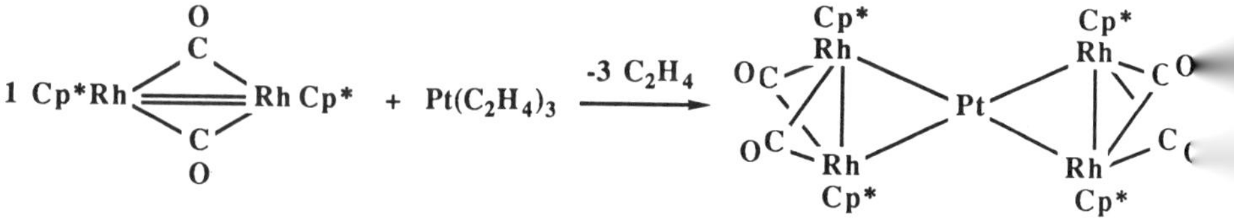

(3.118)

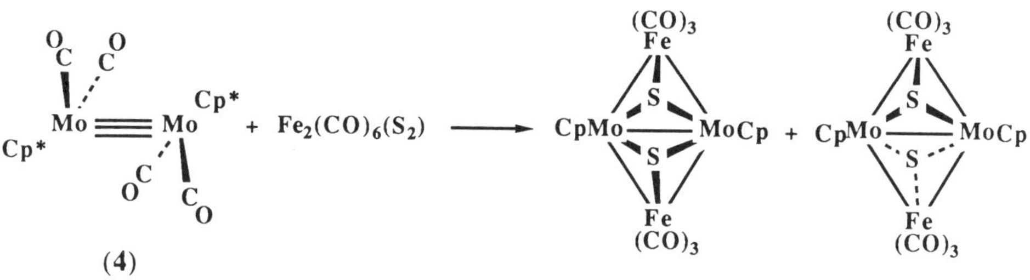

(3.119)

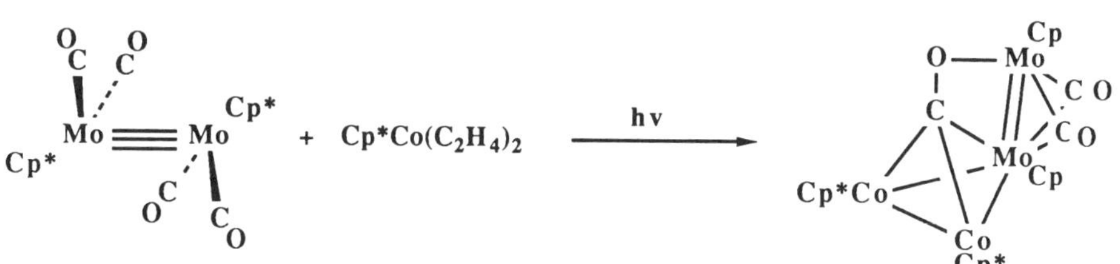

$Os_3(CO)_{10}(\mu\text{-H})_2$ (**28**) is well known for a high reactivity that is believed to be related to its "electron deficient" 46-electron configuration. It has been shown to add a variety of metal-containing groupings to yield higher nuclearity heteronuclear cluster complexes, equations (3.121),[155] (3.122),[156] and (3.123).[157] The presence of a hydrogen atmosphere has been shown to have a beneficial effect in some syntheses that use (**28**).[157,158]

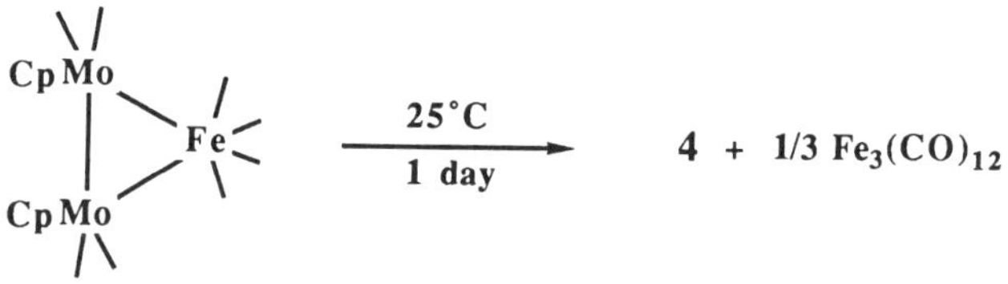

(3.121)

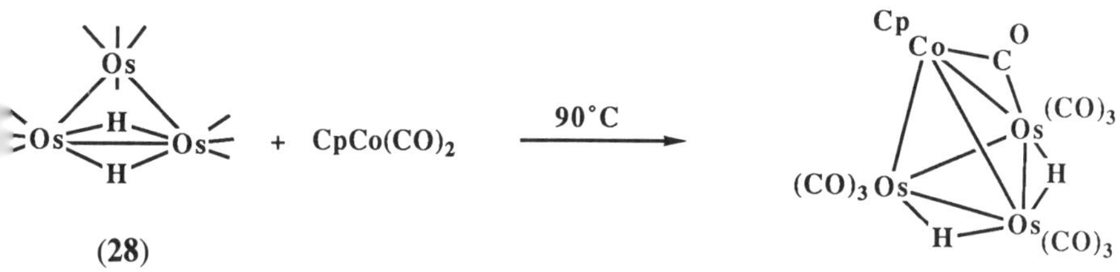

$$(28) \quad + \quad Pt(C_2H_4)_2PR_3 \longrightarrow \qquad (3.122)$$

$$(28) \quad + \quad 4 \quad \xrightarrow{H_2} \qquad (3.123)$$

Stone and co-workers have emphasized the analogy of metal-carbene complexes to olefins and of metal-carbyne complexes to alkynes to explain their great success in using these compounds to prepare a new class of heteronuclear metal complexes containing bridging carbene and carbyne ligands.[159,160] These reactions give the best yields when the metal grouping to be added contains ligands that are easily displaced (e.g., COD, C_2H_4, thf), equations (3.124)[161] and (3.125).[146]

$$(CO)_5M{=}C\overset{OMe}{\underset{Ph}{\diagup}} \quad + \quad Pt(COD)_2 \longrightarrow \qquad (3.124)$$

$$M = Cr, Mo, W$$

$$(CO)_5M{=}C\overset{OMe}{\underset{Ph}{\diagup}} \quad + \quad 2\ Pt(C_2H_4)_2(PR_3) \longrightarrow \qquad (3.125)$$

$$M = Cr, W$$

It is notable that in reaction (3.125) the carbene ligand was separated completely from the Cr or W atom to which it was originally attached. Significant amounts of polynuclear platinum carbene complexes that contain no chromium or tungsten were also obtained from these reactions.

Reactions of the metal-carbyne complexes have produced a greater variety of new polynuclear metal complexes.[159] It is possible to add one and two metal groupings to a single metal-carbyne complex, equations (3.126),[162] (3.127),[163] and (3.128).[164] The $M\equiv C-R$ can be viewed as π-bonded to the second metal atom. It is believed that the $M-C$ bond in the dinuclear products still contains a significant amount of unsaturation. This is not present in the trinuclear metal complexes where the carbyne ligand serves as a triply bridging ligand. By the sequential addition of two different metal groupings, chiral $MM'M''$ (μ_3-CR) cluster units can be made, equation (3.129).[165]

$$CpW(CO)_2(\equiv C\text{-tol}) + Pt(C_2H_4)(PR_3)_2 \longrightarrow (CO)_2W\text{---}Pt(PR_3)_2 \quad (3.126)$$

(21)

$$(3.127)$$

$$(CO)_5Re\text{-}M(CO)_4(\equiv C\text{-tol}) + Fe_2(CO)_9 \longrightarrow \quad \xrightarrow{-2\ CO} \quad (3.127)$$

$$M = Mo, W$$

$$(21) + Co_2(CO)_8 \longrightarrow (CO)_2W\text{---}Co(CO)_3 \quad (3.128)$$

$$(CO)_2W\text{---}Rh(C_9H_7) + Fe_2(CO)_9 \longrightarrow (CO)_2W\text{---}Rh(C_9H_7) \quad (3.129)$$

Techniques for resolving racemic mixtures of such chiral products have been developed.[166,167] In some cases, it is possible to add two metal-carbyne complexes to yield linear or bent chains of metal-containing groups.[168] These chains can be lengthened by a sequence of alternating additions of ML_n and $M\equiv C-R$, equation (3.130).[159,169] Interestingly, (29) reacts with Ni(COD)$_2$ to yield the cyclized product (30) Ni$_2$Pt$_2$[W(CO)$_2$Cp]$_4$(μ_3-C—tol)$_4$ that has been referred to as the "star" cluster, equation (3.131).[170] In a few cases, coupling of the carbyne ligands to form bridging alkyne ligands is observed when two equivalents of (21) are combined in the same molecule, equation (3.132).[171,172]

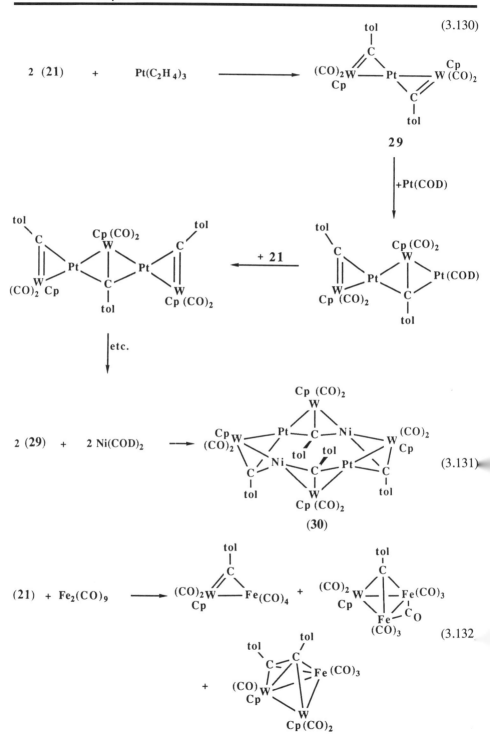

(3.130)

$$2 \ (21) \quad + \quad Pt(C_2H_4)_3 \longrightarrow$$

29

+Pt(COD)

+ **21**

etc.

$$2 \ (29) \quad + \quad 2 \ Ni(COD)_2 \longrightarrow$$

(3.131)

(30)

$$(21) + Fe_2(CO)_9 \longrightarrow$$

(3.132)

3.7. Metal-Metal Exchange Reactions

In these reactions, one or more metal-ligand groups of a cluster is replaced by a different metal-ligand group to yield a new cluster that contains the same total number of metal atoms. The reactions usually proceed in a stepwise fashion by either of two processes: (1) an associative process that involves the addition of the metal-ligand grouping to the cluster. Sometimes the expanded intermediate(s) can be isolated and provide valuable mechanistic information. (2) A dissociative process that involves the elimination of the metal-ligand grouping followed by addition of the new metal-ligand grouping. The dissociative route could involve either even-electron fragments (14- or 16-electron complexes) or odd-electron fragments (17-electron species[19]). In a few cases, intermediates have been isolated and characterized.

Vahrenkamp has shown that metal groupings containing the $AsMe_2$ ligand are readily substituted for cobalt-containing groupings in a variety of cluster complexes, equation (3.133).[173,174] These reactions are facilitated by the ability of the $AsMe_2$ group to serve as a bridging ligand to introduce the new metal grouping, and by the tendency of $[(CO)_3CoAsMe_2]_x$ to eliminate as an insoluble oligomer. Multiple applications of the $CpM(CO)_3AsMe_2$ reagent can lead to multiple exchanges (3.133).[175]

$$(3.133)$$

By applying this methodology to the prochiral cluster (31) $FeCo_2(CO)_9(\mu_3-S)$, Vahrenkamp was able to prepare and subsequently separate the enantiomers of the first cluster complexes $FeCoM(CO)_7Cp_2(\mu_3-S)$, (35) M = Mo, W to possess chirality due to the presence of four different atoms FeCoMS at the corners of a tetrahedral grouping, see Scheme 3.7.[176,177] This reaction has been studied in great detail and several intermediates have been isolated and characterized.[178] The reaction begins by the attachment of the $CpM(CO)_3AsMe_2$ molecule to a cobalt atom in (31) by using the $AsMe_2$ group as a bridging ligand, see (32). With loss of three CO ligands, a $CpM(CO)$ group is drawn into the cluster and three metal-metal bonds are formed. This yields the cluster complexes $MCo_2Fe(CO)_8Cp(\mu\text{-}AsMe_2)(\mu_3\text{-}S)$, (33), M = Mo, W. Compound (33) has recently been shown to exist in two isomeric forms that are believed to be (33a) and (33b).[167] In compounds (33), the $AsMe_2$ ligand has been separated from the metal M to which it was originally attached. Clearly, several steps were involved in the transformation of (32) into (33), but information about these has not yet been obtained. However, it is known that both isomers of (33) add two equivalents of CO to form the open cluster (34) $MCo_2Fe(CO)_{10}Cp(\mu\text{-}AsMe_2)(\mu_3\text{-}S)$ that is believed to have the structure (34a). However, it was not possible to distinguish (34a) from a possible isomer (34b) by the X-ray crystallographic analysis. It was shown that (34) eliminates $[(CO)_3CoAsMe_2]_x$ under 1 atm CO at 50°C to yield (35). Compound (34a) could yield (35) after a CO addition and a considerable amount of rearrangement, possibly via (34b), but the ease of this latter reaction seems to suggest that the structure of (34) might actually be that of (34b) and the CO addition simply cleaves a $Co(CO)_3(AsMe_2)$ group to yield (35). The related phosphinidene complexes $FeCo_2(CO)_9(\mu_3\text{-}PR)$, R = Me, Bu^t, and Ph react similarly with $CpM(CO)_3AsMe_2$, M = Mo, W.[179]

Clusters containing bridging ligands that may interact with metal-containing groups also engage in facile metal-metal exchange reactions. In reaction (3.134) an osmium-containing fragment from a basal position in the cluster $Os_5(CO)_{15}(\mu_4\text{-}S)$ is replaced with a platinum-containing group to form (36) $Os_4Pt(CO)_{13}(PPh_3)(\mu_4\text{-}S)$.[180] An interesting higher nuclearity intermediate, (37) $Os_5Pt(CO)_{15}(PPh_3)_2(\mu_4\text{-}S)$, that was stabilized by a PPh_3 addition was isolated. The structure of (37) shows the platinum atom fully incorporated into the body of the cluster while the departing osmium group is still clinging to a basal edge of the cluster on a side opposite to that of the platinum atom. This osmium group can be removed easily as $Os(CO)_4(PPh_3)$ in a separate step by treatment with CO. The observation of Pt—S interactions in (36) strongly implies the importance of the bridging sulfido in facilitating the exchange process.

(3.134)

(37)   (36)

The reaction of (38) $Ru_3(CO)_9(\mu_3\text{-}CO)(\mu_3\text{-}S)$ with $[CpMo(CO)_2]_2$ yields the product $RuMo_2(CO)_7Cp_2(\mu_3\text{-}S)$ through the simultaneous exchange of two metal atoms, equation (3.135).[181] The expanded cluster (39) $Ru_3Mo_2(CO)_{12}Cp_2(\mu_4\text{-}S)$ was isolated and shown to be an intermediate in the reaction. (39) was formed by the insertion of the Mo≡Mo grouping into one of the Ru—S bonds in (38).

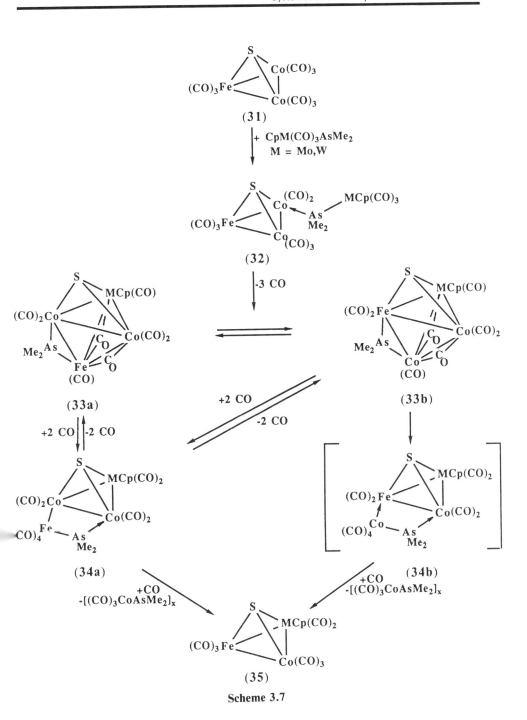

Scheme 3.7

$$(3.135)$$

(38)   **(39)**

Metal carbonylate anions have been used effectively to displace metal group-ings from clusters, equations (3.136),[182] (3.137),[183] and (3.138).[184] Good product yields can be obtained by this method.

$$Os_3(CO)_{12} \ + \ M(CO)_5^- \ \xrightarrow{\ M = Mn,Re\ } \ MOs_2(CO)_{12}^- \qquad (3.136)$$

$$(3.137)$$

$$(3.138)$$

$$(3.139)$$

M = Mn(CO)$_5$,CpFe(CO)$_2$,
   CpMo(CO)$_3$,CpW(CO)$_3$

M = Mo,W
(40)

Wojcicki has used the unsaturated $C\equiv C$ bond in the propargyl complexes $M-CH_2-C\equiv CPh$, $M = Mn(CO)_5$, $CpFe(CO)_2$, $CpMo(CO)_3$, $CpW(CO)_3$ to facilitate the addition of these molecules to $Co_2(CO)_8$ by formation of a bridging alkynyl group, equation (3.139).[185] When treated with H^+ the $M-CH_2$ bond was cleaved and the proton was added to the CH_2 group to form a bridging $MeC\equiv CPh$ ligand. When $M = Mn(CO)_5$ or $CpFe(CO)_2$, this metal-containing group was eliminated, but when $M = CpMo(CO)_3$ and $CpW(CO)_3$, a cobalt-containing group was eliminated and the heterobinuclear alkyne complexes (**40**), $CoM(CO)_5Cp(\mu\text{-}MeC_2Ph)$, $M = Mo$, W were formed.

Vahrenkamp has prepared twenty-one heterodinuclear metal complexes by simple redistribution reactions from the homonuclear precursors, equation (3.140), see Table 3.2.[19] These reactions are reversible and the yields of heteronuclear product depend on the state of the equilibrium. Some compounds that are not sufficiently reactive to undergo a significant exchange thermally can be activated by photochemical methods. Mechanistically, they are believed to proceed by homolytic cleavage of the metal-metal bonds to give 17-electron intermediates. Sometimes, however, these heteronuclear products can be prepared in higher yields through the coupling of metal carbonylate anions with metal carbonyl halide complexes, vide supra.

$$[ML_n]_2 + [M'L'_m]_2 \rightleftharpoons 2\,MM'L_nL'_m \qquad (3.140)$$

Some cluster complexes participate in metathesis reactions with homonuclear dimetallic complexes also.[174,186–189] By using this method, several $MM'M''(\mu_3\text{-}L)$ chiral clusters have been prepared from prochiral precursors, equations (3.141)[186] and (3.142).[166,189] Shriver has used $Co_2(CO)_8$ to produce $Co(CO)_3$ substitutions in selected anionic cluster complexes and has obtained evidence for radical intermediates.[55]

There are few examples of metal-metal exchange reactions that are initiated by cluster fragmentation. The formation of the mixed clusters $Ru_2Os(CO)_{12}$ and $RuOs_2(CO)_{12}$ by pyrolysis of mixtures of $Ru_3(CO)_{12}$ and $Os_3(CO)_{12}$ may proceed in this way, equation (3.143).[190] The formation of platinum-ruthenium compounds from the reaction of $Ru_3(CO)_{12}$ with mononuclear platinum phosphine complexes may proceed similarly.

Table 3.2 • Mixed-metal clusters generated by Eq. 3.140

$CpCr(CO)_3$	$CpMo(CO)_3$	$CpW(CO)_3$	$Mn(CO)_5$	$CpFe(CO)_2$
Cr—Cr	Cr—Mo	Cr—W	Cr—Mn	Cr—Fe
	Mo—Mo	Mo—W	Mo—Mn	Mo—Fe
		W—W	W—Mn	W—Fe
			Mn—Mn	Mn—Fe
				Fe—Fe

		$Co(CO)_4$	$CpNi(CO)$	M/M′
		Cr—Co	Cr—Ni	$CpCr(CO)_3$
		Mo—Co	Mo—Ni	$CpMo(CO)_3$
		W—Co	W—Ni	$CpW(CO)_3$
		Mn—Co	Mn—Ni	$Mn(CO)_5$
		Fe—Co	Fe—Ni	$CpFe(CO)_2$
		Co—Co	Co—Ni	$Co(CO)_4$
			Ni—Ni	$CpNi(CO)$

$$\begin{array}{c} Ru_3(CO)_{12} \\ + \\ Os_3(CO)_{12} \end{array} \longrightarrow \begin{array}{c} Ru(CO)_5 + \text{"}Ru_2(CO)_7\text{"} \\ Os(CO)_5 + \text{"}Os_2(CO)_7\text{"} \end{array} \longrightarrow \begin{array}{c} OsRu_2(CO)_{12} \\ + \\ Os_2Ru(CO)_{12} \end{array} \qquad (3.143)$$

$$(3.144)$$

$$(3.145)$$

Oligomerization of Clusters

Some carbonyl cluster complexes containing bridging ligands with lone pairs of electrons have been shown to exhibit a tendency to lose CO and oligomerize by using the lone pair of electrons on one molecule to fill the vacant coordination site on a second molecule. Some examples of these reactions are the formation of the cyclodimer $[Ru_3(CO)_8(\mu_3\text{-}HC_2Ph)(\mu_4\text{-}S)]_2$ formed by the decarbonylation of $Ru_3(CO)_9(\mu_3\text{-}HC_2Ph)(\mu_3\text{-}S)$, Eq. (144),[191] and the cyclotrimer $[Ru_3(CO)_8(\mu_4\text{-}S)(\mu\text{-}H)_2]_3$ formed by the decarbonylation of $Ru_3(CO)_9(\mu_3\text{-}S)(\mu\text{-}H)_2$, Eq. (145).[192] The latter contains a slightly puckered chair cyclohexane-like six-membered Ru_3S_3 ring. The compounds $Co_3(CO)_9(\mu_3\text{-}E)$, E = P, As also exhibit this tendency to form cyclotrimers.[193] The ability of cluster complexes such as these to oligomerize has not been thoroughly investigated. The oligomerization of clusters could lead to interesting new materials.

3.8. Summary

Our understanding of how metal cluster complexes are formed has advanced greatly over the last 20 years, but it is not nearly as developed as that of organic synthesis. Progress in cluster synthesis is strongly tied to developments in the understanding of cluster bonding and reactivity. Fortunately, great advances have been made in these areas also. Today, we can predict in a qualitative fashion whether or not a particular cluster complex will be stable and with a certain degree of confidence, we can design a synthesis for it. Certainly, our current state of knowledge still has much room for expansion and refinement. The development of reliable and systematic routes to large metal clusters remains a major challenge. The transition from molecular clusters to colloids and small metal particles is the frontier.

References

1. G. L. Geoffroy, in *Metal clusters in catalysis*, B. C. Gates, L. Guczi and H. Knozinger (Eds.). New York: Elsevier, 1986, Ch. 1.
2. D. A. Roberts and G. L. Geoffroy, in *Comprehensive organometallic chemistry*, G. Wilkinson, F. G. A. Stone and E. Abel (Eds.). Oxford: Pergamon, 1982, Ch. 40.
3. M. D. Vargas and J. N. Nicholls, *Adv. Inorg. Chem. Radiochem.*, 1987, **30**, 123.
4. H. Vahrenkamp, *Adv. Organomet. Chem.*, 1983, **22**, 169.
5. H. Vahrenkamp, *Angew. Chem. Int. Ed.*, 1978, **17**, 379.
6. R. Hoffmann, *Angew. Chem. Int. Ed. Engl.*, 1982, **21**, 711.
7. F. A. Cotton, *Accts. Chem. Res.*, 1969, **2**, 240.
8. L. F. Dahl, E. Ishishi and R. E. Rundle, *J. Chem. Phys.*, 1957, **26**, 1750.
9. F. W. B. Einstein, T. Jones, R. K. Pomeroy and P. Rushman, *J. Am. Chem. Soc.*, 1984, **106**, 2707.
10. F. W. B. Einstein, T. Jones, R. K. Pomeroy and P. Rushman, *Organometallics*, 1985, **4**, 250.
11. F. W. B. Einstein, T. Jones, R. K. Pomeroy and P. Rushman, *J. Chem. Soc. Chem. Commun.*, 1983, 854.
12. H. B. Davis, F. W. B. Einstein, V. J. Johnson and R. K. Pomeroy, *J. Organomet. Chem.*, 1987, **319**, C25.
13. V. J. Johnson, F. W. B. Einstein and R. K. Pomeroy, *J. Am. Chem. Soc.*, 1987, **109**, 7220.

14. W. I. Bailey, D. M. Collins, F. A. Cotton, J. C. Baldwin and W. C. Kaska, *J. Organomet. Chem.*, 1979, **165**, 373.
15. R. E. Ginsburg, L. M. Cirjak and L. F. Dahl, *J. Chem. Soc. Chem. Commun.*, 1979, 468.
16. R. J. Klingler, W. M. Butler and M. D. Curtis, *J. Am. Chem. Soc.*, 1978, **100**, 5034.
17. E. L. Muetterties, R. R. Burch and A. M. Stolzenberg, *Ann. Rev. Phys. Chem.*, 1982, **33**, 89.
18. M. S. Wrighton and D. S. Ginley, *J. Am. Chem. Soc.*, 1975, **97**, 2065.
19. T. Madach and H. Vahrenkamp, *Chem. Ber.*, 1980, **113**, 2675.
20. K. H. Whitmire, *J. Coord. Chem.*, 1988, **17**, 95.
21. R. B. King, *Organomet. Syn.*, 1965, **1**, 93.
22. J. R. Moss and W. A. G. Graham, *J. Chem. Soc. Dalton Trans.*, 1977, 95.
23. O. S. Mills and E. F. Paulus, *J. Organomet. Chem.*, 1967, **10**, 337.
24. O. S. Mills and J. P. Nice, *J. Organomet. Chem.*, 1967, **10**, 331.
25. H. B. Davis, F. W. B. Einstein, V. J. Johnston and R. K. Pomeroy, *J. Am. Chem. Soc.*, 1988, **110**, 4451.
26. J. K. Ruff, *Inorg. Chem.*, 1968, **7**, 1818.
27. E. Burkhardt and G. L. Geoffroy, *J. Organomet. Chem.*, 1980, **198**, 179.
28. P. W. Jolly and G. Wilke, *The organic chemistry of nickel*. New York: Academic Press, 1974, Vol. 1, Ch. 1.
29. C. R. Eady, B. F. G. Johnson and J. Lewis, *J. Chem. Soc. Dalton Trans.*, 1975, 2606.
30. M. I. Bruce, in *Comprehensive organometallic chemistry*, G. W. Wilkinson, F. G. A. Stone and E. Abel (Eds.). Oxford: Pergamon, 1982, Ch. 32.2.
31. H. G. Cutforth and P. W. Selwood, *J. Am. Chem. Soc.*, 1943, **65**, 2414.
32. F. Ungvary and L. Markó, *J. Organomet. Chem.*, 1974, **71**, 283.
33. R. B. King, *Inorg. Chem.*, 1966, **5**, 2227.
34. I. T. Horváth, G. Bor, M. Garland and P. Pino, *Organometallics*, 1986, **5**, 1441.
35. B. F. G. Johnson and J. Lewis, *Adv. Inorg. Radiochem.*, 1981, **24**, 225.
36. M. I. Bruce, *J. Organomet. Chem.*, 1983, **242**, 147.
37. J. Knight and M. J. Mays, *J. Chem. Soc. (A)*, 1970, 654.
38. L. R. Byers, V. A. Uchtman and L. F. Dahl, *J. Am. Chem. Soc.*, 1981, **103**, 1942.
39. D. H. Farrar, B. F. G. Johnson, J. Lewis, P. R. Raithby and M. J. Rosales, *J. Chem. Soc. Dalton Trans.*, 1982, 2051.
40. R. J. Goudsmit, B. F. G. Johnson, J. Lewis, P. R. Raithby and K. H. Whitmire, *J. Chem. Soc. Chem. Commun.*, 1982, 640.
41. F. G. A. Stone, *Inorg. Chim. Acta.*, 1981, **50**, 33.
42. M. G. Thomas, W. R. Pretzer, B. F. Beier, F. J. Hirsekorn and E. L. Muetterties, *J. Am. Chem. Soc.*, 1977, **99**, 743.
43. M. Green, J. A. K. Howard, M. Murray, J. L. Spencer and F. G. A. Stone, *J. Chem. Soc. Dalton Trans.*, 1977, 1509.
44. M. I. Bruce, G. Shaw and F. G. A. Stone, *J. Chem. Soc. Dalton Trans.*, 1972, 1082.
45. J. C. Jeffrey, H. Razay and F. G. A. Stone, *J. Chem. Soc. Chem. Commun.*, 1981, 243.
46. (a) Y. Shvo and E. Hazum, *J. Chem. Soc. Chem. Commun.*, 1975, 829. (b) T. Y. Luh, *Coord. Chem. Rev.*, 1984, **60**, 255.
47. J.-K. Shen, Y.-L. Shi, Y.-C. Gao, Q.-Z. Shi and F. Basolo, *J. Am. Chem. Soc.*, 1988, **110**, 2414.
48. R. J. Lawson and J. R. Shapley, *J. Am. Chem. Soc.*, 1976, **98**, 7433.
49. R. H. Dawson and A. K. Smith, *J. Chem. Soc. Chem. Commun.*, 1987, 826.
50. R. D. Adams, J. E. Babin and H. S. Kim, *Inorg. Chem.*, 1986, **25**, 1122.
51. (a) C. R. Eady, J. J. Guy, B. F. G. Johnson, J. Lewis, M. C. Malatesta and G. M.

Sheldrick, *J. Chem. Soc. Chem. Commun.*, 1976, 602. (b) A. P. Humphries and H. D. Kaesz, *Prog. Inorg. Chem.*, 1979, **25**, 145.

52. B. F. G. Johnson, J. Lewis, W. J. H. Nelson, M. D. Vargas, D. Braga, K. Henrick and M. McPartlin, *J. Chem. Soc. Dalton Trans.*, 1984, 2151.

53. P. Chini, G. Longoni and V. G. Albano, *Adv. Organomet. Chem.*, 1976, **14**, 285.

54. P. Chini, *J. Organomet. Chem.*, 1980, **200**, 37.

55. C. P. Horwitz, E. M. Holt and D. F. Shriver, *Organometallics*, 1985, **4**, 1117.

56. (a) M. Arewgoda, B. H. Robinson and J. Simpson, *J. Am. Chem. Soc.*, 1983, **105**, 1893. (b) M. I. Bruce, D. C. Kehoe, J. G. Mattsons, B. K. Nicholson, P. H. Rieger and M. L. Williams, *J. Chem. Soc. Chem. Commun.*, 1982, 442.

57. E. W. Abel, A. Singh and G. Wilkinson, *J. Chem. Soc.*, 1960, 1321.

58. R. B. King, P. M. Treichel and F. G. A. Stone, *Chem. Ind. (London)*, 1961, 747.

59. P. Braunstein and J. Dehand, *J. Chem. Soc. Chem. Commun.*, 1972, 164.

60. R. Bender, P. Braunstein, Y. Dusavsoy and J. Protas, *J. Organomet. Chem.*, 1979, **172**, C51.

61. P. Braunstein, J. Dehand and J. F. Nennig, *J. Organomet. Chem.*, 1975, **92**, 117.

62. G. Doyle, K. A. Eriksen and D. Van Engen, *J. Am. Chem. Soc.*, 1986, **108**, 445.

63. A. Cerotti, F. Demartin, G. Longoni, M. Manassero, M. Marchionna, G. Piva and M. Sansoni, *Angew. Chem. Int. Ed. Engl.*, 1985, **24**, 697.

64. T. J. Henly, J. R. Shapley, A. L. Rheingold and S. J. Geib, *Organometallics*, 1988, **7**, 441.

65. C. E. Coffey, J. Lewis and R. S. Nyholm, *J. Chem. Soc.*, 1964, 1741.

66. J. W. Lauher and K. Wald, *J. Am. Chem. Soc.*, 1981, **103**, 7648.

67. P. L. Bogdan, C. P. Horwitz and D. F. Shriver, *J. Chem. Soc. Chem. Commun.*, 1986, 553.

68. U. Anders and W. A. G. Graham, *J. Am. Chem. Soc.*, 1967, **89**, 539.

69. A. Fumagalli, T. Koetzle, F. Takusagawa, P. Chini, S. Martinengo and B. T. Heaton, *J. Am. Chem. Soc.*, 1980, **102**, 1740.

70. W. Hieber and E. H. Schubert, *Z. Anorg. Allg. Chem.*, 1965, **338**, 32.

71. A. A. Bhattacharyya, C. C. Nagel and S. G. Shore, *Organometallics*, 1983, **2**, 1187.

72. D. M. Washecheck, E. J. Wucherer, L. F. Dahl, A. Ceriotti, G. Longoni, M. Manassero, M. Sansoni and P. Chini, *J. Am. Chem. Soc.*, 1979, **101**, 6110.

73. M. Tachikawa and J. R. Shapley, *J. Organomet. Chem.*, 1977, **124**, C19.

74. F. G. A. Stone, *Phil. Trans. R. Soc. Lond.*, 1982, **A308**, 87.

75. M. J. Freeman, A. D. Miles, M. Murray, A. G. Orpen and F. G. A. Stone, *Polyhedron*, 1984, **3**, 1093.

76. (a) M. Tachikawa, R. L. Geerts and E. L. Muetterties, *J. Organomet. Chem.*, 1981, **213**, 11. (b) M. Tachikawa and E. L. Muetterties, *Prog. Inorg. Chem.*, 1981, **28**, 203.

77. E. J. Ditzel, H. D. Holden, B. F. G. Johnson, J. Lewis, A. Saunders and M. J. Taylor, *J. Chem. Soc. Chem. Commun.*, 1982, 1373.

78. B. F. G. Johnson, R. Khattar, J. Lewis and M. McPartlin, *J. Chem. Soc. Chem. Commun.*, 1986, 507.

79. M. R. Churchill, F. J. Hollander, R. A. Lashewycz, G. A. Pearson and J. R. Shapley, *J. Am. Chem. Soc.*, 1981, **103**, 2430.

80. M. Akhtar and H. C. Clark, *J. Organomet. Chem.*, 1970, **22**, 233.

81. C. Courture and D. H. Farrar, *J. Chem. Soc. Dalton Trans.*, 1986, 1395.

82. L. R. Martin, F. W. B. Einstein and R. K. Pomeroy, *Organometallics*, 1988, **7**, 294.

83. H. W. Sternberg, I. Wender, R. A. Friedel and M. Orchin, *J. Am. Chem. Soc.*, 1953, **75**, 2717.

84. J. R. Norton, *Accts. Chem. Res.*, 1979, **12**, 139.

85. M. J. Nappa, R. Santi, S. P. Diefenbach and J. Halpern, *J. Am. Chem. Soc.*, 1982, **104**, 619.

86. K. E. Warner and J. R. Norton, *Organometallics*, 1985, **4**, 2150.
87. R. J. Haines, R. S. Nyholm and M. H. B. Stiddard, *J. Chem. Soc. A*, 1968, 46.
88. D. J. Chandler, R. A. Jones, A. L. Stuart and T. C. Wright, *Organometallics*, 1984, **3**, 1830.
89. R. A. Jones, J. G. Lasch, N. C. Norman, A. L. Stuart, T. C. Wright and B. R. Whittlesey, *Organometallics*, 1984, **3**, 114.
90. W. Ehrl and H. Vahrenkamp, *Chem. Ber.*, 1973, **106**, 2563.
91. P. J. Hay, R. R. Ryan, K. V. Salazar, D. A. Wrobleski and A. P. Sattleberger, *J. Am. Chem. Soc.*, 1986, **108**, 313.
92. F. Richter and H. Vahrenkamp, *Organometallics*, 1982, **1**, 756.
93. F. Richter and H. Vahrenkamp, *Angew. Chem. Int. Ed.*, 1979, **18**, 531.
94. R. D. Adams, I. T. Horváth and S. Wang, *Inorg. Chem.*, 1985, **24**, 1728.
95. R. D. Adams, I. T. Horváth and P. Mathur, *J. Am. Chem. Soc.*, 1984, **106**, 6296.
96. R. D. Adams, I. T. Horváth and H. S. Kim, *Organometallics*, 1984, **3**, 548.
97. R. D. Adams, *Polyhedron*, 1985, **4**, 2003, and references therein.
98. R. D. Adams, J. E. Babin and M. Tasi, *Inorg. Chem.*, 1987, **26**, 2807.
99. D. J. Darensbourg, D. J. Zalewski, K. M. Sanchez and T. Delord, *Inorg. Chem.*, 1988, **27**, 821.
100. R. D. Adams and T. S. A. Hor, *Inorg. Chem.*, 1984, **23**, 4723.
101. L. E. Bogan, D. A. Lesch and T. B. Rauchfuss, *J. Organomet. Chem.*, 1983, **250**, 429.
102. H. Vahrenkamp and E. Wucherer, *Angew. Chem. Int. Ed. Engl.*, 1981, **20**, 680.
103. D. Seyferth, R. S. Henderson and L.-C. Song, *Organometallics*, 1982, **1**, 125.
104. C. K. Schauer and D. F. Shriver, *Angew. Chem. Int. Ed. Engl.*, 1987, **26**, 255.
105. S. B. Colbran, B. F. G. Johnson, J. Lewis and R. M. Sorrell, *J. Chem. Soc. Chem. Commun.*, 1986, 525.
106. R. D. Adams, J. E. Babin and J. Tanner, *Organometallics*, 1988, **7**, 765.
107. C. P. Horwitz and D. F. Shriver, *Adv. Organomet. Chem.*, 1984, **23**, 219.
108. R. D. Adams, J. E. Babin and M. Tasi, *Inorg. Chem.*, 1988, **27**, 2618.
109. E. Roland, W. Bernhardt and H. Vahrenkamp, *Chem. Ber.*, 1986, **119**, 2566.
110. D. Seyferth, J. B. Hoke, A. L. Rheingold, M. Cowie and A. D. Hunter, *Organometallics*, 1988, **7**, 2163.
111. G. Joaven, A. Marinetti, B. Mentzen, R. Mutin, J.-Y. Saillard, B. G. Sayer and M. J. McGlinchey, *Organometallics*, 1982, **1**, 753.
112. J. A. Hriljac, P. N. Swepston and D. F. Shriver, *Organometallics*, 1985, **4**, 158.
113. (a) W. L. Gladfelter, *Adv. Organomet. Chem.*, 1985, **24**, 41. (b) M. L. Blohm and W. L. Gladfelter, *Organometallics*, 1985, **4**, 45.
114. G. Bor, L. Markó and B. Markó, *Chem. Ber.*, 1962, **95**, 333.
115. A. Vizi-Orosz, V. Galamb, G. Palyi, L. Marko, G. Bor and G. Natile, *J. Organomet. Chem.*, 1976, **107**, 235.
116. T. J. Marks and A. R. Newman, *J. Am. Chem. Soc.*, 1973, **95**, 769.
117. R. J. Haines, C. R. Nolte, R. Greatrex and N. N. Greenwood, *J. Organomet. Chem.*, 1971, **26**, C45.
118. W. Ehrl and H. Vahrenkamp, *Chem. Ber.*, 1973, **106**, 2550.
119. M. Müller and H. Vahrenkamp, *Chem. Ber.*, 1983, **116**, 2322.
120. G. Huttner, U. Weber, B. Sigwarth, O. Scheidsteger, H. Lang and L. Zsolnai, *J. Organomet. Chem.*, 1985, **282**, 331.
121. V. G. Albano, P. Chini, S. Martinengo, M. Sansoni and D. Strumolo, *J. Chem. Soc. Chem. Commun.*, 1974, 299.
122. G. Huttner and K. Knoll, *Angew. Chem. Int. Ed. Engl.*, 1987, **26**, 743.
123. G. Huttner and K. Evertz, *Accts. Chem. Res.*, 1986, **19**, 406.
124. G. Huttner, G. Mohr, P. Friedrich and H. G. Schmid, *J. Organomet. Chem.*, 1978, **160**, 59.
125. R. L. De, J. von Seyerl and G. Huttner, *J. Organomet. Chem.*, 1979, **178**, 319.

126. J. Borm, K. Knoll, L. Zsolnai and G. Huttner, *Z. Naturforsch.*, 1986, 532.
127. P. M. Treichel, W. K. Dean and W. M. Douglas, *Inorg. Chem.*, 1972, **11**, 1609.
128. R. Ball, M. G. Bennett, E. H. Brooks, W. A. G. Graham, J. Hoyano and S. M. Illingworth, *J. Chem. Soc. Chem. Commun.*, 1970, 592.
129. S. A. Khattab, L. Markó, G. Bor and B. Markó, *J. Organomet. Chem.*, 1964, **1**, 373.
130. J. Schneider, L. Zsolnai and G. Huttner, *Chem. Ber.*, 1982, **115**, 989.
131. M. Müller and H. Vahrenkamp, *Chem. Ber.*, 1983, **115**, 2311.
132. G. Suss-Fink, U. Thewalt and H. P. Klein, *J. Organomet. Chem.*, 1984, **262**, 315.
133. F. E. Wood, M. M. Olmstead and A. L. Balch, *J. Am. Chem. Soc.*, 1983, **105**, 6332.
134. J. A. Osborn and G. G. Stanley, *Angew. Chem. Int. Ed. Engl.*, 1980, **19**, 1025.
135. A. A. Bahsoun, J. A. Osborn, J. P. Kintzinger, P. H. Bird and U. Siriwardane, *Nouv. J. Chim.*, 1984, **8**, 125.
136. R. M. Bullock and C. P. Casey, *Accts. Chem. Res.*, 1987, **20**, 167.
137. C. O. Pioresana, T. Tarantelli and P. F. Zanazzi, *Inorg. Chem.*, 1985, **24**, 366.
138. J. A. Schuerman, F. R. Fronczek and J. Selbin, *J. Am. Chem. Soc.*, 1986, **108**, 336.
139. E. L. Muetterties, R. R. Burch and A. M. Stolzenberg, *Ann. Rev. Phys. Chem.*, 1982, **33**, 89.
140. R. G. Teller, J. M. Williams, T. F. Koetzle, R. R. Burch, R. M. Gavin and E. L. Muetterties, *Inorg. Chem.*, 1981, **20**, 1806.
141. R. K. Brown, J. M. Williams, A. J. Sivak and E. L. Muetterties, *Inorg. Chem.*, 1980, **19**, 370.
142. M. D. Fryzuk, *Organometallics*, 1982, **1**, 408.
143. S. Otsuka, T. Yoshida, M. Matsumoto and K. Nakatsu, *J. Am. Chem. Soc.*, 1976, **98**, 5850.
144. M. Green, J. A. K. Howard, M. Martin, J. L. Spenser and F. G. A. Stone, *J. Chem. Soc.*, 1977, 1509.
145. A. Albinati, *Inorg. Chim. Acta*, 1977, **22**, L31.
146. T. V. Ashworth, M. Berry, J. A. K. Howard, M. Laguna and F. G. A. Stone, *J. Chem. Soc. Dalton Trans.*, 1980, 1615.
147. M. D. Curtis, *Polyhedron*, 1987, **6**, 759.
148. M. Green, R. M. Mills, G. N. Pain, F. G. A. Stone and P. Woodward, *J. Chem. Soc. Dalton Trans.*, 1982, 1309.
149. M. L. Aldridge, M. Green, J. A. K. Howard, G. N. Pain, S. J. Porter, F. G. A. Stone and P. Woodward, *J. Chem. Soc. Dalton Trans.*, 1982, 1333.
150. M. Green, J. A. K. Howard, G. N. Pain and F. G. A. Stone, *J. Chem. Soc. Dalton Trans.*, 1982, 1327.
151. P. Braunstein, J. M. Jud, A. Tiripicchio, M. Camellini-Tiripicchio and E. Sappa, *Angew. Chem. Int. Ed. Engl.*, 1982, **21**, 307.
152. P. D. Williams, M. D. Curtis, D. N. Duffy and W. M. Butler, *Organometallics*, 1983, **2**, 165.
153. P. Brun, G. M. Dawkins, M. Green, A. D. Miles, A. G. Orpen and F. G. A. Stone, *J. Chem. Soc. Chem. Commun.*, 1982, 926.
154. M. D. Curtis and R. J. Klinger, *J. Organomet. Chem.*, 1978, **161**, 23.
155. M. R. Churchill, C. Bueno, S. Kennedy, J. C. Bricker, J. S. Plotkin and S. G. Shore, *Inorg. Chem.*, 1982, **21**, 627.
156. L. J. Farrugia, J. A. K. Howard, P. Mitrprachachon, F. G. A. Stone and P. Woodward, *J. Chem. Soc. Dalton Trans.*, 1981, 155.
157. L.-Y. Hsu, W.-L. Hsu, D.-Y. Jan and S. G. Shore, *Organometallics*, 1986, **5**, 1041.
158. D.-Y. Jan, L.-Y. Hsu, W.-L. Hsu and S. G. Shore, *Organometallics*, 1987, **6**, 274.
159. F. G. A. Stone, *Pure Appl. Chem.*, 1986, **58**, 529.
160. F. G. A. Stone, *Angew. Chem. Int. Ed. Engl.*, 1984, **23**, 89.

161. T. V. Ashworth, J. A. K. Howard, M. Laguna and F. G. A. Stone, *J. Chem. Soc. Dalton Trans.*, 1980, 1593.
162. T. V. Ashworth, J. A. K. Howard and F. G. A. Stone, *J. Chem. Soc. Dalton Trans.*, 1980, 1609.
163. D. G. Evans, J. A. K. Howard, J. C. Jeffrey, D. B. Lewis, G. E. Lewis, M. J. Grosse-Ophoff, M. J. Parrot and F. G. A. Stone, *J. Chem. Soc. Dalton Trans.*, 1986, 1723.
164. M. J. Chetcuti, P. A. M. Chetcuti, J. C. Jeffrey, R. M. Mills, P. Mitrprachachon, S. J. Pickering, F. G. A. Stone and P. Woodward, *J. Chem. Soc. Dalton Trans.*, 1982, 699.
165. M. Green, J. C. Jeffrey, S. J. Porter, H. Razay and F. G. A. Stone, *J. Chem. Soc. Dalton Trans.*, 1982, 2475.
166. R. Blumhofer and H. Vahrenkamp, *Chem. Ber.*, 1986, **119**, 683.
167. M. Müller and H. Vahrenkamp, *Chem. Ber.*, 1983, **116**, 2748.
168. T. V. Ashworth, M. J. Chetcuti, J. A. K. Howard, F. G. A. Stone, S. J. Wisbey and P. Woodward, *J. Chem. Soc. Dalton Trans.*, 1981, 763.
169. (a) S. J. Davies, G. P. Elliot, J. A. K. Howard, C. M. Nunn and F. G. A. Stone, *J. Chem. Soc. Dalton Trans.*, 1987, 2177. (b) S. J. Davies, J. A. K. Howard, R. J. Musgrove and F. G. A. Stone *J. Chem. Soc. Dalton Trans.*, 1989, 2269.
170. (a) G. P. Elliot, J. A. K. Howard, T. Mise, C. M. Nunn and F. G. A. Stone, *J. Chem. Soc. Dalton Trans.*, 1987, 2189. (b) G. P. Elliot, J. A. K. Howard, T. Mise, C. M. Nunn and F. G. A. Stone, *Angew. Chem. Int. Ed. Engl.*, 1986, **25**, 190.
171. L. Busetto, J. C. Jeffrey, R. M. Mills, F. G. A. Stone, M. J. Went and P. Woodward, *J. Chem. Soc. Dalton Trans.*, 1983, 101.
172. J. R. Shapley, J. T. Park, M. R. Churchill, C. Bueno and H. J. Wasserman, *J. Am. Chem. Soc.*, 1981, **103**, 7385.
173. H. Beurich and H. Vahrenkamp, *Chem. Ber.*, 1982, **115**, 2385.
174. H. Beurich, R. Blumhofer and H. Vahrenkamp, *Chem. Ber.*, 1982, **115**, 2409.
175. R. Blumhofer, K. Fischer and H. Vahrenkamp, *Chem. Ber.*, 1986, **119**, 194.
176. F. Richter and H. Vahrenkamp, *Angew. Chem. Int. Ed. Engl.*, 1979, **18**, 531.
177. F. Richter and H. Vahrenkamp, *Chem. Ber.*, 1982, **115**, 3243.
178. F. Richter, M. Müller, N. Gartner and H. Vahrenkamp, *Chem. Ber.*, 1984, **117**, 2438.
179. M. Müller, H. Schacht, K. Fischer, J. Ensling, P. Gutlich and H. Vahrenkamp, *Inorg. Chem.*, 1986, **25**, 4032.
180. R. D. Adams, J. E. Babin, R. Mahtab and S. Wang, *Inorg. Chem.*, 1986, **25**, 1623.
181. R. D. Adams, J. E. Babin and M. Tasi, *Organometallics*, 1988, **7**, 219.
182. J. Knight and M. Mays, *J. Chem. Soc. Dalton Trans.*, 1972, 1022.
183. R. A. Epstein, H. W. Withers and G. L. Geoffroy, *Inorg. Chem.*, 1979, **18**, 942.
184. D. Mani and H. Vahrenkamp, *Chem. Ber.*, 1986, **119**, 3639.
185. T. Wido, G. H. Young, A. Wojcicki, M. Calligaris and G. Nardin, *Organometallics*, 1988, **7**, 452.
186. E. Roland and H. Vahrenkamp, *Chem. Ber.*, 1984, **117**, 1039.
187. P. Gusbeth and H. Vahrenkamp, *Chem. Ber.*, 1983, **118**, 1770.
188. M. Muller and H. Vahrenkamp, *Chem. Ber.*, **116**, 2675.
189. (a) H. Beaurich and H. Vahrenkamp, *Angew. Chem. Int. Ed.*, 1981, **20**, 98. (b) R Blumhofer, K. Fischer and H. Vahrenkamp, *Chem. Ber.*, 1986, **119**, 194.
190. R. P. Ferrari, G. A. Vaglio and M. Valle, *J. Chem. Soc. Dalton Trans.*, 1978 1164.
191. R. D. Adams, J. E. Babin and T. A. Wolfe, *Polyhedron* 1989, **8**, 1123.
192. R. D. Adams, D. Männig and B. E. Segmüller, *Organometallics* 1983, **2**, 149.
193. A. Vizi-Orosz, V. Galamb, G. Palyi, L. Markó, G. Bor and G. Natile, *J. Organomet Chem.* 1976, **107**, 235.

Ligand Substitution Reactions

Donald J. Darensbourg

4.1. Introduction

In this chapter an attempt will be made to summarize the current understanding of ligand substitutional pathways involving polynuclear transition metal complexes. Metal clusters will be defined rather liberally as compounds containing more than one transition metal atom directly bonded to each other. This presentation is not intended to be an exhaustive review of the literature in the area, and the selection of references is chosen to illustrate important mechanistic aspects of this class of reactions. Since there are often several references which fulfill this requirement the selection of references is to some degree arbitrary. Nevertheless, the pertinent works in this general area are included for the reader's benefit in the list of references.[1] Included as well are publications covering the closely related ligand substitution processes involving mononuclear transition metal complexes.[2]

Mechanistic investigations of ligand substitution reactions at multinuclear metal complexes are not only of academic interest but are of significance in providing a detailed analysis of homogeneous catalytic processes. For example, in the presence of dihydrogen, $H_4Ru_4(CO)_{12}$ catalyzes the homogeneous hydrogenation of alkenes or alkynes, where dissociation or displacement of a carbon monoxide ligand is regarded as the initial step in the process (Scheme 4.1).[3-8] Derivatives of $H_4Ru_4(CO)_{12}$ substituted by phosphorus donor ligands exhibit similar catalytic behavior. Indeed asymmetric hydrogenation of prochiral alkenes has been reported employing the chiral ruthenium cluster $H_4Ru_4(CO)_8L_2$ as catalyst, where L = (−)-DIOP, a chiral ditertiary phosphine ligand.[9]

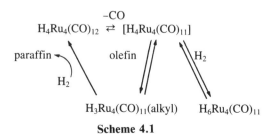

Scheme 4.1

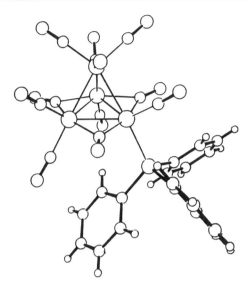

Figure 4.1 ▪ Perspective drawing of the $Co_4(CO)_{11}[PPh_3]$ molecule (from ref. 11).

In addition, kinetic measurements of ligand substitutional processes are useful in defining the reactivity of reaction intermediates, resulting from ligand dissociation. Hence, the kinetic parameters governing ligand substitution reactions in metal clusters provide invaluable information for designing new and selective homogeneous catalysts. Furthermore this knowledge, when applied correctly, can greatly enhance our understanding of heterogeneous catalytic processes.

In both homogeneous and heterogeneous catalysis, catalytic activity is associated with specific sites in metal complexes or on metal surfaces. One question which mechanistic investigations of metal clusters are often unable to definitively answer is the initial site of ligand dissociation when multiple sites are available. This is due to the fact that ligands capable of multiple-coordination modes often possess the ability to migrate about the cluster (see reference 10 for reviews of ligand mobility in metal clusters). An illustration of this phenomenon is provided here for the $Co_4(CO)_{12}$ cluster which has four different types of CO ligands, that is, apical, equatorial, axial, and bridging. Dissociation of carbon monoxide from $Co_4(CO)_{12}$ followed by addition of L results in formation of $Co_4(CO)_{11}L$, equation (4.1). The derivative where L = PPh_3 has been structurally characterized with PPh_3 being shown to occupy an axial site in the cluster (Figure 4.1).[11] This product may indeed result from dissociation of an axial CO ligand or it may be derived from dissociation of CO from one of the other sites followed by vacant site migration in the unsaturated intermediate. [This latter possibility is generally not applicable when the incoming ligand (L) equals ^{13}CO.[12]] Alternatively the initially formed $Co_4(CO)_{11}L$ species may undergo rapid intramolecular ligand migration leading to formation of the final product.

$$Co_4(CO)_{12} \rightleftarrows \{Co_4(CO)_{11}\} + CO$$

$$\downarrow L \qquad\qquad (4.1)$$

$$Co_4(CO)_{11}L$$

The interchange between linear and bridging carbonyl sites in metal carbonyl clusters usually requires only a small activation barrier, implying similar binding energies in the two sites. In heterogeneous catalysis, studies of the adsorption of CO on single-crystal surfaces, for example, the Pt(111) surface (Figure 4.2), has allowed for a detailed analysis of surface binding sites.[13] That is, the CO molecule may bind to one metal atom site or two- or three-fold bridging sites depending on the energetically most favorable situation at a particular coverage. Thermal desorption studies reveal the binding energy to be very similar for these different sites. These various modes of CO coordination each give rise to a distinct CO stretching frequency on either metal surfaces or in metal cluster compounds.

4.2. Classification of Ligand Substitution Mechanisms

Langford and Gray have classified the three possible intimate mechanisms for ligand substitution processes in mononuclear metal complexes as (a) dissociative (D), (b) associative (A), and (c) interchange (I).[14] The latter designation may be further subdivided into I_d and I_a, depending on the extent to which both the entering and leaving groups participate in the transition state. In addition to these ligand substitutional pathways, polynuclear metal compounds have other mechanisms for ligand substitution available to them. These include metal-metal bond dissociation without fragmentation and with fragmentation.[15,16]

4.2.1. The Dissociative Pathway

The dissociative mechanism, equations (4.2) and (4.3), which affords an intermediate of reduced coordination number, is one of the most common pathways for ligand substitution reactions. The rate constant expression depicted in equation (4.4) reduces to $k_{obs} = k_1$ for the condition that is usually satisfied, $k_{-1}[A] \ll k_2[B]$. That is, reactions are generally carried out in solutions where the concentration of the incoming ligand (B) exceeds that of the leaving ligand (A). Differences in k_{-1} and k_2 would define the selectivity of the intermediate, $\{M_nL_m\}$ for A or B, respectively.

$$M_nL_mA \underset{k_{-1}}{\overset{k_1}{\Leftrightarrow}} \{M_nL_m\} + A \qquad (4.2)$$

$$\{M_nL_m\} + B \xrightarrow[\text{rapid}]{k_2} M_nL_mB \qquad (4.3)$$

plane view

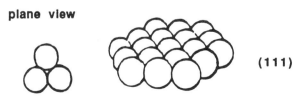

(111)

Figure 4.2 ▪ 111 plane of face-centered metal.

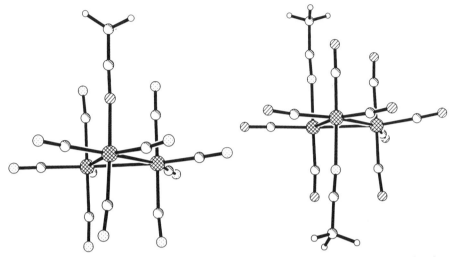

Figure 4.3 ▪ Perspective drawings of $Os_3(CO)_{11}(NCMe)$ and $Os_3(CO)_{10}(NCMe)_2$ molecules (from ref. 18).

$$k_{obs} = \frac{k_1 k_2 [B]}{k_{-1}[A] + k_2[B]} \qquad (4.4)$$

A consideration of the substitution kinetics of $Os_3(CO)_{11}(NCMe)$ and $Os_3(CO)_{10}(NCMe)_2$ will serve to illustrate ligand substitution by the dissociative pathway.[17] These derivatives of $Os_3(CO)_{12}$ contain strong metal-metal bonds and labile acetonitrile ligands. The structures of these two derivatives have been determined crystallographically and are shown in Figure 4.3.[18] Because of the facile replacement of the acetonitrile ligand by more strongly bonding ligands, such as phosphines, and their easy synthesis from the reaction of the parent carbonyl with trimethylamine oxide in acetonitrile, these species are often utilized as intermediates in the synthesis of $Os_3(CO)_{11}PR_3$ and $Os_3(CO)_{10}(PR_3)_2$ derivatives.

The ligand substitution reaction of $Os_3(CO)_{11}(NCMe)$ with phosphines has been shown to be quantitative, resulting in replacement of the CH_3CN ligand. The rate constants were found to be independent of both the nature and concentration of the substituting phosphine ligand (see Table 4.1). At lower concentrations of the incoming ligand (L) the first-order rate constants decreased slightly with time. These observations are characteristic of a simple dissociative mechanism where the reverse of reaction (4.5) competes with reaction (4.6) when [L]/[NCMe] is small. When reactions were performed in the presence of added MeCN the plots in Figure 4.4 were obtained, which are in excellent agreement with equation (4.7). A $k_2/k_{-1} = 0.103 \pm 0.002$ was obtained from the intercept and gradient of the linear plot depicted in Figure 4.4. That is, the unsaturated intermediate $\{Os_3(CO)_{11}\}$ is more reactive towards CH_3CN than PPh_3 by a factor of about 10. Triphenylphosphine is slightly more competitive than CO for reaction with the coordinatively unsaturated $\{Ru_3(CO)_{11}\}$ cluster.[19] In any instance, as is observed in unsaturated

Table 4.1 ▪ Limiting First-Order Rate Constants for Reactions of $Os_3(CO)_{11}(NCMe)$ with L in p-xylene at 30°C[a]

L	$10^2 \times k_{obs}$ (sec^{-1})[b]
PPh_3[c]	1.45 ± 0.04
$AsPh_3$[c]	1.52 ± 0.04
$P(OPh)_3$[d]	1.59 ± 0.04

[a] Conc. of $Os_3(CO)_{11}(NCMe)$ = 1×10^{-4} M. [b] The average rate constant for several measurements. [c] Conc. range of [L] = 0.01–0.50 M. [d] Conc. range of [L] = 0.015–0.38 M.

mononuclear metal carbonyls,[2f] there is high reactivity and little selectivity of these intermediates for sterically unencumbered nucleophiles.

$$Os_3(CO)_{11}(NCMe) \overset{k_1}{\underset{k_{-1}}{\rightleftarrows}} \{Os_3(CO)_{11}\} + MeCN \qquad (4.5)$$

$$\{Os_3(CO)_{11}\} + L \overset{k_2}{\longrightarrow} Os_3(CO)_{11}L \qquad (4.6)$$

$$1/k_{obs} = 1/k_1 + (k_{-1}/k_1k_2)[MeCN]/[PPh_3] \qquad (4.7)$$

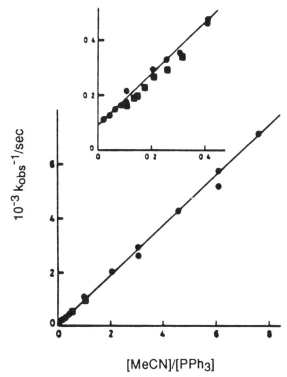

Figure 4.4 ▪ Dependence of k_{obs}^{-1} on [MeCN]/[PPh₃] for reaction of $Os_3(CO)_{11}(NCMe)$: (●) [PPh₃] = 0.0153, [MeCN] = 0–0.116 M; (■) [MeCN] = 0.00154, [PPh₃] = 0.0015–0.015 M.

Table 4.2 ▪ Activation Parameters of Dissociative Ligand Substitution Reactions of the Group 8 Trinuclear Species

Complex	Ligand Dissociated	$\Delta H^{\neq}$ (kJ/mol)	$\Delta S^{\neq}$ (J/K-mol)
$Fe_3(CO)_{12}$ [a]	CO	123.4	79.5
$Ru_3(CO)_{12}$ [b]	CO	133.1	84.5
$Os_3(CO)_{12}$ [c]	CO	137.5	31.8
		(161.5) [a]	(102.1) [a]
$Os_3(CO)_{11}(NCMe)$ [d]	MeCN	112.4	92.2
$HRu_3(CO)_{11}^{-}$ [e]	CO	66.9	−7.9
$HRu_3(CO)_{10}PPh_3^{-}$ [e]	PPh$_3$	76.1	4.2

[a] A. Shojaie and J. D. Atwood, *Organometallics*, 1985, **4**, 187. [b] A. J. Poe and M. V. Twigg, *J. Chem. Soc. Dalton Trans.*, 1974, 1860. [c] A. J. Poe and V. C. Sekhar, *Inorg. Chem.*, 1985, **24**, 4376. [d] K. Dahlinger, A. J. Poe, P. K. Sayala and V. C. Sekhar, *J. Chem. Soc. Dalton Trans.*, 1986, 2145. [e] D. J. Taube and P. C. Ford, *Organometallics*, 1986, **5**, 99.

The activation parameters listed in Table 4.2 for the ligand-independent substitution reaction of $Os_3(CO)_{11}(NCMe)$ with phosphines (L) to provide $Os_3(CO)_{11}L$ are consistent with a dissociative mechanism. It is also evident from the data contained in Table 4.2 that loss of acetonitrile from the triosmium unit is less energetic than the corresponding loss of CO from $Os_3(CO)_{12}$. This is to be expected since metal-NCMe bonds are generally weaker than metal-CO bonds. It is noteworthy that the $\Delta H^{\neq}$ values for CO dissociation in the group 8 metals dodecacarbonyls increase slightly as one proceeds down the group, that is, proceeding from Fe to Os the $\Delta H^{\neq}$ values increase from 123.4 to 137.5 kJ/mol.

The trinuclear ruthenium hydride anion, $HRu_3(CO)_{11}^{-}$, undergoes more facile CO substitution with PPh$_3$ in tetrahydrofuran relative to the parent $Ru_3(CO)_{12}$ complex.[20] The reaction has been shown to be reversible, equation (4.8). Plots of k_{obs} vs. [PPh$_3$] were nonlinear and reached limiting values at high [PPh$_3$]. This observation, coupled with the fact that at a given [PPh$_3$], k_{obs} decreased with increasing [CO] (Figure 4 5), suggested a reaction pathway proceeding by CO dissociation (Scheme 4.2). As is noted in Table 4.2, dissociative loss of CO or PPh$_3$ to give [$HRu_3(CO)_{10}^{-}$] occurs with about equal facility. Furthermore, the ratio of k_{-1}/k_2 was found to be about 14 for both PPh$_3$ and $PnBu_3$. That is, the proposed intermediate [$HRu_3(CO)_{10}^{-}$] reacts with CO an order of magnitude faster than with phosphines. This is in contrast with the reactivity of the intermediate resulting from CO dissociation in the neutral species, [$Ru_3(CO)_{11}$], which reacts with phosphines about an order of magnitude faster than with CO. These observations presumably reflect the greater nucleophilicity of [$HRu_3(CO)_{10}^{-}$] as compared with [$Ru_3(CO)_{11}$]

$$HRu_3(CO)_{11}^{-} + PPh_3 \rightleftarrows HRu_3(CO)_{10}PPh^{-}{}_3 + CO \qquad (4.8$$

The enthalpy of activation for CO dissociation in $HRu_3(CO)_{11}^{-}$ is about 66 kJ/mole lower than that determined for the analogous reaction involving the neutral $Ru_3(CO)_{12}$ complex. This rate enhancement is ascribed to a nucleophilic attack by the bridging CO ligand on an axial carbonyl group of the unique ruthenium atom, intermediate (**1**). This explanation is consistent with results in the literature which demonstrate that nucleophiles capable of forming adducts with coor

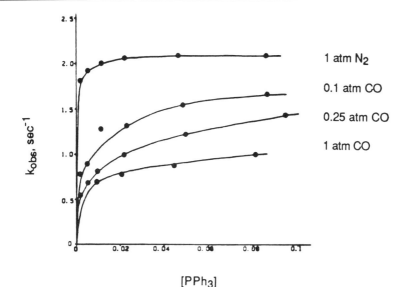

Figure 4.5 ▪ Plots of k_{obs} vs. [PPh$_3$] for the reaction of HRu$_3$(CO)$_{11}^-$ and PPh$_3$ in THF under varied P$_{CO}$ at 25°C.

$$HRu_3(CO)_{11}^- \underset{k_{-1}}{\overset{k_1}{\rightleftarrows}} HRu_3(CO)_{10}^- + CO$$

$$HRu_3(CO)_{10}^- + PPh_3 \underset{k_{-2}}{\overset{k_2}{\rightleftarrows}} HRu_3(CO)_{10}PPh_3^-$$

Scheme 4.2

dinated CO (e.g., OMe$^-$) are catalysts for CO substitution reactions of metal clusters.[21-25] Indeed this process has been employed in the preparation of the very useful Ru$_3$(^{13}CO)$_{12}$ (>99% ^{13}C-enriched) complex.[24]

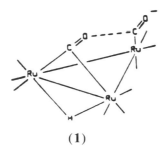

(1)

In these instances where more polar solvents are required to dissolve the organometallic salt, the solvent itself is a potential nucleophile. Hence, it is necessary to establish that the CO lability in the HRu$_3$(CO)$_{11}^-$ derivative does not reflect an associative reaction involving the solvent molecule tetrahydrofuran (THF). This was accomplished by measuring the rates in both THF and the sterically encumbered and less coordinating 2,5-dimethyltetrahydrofuran (DMTHF) solvents. The reaction rates were found to be essentially the same, and the activation parameters were within experimental error in the two solvents. Further evidence for the dissociative mechanism was obtained from the volume of activation ($\Delta V^{\neq}$) determined for this reaction in THF, that is, $\Delta V^{\neq}$ was found to be $+21.2 \pm 1.4$ cm^3/mol.[26]

4.2.2. The Associative Pathway

The associative mechanism, equations (4.9) and (4.10), involves addition of an incoming ligand to one of the metal centers in the cluster in the rate-determining step to afford an intermediate of increased coordination number. Because most mechanistic ligand substitution studies have been concerned with low-nuclearity metal carbonyl clusters, where the metal centers generally adhere to the 18-electron rule, the associative pathway is not common. In this regard Basolo has stated the following rule: Substitution reactions by 18-electron transition metal organometallic compounds may proceed by an associative mechanism provided the metal complex can delocalize a pair of electrons onto one of its ligands.[27]

$$M_nL_mA + B \xrightarrow{k_2} M_nL_m(A)B$$
$$\downarrow$$
$$M_nL_mB + A \tag{4.9}$$

$$\text{rate} = k_2[M_nL_mA][B] \tag{4.10}$$

The rate-constant expression observed for ligand substitution reactions for a variety of low-nuclearity metal carbonyl clusters, including Ru$_3$(CO)$_{12}$[28] and Ir$_4$(CO)$_{12}$,[29] is comprised of incoming ligand-independent and ligand-dependent terms, equation (4.11). The ligand-dependent term may be accounted for by several reaction pathways, including an associative process, an interchange (I$_d$ or I$_a$) process, or a heterolytic fission of the metal-metal bond. Of these, the associative mechanism is not viable for electron-precise metal carbonyl clusters in the absence of ligands like NO, cyclopentadienyl, or arenes, for the aforementioned reason.

$$k_{\text{obs}} = k_1 + k_2[L] \tag{4.11}$$

On the other hand, the associative mechanism may hold for electron-poor metal clusters. For example, the triplatinum clusters Pt$_3$(CO)$_3$L$_3$ (L = phosphine) have been found to undergo a facile ligand substitution reaction with phosphines, equation (4.12).[30] In these complexes each metal center formally contains 16 electrons. Although no quantitative rate data is available, the reaction rate was found to be dependent on the nature and concentration of the incoming phosphine ligand (L'). The substitution process was proposed to proceed by an associative pathway, where an intermediate involving attack at the metal center (2) is plausible.

$$Pt_3(CO)_3L_3 + 3L' \rightarrow Pt_3(CO)_3L_3' + 3L \tag{4.12}$$

$$(2)$$

4.2.3. The Interchange Pathway

Concerted or interchange pathways, designated by I_d or I_a, are distinguished from the previously discussed (D and A) mechanisms by "the absence of an intermediate in which the primary coordination number of the metal is modified."[14] The I_d designation applies to processes where the transition state involves only a weak bonding to both the incoming and leaving ligands, whereas in I_a processes the transition state entails substantial bonding of both the incoming and leaving ligands. Hence, I_d processes have $\Delta H^{\neq}$ values resembling D processes, and I_a processes have $\Delta H^{\neq}$ values similar to A processes.

The proposed mechanism for an interchange ligand substitution that proceeds to completion is provided by equations (4.13–4.15). The rate-constant expressions, equations (4.16 and 4.17) are:

$$M_nL_mA + B \overset{K_1}{\rightleftharpoons} M_nL_mA \cdot B \text{ (rapid)} \qquad (4.13)$$

$$M_nL_mA \cdot B \xrightarrow{k_2} M_nL_mB \cdot A \qquad (4.14)$$

$$M_nL_mB \cdot A \xrightarrow{\text{fast}} M_nL_mB + A \qquad (4.15)$$

$$k_{obs} = \frac{k_2 K_1[B]}{1 + K_1[B]} \qquad (4.16)$$

$$1/k_{obs} = 1/k_2 + 1/k_2 K_1[B] \qquad (4.17)$$

Recent examples from the literature serve to illustrate the interchange mechanism. Basolo and co-workers[31] have reported upon the kinetics and mechanism of CO substitution reactions of $M_3(CO)_{12}$ (M = Fe, Ru, Os) in the presence of trimethylamine N-oxide, equation (4.18). The rate of reaction (4.18) was too fast in aprotic solvents to be measured by conventional techniques. However, in protic solvents such as ethanol where Me_3NO is involved in hydrogen bonding, $Me_3NO \cdots HOC_2H_5$, the concentration of free Me_3NO is low and the reactions can be readily monitored.

$$M_3(CO)_{12} + Me_3NO + L \rightarrow M_3(CO)_{11}L + Me_3N + CO_2 \qquad (4.18)$$

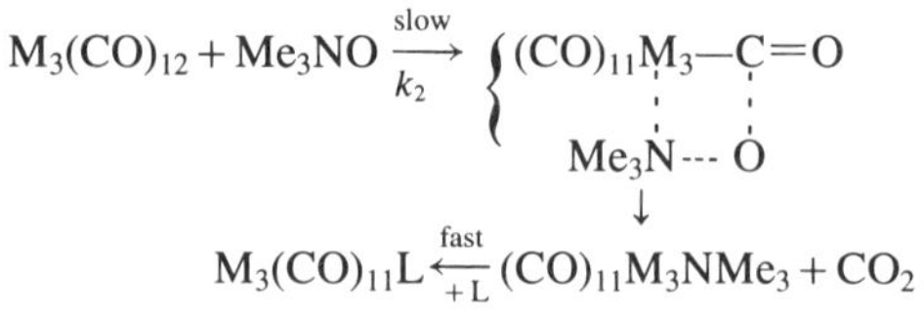

$$M_3(CO)_{12} + Me_3NO \xrightarrow[k_2]{slow} \left\{ \begin{array}{c} (CO)_{11}M_3-\overset{|}{\underset{|}{C}}{=}O \\ \\ Me_3N \cdots \overset{|}{O} \end{array} \right.$$

$$\downarrow$$

$$M_3(CO)_{11}L \underset{+L}{\overset{fast}{\longleftarrow}} (CO)_{11}M_3NMe_3 + CO_2$$

Scheme 4.3

The rates of formation of $M_3(CO)_{11}L$ were found to be first-order in $[M_3(CO)_{12}]$ and $[Me_3NO]$ but zero-order in the concentration of L. The suggested reaction pathway involves nucleophilic attack of Me_3NO on the C atom of a CO ligand (i.e., an outer-sphere interaction), resulting in oxidation of CO to CO_2 and the concomitant production of a reactive metal cluster species (Scheme 4.3). An intermediate which contains the labile trimethylamine ligand is indicated for consistency with the reaction of $Os_3(CO)_{10}(NO)_2$ with Mc_3NO, where the analogous $Os_3(CO)_9(NO)_2(NMe_3)$ species was isolated and characterized crystallographically.[32]

The second-order rate constants and activation parameters for these reactions are compiled in Table 4.3, where the order of reactivity, $Fe_3(CO)_{12} > Ru_3(CO)_{12} > Os_3(CO)_{12}$, is noted. Reactions involving nucleophilic attack at a carbon atom in metal carbonyls generally display an increase in reac-

Table 4.3 ▪ **Second-Order Rate Constants and Activation Parameters for Reactions (4.18)**

$M_3(CO)_{12}$	L	T, °C	k_2,[a] M^{-1} s^{-1}	$\Delta H^{\neq}$, kJ mol^{-1}	$\Delta S^{\neq}$, J mol^{-1}K^{-1}
$Fe_3(CO)_{12}$	PPh_3	5.6	0.854	52.26 ± 2.55	-58.37 ± 8.79
		13.1	1.53		
		17.3	2.02		
		25.6	4.18		
	$P(OPh)_3$	5.6	0.852	51.63 ± 2.30	-60.71 ± 7.95
		13.1	1.50		
		17.3	2.01		
		25.6	4.08		
	$AsPh_3$	5.6	0.805	57.91 ± 0.79	-38.41 ± 2.80
		13.1	1.63		
		17.3	2.27		
		25.2	4.62		
$Ru_3(CO)_{12}$	PPh_3	14.1	0.350	50.67 ± 0.67	-76.99 ± 2.26
		20.1	0.538		
		25.6	0.822		
		33.4	1.41		
$Os_3(CO)_{12}$	PPh_3	14.1	0.0307	71.46 ± 1.21	-24.77 ± 4.06
		20.2	0.0575		
		25.6	0.104		
		33.4	0.213		

[a] Solvent $CHCl_3-C_2H_5OH$ (v/v, 2:1).

tion rates with increasing values of ν_{CO} or F_{CO}, quantities which correlate well with the ground-state positive charge on carbon.[33] Because the relative reaction rates show exactly the opposite trend, it is necessary to consider factors that affect the stabilities of the transition states. Hence, the order of reactivity was ascribed to bridging CO groups which are more easily formed for iron and are better able to accommodate charge buildup in the transition state. A similar rate order and explanation was noted for the reaction of $M_3(CO)_{12}$ with MeO^- to afford $[M_3(CO)_{11}C(O)OMe^-]$.[34,35]

The kinetics of the reaction of $Ir_4(CO)_{12}$ with P-donor ligands to afford multisubstituted tetrairidium clusters have been shown to be first-order in the concentrations of both the metal cluster and the incoming phosphorus ligand.[36-37] The activation parameters derived for these processes resemble those commonly seen for associative processes, for example, for $L = P(OEt)_3$ $\Delta H^{\neq} = 76.1$ kJ/mol and $\Delta S^{\neq} = -41.8$ J/mol-K compared to $\Delta H^{\neq} = 134.3$ kJ/mol and $\Delta S^{\neq} = 26.8$ J/mol-K for dissociative CO substitution in $Ir_4(CO)_{12}$.[38] Indeed, this reaction has been described as an associative process, where interaction of an incoming P-donor ligand occurs at an iridium center. Because the metal centers are 18-electron moieties this interaction is achieved at the expense of weakening the bonding within the Ir_4 cluster framework by reducing the electrons involved in cluster bonding from 12 to 10. It is noteworthy that in several 18-electron mononuclear metal carbonyls, where an analogous process is obviously not possible, similar ligand-dependent pathways are observed and have been assigned to an interchange mechanism. For example, the activation parameters determined for CO substitution in $Cr(CO)_6$ by tri-n-butylphosphine for the dissociative pathway are $\Delta H_1^{\neq} = 168.2$ kJ/mol and $\Delta S^{\neq} = 94.6$ J/mol-K and for the ligand-dependent pathway $\Delta H_2^{\neq} = 106.7$ kJ/mol and $\Delta S_2^{\neq} = -61.1$ J/mol-K.[39]

Hence, as previously mentioned, the ligand-dependent term in the kinetic expression for ligand substitutional processes involving metal carbonyl clusters can be alternatively accounted for via an interchange mechanism, or more likely, by way of a pathway which entails metal-metal bond rupture. This latter mechanism is discussed in more detail in the following section.

4.2.4. Metal-Metal Bond Dissociation without Fragmentation

A possible mechanism for CO substitution reactions in metal carbonyl cluster derivatives involves metal-metal bond dissociation, either heterolytic or homolytic, to generate a polynuclear metal unit containing an unsaturated, 16-electron metal center. This is represented for the heterolytic fission in a trimetal cluster (3)[40] and for the homolytic fission in a tetranuclear cluster (4).[41]

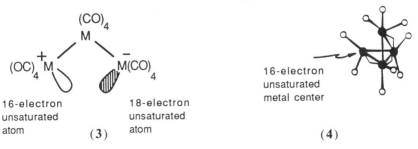

$(OC)_4\overset{+}{M}$　$(CO)_4$ M　$M(CO)_4^-$

16-electron unsaturated atom

(3)

18-electron unsaturated atom

16-electron unsaturated metal center

(4)

Johnson has proposed the heterolytic metal-metal bond fission mechanism to explain the kinetic behavior exhibited by the group 8 trinuclear clusters.[40] The pathways of relevance to ligand substitution at an intact cluster are depicted in equations (4.19)–(4.22). Fragmentation of $LM_3(CO)_{12}$ or $L_2M_3(CO)_{11}$ via equations (4.23) and (4.24) gives rise to the mononuclear species observed during these reactions. This scheme accounts for the observation that the $M_3(CO)_{12}$ and $M_3(CO)_9L_3$ derivatives, where there is little M—M bond polarity, resist substitution to a greater degree than $M_3(CO)_{11}L$ and $M_3(CO)_{10}L_2$ derivatives.

$$M_3(CO)_{12} \rightleftarrows (CO)_4\overset{O}{M}-M(CO)_4\text{-}\overset{\bullet}{M}(CO)_4 \qquad (4.19)$$

$$(3)$$

$$(3) + L \rightarrow L(CO)_4M-M(CO)_4\text{-}M(CO)_4 \xrightarrow{-CO} M_3(CO)_{11}L \qquad (4.20)$$

$$M_3(CO)_{11}L \rightleftarrows L(CO)_3M-M(CO)_4\text{-}M(CO)_4 \qquad (4.21)$$

$$(5)$$

$$(5) + L \rightarrow L(CO)_3M-M(CO)_4\text{-}M(CO)_4L \xrightarrow{-CO} M_3(CO)_{10}L_2 \qquad (4.22)$$

$$L(CO)_4M-M(CO)_4\text{-}M(CO)_4 \rightleftarrows M(CO)_4L + M_2(CO)_8 \qquad (4.23)$$

$$L_2(CO)_3M-M(CO)_4\text{-}M(CO)_4 \rightleftarrows M(CO)_3L_2 + M_2(CO)_8 \qquad (4.24)$$

$$M_2(CO)_8 + 2L \rightleftarrows 2M(CO)_4L \qquad (4.25)$$

Since L is, in general, more basic than CO, heterolytic bond fission of substituted derivatives would be expected to lead to intermediates where the substituted metal center is electronically unsaturated. For example, $M_3(CO)_{11}L$ would dissociate as is indicated in equation (4.26) as opposed to equation (4.27). It should nevertheless be remembered that the metal center of initial unsaturation need not be the metal center which has undergone substitution as revealed by the stereochemistry of the cluster product because of ligand migration.

$$M_3(CO)_{11}L \rightleftarrows L(CO)_3\underset{+}{\overset{O}{M}}-M(CO)_4\text{-}\underset{-}{\overset{\bullet}{M}}(CO)_4 \qquad (4.26)$$

$$M_3(CO)_{11}L \rightleftarrows L(CO)_3\underset{-}{\overset{\bullet}{M}}-M(CO)_4\text{-}\underset{+}{\overset{O}{M}}(CO)_4 \qquad (4.27)$$

Alternative intermediates to Johnson's $L(CO)_4M-M(CO)_4-M(CO)_4$ species[40] have been suggested. These as well involve a weakening of the metal cluster bonding which is offset by M—L bond formation. In these instances M—M bond rupture is homolytic in nature, for example, as in species (6) and (7). Species of these types are thought to be more likely than those resulting from heterolytic M—M bond rupture since the reactions are carried out in nonpolar solvents.

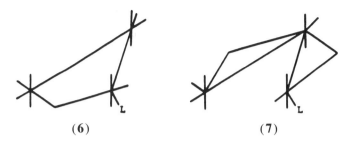

(6)   (7)

Similarly, ligand substitution reactions have been investigated which involve the closed tetrahedral clusters $[RPFe_3(CO)_{10-n}L_n]$ (R = alkyl, aryl; L = phosphite, isonitrile; $n = 0, 1, 2$) $[RPFe_3(CO)_{10-n}L_{n+1}]$ and $[RPFe_3(CO)_{10-n}L_{n+2}]$ in a stepwise manner.[15] Elimination of CO or L from these M—M bond-opened species results in ligand substitution in the closed tetrahedral derivatives as outlined in Scheme 4.4. The M—M bond-opened intermediate, where L and L' are trimethylphosphite, has been isolated and characterized by X-ray crystallography (8). Hence, ligand substitution occurs by an associative process encompassing a series of addition-elimination steps involving bond-opened intermediates.

(8)

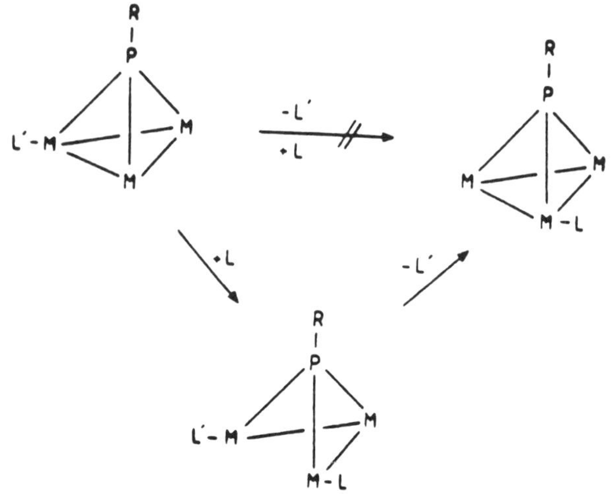

Scheme 4.4

4.2.5. Metal-Metal Dissociation with Fragmentation

Originally the reactions of $Ru_3(CO)_{12}$ with phosphine ligands were proposed to proceed via radical pathways in which the cluster underwent homolytic bond fission to produce $Ru(CO)_4$ diradicals. Species such as $Ru(CO)_4$ are known to undergo facile CO substitutional processes.[42] Radical recombination reactions would lead to the observed products: $Ru_3(CO)_{11}L$, $Ru_3(CO)_{10}L_2$, and $Ru_3(CO)_9L_3$.

Although it now appears that these processes proceed by way of the metal-metal bond rupture pathway as discussed in the previous section, concurrent reaction pathways for associative reactions of these metal carbonyl clusters often lead to fragmentation of the cluster. For example, the reaction of $Ru_3(CO)_{12}$ with $PnBu_3$ occurs almost exclusively by a ligand-dependent mechanism and the products at high $[PnBu_3]$ were found to be $Ru(CO)_4(PnBu_3)$ and $Ru(CO)_3(PnBu_3)_2$ in a mole ratio of 2:1.[43] It was concluded from these studies that $Ru_3(CO)_{11}(PnBu_3)$ was the initially formed product and that this species subsequently led to the formation of mononuclear derivatives. Kinetic studies showed that the fragmentation is induced by nucleophilic attack in the cluster and Poë has designated these types of pro-

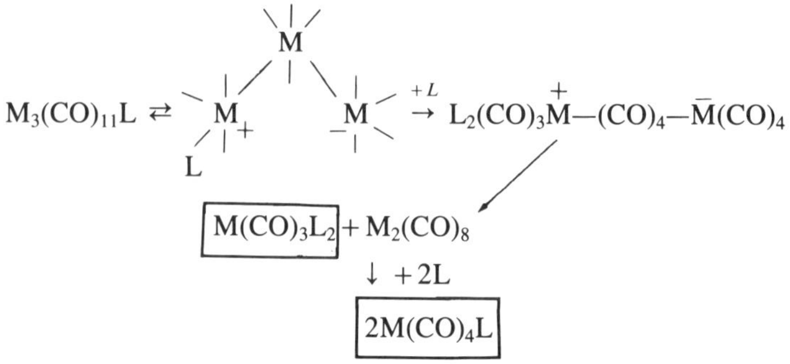

Scheme 4.5

cesses as F_N2 in nature, that is, bimolecular nucleophilic fragmentation.[16a] Similar observations were noted for the reaction of $Os_3(CO)_{11}(PnBu_3)$ with $PnBu_3$.[16b]

As alluded to in section 4.2.4, routes to the formation of the mononuclear species, $Ru(CO)_4L$ and $Ru(CO)_3L_2$, involve equations (4.24) and (4.25). This mechanism, which is reiterated in Scheme 4.5, readily accounts for the observed ratio of $Ru(CO)_3L_2/Ru(CO)_4L$ in the product mixture of 1:2.

4.3. Isotopic Labeling Investigations

The use of isotopic labels, either located in the metal framework or incorporated in the ligand polyhedron, in the investigation of ligand substitutional pathways in metal carbonyl clusters is vital to an understanding of these important reactions. In this section an attempt is made to: (a) describe methods for the preparation and characterization of isotopically labeled clusters, (b) define the uses of these species in the determination of the kinetic parameters for CO dissociation, and (c) ascertain the role of cluster fragmentation during ligand substitution reactions in a definitive manner employing isotopically labeled cluster derivatives.

4.3.1. Synthesis and Characterization of Isotopically Labeled Metal Carbonyl Clusters

The isotopic label in the carbonyl ligands in metal carbonyl clusters can reside at either the C or O center, that is, ^{13}C or ^{17}O and ^{18}O. Because carbonyl ligands in metal clusters are often not very labile, it is generally necessary to introduce a CO-labilization method or to synthesize the metal cluster from labeled carbon monoxide. This latter method could be extremely expensive since in general high pressures of CO are required in these synthetic procedures. Some of the available routes to isotopically labeled metal carbonyl clusters are listed in equations (4.28)–(4.32).

$$Co_4(CO)_{12} + {}^{13}CO \rightleftharpoons Co_4(CO)_{12-n}({}^{13}CO)_n + {}^{12}CO \qquad (4.28)^{41}$$

$$Mn_2(CO)_{12} + {}^{13}CO \overset{nBu_3PO}{\underset{\substack{or \\ Me_3NO}}{\rightleftharpoons}} Mn_2(CO)_{10-n}({}^{13}CO)_n + {}^{12}CO \qquad (4.29)^{44,45}$$

$$Os_3(CO)_{12} + {}^{13}CO \overset{Ph_2CO^-}{\rightleftharpoons} Os_3(CO)_{12-n}({}^{13}CO)_n + {}^{12}CO \qquad (4.30)^{46}$$

$$Ru_3(CO)_{12} + {}^{13}CO \overset{OMe^-}{\rightleftharpoons} Ru_3(CO)_{12-n}({}^{13}CO)_n + {}^{12}CO \qquad (4.31)^{24}$$

$$Na_3[IrCl_6] + NaI \overset{{}^{13}CO}{\underset{1\,bar}{\longrightarrow}} Na[Ir(CO)_2I_2] \overset{{}^{13}CO}{\underset{K_2CO_3}{\longrightarrow}} Ir_4({}^{13}CO)_{12} \qquad (4.32)^{47}$$

The most general method for monitoring the course of labeled carbon monoxide in ligand substitution reactions is by observing frequency shifts in the $\nu(CO)$ vibrational modes as a consequence of isotopically labeled CO being incorporated or lost in the substrate molecule. Similar shifts in the $\nu(CO)$ vibrational modes are observed upon either ^{13}CO or $C^{18}O$ substitution. The reliability of simplified restricted CO force field computations at deducing structural information has immeasurably aided in the utilization of this procedure.[48–50] Nevertheless, this spectroscopic technique is often not straightforward in its application due to difficulties associated with quantitatively assessing the various isotopically substituted species present. This is primarily due to the fact that in metal carbonyl clusters containing several CO ligands an array of species is possible in which the molecules possess electronically equivalent, but symmetry nonequivalent, CO ligands, hence giving rise to a large number of overlapping or degenerate infrared active bands.

Notwithstanding the previously mentioned shortcomings of the $\nu(CO)$ vibrational technique, it is possible to extract rapid information by this procedure on ligand substitutional processes of metal carbonyl clusters. Because of the sensitivity of this technique only small sample sizes are required. An example which serves to illustrate the usefulness of this procedure is described in detail in the following for the thermal CO-exchange reactions involving $Co_4(CO)_{12}$, equation (4.30).[41]

The infrared spectra in the $\nu(CO)$ bridging region for reaction (4.30) in hydrocarbon solvent are shown at various stages during the ligand substitution process in Figure 4.6. It is possible to focus attention exclusively on the bridging CO groups because calculations have revealed that the interaction force constants between terminal and bridging CO groups in the cobalt dodecacarbonyl species may be considered as being zero.[51] Since the carbonyl ligands are intramolecularly fluxional on the time scale of intermolecular CO ligand exchange, the bridging $\nu(CO)$ region will be indicative of progressive formation of three ^{13}CO-substituted cluster fragments in addition to the starting all-^{12}CO species (see Figure 4.7) regardless of any preferential CO dissociation which may be taking place. Spectral band assignments for the various species are provided in Table 4.4 and Figure 4.8, where

Table 4.4 ▪ Calculated and Observed CO Stretching Frequencies in the Bridging Region of $Co_4(CO)_{12}$[a]

| Molecule | $\nu(CO)$, cm^{-1} | | Symmetry | Symmetry Coordinate |
	Obs[b]	Calc[c]		
all-^{12}CO	1899.7	1900.3	A_1	$(1/3^{1/2})(r_1 + r_2 + r_3)$
	1867.0	1866.0	E	$(1/6^{1/2})(2r_2 - r_1 - r_3)$
		1866.0		$(1/2^{1/2})(r_3 - r_1)$
mono-^{13}CO	1891.5	1893.3	A'	$(1/2^{1/2})(r_2 + r_3)$
	1831.2	1831.2	A'	r_1
	1867.0	1866.0	A''	$(1/2^{1/2})(r_3 - r_2)$
di-^{13}CO	1882.9	1884.3	A'	r_3
	1840.5	1840.0	A'	$(1/2^{1/2})(r_1 + r_2)$
	1825.0	1824.4	A''	$(1/2^{1/2})(r_2 - r_1)$
all-^{13}CO		1858.0	A_1	$(1/3^{1/2})(r_1 + r_2 + r_3)$
	1825.0	1824.4	E	$(1/6^{1/2})(2r_2 - r_1 - r_3)$
		1824.4		$(1/2^{1/2})(r_3 - r_1)$

[a] Spectra were recorded in heptane solution. [b] The observed frequencies are accurate to ± 1.0 cm^{-1}. [c] The CO stretching force field arrived at in this computation was $F_{CO} = 14.23$ and $F_{CO,CO} = 0.17$ mdyn/Å. A similar value for F_{CO} (14.23 mdyn/Å) has been reported in ref. 51.

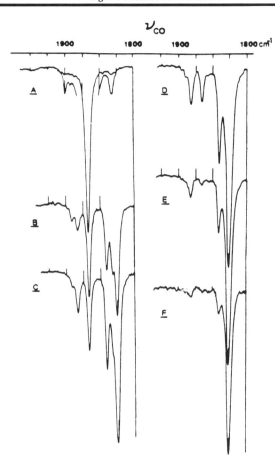

ν_{CO}

Figure 4.6 ▪ Time-dependent infrared spectra in the $\nu(CO)$ bridging region for the exchange reaction between $Co_4(CO)_9(\mu\text{-}CO)_3$ and ^{13}CO: A, initial spectrum (overlay at very high concentration); B, spectrum after 42 h; C, spectrum after 62 h; D, spectrum after 90 h; E, spectrum after 120 h; F, spectrum after 132 h.

a restricted force field involving only the bridging CO ligands was employed in the computation of $\nu(CO)$ positions.

On the other hand, examination of the terminal $\nu(CO)$ spectral region for the $[Co_4(CO)_9]$ molecular fragment during progressive ^{13}CO incorporation into the $Co_4(CO)_{12}$ cluster presents a much more complicated situation, that is, 80 different isotopic molecules are to be expected for the $Co_4(^{12}CO)_{9-n}(^{13}CO)_n$ $(n = 0\text{-}9)$ fragments. It is possible to generate the frequencies of all of the anticipated terminal $\nu(CO)$ vibrational modes afforded by systematic ^{12}CO substitution by ^{13}CO in a completely fluxional metal-cluster species using the restricted CO stretching force field defined by Bor et al.[51] These computations reveal, as expected, that many of the CO stretching vibrations in these isotopically related molecules are degenerate or are very close in frequency to one another, making it extremely difficult to

Figure 4.7 ▪ Possible isotopic species involving the bridging CO ligands in $Co_4(CO)_{12}$.

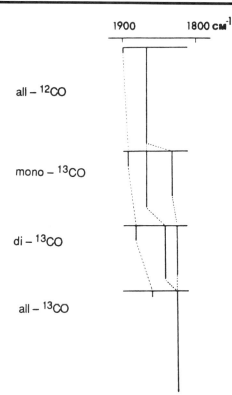

all – ^{12}CO

mono – ^{13}CO

di – ^{13}CO

all – ^{13}CO

Figure 4.8 ▪ Line drawings of the $\nu(CO)$ bridging region for the various ^{13}CO-substituted $Co_4(CO)_{12}$ species. The relative intensities are only approximate.

follow the kinetics of CO exchange via monitoring this region of the infrared spectrum.

It is important to verify that all the $\nu(CO)$ vibrational changes observed during CO ligand substitution reactions employing ^{13}CO as the incoming ligand are due to isotopic substitution into the cluster species. This was done in the case involving $Co_4(CO)_{12}$, where the once formed highly ^{13}CO-enriched $Co_4(CO)_{12}$ sample was subjected to the reverse reaction with ^{12}CO. As is evident in Figure 4.9, the $\nu(CO)$ bands reverted back to those assigned to the $Co_4(^{12}CO)_{12}$ species. Hence, the CO exchange is quite clean with no side reactions occurring.

4.3.2. Kinetic Parameters for CO Dissociation Derived from Isotopic Labeling Studies

As previously mentioned ligand substitution reactions of metal carbonyl clusters with the more basic ligands (L) commonly react according to the rate expression, equation (4.33), where the ligand-dependent pathway dominates, that is, $k_1 \ll k_2[L]$. This in turn often makes it difficult to extract information about CO dissociation processes. Because of the low nucleophilicity of the carbon monoxide ligand, CO substitution in metal clusters using isotopically labeled carbon monoxide (^{13}CO or $C^{18}O$) generally occurs via the k_1 term, that is, $k_1 \gg k_2[(CO)]$. This is particularly true for reactions carried out at moderate pressures of carbon

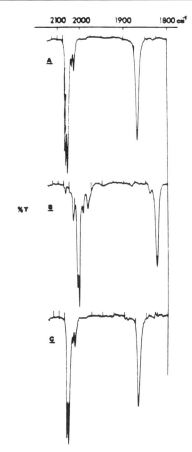

Figure 4.9 ■ Infrared spectra in the ν(CO) region during the exchange reaction of $Co_4(CO)_{12}$ and carbon monoxide: A, initial spectrum; B, spectrum after 168 h of reaction with ^{13}CO at 24.6°C; C, spectrum after ^{13}CO atmosphere in part B was removed and replaced by ^{12}CO for an additional 288 h at 24.6°C.

monoxide. It should be recalled that for thermodynamic reasons high pressures of CO often cause declusterification to occur, for example, reaction (4.34).[52,53] The reaction of $Co_4(CO)_{12}$ with CO to afford $Co_2(CO)_8$ at elevated pressures, between 5 and 120 bar, has been investigated in detail.[54]

$$rate = k_{obs}[M_n(CO)_m] = \{k_1 + k_2[L]\}[M_n(CO)_m] \tag{4.33}$$

$$Co_4(CO)_{12} + 4CO \rightarrow 2Co_2(CO)_8, \Delta H° = 213 \text{ kJ} \tag{4.34}$$

For example, the incoming ligand-independent term, k_1, for the reaction described in equation (4.35) has been measured via the ^{13}CO exchange procedure.[55] Because the reactions are carried out in a large excess of labeled carbon monoxide the reverse reaction is negligible. Figure 4.10 contains a representative plot of rate data obtained by the ^{13}CO exchange technique, whereas Table 4.5 depicts comparative rate constants and activation parameters for CO dissociation in $Co_4(CO)_{11}L$ species. As is evident in Table 4.5 for L groups of similar steric requirements, as

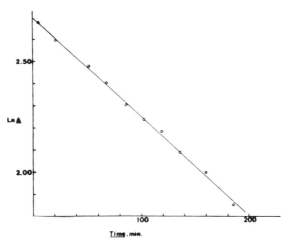

Figure 4.10 ▪ First-order rate plot for the disappearance of substrate for the reaction of $Co_4(CO)_{11}P(OEt)_3$ with ^{13}CO in heptane at $40°C$. $k_{obs} = 7.49 \times 10^{-5}$ s^{-1}, which when multiplied by 9 and divided by 2 affords $k = 3.37 \times 10^{-4}$ s^{-1}.

determined by their cone angles,[56] the rate constants are fairly independent of the nature of the ligand L. On the other hand for the sterically more demanding PEt$_3$ ligand a significant acceleration in the rate of CO loss was noted.

$$Co_4(CO)_{11}L + n^{13}CO \rightleftarrows Co_4(CO)_{11-n}(^{13}CO)_nL + n^{12}CO \quad (4.35)$$

where L = CO or phosphorus donor ligand

    The observed first-order rate constants were interpreted in light of the fact that the reactions were monitored in the $\nu(CO)$ region (vide infra) by a decrease in the all-^{12}CO species. Hence because intramolecular CO rearrangement is fast relative to dissociative CO loss incorporation of ^{13}CO at the eight (L = phosphorus donor ligand) terminal CO positions goes unnoticed, i.e., the k_{obs} must be multiplied by the factor 9, since there are nine positions which among the single incoming ^{13}CO

Table 4.5 ▪ Comparative Rate and Activation Parameters for Carbon Monoxide Displacement in $Co_4(CO)_{11}L$

L	Cone angle,[a] deg	10^4k, s^{-1}[b]	ΔH^c, kJ mol^{-1}	ΔS^c, J mol^{-1}K^{-1}
P(OMe)$_3$	107	2.03 (1.00)	112.1 ± 4.2	34.3 ± 14.6
CO	~95	3.27 (1.61)	104.2 ± 7.9	12.1 ± 24.7
P(OEt)$_3$	109	3.37 (1.66)	115.1 ± 13.8	46.0 ± 42.7
PEt$_3$	132	15.6 (7.68)	d	d

[a] From ref. 56. [b] Relative rate data are listed in parentheses. Reactions were carried out at $40.0°C$. [c] Error limits for activation parameters represent 95% confidence limits. [d] These parameters were not measured in this instance.

ligand may distribute itself. The k_{obs} values were further divided by 2 since it is assumed that there is selective dissociation of one of the two axial CO groups. The k_{obs} for the dissociative CO loss in the $Co_4(CO)_{12}$ parent species must be multiplied by 10 and divided by 3 for similar reasons. Obviously when comparing kinetic parameters involving CO loss in metal carbonyl clusters careful attention must be paid to the assumptions made in converting the measured rate constants (k_{obs}) to a specific rate constant (k).

4.3.3. Assessment of the Importance of Cluster Fragmentation from Isotopic Labeling Studies. Crossover Experiments

In very elegant experiments designed to definitively distinguish between reversible dissociation of carbon monoxide (Scheme 4.6) and metal-metal bond homolysis (Scheme 4.7) mechanisms of substitution reactions of the group 7 metal carbonyl dimers, Muetterties and co-workers[57,58] have synthesized and investigated reactions of the isotopically labeled species $^{185}Re_2(CO)_{10}/^{187}Re_2(CO)_{10}$ and $Mn_2(^{13}CO)_{10}/Mn_2(^{12}CO)_{10}$. In the presence of an excess of incoming ligand (L), both mechanisms lead to rate expressions which are first-order in metal carbonyl dimer and independent of the incoming ligand concentration. Hence, as is quite common in mechanistic studies, it is not possible to discriminate between these two reaction pathways via their rate laws alone. When the reactions defined in equations (4.36) and (4.37) were carried out for an extended period of time ($\sim$14 half-lives) at 150°C no crossover products, for example, $^{185}Re^{187}Re(CO)_{10-n}(^{13}CO)_n$, were observed. Similarly, further substitution of $Re_2(CO)_9PPh_3$ with triphenylphosphine to afford $Re_2(CO)_8[PPh_3]_2$ proceeded without detection of mononuclear rhenium carbonyl species. These observations strongly support a dissociation CO loss pathway (Scheme 4.6) for these processes.[57] However, upon photolysis of $^{185}Re_2(CO)_{10}/^{187}Re_2(CO)_{10}$ in the presence of PPh$_3$ complete crossover occurred.

$$M_2(CO)_{10} \rightleftharpoons [M_2(CO)_9] + CO$$

$$[M_2(CO)_9] + L \rightarrow M_2(CO)_9L$$

Scheme 4.6

$$M_2(CO)_{10} \rightleftharpoons 2[M(CO)_5]$$

$$[M(CO)_5] + L \rightarrow [M(CO)_4L] + CO$$

$$2[M(CO)_4L] \rightarrow M_2(CO)_8L_2$$

$$[M(CO)_5] + [M(CO)_4L] \rightarrow M_2(CO)_9L$$

Scheme 4.7

$$^{185}Re_2(CO)_{10}/^{187}Re_2(CO)_{10} + {}^{13}CO \rightarrow Re_2(CO)_{10-n}(^{13}CO)_n \qquad (4.36)$$

$$^{185}Re_2(CO)_{10}/^{187}Re_2(CO)_{10} + PPh_3 \rightarrow Re_2(CO)_9PPh_3 \qquad (4.37)$$

Analogous experiments performed employing the $Mn_2(CO)_{10}$ and $Mn_2(^{13}CO)_{10}$ clusters led to similar conclusions.[58] That is, thermal ligand substitution reactions involving $Mn_2(CO)_{10}$ occurred by $Mn-CO$ and not $Mn-Mn$ bond scission, whereas the photoinitiated ligand substitution reactions occurred with $Mn-Mn$ bond cleavage. This technique of using a completely ^{13}CO-labeled dimer for unambiguously distinguishing between $M-CO$ and $M-M$ bond dissociation during ligand substitution reactions has been suggested to be applicable generally to polynuclear metal carbonyl clusters. Indeed, it has been used to rule out declusterification processes in ligand substitution reactions of $Co_4(CO)_{12}$, equation (4.38) in experiments carried out with a mixture of $Co_4(CO)_{12}/Co_4(^{13}CO)_{12}$.[59]

$$Co_4(CO)_{12} + L \rightarrow Co_4(CO)_{11}L + CO \tag{4.38}$$

Despite the fact that the debate over either thermal $M-CO$ bond dissociation or $M-M$ homolytic bond dissociation in group 7 $M_2(CO)_{10}$ dimers has gone on for over a decade,[60-74] and has only been definitively decided in favor of CO dissociation by the crossover experiments involving metal or carbon isotopes described earlier,[57-58] it should not be inferred that all related processes proceed by way of this pathway. For example, reactions of a number of $Mn_2(CO)_8L_2$ derivatives with ligands (L) exhibit a strong dependence on the ligand L and deviate from first-order kinetics.[75] These substitution reactions are believed to proceed via metal-metal bond homolysis.

Isotopically metal-labeled derivatives of triruthenium dodecacarbonyl ($^{100}Ru_3(CO)_{12}$, $^{101}Ru_3(CO)_{12}$, and $^{104}Ru_3(CO)_{12}$) have been utilized in monitoring thermal and photochemical initiated intermolecular metal atom scrambling reactions.[76] The rate of metal scrambling in $^{101}Ru_3(CO)_{12}$ and $^{104}Ru_3(CO)_{12}$ was found by mass spectroscopy to be independent of the CO concentration and to be two orders of magnitude slower than CO exchange as assessed by the rate of ^{13}CO incorporation. Furthermore, metal atom scrambling reactions involving equimolar mixtures of $^{100}Ru_3(CO)_{12}$, $^{101}Ru_3(CO)_{12}$, and $^{104}Ru_3(CO)_{12}$ provided nonstatistical distributions of isotopomers, indicative of fragmentation reactions implicating long-lived dimeric intermediates. This latter observation is consistent with equation (4.23), with the exception of being CO-independent. On the contrary, photochemically initiated metal-scrambling reactions using the three isotopically labeled metal clusters showed no indication of dimeric intermediates.

4.4. Substitution Reactions Based on Cluster Nuclearity

In the concluding section to this overview of ligand substitution reactions involving polynuclear metal complexes a few of the major accounts will be highlighted that have unfolded during investigations of these processes, as well as directions currently being pursued. Both aspects of the subject will be discussed within the framework of trinuclear and tetranuclear metal derivatives.

4.4.1. Trinuclear Metal Clusters

In addition to previous examples, a noteworthy development involves ligand substitution reactions of mixed group 8 trimetal carbonyl clusters. The reader is re-

Table 4.6 ▪ Activation Parameters for CO Dissociation in Mixed-Metal Clusters

	$\Delta H^{\neq}$ (kJ mol^{-1})	$\Delta S^{\neq}$ (L mol^{-1}K^{-1})
$Fe_3(CO)_{12}$[a]	123.4	79.5
$Fe_2Ru_2(CO)_{12}$[b]	108.8	36.0
$Fe_2Ru(CO)_{12}$[c]	117.2	66.90
$Fe_2Os(CO)_{12}$[c]	113.0	29.3

[a] From ref. 78. [b] From ref. 79. [c] From ref. 80.

ferred to an excellent discussion of mixed-metal clusters which has appeared in the literature.[77]

Atwood and co-workers have recently examined the mixed-metal clusters $Fe_2Ru(CO)_{12}$, $FeRu_2(CO)_{12}$, and $Fe_2Os(CO)_{12}$.[78-80] The structures of $Fe_2M(CO)_{12}$ (M = Ru and Os) adopt the $Fe_3(CO)_{12}$ structure with the two iron centers possessing two bridging CO ligands, whereas $FeRu_2(CO)_{12}$ mimics the structure of $Ru_3(CO)_{12}$, which has all terminal CO ligands. For comparative purpose it should be recalled that the order of reactivity of the parent group 8 metal trimers, $M_3(CO)_{12}$, towards dissociative loss of carbon monoxide has been found to be Fe > Ru > Os, with the activation parameters determined for these processes listed in Table 4.2.

The reactions were observed to be first-order in metal cluster and exhibited little to no dependence on the concentration or nature of the entering ligand. These data, coupled with the activation parameters (Table 4.6), are consistent with a D or I_d mechanism. Substitution on $Fe_2M(CO)_{12}$ (M = Ru and Os) occurs initially at the M metal center, with subsequent substitution occurring at the iron center (e.g., see Figure 4.11). Similarly, $FeRu_2(CO)_{12}$ undergoes CO substitution preferentially at the ruthenium centers. As is evident in Table 4.6 the mixed-metal species which all contain at least one iron center have very similar activation enthalpies which compare well with that determined for the parent $Fe_3(CO)_{12}$ cluster. Furthermore, these $\Delta H^{\neq}$ are all significantly lower than the corresponding values in the $Ru_3(CO)_{12}$ and $Os_3(CO)_{12}$ analogs. It was concluded from these investigations that the site of CO dissociation was the iron center (see Scheme 4.8).

Similar conclusions have been arrived at from mixed-metal cluster reactions (hydrogenation and carbonylation) depicted in equation (4.39).[81-82] That is, the relative rates of hydrogenation of $HM_3(\mu\text{-COMe})(CO)_{10}$ to $H_3M_3(\mu\text{-COMe})(CO)_9$, which is ascribed to the relative rate of CO dissociation, are: $M_3 = Ru_3(4500) > Ru_2Os(1100) > RuOs_2(220) \gg Os_3(1)$. Likewise, the relative rates for carbonylation of $H_3M_3(\mu\text{-COMe})(CO)_9$ to $HM_3(\mu\text{-COMe})(CO)_{10}$ are: $M_3 = Ru_3(210) > Ru_2Os(72) > RuOs_2(38) \gg Os_3(1)$. The similarity in rates of decarbonylation and carbonylation for all the clusters which contain at least one ruthenium atom, coupled with the decrease in reactivity of the Os_3 cluster, has led to the suggestion that M—CO dissociation and reductive-elimination of dihydrogen occur from a ruthenium center.

$$HM_3(\mu\text{-COMe})(CO)_{10} + H_2 \rightleftharpoons H_3M_3(\mu\text{-COMe})(CO)_9 + CO \qquad (4.39)$$

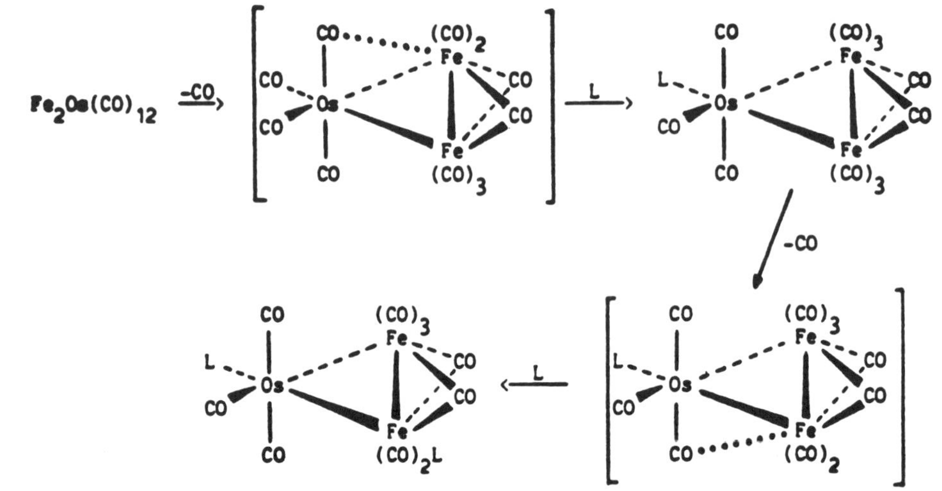

Scheme 4.8

4.4.2. Tetranuclear Metal Clusters

The early investigations by Karel and Norton[36] of ligand substitution reactions of $Ir_4(CO)_{12}$ with triphenylphosphine revealed a significant increase in the dissociative CO rate constant with an increase in the extent of phosphorus-ligand substitution. Equation (4.40) indicates the enormous differences in rate constants observed with progressive triphenylphosphine substitution. This result was interpreted as a cooperative effect, where substitution of CO by PPh_3 at one metal center served to enhance the rate of CO dissociation from an adjacent metal center. It should be noted that in this instance some of the rate increase may be attributed to a change in structure in going from the nonbridging $Ir_4(CO)_{12}$ to the bridging $Ir_4(CO)_{12-n}(PPh_3)_n$ systems.

$$Ir_4(CO)_{12} \xrightarrow{1} Ir_4(CO)_{11}(PPh_3) \xrightarrow{1320} Ir_4(CO)_{10}(PPh_3)_2 \xrightarrow{41800} Ir_4(CO)_9[PPh_3]_3$$

$$(4.40)$$

Since this pivotal study in ligand substitution reactions several, more thorough, investigations have been carried out for the reaction of $Ir_4(CO)_{12}$ with a series of phosphorus donor ligands of varying steric and electronic properties.[36,37,83] In general, further examinations of ligand substitutional processes involving the $Ir_4(CO)_{12}$ cluster have indicated that the extent of the enhancement of CO dissociation is dependent on both the steric requirements as well as electronic properties of the phosphorus donor ligands.

For example, the rate parameters for the dissociation of CO in $Ir_4(CO)_9(PR_3)_3$ species all exhibit CO labilization in proceeding from $Ir_4(CO)_{12}$ to $Ir_4(CO)_9(PR_3)_3$, with the relative order of CO labilization being $PPh_3(78400) >$ P-i-$Pr_3(45100) >$ $PEt_3(8870) >$ P-n-$Bu_3(8470) >$ $PMe_3(1150) > CO(1)$ (see Table 4.7).[83] As noted in Table 4.7 the rate acceleration attributed to phosphine sub-

Table 4.7 ▪ Rate Constants for CO Dissociation in
$Ir_4(CO)_9(PR_3)_3$ Derivatives in Tetrachloroethylene[a]

R	10^3k, s^{-1}	$t_{1/2}$, min	θ,[b] deg
Me	0.173	66.8	118
Et	1.33	8.69	132
n–Bu	1.27	9.06	132
i–Pr	6.76	1.71	160
Ph	7.84	1.47	145

[a] The reaction temperature was 80°C. [b] From C. A. Tolman, *Chem. Rev.,*
1977, **77**, 313.

stitution is attenuated as the spatial requirements for the substituted PR_3 ligands
are lessened, while simultaneously holding their basicities constant. This is best
illustrated for the trialkylphosphine series of ligands, where there is little variation
in ligand basicity and the ligand cone angles span a wide range from 118° to 160°.
A smaller electronic effect of the phosphorus ligand is superimposed on this steric
acceleration phenomenon as noted for the PPh_3 ligand.

Additional evidence for the importance of steric considerations in ligand
substitution reactions of Ir_4 clusters is reflected in the rate data for phosphine dissociation from the $Ir_4(CO)_8(PR_3)_4$ derivatives, equation (4.41). The
rate of Ir—PR_3 bond dissociation increased by a factor of 3300 in the series
$PMe_3 < PnBu_3 < PEt_3 < PPh_2Me$. The origin of the steric crowding is evident
in the solid-state structure determined for one of these species, $Ir_4(CO)_8(PMe_3)_4$,
where interligand repulsions between the two axial PMe_3 ligands is manifested in
a significantly elongated Ir—Ir bond, Figure 4.11.[84]

$$Ir_4(CO)_8(PR_3)_4 + CO \rightarrow Ir_4(CO)_9(PR_3)_3 + PR_3 \qquad (4.41)$$

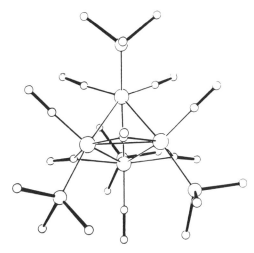

Figure 4.11 ▪ Solid-state structure of
$Ir_4(CO)_8(PMe_3)_4$ as determined in ref.
84.

$$R_3P—M—M—CO \xrightarrow{rds} \left\{ R_3P—M—M—CO \right\} \longrightarrow$$

$$R_3P—M—M—CO \xrightarrow{PR_3} R_3P—M—M—CO$$

Scheme 4.9

It is worth reiterating at this point the possibility that CO loss may be occurring at a phosphine-substituted metal center,[38,83] for example, analogous to the transition-state phenomenon of *cis* labilization seen in mononuclear metal carbonyl derivatives.[85] The skeletal sequence depicted in Scheme 4.9 could be operative, hence negating the necessity for an electronic cooperativity between metal centers.

The lack of a significant rate enhancement upon prior phosphorus ligand substitution in the Co_4 tetramers has also been reported based on quantitative kinetic measurements of CO dissociation. The relative order of reactivity for dissociative CO substitutional processes in $Co_4(CO)_{12}$ with progressive substitution by the small, good π-acceptor $P(OMe)_3$ ligand indicated in equation (4.42).[55] Furthermore, the $Co_4(CO)_7(tripod)(dppm)$ (tripod = $HC(PPh_2)_3$ and dppm = $H_2C(PPh_2)_2$) derivative, Figure 4.12,[86,87] has been observed to undergo stereoselective CO exchange of the apical carbon monoxide ligands via a dissociative pathway at a rate quite similar to that noted for CO dissociation in the parent species, $Co_4(CO)_9(tripod)$ and $Co_4(CO)_{12}$, equation (4.43). This cluster molecule represents the only reported example of a tetranuclear cluster carbonyl derivative where intermolecular CO exchange takes place at a rate faster than intramolecular CO rearrangement.

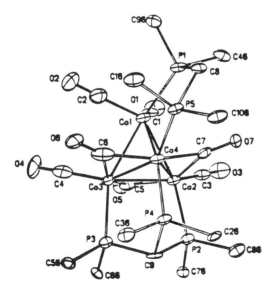

Figure 4.12 ▪ Molecular structure of $Co_4(CO)_7(tripod)(dppm)$. Only the ipso carbon atoms are shown for the six phenyl rings of the tripod and dppm ligands (ref. 87).

$$Co_4(CO)_{12} \xrightarrow{1.00} Co_4(CO)_{11}P(OMe)_3 \xrightarrow{0.62} Co_4(CO)_{10}[P(OMe)_3]_2$$

$$\xrightarrow{1.46} Co_4(CO)_9[P(OMe)_3]_3 \quad (4.42)$$

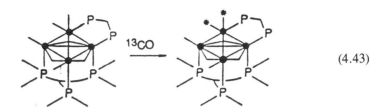

$$(4.43)$$

Similar to the reactivity of $Co_4(CO)_{12}$, the cobalt tetramer (**9**) has been observed to undergo sequential CO ligand substitution reactions with trimethylphosphite to afford mono, bis, tris, and tetrakis derivatives, where the phosphite ligands are bound to a separate cobalt center as demonstrated by X-ray crystallography.[88] Kinetic parameters are consistent with an I_a or A process for the mono- and bis- substitution, whereas the tris- and tetrakis- substitution occurs by way of a dissociative pathway. Analogous, less facile, reactions involving triphenylphosphine as the incoming ligand were observed. On the contrary, the radical anion $[Co_4(CO)_{10}(PPh_2)]^-$ was noted to be substitutionally quite labile, thus allowing for the selective synthesis of a variety of monosubstituted derivatives.[89] A dissociative mechanism was proposed for the electrocatalytic substitution process, Scheme 4.10, where E_i represents the electrode of chemical potential necessary to reduce a portion of the tetracobalt cluster to the anion radical.

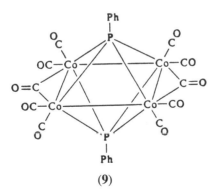

(**9**)

The radical-catalyzed ligand substitution reaction, initiated electrochemically or chemically, appears to be a general one for metal cluster species. For example, other ligand substitution processes which have been investigated include:[46,90,91]

$$M_3(CO)_{12}(M = Fe, Ru, Os) + nL \xrightarrow{Ph_2CO\cdot^-} M_3(CO)_{12-n}L_n + nCO \quad (4.44)$$

$$Fe_3(CO)_9(PPh_2)_2 + nL \rightarrow Fe_3(CO)_{9-n}(PPh_2)_2L_n + nCO \quad (4.45)$$

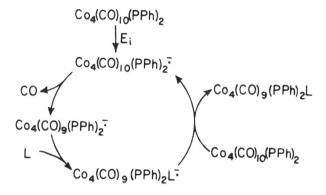

Scheme 4.10

4.4.3. Larger Clusters

Presently there are few mechanistic studies of ligand substitutional processes involving higher nuclearity metal clusters.[92,93] It should be evident from the preceding discussions that the complications introduced by even two metal centers makes interpretation of kinetic data difficult. Nevertheless it is anticipated that mechanistic investigations of these larger clusters will be forthcoming and will undoubtedly be quite challenging to elucidate.

References

1. (a) E. L. Muetterties, R. R. Burch, Jr. and A. M. Stolzenberg, *Ann. Rev. Phys. Chem.*, 1982, **33**, 89. (b) M. V. Twigg (Ed.), *Mechanisms of inorganic and organometallic reactions*, 1–5. New York: Plenum, 1983–1987. (c) J. D. Atwood, M. J. Wovkulich and D. C. Sonnenberger, *Acc. Chem. Res.*, 1983, **16**, 350. (d) A. J. Poë, *Metal clusters*, M. Moskovits (Ed.). New York: Wiley-Interscience, 1986, 53. (e) G. Lavigne and H. D. Kaesz, in *Metal clusters in catalysis*, B. C. Gates, L. Guczi and H. Knözinger (Eds.). Amsterdam: Elsevier, 1986, 43.
2. (a) F. Basolo, *Inorg. Chim. Acta*, 1981, **50**, 65. (b) R. J. Angelici, *Organomet. Chem. Rev.*, 1968, **3**, 173. (c) D. A. Brown, *Inorg. Chim. Acta Rev.*, 1967, **1**, 35. (d) H. Werner, *Angew. Chem. Int. Ed. Engl.*, 1968, **7**, 930. (e) G. R. Dobson, *Acc. Chem. Res.*, 1978, **9**, 300. (f) D. J. Darensbourg, *Adv. Organomet. Chem.*, 1982, **21**, 113. (g) J. A. S. Howell and P. M. Burkinshaw, *Chem. Rev.*, 1983, **83**, 557.
3. J. L. Graff and M. S. Wrighton, *J. Am. Chem. Soc.*, 1980, **102**, 2123.
4. Y. Doi, K. Koshizuka and T. Keii, *Inorg. Chem.*, 1982, **21**, 2732.
5. Y. Doi, S. Tamura and K. Koshizuka, *Inorg. Chim. Acta*, 1982, **65**, L63.
6. Y. Doi, S. Tamura and K. Koshizuka, *J. Mol. Catal.*, 1983, **19**, 213.
7. P. M. Lausarot, G. A. Vaglio and M. Valle, *Inorg. Chim. Acta*, 1977, **25**, L107.
8. P. M. Lausarot, G. A. Vaglio and M. Valle, *Inorg. Chim. Acta*, 1979, **36**, 213.
9. T. P. Dang, J. C. Poulin and H. B. Kagan, *J. Organomet. Chem.*, 1975, **91**, 105.
10. (a) B. F. G. Johnson and R. E. Benfield, in *Transition metal clusters*, B. F. G. Johnson (Ed.). New York: Wiley, 1980, 471. (b) E. Band and E. L. Muetterties, *Chem. Rev.*, 1978, 639.
11. D. J. Darensbourg and M. J. Incorvia, *Inorg. Chem.*, 1981, **20**, 1911.

12. W. G. Jackson, *Inorg. Chem.*, 1987, **26**, 3004 and references therein.
13. A. M. Baro and H. Ibach, *J. Chem. Phys.*, 1979, **71**, 4812.
14. C. H. Langford and H. B. Gray, in *Ligand substitution processes*. New York: Benjamin, 1965.
15. K. Knoll, G. Huttner, L. Zsolnai, I. Jibril and M. Wasincionek, *J. Organomet. Chem.*, 1985, **294**, 91.
16. (a) N. Brodie, A. J. Poë and V. Sekhar, *J. Chem. Soc. Chem. Commun.*, 1985, 1090. (b) A. J. Poë and V. C. Sekhar, *Inorg. Chem.*, 1985, **24**, 4376.
17. K. Dahlinger, A. J. Poë, P. K. Sayal and V. C. Sekhar, *J. Chem. Soc. Dalton Trans.*, 1986, 2145.
18. P. A. Dawson, B. F. G. Johnson, J. Lewis, J. Puga, P. R. Raithby and M. J. Rosales, *J. Chem. Soc. Dalton Trans.*, 1982, 233.
19. A. J. Poe and M. V. Twigg, *J. Chem. Soc. Dalton Trans.*, 1974, 1860.
20. D. J. Taube and P. C. Ford, *Organometallics*, 1986, **5**, 99.
21. M. Anstock, D. J. Taube, D. C. Gross and P. C. Ford, *J. Am. Chem. Soc.*, 1981, **106**, 3696.
22. D. E. Morris and F. Basolo, *J. Am. Chem. Soc.*, 1968, **90**, 2536.
23. T. L. Brown and P. A. Bellus, *Inorg. Chem.*, 1978, **17**, 3726.
24. D. J. Darensbourg, R. L. Gray and M. Pala, *Organometallics*, 1984, **3**, 1928.
25. G. Lavigne and H. D. Kaesz, *J. Am. Chem. Soc.*, 1984, **106**, 4647.
26. D. J. Taube, R. van Eldik and P. C. Ford, *Organometallics*, 1987, **6**, 125.
27. F. Basolo, *Inorg. Chim. Acta*, 1981, **50**, 65.
28. J. P. Candlin and A. C. Shortland, *J. Organomet. Chem.*, 1969, **16**, 289.
29. K. J. Karel and J. R. Norton, *J. Am. Chem. Soc.*, 1974, **96**, 6812.
30. C. S. Browning, D. H. Farrar, R. R. Gukathasan and S. A. Morris, *Organometallics*, 1985, **4**, 1750.
31. J.-K. Shen, Y.-L. Shi, Y.-C. Gao, Q.-Z. Shi and F. Basolo, *J. Am. Chem. Soc.*, 1988, **110**, 2414.
32. B. F. G. Johnson, J. Lewis, P. P. Raithby and C. Zuccaro, *J. Chem. Soc. Chem. Commun.*, 1979, 916.
33. D. J. Darensbourg and M. Y. Darensbourg, *Inorg. Chem.*, 1970, **9**, 1691.
34. D. C. Gross and P. C. Ford, *J. Am. Chem. Soc.*, 1985, **107**, 585.
35. R. J. Trautman, D. C. Gross and P. C. Ford, *J. Am. Chem. Soc.*, 1985, **107**, 2355.
36. K. J. Karel and J. R. Norton, *J. Am. Chem. Soc.*, 1974, **96**, 6812.
37. K. Dahlinger, F. Falcone and A. J. Poe, *Inorg. Chem.*, 1986, **25**, 2654.
38. D. C. Sonnenberger and J. D. Atwood, *J. Am. Chem. Soc.*, 1982, **104**, 2113.
39. J. R. Graham and R. J. Angelici, *Inorg. Chem.*, 1967, **6**, 2082.
40. B. F. G. Johnson, *Inorg. Chim. Acta*, 1986, **115**, L39.
41. D. J. Darensbourg and M. J. Incorvia, *Inorg. Chem.*, 1980, **19**, 2585.
42. For a recent compilation of references on this subject in general see M. J. Therien and W. C. Trogler, *J. Am. Chem. Soc.*, 1988, **110**, 4942.
43. A. J. Poe and M. V. Twigg, *Inorg. Chem.*, 1974, **13**, 2982.
44. (a) D. J. Darensbourg, N. Walker and M. Y. Darensbourg, *J. Am. Chem. Soc.*, 1980, **102**, 1213. (b) D. J. Darensbourg, M. Y. Darensbourg and N. Walker, *Inorg. Chem.*, 1981, **20**, 1918.
45. U. Koelle, *J. Organomet. Chem.*, 1977, **133**, 53.
46. M. I. Bruce, D. C. Kehoe, J. G. Matisons, B. K. Nicholson, P. H. Rieger and M. L. Williams, *J. Chem. Soc. Chem. Commun.*, 1982, 442.
47. L. Malatesta, G. Caglio and M. Angoletta, *Inorg. Synth.*, 1974, **13**, 95.
48. F. A. Cotton and C. S. Kraihanzel, *J. Am. Chem. Soc.*, 1964, **84**, 4432.
49. R. N. Perutz and J. J. Turner, *Inorg. Chem.*, 1975, **14**, 262.
50. D. J. Darensbourg, H. H. Nelson III and M. A. Murphy, *J. Am. Chem. Soc.*, 1977, **99**, 896.
51. G. Bor, G. Sbrignadello and K. Noack, *Helv. Chim. Acta*, 1975, **58**, 815.

52. J. A. Connor, H. A. Skinner and Y. Virmani, *Faraday Symp. Chem. Soc.*, 1974, **8**, 18.
53. P. J. Gardner, A. Cartner, R. Cunninghame and B. H. Robinson, *J. Chem. Soc. Dalton*, 1975, 2582.
54. G. Bor, U. K. Dietler, P. Pino and A. J. Poë, *J. Organomet. Chem.*, 1978, **154**, 301.
55. D. J. Darensbourg, B. S. Peterson and R. E. Schmidt, Jr., *Organometallics*, 1982, **1**, 306.
56. C. A. Tolman, *Chem. Rev.*, 1977, **77**, 313.
57. A. M. Stolzenberg and E. L. Muetterties, *J. Am. Chem. Soc.*, 1983, **105**, 822.
58. N. J. Coville, A. M. Stolzenberg and E. L. Muetterties, *J. Am. Chem. Soc.*, 1983, **105**, 2499.
59. D. J. Darensbourg and D. J. Zalewski, *Inorg. Chem.*, 1984, **23**, 4382.
60. H. Wawarsik and F. Basolo, *Inorg. Chim. Acta*, 1968, **3**, 113.
61. L. I. B. Haines, P. Hopgood and A. J. Poë, *J. Chem. Soc. A*, 1968, 421.
62. L. I. B. Haines and A. J. Poë, *J. Chem. Soc. A*, 1969, 2826.
63. J. P. Fawcett, A. J. Poë and K. R. Sharma, *J. Am. Chem. Soc.*, 1976, **98**, 1401.
64. J. P. Fawcett and A. J. Poë, *J. Chem. Soc. Dalton Trans.*, 1976, 2039.
65. D. G. DeWit, J. P. Fawcett and A. J. Poë, *J. Chem. Soc. Dalton Trans.*, 1976, 528.
66. J. P. Fawcett and A. J. Poë, *J. Chem. Soc. Dalton Trans.*, 1977, 1302.
67. D. M. Cowdhury, A. J. Poë and K. R. Sharma, *J. Chem. Soc. Dalton Trans.*, 1977, 2352.
68. J. P. Fawcett, R. A. Jackson and A. J. Poë, *J. Chem. Soc. Dalton Trans.*, 1978, 789.
69. J. P. Fawcett, A. J. Poë and K. R. Sharma, *J. Chem. Soc. Dalton Trans.*, 1979, 1886.
70. D. Sonnenberger and J. D. Atwood, *J. Am. Chem. Soc.*, 1980, **102**, 3484.
71. A. J. Poë, *Inorg. Chem.*, 1981, **20**, 4029.
72. J. D. Atwood, *Inorg. Chem.*, 1981, **20**, 4031.
73. A. J. Poe, *Inorg. Chem.*, 1981, **20**, 4032.
74. S. P. Schmidt, W. C. Trogler and F. Basolo, *Inorg. Chem.*, 1982, **21**, 1698.
75. A. J. Poe, *Chem. Brit.*, 1983, **19**, 997.
76. D. M. Heinekey and E. L. Muetterties, unpublished observations.
77. D. A. Roberts and G. L. Geoffroy, *Comprehensive Organometallic Chemistry*, G. Wilkinson, F. G. A. Stone and E. W. Abel (Eds.). Oxford: Pergamon, 1982, Ch. 40.
78. A. Shojaie and J. D. Atwood, *Organometallics*, 1985, **4**, 187.
79. R. Shojaie and J. D. Atwood, *Inorg. Chem.*, 1987, **26**, 2199.
80. R. Shojaie and J. D. Atwood, *Inorg. Chem.*, 1988, **27**, 2558.
81. L. M. Bavaro, P. Montangero and J. B. Keister, *J. Am. Chem. Soc.*, 1983, **105**, 4977.
82. J. B. Keister and C. C. O. Onyeso, *Organometallics*, 1988, **7**, 2364.
83. D. J. Darensbourg and B. J. Baldwin-Zuschke, *J. Am. Chem. Soc.*, 1982, **104**, 3906.
84. D. J. Darensbourg and B. J. Baldwin-Zuschke, *Inorg. Chem.*, 1981, **20**, 3846.
85. D. L. Lichtenberger and T. L. Brown, *J. Am. Chem. Soc.*, 1978, **100**, 366 and other contributions to this series.
86. D. J. Darensbourg and D. J. Zalewski, *Organometallics*, 1985, **4**, 92.
87. D. J. Darensbourg, D. J. Zalewski, A. L. Rheingold and R. L. Durney, *Inorg. Chem.*, 1986, **25**, 3281.
88. M. G. Richmond and J. K. Kochi, *Inorg. Chem.*, 1986, **25**, 1334.
89. M. G. Richmond and J. K. Kochi, *Inorg. Chem.*, 1986, **25**, 656.
90. H. H. Ohst and J. K. Kochi, *Inorg. Chem.*, 1986, **25**, 2066.
91. H. H. Ohst and J. K. Kochi, *J. Am. Chem. Soc.*, 1986, **108**, 2897.
92. K. Nomiya and H. Suzuki, *J. Organomet. Chem.*, 1979, **168**, 115.
93. G. R. John, B. F. G. Johnson, J. Lewis and A. L. Mann, *J. Organomet. Chem.* 1979, **171**, C9.

Cluster-Assisted Ligand Transformations

Guy Lavigne

5.1. Introduction

Dramatic progress has been made during the past decade in studies of the reactivity of metal cluster complexes as evidenced by numerous review articles,
both general[1-10] and specific,[11-28] and by modern textbooks[29a] and treatises on
organometallic chemistry.[29b,c]

A selected survey is presented in this chapter to show how organic ligands
have been tailored on the faces or edges of metal carbonyl cluster complexes,
paying particular attention to some recent results which offer novel opportunities
for organic synthesis and catalysis.

5.1.1. Early Thermally Activated Reactions

Historically, and logically, cluster reactions were first examined under thermal
activation in the range of 80–100°C or higher. Quite a complex mixture of products
was obtained in many of these, not amenable to interpretation in terms of reaction
mechanisms. An additional complicating factor arises from the fact that metal-to-
metal and metal-to-ligand bond enthalpies can be of comparable magnitude (see
Chapter 2), leading to cluster fragmentation. More recently, the means to carry
out reactions under mild conditions have led to a greater degree of selectivity in
the reaction products.

5.1.2. Achieving Greater Selectivity

As is illustrated in the following, greater selectivity is achieved under a variety of
conditions for carbonyl cluster complexes (a) that are electronically unsaturated,
or (b) that have been chemically modified to contain good leaving groups (lightly

stabilized), or (c) that contain bridging groups which can vary in their hapticity (lightly ligand-bridged), or conversely (d) that contain strong bridging groups and labile metal-metal interactions,[27] or finally (e) and (f), whose reactions are promoted by external chemical reagents, either electrophilic or nucleophilic. By the use of such methods as well as more general procedures like photochemical activation or electronic activation,[26] investigators have been able to trace the stepwise transformations of a wide variety of organic or inorganic molecules,[1-28] observing elementary reaction steps on polynuclear ensembles, possibly serving as models for surface reactions.[30] Thus far, these have been achieved principally on low-nuclearity cluster complexes, though there is presently a growing interest in studies of the reactivity of high-nuclearity species.[24]

5.1.3. Stabilization of Molecular Fragments vs. Observation of Complete Catalytic Cycles

In many cases, an organic or inorganic fragment having no significant lifetime in the free state may be stabilized by interaction with several metal centers. The resulting complexes are of interest in model studies of the activation of small molecules.[30] A more extreme form of fragment stabilization is represented by the partial or total "encapsulation" of nontransition metal atoms such as carbon,[13,31] nitrogen,[18] sulfur,[20] and other main group elements.[11,16,23] In these complexes, the caged element is an integral part of the cluster core and the hetero-atom no longer participates in catalytic cycles occurring at the surface of the complex (unless a partial degradation of the metal framework is carried out to expose the hetero-atom).[13] Instead, it may serve as a stabilizing agent for the polynuclear architecture.[23]

To connect the chemistry of clusters to organic synthesis or catalysis,[32] one must find the means to achieve the elimination of the modified substrate. The problem is illustrated in the stepwise reduction of nitriles on the face of a tri-iron cluster, Scheme 5.1.[33,34]

The formation of a stable nitrene complex proved to be a "dead end" in the cycle, preventing closure with a reductive elimination of amine (the hypothetical missing step is shown in brackets in Scheme 5.1). Similar cycles on analogous cluster complexes of osmium[35] or ruthenium[36] came to a halt at the same critical step.

5.1.4. On the Way to "Ideal" Cluster Systems

For a cluster complex to achieve a complete catalytic cycle while itself remaining intact, a number of requirements must be fulfilled which seldom go together:

1) The metal atom polyhedron has to be sufficiently stable; it may be stabilized either with appropriate ancillary ligands acting as nonfluxional building blocks,[20,23,27] or by grafting the metal cluster on a variety of supports.[37] In many cases, yet, the efficiency of the supporting ligand is questioned.

2) The cluster complex must possess substitutional lability to allow reaction with a given substrate.

3) Irreversible accumulation of stable thermodynamic products must be avoided by suitably mild reaction conditions still permitting the transformation of the coordinated substrate.

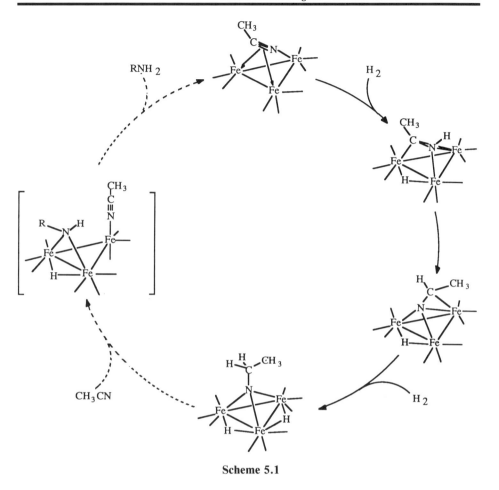

Scheme 5.1

4) An appropriate electronic polarity that is achieved in heterometallic clusters[32h] may be necessary to orient the substrate transformation in a given direction.[38] For example, $Ru_3(\mu_3\text{-}S)(CO)_9(\mu_3\text{-}CO)$ reacts with alkynes to yield a stable complex; by contrast, an appropriate metal atom substitution within this species gives the heterometallic derivative $RuMo_2(C_5H_5)_2(\mu_3\text{-}S)(CO)_7$ which becomes active toward alkyne oligomerization (see Section 5.7 of this chapter for details).[39]

5) Efficient means to selectively labilize the metal-ligand bonds of the modified substrate as opposed to those of the supporting ligands must be found.

Though there is a long way to design "ideal" cluster systems for organic synthesis, we now see a growing number of favorable cases where complete sequences of cluster-assisted ligand transformations can be carried out, at least on a laboratory scale.

The attractive possibilities offered by activated cluster complexes for selective transformations of a variety of organic substrates are first illustrated by representative examples given in Section 5.2. More specific transformations of such organic substrates on polynuclear ensembles are examined later according to a classification by ligand types.

5.2. Recent Advances in the Chemistry of Activated Cluster Complexes

5.2.1. Photochemical Activation

Control of photosubstitution and photofragmentation processes for $M_3(CO)_{12}$. Recently, significant progress has been made in the elucidation of the factors which govern photofragmentation or photosubstitution processes for $Ru_3(CO)_{12}$ (1)[40,41] and $Os_3(CO)_{12}$ (2);[42,43] kinetic evidence has been obtained for intermediates which have not as yet been spectroscopically characterized.

For $Ru_3(CO)_{12}$ (1), there are two distinct processes as shown in Scheme 5.2.

The first involves electronic excitation at low wavelength and in the presence of CO or phosphines. This leads to photofragmentation as the only observable photoprocess, which is believed to occur from a low energy state, ES_1; in the presence of CO and a radical trap (CCl_4), $Ru(CO)_5$ is the primary photoproduct. This process is wavelength independent, and is believed to involve a nonradical isomeric form of (1), $\{Ru_3(CO)_{12}\}^*$, (1*).

This intermediate is electronically unsaturated and may either return to starting material or react nonselectively with electron donor ligands to give $Ru_3(CO)_{12}L$; only fragmentation products are obtained from the latter. By contrast, the path to photosubstitution is wavelength dependent and proceeds by CO dissociation from a higher energy state ES_2 involving "$Ru_3(CO)_{11}$" which reacts selectively with

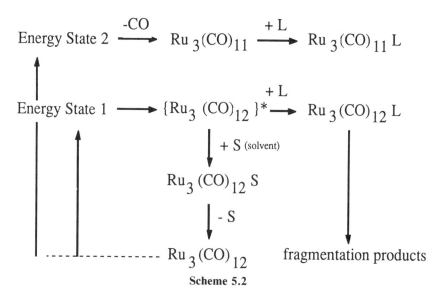

Scheme 5.2

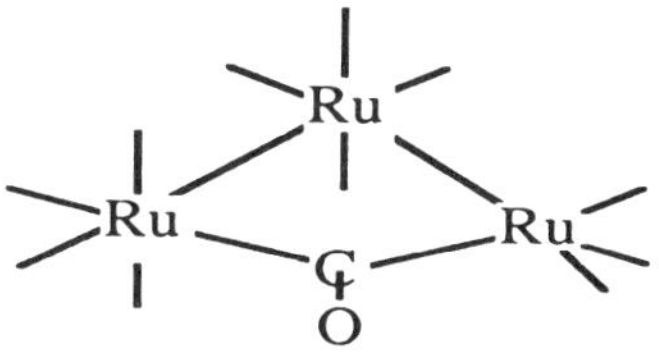

$$\{Ru_3(CO)_{12}\}^*$$
$$(1^*)$$

substrates to give substituted derivatives.[40] The osmium system bears close similarities, though only the low energy state has been reached by 436 nm irradiation; it differs in that the excited complex $\{Os_3(CO)_{12}\}^*$ may be a source of substitution or fragmentation products, depending on the nature of the ligand; in this respect, it is noteworthy that olefins can cause cluster degradation, while CO, PPh$_3$, P(OEt)$_3$, or even P(n-Bu)$_3$ do not.[42]

Selective photogeneration of "M$_3$(CO)$_{11}$" (M = Fe, Ru, Os) has led to a variety of mono-substituted complexes M$_3$(CO)$_{11}$L ((**3**), L = N$_2$; (**4**), L = C$_2$H$_4$; (**5**), L = 2-MeTHF) that cannot be obtained through other routes.[41,43]

Ligand transformations via photochemistry. Photochemical activation may also lead to ligand transformations, as exemplified by the conversion of a coordinated methylidyne group in Ru$_3$(μ-H)(μ-COCH$_3$)(CO)$_{10}$ (**6**) into an acyl group in Ru$_3$(μ-H)(μ-C(O)CH$_3$)(CO)$_{10}$ (**7**), Scheme 5.3.[44] The migration of a methyl group from oxygen to carbon is unprecedented. Though there is no gain of CO in the overall reaction, the dependence of quantum yields on CO concentration indicates association with CO at an intermediate step. Long-term photolysis leads to cluster fragmentation to Ru(CO)$_5$ and formation of acetaldehyde.

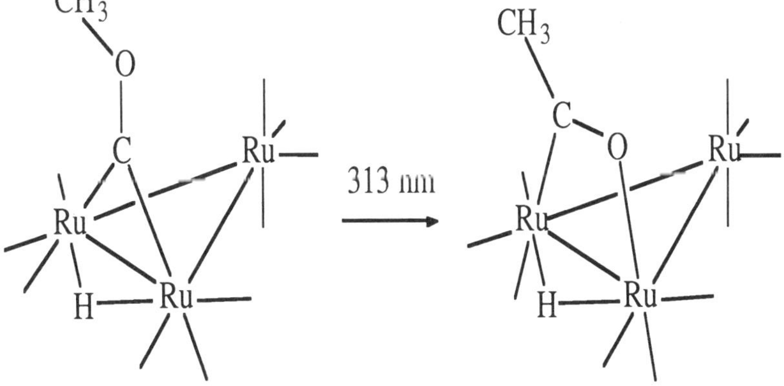

Scheme 5.3

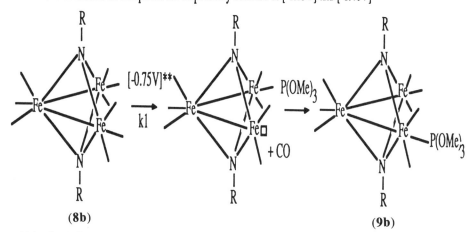

(8a)   (9a)

* di- and tri-substituted complexes are respectively obtained at [-1.15V] and [-1.40V]

(8b)   (9b)

** the di-substituted derivative is obtained at [-1.0V]

Scheme 5.4

5.2.2. Electron-Induced Nucleophilic Substitutions

Following an early report on electron-induced nucleophilic substitution in a binuclear complex,[45] there has been a wide extension of such reactions to metal clusters,[21,46] particularly those for which a relatively long-lived radical anion is detectable.

Electrode-initiated substitutions. It has been observed that passing a cathodic current at low potential promotes substitution reactions on metal cluster complexes. This is very attractive, since it appears that the degree of substitution can be controlled by tuning the reduction potential. This applies to ETC (electron transfer chain) catalysis of ligand substitution in the bicapped cluster species $[Fe_3(\mu_3\text{-}E)_2(CO)_9]$ (**8**) [(**8a**), E = PPh;[47] (**8b**), E = NPh; (**8c**), E = S; (**8d**), E = Se[48]] recently investigated by Kochi and co-workers, Scheme 5.4. The activation process is dependent on the nature of the capping group. Addition of one electron to (**8a**) gives the radical anion [**8a**]$^{\div}$ which tends to relieve its supersaturation by scission of a P—Fe bond. The slippage of the capping phosphinidene bridge is thus the rate limiting process in activation of (**8a**) toward substitution to give $Fe_3(\mu_3\text{-PPh})_2(CO)_{9-n}L_n$ (**9a**).[47] By contrast, the radical anions [**8b-d**]$^{\div}$ undergo dissociative first-order CO loss to generate coordinatively unsaturated clusters (the rates observed for substitution in this case are 10^6 times faster than for PPh).

Chemical reduction. Despite some attractive features mentioned previously, electrochemical reduction is inefficient and unselective in promoting substitution reactions within $Ru_3(CO)_{12}$ (**1**).[49,50] This is in sharp contrast with the high efficiency of the chemical reduction procedure based on sodium benzophenone-ketyl (BPK), developed by Bruce and co-workers, providing selective access to mono- and di-substituted phosphane derivatives of (**1**) which are not available through thermal routes.[51] The discrepancy between electrode and BPK as well as the fact that Na-benzophenone reacts with (**1**) to give a variety of reduced species,[52] raise mechanistic problems which have been discussed elsewhere.[26,49,50] Also of interest are observations that some metal dimers, like [{$Fe(CO)_2(C_5H_5)$}$_2$],[53,54] [$Cp_2Mo_2(CO)_6$],[55] or [$Fe_2(CO)_6(SMe)_2$],[56,57,58] may be used as catalyst precursors for substitution reactions (sometimes in combination with thermal activation), involving organic substrates such as alcohols or thiols,[57] and amines.[58]

Electron-induced transformations of organic substrates. Besides nucleophilic substitutions considered earlier, electrons are also prone to promote ligand transformations: in some cases, electrochemical reduction of a cluster containing coordinated hydrocarbon fragments results in a saturation which is balanced by a reductive coupling reaction leading to carbon-carbon bond formation. A representative example from the work of R. Mathieu on alkylidyne complexes is provided in Section 5.7 (see Scheme 5.53 and relevant discussion).

5.2.3. Unsaturated Metal Clusters

Aspects of the chemistry of $Os_3(\mu\text{-H})_2(CO)_{10}$. The prototype $Os_3(\mu\text{-H})_2(CO)_{10}$ (**10**) represents a rare example for which an extensive chemistry has been developed.[15,25,59] A systematic extension of such unsaturated species is limited by the fact that clusters generally remove electronic unsaturation by condensation through metal-metal bond formation. Typically, while $Os_3(\mu\text{-H})_2(CO)_{10}$ can be prepared in high yield through a simple hydrogenation of $Os_3(CO)_{12}$ (**2**),[60] parallel reaction of hydrogen with $Ru_3(CO)_{12}$ (**1**) gives only the electronically saturated tetranuclear complex $Ru_4(\mu\text{-H})_4(CO)_{12}$ (**11**). Forcing conditions are required to obtain the analogous tetranuclear osmium species;[60] by contrast, attempts to retain the trinuclear ruthenium structure with bridging phosphine ligands failed to produce an unsaturated species upon hydrogenation: in the reaction of the stabilized complex $Ru_3(CO)_8(\mu\text{-P}(C_6H_5)_2CH_2P(C_6H_5)_2)_2$ (**12**) with hydrogen, the expected unsaturation was released by oxidative cleavage of phosphorus—carbon bonds to give $Ru_3(\mu\text{-H})_2(CO)_6(\mu\text{-P}(C_6H_5)CH_2P(C_6H_5)_2)_2$ (**13**) (see Section 5.3 for details).[61]

The 46-e complex $Os_3(\mu\text{-H})_2(CO)_{10}$ (**10**) undergoes associative reaction with a variety of reagents under mild conditions. The addition process involves a shift of one bridging hydride in terminal position, leading to the 48-e species $Os_3H(\mu\text{-}$

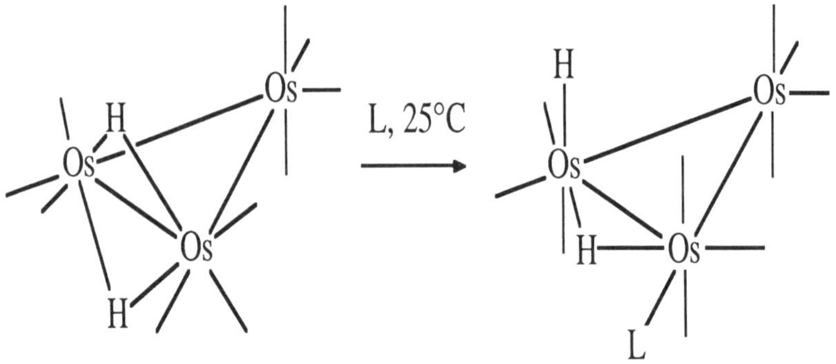

(10)   (14)

Scheme 5.5

$H)(CO)_{10}L$ (14) (Scheme 5.5).[62] The incoming ligand L in (14) occupies either an axial or an equatorial site, depending on its steric bulk. The two isomeric forms have been detected in the case of the anionic nucleophile CN^-: the formation of $[PPN][Os_3H(\mu\text{-}H)(CO)_{10}(CN)]$, ($[PPN][14a]$) allows further reduction of the multiple bond of the cyanide group at several metal centers.[63]

Another remarkable example of the possibilities offered by complex (10) is given in Scheme 5.6. This contains the complete sequence involving stoichiometric conversion of diazomethane to methane starting from $Os_3(\mu\text{-}H)_2(CO)_{10}$ (10), and ending at $(\mu\text{-}H)_2Os_3(CO)_9(\mu_3\text{-}O_3SO)$ (18).[64]

The protonation by 98% H_2SO_4 at the final step is believed to occur at metal-carbon bonds leading to methane, while the SO_4^{2-} dianion moves in to occupy the vacant coordination sites thus created.[64d] The unusual species (18) serves as a model for the chemisorption of a cluster complex and an oxide support.

It should be noted that the above-mentioned behavior of CH_2N_2 is unique, since most diazoalkanes do not undergo N_2 elimination in this reaction; the classic path involving proton transfer to nitrogen is followed with $t\text{-BuC}(H)N_2$, to end up with $Os_3(\mu\text{-}H)(CO)_{10}\{\mu\text{-}N(H)NC(H)(t\text{-Bu})\}$, (19), reaction (i) in Scheme 5.7.[65]

In the substituted complex $Os_3(\mu\text{-}H)_2(CO)_9PR_3$ (20), the basic phosphine ligand reduces the acidity of the hydrides, thus preventing proton transfer. As a consequence, the strongly basic nitrogen attacks at the electrophilic carbon of a coordinated CO, generating the μ_3 isocyanate complex $Os_3(\mu\text{-}H)(Bu\text{-}tCH{=}NNCO)(CO)_8(PMe_2Ph)$ (21). Similar coupling reactions are now observable for anionic ruthenium complexes (see Section 5.2.8). The carbon-nitrogen bond can be cleaved by H^+. It thus appears here that a modification of the basicity of a cluster by the use of ancillary phosphine ligands may provide means to control the transformation of a given ligand on a metal cluster.

Other Unsaturated Cluster Complexes. Although a number of other unsaturated cluster complexes have been designed,[8] most of them have not yet been extensively used in studies of ligand transformations, except for some rhenium clusters which exhibit a fascinating chemistry.[66,67] For example, the complete stepwise reduction of a CO ligand to methanol may be observed on the face of $[Re_3(\mu\text{-}H)_4(CO)_{10}]^-$ [22], during which the cluster complex relieves its unsaturation, Scheme 5.8.[66b] In the first step, there is an attack of hydride at the electrophilic

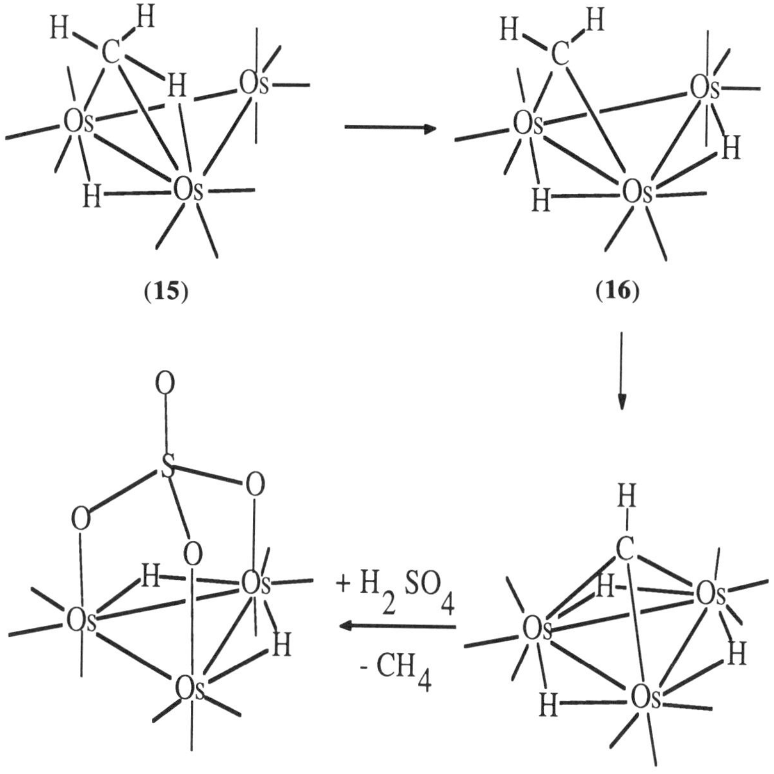

Scheme 5.6

carbon of an axial CO ligand on [22]; this gives the intermediate formyl complex $[Re_3(\mu\text{-}H)_4(\mu\text{-}CHO)(CO)_9]^{2-}$ [23] which rearranges to the oxymethyl complex $[Re_3(\mu\text{-}H)_3(\mu\text{-}CH_2O)(CO)_9]^{2-}$ [24]. Protonation of this complex occurs at oxygen to give the unstable hydroxymethyl complex $[Re_3(\mu\text{-}H)_3(\mu\text{-}CH_2OH)(CO)_9]^-$ [25] which releases methanol quantitatively under CO to give $[Re_3(\mu\text{-}H)_2(CO)_{12}]^-$ [26].

The hydridic character of the complex $[Re_3(\mu\text{-}H)_4(CO)_{10}]^-$ [22] is also evidenced in the facile reduction of acetone which occurs under mild conditions to provide the new species $[Re_3(\mu\text{-}H)_3(\mu\text{-}OCHMe_2)(CO)_{10}]^-$ [27] and $[Re_3(\mu\text{-}H)_3(\mu_3\text{-}OCHMe_2)(CO)_9]^-$ [28] in which acetone has been reduced to an isopropylate group (Scheme 5.9).[66c]

An even more reactive species may be derived from [22] by selective introduction of labile ligands;[66d] the resulting species $[Re_3(\mu\text{-}H)_4(CO)_9L]^-$ [29] (L = pyridine or acetonitrile) is reactive toward methanol, leading to $[Re_3(\mu\text{-}H)_3(\mu\text{-}OMe)(CO)_9]^-$ [30].

Finally, a doubly unsaturated (44 valence electrons) triangular species, $Re_3(\mu\text{-}H)_2(\mu\text{-}PPh_2)_3(CO)_6$ (32) has been prepared by hydrogenation of the phosphido-bridged species $Re_3(\mu\text{-}PPh_2)_3(CO)_9$ (31).

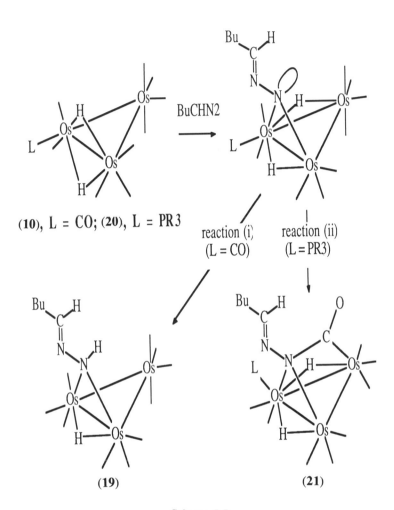

(10), L = CO; (20), L = PR3

reaction (i)
(L = CO)

reaction (ii)
(L = PR3)

(19)   (21)

Scheme 5.7

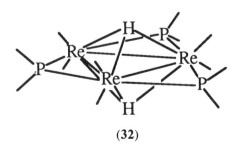

(32)

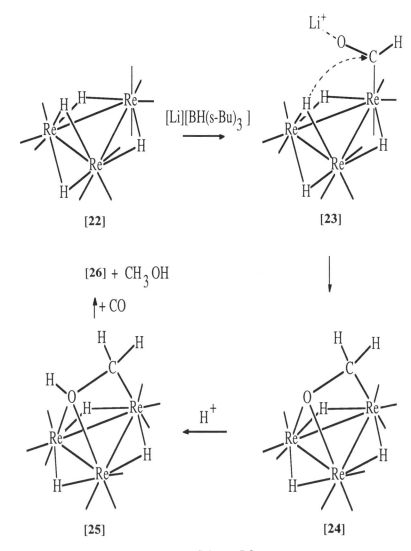

Scheme 5.8

The equally shortened metal-metal vectors in (**32**) suggest delocalization of the four π electrons over the three-membered ring, while the occurrence of two face-bridging hydrides is implied by NMR spectroscopy. This complex is a precursor for the hydrogenation of cyclohexene at very mild conditions.[67]

Activation of hydrogen by unsaturated cluster complexes. Activation of hydrogen is rarely achieved under mild conditions, even by unsaturated cluster complexes.[68–70] A notable exception is the newly designed complex $[Rh_3(\mu_3\text{-}CO)_2(\eta^5\text{-}C_5Me_5)_3]$ (**33**) and related mixed-metal species.[70] These undergo unusual

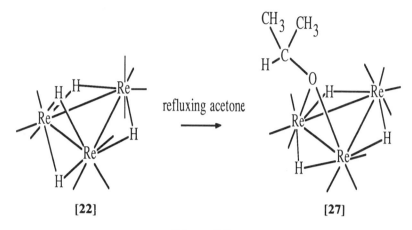

[22]   **[27]**

Scheme 5.9

reversible addition of H_2 under ambient conditions (25°C, 1 atm) to give $[Rh_3(\mu\text{-}H)_2(\mu\text{-}CO)(\mu_3\text{-}CO)(\eta^5\text{-}C_5Me_5)_3]$ (**34**) (Scheme 5.10).

5.2.4. Lightly Stabilized Metal Clusters

Replacement of CO by weakly bound ligands. The first "lightly stabilized" cluster compound reported so far, $Os_3(CO)_{10}(C_6H_8)$ (**35**) was isolated by the research group of Johnson and Lewis[71] from the reaction of (**10**) with cyclohexa-1,3 diene. The term "lightly stabilized" was subsequently coined by Shapley[72] to define complexes that contain good leaving groups such as earlier demonstrated in the case of mononuclear complexes.[73] Such weakly bound ligands involve principally acetonitrile,[74] but also cyclooctene,[72] cyclohexadiene,[71,75] or ammonia.[76] The synthesis of lightly stabilized species is generally carried out by nucleophilic

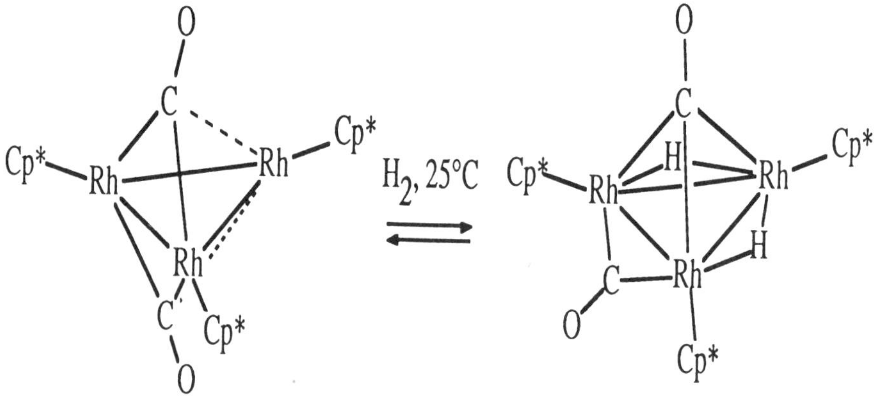

(**33**)   (**34**)

Scheme 5.10

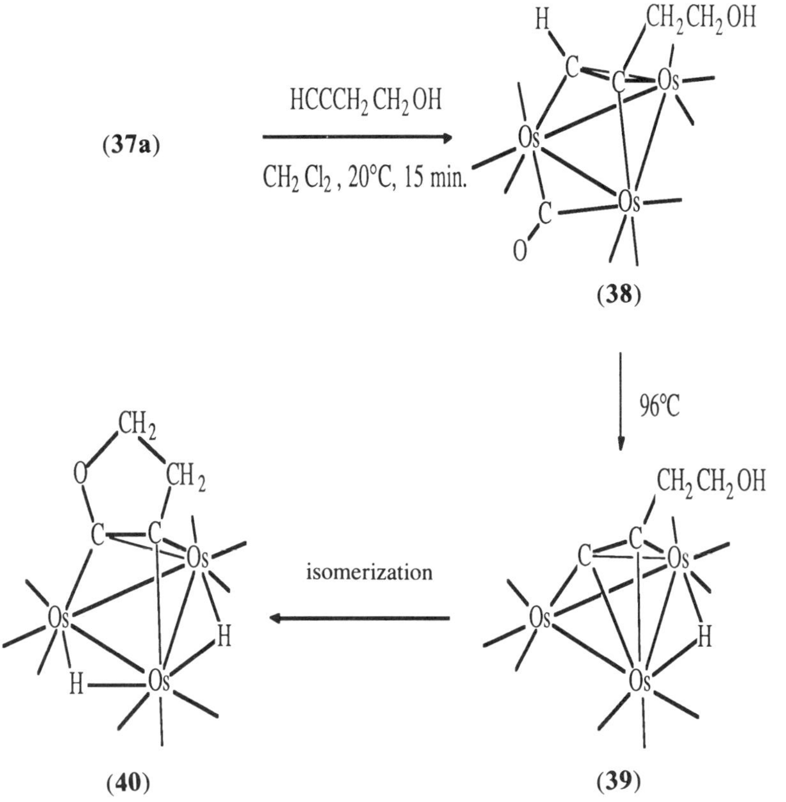

(37a) $\xrightarrow[\text{CH}_2\text{Cl}_2,\ 20°C,\ 15\ \text{min.}]{\text{HCCCH}_2\text{CH}_2\text{OH}}$ (38)

↓ 96°C

(40) ← isomerization ← (39)

Scheme 5.11

attack of trimethylamine *n*-oxide at the electrophilic carbon of coordinated car-bonyl groups to release CO_2,[77] while the resulting vacant coordination site is temporarily protected by transient coordination of the amine.[78,79] In general, the reaction must be carried at low temperature. If the reagent trimethylamine *n*-oxide is not carefully dehydrated, reaction of unsaturated intermediates with water may be eventually observed.[79]

Chemistry of $M_3(CO)_{12-n}(CH_3CN)_n$ (M = Os, Ru; n = 1, 2). The rich chemistry available to $Os_3(CO)_{11}(CH_3CN)$ (36a) and $Os_3(CO)_{10}(CH_3CN)_2$ (37a)[74] has been reviewed.[15,25] The initial step in reactions of these complexes in-volves dissociative loss of the weakly bound ligand.[80] The more unstable and highly reactive ruthenium analogs $Ru_3(CO)_{11}(CH_3CN)$ (36b) and $Ru_3(CO)_{10}(CH_3CN)_2$ (37b) have been only recently prepared,[81] and investigation of their chemistry is presently underway.[82]

A typical example of possibilities offered by the lightly stabilized species (37a) is given in Scheme 5.11.[83] The derivative $Os_3(\mu\text{-}H)_2(\mu_3\text{-}C_2CCH_2CH_2O)$ $(CO)_9$ (40) can be obtained from the thermal reaction of butynol with $Os_3(CO)_{12}$. However, the paths for this reaction were traced from the lightly stabi-lized species: (37a) reacts rapidly at room temperature with butynol to give

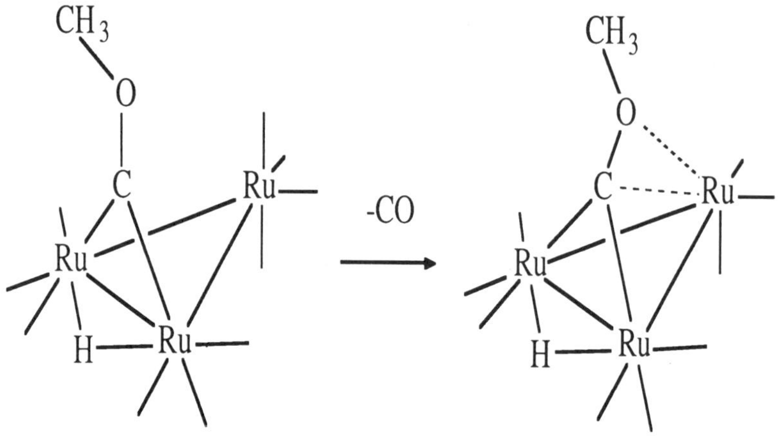

Scheme 5.12

$Os_3(\mu_3\text{-HCCCH}_2CH_2OH)(CO)_{10}$ (**38**) which further isomerizes to $Os_3(\mu\text{-H})(\mu_3\text{-}$
$CCCH_2CH_2OH)(CO)_{10}$ (**39**), and finally cyclizes to give the complex $Os_3(\mu\text{-}$
$H)_2(\mu_3\text{-CCCH}_2CH_2O)(CO)_9$ (**40**).

5.2.5. Cluster Complexes Containing Lightly Coordinated Bridging Ligands

Closely related to the lightly stabilized species mentioned previously are cluster
complexes that contain bridging ligands capable of donating a variable number of
electrons to the metal core. The importance of such ligands is that their variable
modes of coordination are easily reversible, thus facilitating both a coordination
and an elimination in sequential reaction steps.

Substitutional lability of edge-bridged species $Ru_3(\mu\text{-H})(\mu\text{-CX})(CO)_{10}$;
implication for the mechanism of cluster hydrogenation. The edge-bridging
alkylidyne group in $Ru_3(\mu\text{-H})(\mu\text{-CX})(CO)_{10}$ [(**6**), X = OR; (**41**), X = NMe_2][84,85]
provides a noteworthy example of a versatile ligand capable of stabilizing an un-
saturated intermediate: the kinetics of substitution in the above species have been
interpreted in terms of a change of the bridging C-X ligand from a $\mu\text{-}\eta^1$ three-
electron donor to a $\mu_3\text{-}\eta^2$ five-electron donor in the transition state, resulting in
stereospecific CO labilization (see Scheme 5.12); indeed, substitutions within this
complex occur essentially at the unique ruthenium atom.

Interestingly, the unsaturated intermediate $(6\text{-CO})^*$ exhibits high selectivity
for CO over hydrogen (competition ratio $k_{CO}/k_{H2} = 700$). This suggests that an
intramolecular rearrangement is required to convert the kinetic product of hydrogen
addition to its stable thermodynamic product $Ru_3(\mu\text{-H})_3(\mu_3\text{-COMe})(CO)_9$ (**42**),
reactions (5.1)–(5.3). The first formed product of H_2 addition is proposed to have
one or more hydrogen atoms in terminal position; the first formed adduct readily
loses H_2 in competition with its isomerization to the stable form, consistent with
the observation that bridging hydrides are more stable than terminal ones.[86]

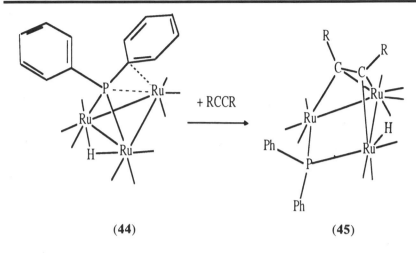

(44) +RCCR → (45)

Scheme 5.13

$$Ru_3(\mu\text{-}H)(\mu\text{-}COMe)(CO)_{10} \underset{k_{-1}}{\overset{k1}{\rightleftharpoons}} Ru_3(\mu\text{-}H)(\mu\text{-}COMe)(CO)_9 + CO \quad (5.1)$$

$$Ru_3(\mu\text{-}H)(\mu\text{-}COMe)(CO)_9 + H_2 \underset{k_{-3}}{\overset{k3}{\rightleftharpoons}} \{H_3Ru_3(COMe)(CO)_9\}^* \quad (5.2)$$

$$\{H_3Ru_3(COMe)(CO)_9\}^* \underset{k_{-4}}{\overset{k4}{\rightleftharpoons}} Ru_3(\mu\text{-}H)_3(\mu_3\text{-}COMe)(CO)_9 \quad (5.3)$$

* Activated isomeric intermediate

Extended observations on other ancillary ligands forming light bridges.

Bridging CO groups. In some cases, a CO group itself may function as a versatile 4-*e* donor ligand as first observed in $Mn_2(CO)_5(dppm)_2$ and related binuclear complexes.[87]

A transition state related to that shown in Scheme 5.12 has been postulated to account for the high substitutional lability of the anionic complex $[Ru_3(\mu\text{-}H)(\mu\text{-}CO)(CO)_{10}]^-$ (**43**).[88]

Bridging phosphido groups. A labile interaction of the same type is also seen in the complex $Ru_3(\mu\text{-}H)(\mu_3\text{-}P(C_6H_5)_2)(CO)_9$ (**44**) (Scheme 5.13).

The weak interaction between a phosphorus-carbon bond of the bridging phosphido group and the unique ruthenium center favors the occurrence of facile ligand additions under mild conditions, as exemplified in Scheme 5.13 by the 4-*e* addition of an alkyne occurring without CO loss to give $Ru_3(\mu\text{-}H)(\mu\text{-}P(C_6H_5)_2)(\mu\text{-}RCCR)(CO)_9$ (**45**).[89]

Halides and pseudo-halides. Amongst other ligands that possess such a property are halides and pseudo-halides; see also Section 5.2.8. For example, the availability of terminal, edge-bridging, and face-bridging modes for the iodide atom accounts for the thermally induced interconversion of the three osmium species $Os_3(\mu\text{-}H)(I)(CO)_{11}$ (**46**), $Os_3(\mu\text{-}H)(\mu\text{-}I)(CO)_{10}$ (**47**), $Os_3(\mu\text{-}H)(\mu_3\text{-}I)(CO)_9$ (**48**) which can be reversed under carbon monoxide.[74] The same equilibrium occurs

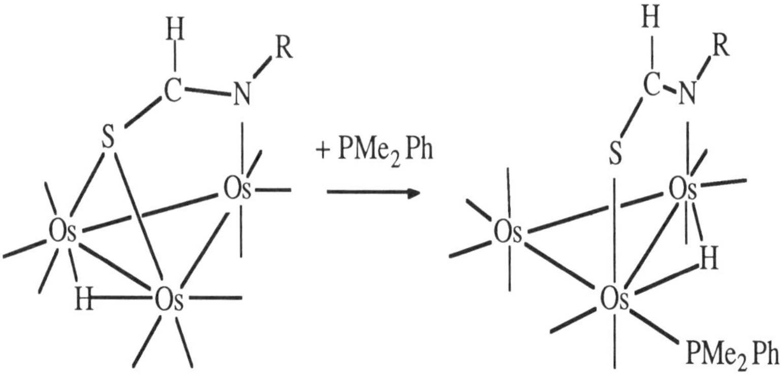

(51)   (52)

Scheme 5.14

under milder conditions between the ruthenium analogs $Ru_3(\mu\text{-}H)(\mu\text{-}I)(CO)_{10}$ (**49**) and $Ru_3(\mu\text{-}H)(\mu_3\text{-}I)(CO)_9$ (**50**) and may account for the high reactivity of these species.[90] Related examples are available for clusters of higher nuclearity;[91,92] in the absence of incoming ligand, a rearrangement of the metal core may occur.[93,94]

X-C(R)-Y linkages. A number of ligands that are coordinated by two donor atoms, X—C(R)—Y, exemplified by amidines, 2-aminopyridines, 2-pyridones,[95] or thioamides SCHNR,[96] are also prone to form lightly coordinated bridges over triangular faces; they thus provide mild paths for the coordination of incoming substrates. One example is given in Scheme 5.14:[96] The complex $Os_3(\mu\text{-}H)(\mu_3\text{-}SCHNR)(CO)_9$ (**51**) undergoes adduct formation in the presence of PMe_2Ph to give $Os_3(\mu\text{-}H)(\mu_2\text{-}SCHNR)(CO)_9(PMe_2Ph)$ (**52**); noticeably, the process is more complex than a simple bridge opening reaction, since a CO shift is observed.

μ-SR and μ-OR groups. (For μ-SR, see under Section 5.2.7.) A dramatic application of bridge opening reactions of the type described earlier is seen in the hydrogenation of ethylene under mild conditions by the silica-grafted surface complex $Os_3(\mu\text{-}H)(\mu_2\text{-}O\text{—}Si\equiv)(CO)_{10}$ (**53a**)[97a] or its molecular analogs $Os_3(\mu\text{-}H)(\mu_2\text{-}OPh)(CO)_{10}$ (**53b**)[97a] or $Os_3(\mu\text{-}H)(\mu_2\text{-}O\text{—}SiEt_3)(CO)_{10}$ (**53c**).[97b] The facile $3e\text{-}1e$ interconversion between bridging $\mu_2\text{-}OR$ and terminal $\eta^1\text{-}OR$ is believed to provide the appropriate energy balance for cluster catalysis without cluster fragmentation.[97a] A limitation of the molecular complex (**53b**) is that loss of phenol and formation of $Os_3(\mu\text{-}H)_2(CO)_{10}$ occur as side reactions under catalytic conditions. (Further information on the use of OR^- ligands for cluster activation is provided under Section 5.2.8.)

5.2.6. Cluster Complexes Involving Strongly Coordinated Bridging Ligands and Labile Metal-Metal Interactions

Control of metal-metal edge opening processes. In contrast to the previous case, when the nuclearity of a cluster is enforced by a strong nonfluxional bridging ligand, the distortions imposed by this ligand on the metal atom polyhedron

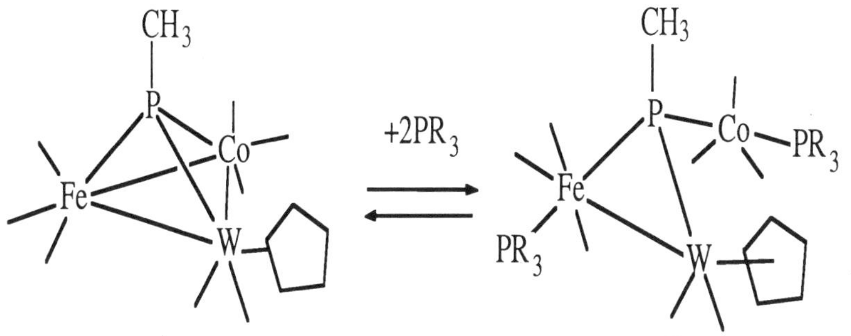

Scheme 5.15

may favor the occurrence of facile and reversible metal-metal edge opening processes under mild conditions.[27,98–107] This observation has led to the proposal by Huttner and co-workers[100] that "clusters behave like breathing objects, which reversibly add substrates to their inner surface, and expire them under reformation of metal-metal bonds." Following on the original report of reversible opening of a metal-metal bond in the case of $Cp(CO)_2MnFe_2(CO)_6(\mu\text{-}PR)$ (**54**),[98] kinetic and mechanism for this process have been investigated.[102] The closed cluster (**54**) is in equilibrium with its valence tautomeric unsaturated form with an opened Mn-Fe bond. The latter species reacts with L to yield $Cp(CO)_2MnFe_2(CO)_6(\mu\text{-}PR)L$ (**55**). The enthalpy of activation for this process is around 90 kJ/mol, closely comparable with the dissociation energy of an Mn—Fe bond. The reverse reaction is initiated by the loss of L. The corresponding ΔH of 100 kJ/mol is in the range expected for the dissociation of L.

Recent mechanistic studies by Vahrenkamp[103] on related mixed-metal cluster complexes provide evidence for a more complete cluster opening via addition of two ligand molecules, as exemplified in Scheme 5.15 by the equilibrium between $FeCoW(\mu_3\text{-}PCH_3)(CO)_8(C_5H_5)$ (**56**) and $FeCoW(\mu_3\text{-}P(CH_3))(CO)_8(PR_3)_2(C_5H_5)$ (**57**).

In such a case, the opening-inversion-closing sequence results in a racemization, which brings a serious limitation in the transfer of stereochemical information by metal clusters.[104]

The extension of the substitution reactions to ligands other than phosphines has provided evidence that a number of supporting groups which were originally expected to be chemically inert, in fact show a dramatic chemical reactivity, the reason being that the enthalpy of metal-metal and metal-ligand bonds is often so close that competing reactivity of such bonds is currently observable.[105] This is illustrated in Schemes 5.16 and 5.17 by two examples taken from the recent literature; other relevant reactions based on phosphorus or sulfur bridged species are discussed in detail in Sections 5.3 and 5.4 respectively.

Scheme 5.16 shows that UV irradiation of the phosphinidene cluster $Fe_3(\mu\text{-}PR)(CO)_{10}$ (**58**) in the presence of diphenylacetylene leads to the complex $Fe_3(\mu\text{-}RPC(Ph)C(Ph))(CO)_9$ (**59**), resulting from the insertion of the acetylene into a metal-phosphorus bond to produce the face-bridging group RPCPhCPh. Further

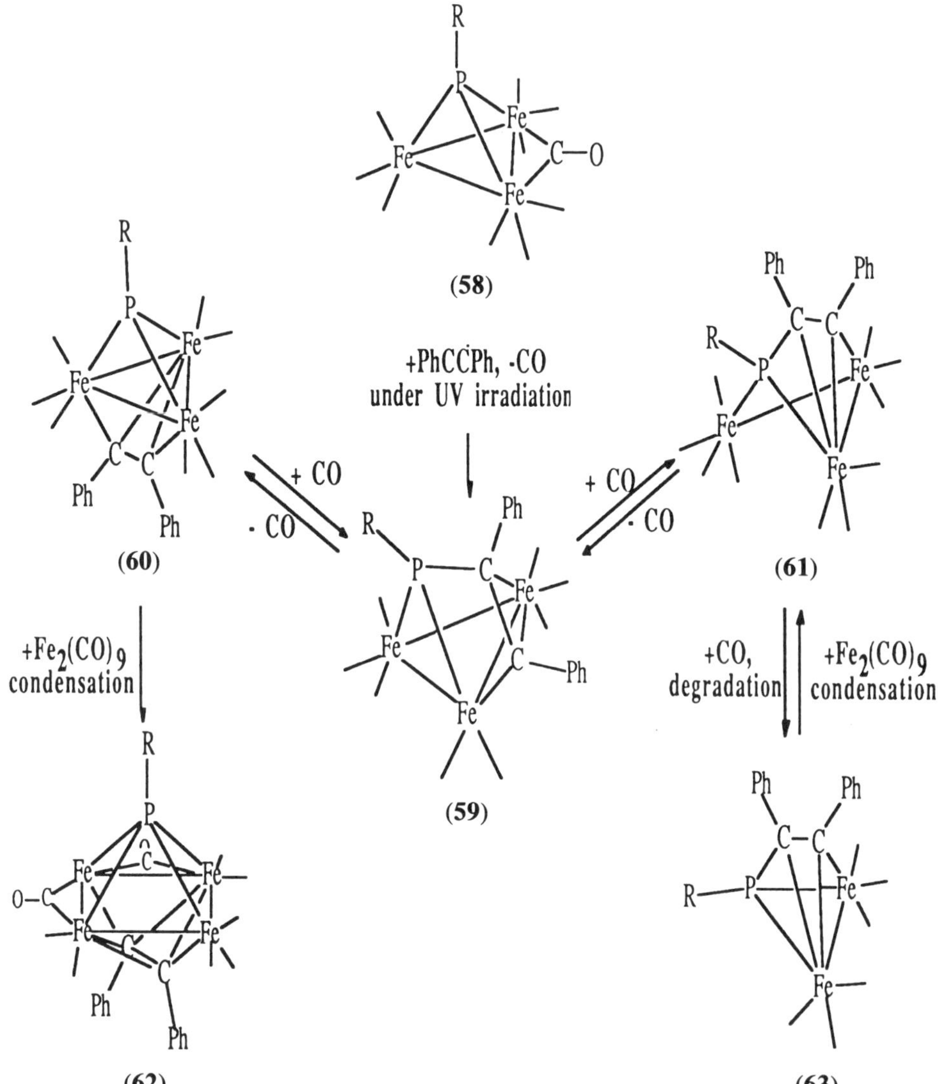

Scheme 5.16

splitting of this group is induced by loss of CO to give $Fe_3(\mu\text{-}PR)(\mu PhCCPh)$ $(CO)_8$ (**60**) where the phosphinidene group is recovered, while the alkyne migrates to the opposite cluster face; the reverse reaction, a CO-induced phosphorus-carbon bond coupling, is also observed. The phosphinidene ligand in (**60**) may accommodate an additional metal fragment to provide the tetranuclear square planar cluster $Fe_4(\mu\text{-}PR)(\mu PhCCPh))(CO)_{11}$ (**62**). Under carbon monoxide, the complex (**59**) is in equilibrium with the "open" species $Fe_3(\mu\text{-}RPCPhCPh)(CO)_{10}$

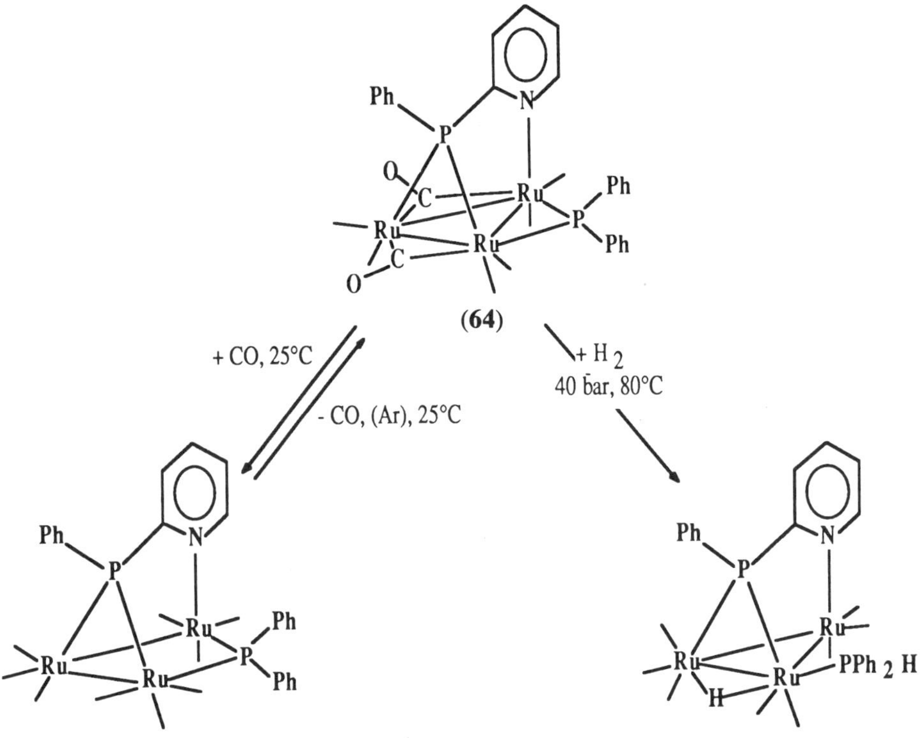

Scheme 5.17

(61); further reaction of the latter with CO leads to the binuclear complex $Fe_2(\mu\text{-}RPCPhCPh)(CO)_6$ (63).[105]

Evidence for the lability of a bridging phosphido group under the typical conditions of catalytic hydrogenation of olefins has been recently obtained (Scheme 5.17).[106] Though electronically saturated, the complex $Ru_3(\mu_3\text{-}P(C_6H_5)(C_5H_4N))(\mu\text{-}P(C_6H_5)_2)(CO)_8$ (64) exhibits the typical behavior of an unsaturated species: in the presence of CO, rapid formation of the open 50-e adduct $Ru_3(\mu_3\text{-}P(C_6H_5)(C_5H_4N))(\mu\text{-}P(C_6H_5)_2)(CO)_9$ (65) is observed under ambient conditions. More surprisingly, (64) also reacts with hydrogen to give the adduct $Ru_3(\mu\text{-}H)(\mu_3\text{-}P(C_6H_5)(C_5H_4N))(P(C_6H_5)_2H)(CO)_8$ (66), in which the bridging phosphido group $\mu\text{-}P(C_6H_5)_2$ has been converted into the terminal phosphine $P(C_6H_5)_2H$. Side products resulting from the intermolecular redistribution of the latter ligand are also observed.

Interestingly, (64) has been effectively used as a precursor for the catalytic hydrogenation of cyclohexanone; the catalysis may be interpreted in terms of the high substitutional lability of the complex and its ability to add hydrogen reversibly.

Thus, the interesting sets of interconversions shown in the preceding examples summarize the principal reactions that may be expected from cluster complexes that are "stabilized" by phosphinidene or phosphido groups:

(i) reversible metal-metal cleavage,* (ii) reversible insertion of various substrates into phosphorus-metal bonds, (iii) intermolecular association with diverse metal fragments (eventually a route to mixed-metal species) or (iv) degradation of the metal framework.

Thus, it appears that in most cases, the stabilization of a metal cluster by a bridging ligand cannot be taken for granted; the frontier between lightly and strongly ligand-bridged species is not well defined; it depends both on the ligand and on the metal.

5.2.7. Electrophilic Activation of Stable Ligand-Bridged Cluster Complexes

Electrophilic attack at main group atoms. Numerous cluster complexes stabilized by main group atoms are not as reactive as those described in the two preceding sections, that is, (i) they do not exhibit labile metal-metal interactions, and (ii) the bridging ligand is not spontaneously labile. In such cases, electrophilic attack at the main group atom exposed on the face of the cluster reduces the number of electrons available to the metal, thereby providing a mild path for coordination of a new substrate. Such an elegant procedure was originally described by Johnson, Lewis, and co-workers for the anion $[Os_3(\mu\text{-H})(\mu_3\text{-S})(CO)_9]^-$ [67]: alkylation was found to occur at the face-bridging sulfido ligand, converting it into an edge-bridging thiolato group, thus permitting coordination of ethylene to give $[Os_3(\mu\text{-H})(\mu_2\text{-SR})(\eta_2\text{-C}_2H_4)(CO)_9]$ (68).[108]

More recently, there have been a number of interesting reports on parallel ways to activate metal clusters. Following on the observation that kinetically controlled protonation may also occur at ligands in metal clusters,[109] Gladfelter and co-workers have nicely applied this to the activation of the tetranuclear nitrido cluster $[Ru_4N(CO)_{12}]^-$ [69].[110] In the absence of ligand, electrophilic attack at the nitrido atom induces subtle structural changes involving the formation of metal-metal bonds (typically, a butterfly cluster will be converted to a closed tetrahedron).[110a] The reactive intermediate may also be trapped by an incoming olefin at very mild conditions as shown in Scheme 5.18; diphenylacetylene is seen to trap the imido cluster formed during the protonation of [69], leading to $Ru_4(NH)(CO)_{11}(Ph_2C_2)$ (70).[110b]

Electrophilic attack at coordinated organic fragments. The preceding procedure may also be applied to coordinated organic fragments on a cluster complex. For example, it has been reported that protonation at the vinylidene fragment (demonstrated by labeling experiments; see Scheme 5.19)[111] of the complex $K[Fe_3(\mu\text{-H})(CO)_9(C{=}CH_2)]^-$ [71] weakens the coordination of the double bond to the unique iron, thereby opening a coordination site for either H_2 addition to give $Fe_3(\mu\text{-H})_3(CO)_9(\mu_3\text{-CCH}_3)$ (72)[111] (Scheme 5.19), or CO addition to give $Fe_3(\mu\text{-H})(\mu\text{-CO})(CO)_9(\mu_3\text{-CCH}_3)$ (73).[112,113] These transformations are similar to those shown in Scheme 5.12.

Acid-mediated coupling reactions. A spectacular example of acid-mediated ligand transformation on a cluster is seen in the sequence appearing in Scheme

---

* Note: when this chapter was completed, we became aware of a novel example of reversible metal-metal cleavage induced by reaction with hydrogen.[177e]

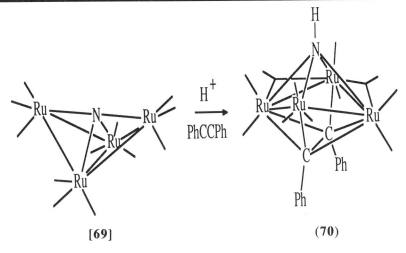

[69]   (70)

Scheme 5.18

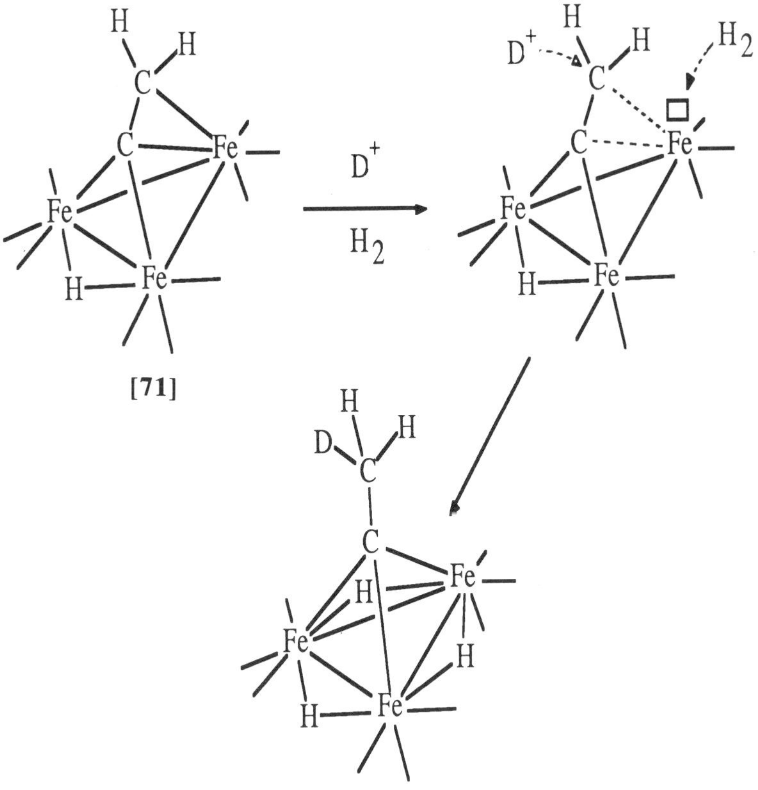

[71]

(72)

Scheme 5.19

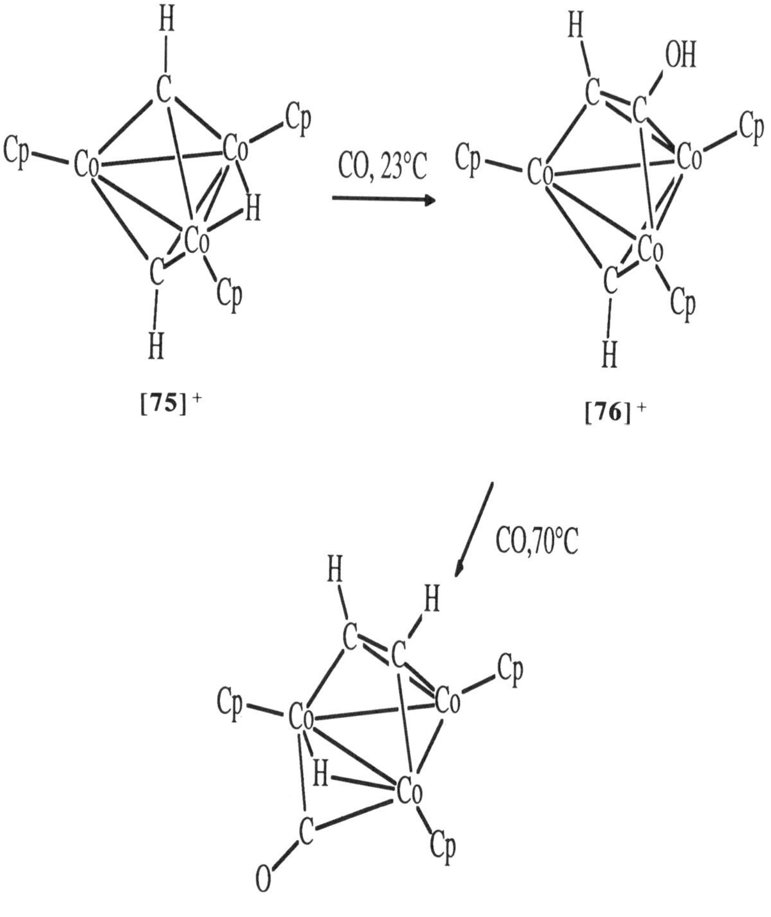

Scheme 5.20

5.20:[114] Although the neutral complex $Co_3Cp_3(\mu_3\text{-}\eta^1\text{-CH})_2$ (**74**) is inert to CO, the protonated complex $[Co_3Cp_3(\mu\text{-H})(\mu_3\text{-}\eta^1\text{-CH})_2]^+$ [**75**] is smoothly carbonylated at ambient temperature to give the ethynol complex $[Co_3Cp_3(\mu_3\text{-}\eta^2\text{-HCCOH})(\mu_3\text{-}\eta^1\text{-CH})]^+$ [**76**], a reaction that can be regarded as the formal insertion of the hydroxymethylidyne cation C—OH$^+$ into a cobalt methylidyne bond. Treatment of [**76**] with CO at 70°C results in apparent CO de-insertion and coupling of the two methylidyne ligands to give $[Co_3Cp_3(\mu\text{-H})(\mu\text{-CO})(\mu_3\text{-}\eta^2\text{-HCCH})]^+$ [**77**].[114]

A comparable sequence leading to C—C bond formation (via intermediate C—N coupling) has been initiated with NO$^+$ (in place of C-OH$^+$).[115] Other examples of acid-mediated coupling reactions involving carbon monoxide are given in Section 5.7.

5.2.8. Nucleophilic Activation; Anion-Promoted Metal Clusters

Brief historical perspective. The promoter effect of anionic nucleophiles is now well documented in reactions of mononuclear or polynuclear carbonyl metal complexes.[116] For the latter species, that is, metal clusters, the developments are relatively recent. A unifying view of the activity of anionic nucleophiles in the chemistry of trimetal clusters of the iron triad has been proposed in earlier literature.[8] Recent results presented next bring further support to such a view.

Perhaps one of the earliest evidences for the affinity of anionic nucleophiles for carbonyl cluster complexes was obtained by the late professor Paolo Chini and his co-workers.[11] These authors noted that "the noninnocence of halides and pseudo-halides should always be considered in reactions of metal clusters," a statement relevant to the observation[117] that such anions react readily with $Rh_6(CO)_{16}$ (**78**) in THF under ambient conditions to give $[Rh_6(CO)_{15}X]^-$ [**79**]. Interestingly, in the same report,[117] parallel reaction of (**78**) with OR^- as a nucleophile was shown to provide $[Rh_6(CO)_{15}COOR]^-$ [**80**] while its reaction with RNH_2 gave $[Rh_6(CO)_{15}CONHR]^-$ [**81**]. At that time, however, these authors did not focus on the reactivity of such anionic cluster complexes, which were just seen as intermediates in the course of more complete reduction reactions.[117] The reason may be simply that there is no need for activating rhodium clusters, which already undergo fast ^{13}CO exchange at 25°C. The problem is much more crucial for $M_3(CO)_{12}$ clusters of the iron triad, ruthenium in particular, due to the lack of unsaturated polynuclear species for this metal (vide supra, Section 5.2.3).

An early indication of nucleophilic activation of $Ru_3(CO)_{12}$ under unprecedented mild conditions (−30°C) was obtained by Kaesz from the reaction of this complex with $HNMe_2$ which provided the carboxamido complex $Ru_3(\mu\text{-H})(\mu\text{-O}=CNMe_2)(CO)_{10}$ (**82**) via nucleophilic attack of the amine at the electrophilic carbon of a CO ligand.[118] The corresponding anion was subsequently isolated as the guanidinium salt $[C(NMe_2)_3][Ru_3(\mu\text{-O}=CNMe_2)(CO)_{10}]$ [**83b**] (see also Table 5.1).[119,120]

[**83b**]

This was reminiscent of earlier observations on mononuclear complexes which indicated that CO-base adducts act as strong labilizing ligands.[121] A parallel reaction had been observed by Deeming between the less basic benzylamine and $Os_3(CO)_{12}$ (**2**),[122] in that case occurring under thermal activation. For the highly

Table 5.1 ■ **Adducts of Various Anionic Nucleophiles with Ru₃(CO)₁₂** [a,b,c]

Nu = Hydride	NR₂, OR	Acetate, halides, pseudo-halides
Initial Adduct		
A1	A2	A3
$[Ru_3(CO)_{11}\{\eta^1\text{-}C(O)H\}]^-$ [85a]	$[Ru_3(CO)_{11}\{\eta^1\text{-}C(O)NMe_2\}]^-$ [83a]	$[Ru_3(CO)_{11}\{\eta^1\text{-}NCO\}]^-$ [87a]
$[Ru_3(CO)_{12}\{\eta^1\text{-}H\}]^-$ [85a*]	$[Ru_3(CO)_{11}\{\eta^1\text{-}C(O)OMe\}]^-$ [86a]	
One CO evolved		
B1	B2	B3
$[Ru_3(\mu\text{-}H)(CO)_{11}]^-$ [85b]	$[Ru_3(CO)_{10}\{\mu\text{-}\eta^2\text{-}C(O)NMe_2\}]^-$ [83b]	$[Ru_3(CO)_{10}\{\mu\text{-}\eta^1\text{-}NCO\}]^-$ [87b]
	$[Ru_3(CO)_{10}\{\mu\text{-}\eta^2\text{-}C(O)OMe\}]^-$ [86b]	
	B4	
	$[Ru_3(CO)_{11}\{\eta^1\text{-}NO\}]^-$ [88b]	
	$[Ru_3(CO)_{11}\{\eta^1\text{-}RCOO\}]^-$ [89b]	
	$[Ru_3(CO)_{11}\{\eta^1\text{-}X\}]^-$ [90b] (X = Cl, Br)	
	$[Ru_3(CO)_{11}\{\eta^1\text{-}CN\}]^-$ [91b]	

Two CO evolved

	C4
$[Ru_3(CO)_{10}\{\mu\text{-}\eta^1\text{-OMe}\}]^-$ [86c]	$[Ru_3(CO)_{10}\{\mu\text{-}\eta^1\text{-NO}\}]^-$ [88c]
	$[Ru_3(CO)_{10}\{\mu\text{-}\eta^2\text{-RCOO}\}]^-$ [89c]
	$[Ru_3(CO)_{10}\{\mu\text{-}\eta^1\text{-X}\}]^-$ [90c]
	(X = Cl, Br, I)
	C4* (dimeric unit)
	$[Ru_6(CO)_{20}\{\mu\text{-}\eta^2\text{-CN}\}_2]^{2-}$ [91c]

Three CO evolved

D4
$[Ru_3(CO)_9\{\mu_3\text{-}\eta^1\text{-X}\}]^-$ [90d]
(X = I only)

Subsequent transformations

E
$[Ru_4(CO)_{13}\{\mu\text{-NCO}\}]^-$ [87e]
$[Ru_4(CO)_{13}\{\mu\text{-Cl}\}]^-$ [90e]

[a] The labeling scheme within this table is as follows: for a given nucleophilic anion Nu$^-$, all adducts are assigned the same compound number followed by a letter indicating the type of adduct (a, initial adduct; b, 1 CO lost; c, 2 CO lost; d, 3 CO lost; e further CO loss and framework rearrangement).

[b] Nu = H$^-$ (adducts 85a,[123] 85a*,[124] 85b[88,125]), Nu = NMe$_2^-$ (adducts 83a-b),[119,120] OMe$^-$ (adducts 86a-b), [126,127] N$_3^-$ (adducts 87a-b, 87e),[128] NO$_2^-$ (adducts 88b-c),[129] RCOO$^-$, with R = H or CH$_3$ (adducts 89b-c),[130] X = Cl$^-$ or Br$^-$ (adducts 90b-c) [131a,136,177h], X = I, adducts 90c-d only),[136b] Nu = CN$^-$ (adducts 91b-c). [132]
The tetranuclear "butterfly" complexes 87e [28] and 90e [133,136b] are the result of thermal degradation of the corresponding trinuclear complexes.

[c] Though the hydride has been included in the present table, it should be regarded as a particular case in that unlike other nucleophiles, it can only function as a one-electron donor.

nucleophilic $HNMe_2$, the complete sequence shown in reactions (5.4)–(5.5) was observed at very mild conditions.[119]

$$Os_3(CO)_{12} + 2HNMe_2 \xrightarrow{\text{THF},0°C} [H_2NMe_3][Os_3(\eta^1\text{-}C(O)NMe_2)(CO)_{11}] \quad (5.4)$$

[84a]

$$[\textbf{84a}] \rightarrow [H_2NMe_3][Os_3(\mu\text{-}\eta^1\text{-}O{=}CNMe_2)(CO)_{10}] + CO \qquad (5.5)$$

[84b]

Such observations were then rapidly generalized to a variety of nucleophilic anions (see following and Table 5.1).

Extended observations on $M_3(CO)_{12}$. The following discussion deals principally with the activation of $Ru_3(CO)_{12}$ by anionic nucleophiles (Table 5.1), with some comments on related osmium analogs being less reactive, but sometimes more easily stabilized.

Under the aprotic conditions that are specified in the next paragraph, the association of an anionic nucleophile Nu^- with $Ru_3(CO)_{12}$ results in the formation of an adduct formulated as "$[Ru_3(CO)_{12}Nu]^-$" [A] which rapidly undergoes stepwise loss of up to three CO ligands (depending on the nature of Nu^-) through the intermediacy of species $[Ru_3(CO)_{12-n}Nu]^-$ [B–D] ($n = 1$ for B, 2 for C, and 3 for D). Further transformations of the metal framework may lead to the stable thermodynamic products E.

Kinetic evidence for an adduct of proposed formula "$[Ru_3(CO)_{12}\{Nu\}]^-$" $[A]^-$ has been obtained in the case of H^-.[124] Early attempts to detect such an adduct by low temperature ^{13}C NMR experiments have suggested its formulation as the formyl complex $[Ru_3(CO)_{11}\{\eta^1\text{-}C(O)H\}]^-$ **[85a]**.[123] The corresponding osmium species has a lifetime of 5 hours under ambient conditions.[134] An isomeric form of **[85a]**, written as the hydrido-anion $[Ru_3(CO)_{12}\{\eta^1\text{-}H\}]^-$ **[85a*]** involving a terminal hydride ligand has been proposed as an intermediate in intermolecular hydride transfer reactions (see following); it was argued that a shift from metal to carbon would be thermodynamically unfavorable.[124] For NR_2^- or OR^-, attachment of the nucleophile is at the electrophilic carbon of a coordinated CO to give an $\eta^1\text{-}C(O)Nu$ group. For other nucleophiles, the lability and high fluxionality of the initial adduct has precluded determination of the initial site of attack. A stable adduct of CH_3^- with $Os_3(CO)_{12}$ is known; low temperature NMR data of this fluxional species are consistent with its formulation as $[Os_3(CO)_{11}\{\eta^1\text{-}C(O)CH_3\}]^-$ **[92]** with the $\eta^1\text{-}C(O)CH_3$ group in equatorial position.[135]

Following the initial interaction, the nature of the incoming nucleophile may be changed. This is observed for the azide anion N_3^- which reacts with coordinated CO presumably via a labile $\eta^1\text{-}C(O)Nu$ interaction, to give the terminal $\eta^1\text{-}NCO$ ligand (type A adduct $[PPN][Ru_3(CO)_{11}(\eta^1\text{-}NCO)]$ **[87a]**)[128] which then behaves as a pseudo-halide and adopts a bridging position in the subsequent type B intermediate $[PPN][Ru_3(CO)_{10}(\mu\text{-}NCO)]$ **[87b]**.

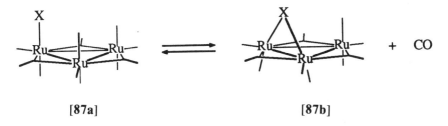

[87a]   [87b]

Scheme 5.21

In a similar way, NO_2^- is converted into NO in reaction with a coordinated carbonyl group to release CO_2,[129] a behavior which parallels that of the amine-oxide (see Section 5.2.4, lightly stabilized species).

Thus, in all type A$^-$ species, the nucleophilic anion *Nu*$^-$ acts as a strong CO-labilizing group, either directly, or via its association with coordinated CO, to produce a new anion [B]$^-$ by loss of one CO. Immediate de-insertion will occur below ambient temperature for the formyl complex [85a] to give the well-known hydrido anion $[Ru_3(\mu\text{-H})(CO)_{11}]^-$ [85b]. By contrast, η^1-C(O)Nu groups such as acyl (not shown in Table 5.1), carboxamido, and carbamoyl will not yet de-insert at this step, but will be converted into the corresponding $\mu\text{-}\eta^2$-C(O)Nu groups (see above the structural drawing of the carbamoxamido adduct 83b).

For acetate, formate, NO, halides, and cyanide, type B4 complexes are often the first spectroscopically detectable species under CO atmosphere. Generally, they are fluxional down to $-100°C$. A formulation based on a terminal nucleophile seems reasonable though only IR data are available for such labile species[136] {note: while this work was completed, we became aware that both the osmium[177a] and ruthenium[177h] derivatives $[PPN][M_3(X)(CO)_{11}]$ have been structurally characterized (for ruthenium, see 90b[177h] in Scheme 5.21). CO labilization in the ruthenium derivatives results in a shift of the terminally bound nucleophile (one-electron donor) in bridging position (three-electron donor) to give a type C complex. This transformation is reversed at $25°C$ under one CO atmosphere in the case of halides[136] (Scheme 5.20).

The only structures of type C species established by crystallographic analysis are those of $[PPN][Ru_3(CO)_{10}\{\mu\text{-RCOO}\}]$ [89c][130] and $[PPN]_2[Ru_6\{CN\}(CO)_{20}]$ [91c].[132] The hexanuclear species (91c) results from the intermolecular association of unsaturated anionic units "$[Ru_3(CO)_{10}\{CN\}]^-$" via CN links. This may reflect the reluctance of linearly hybridized CN groups to form stable edge-bridged species.

Further loss of CO from type C complexes results in the formation of either type D or type E species depending on the nature of the bridging group. The structure of $[Na\text{-Crown}][Ru_3(\mu_3\text{-I})(CO)_9]$ [90d] has now been determined.[136b]

Interestingly, the formation of the tetranuclear butterfly cluster complex $[PPN][Ru_4(CO)_{13}\{\mu\text{-X}\}]$ [90e] from the trinuclear adducts can be cleanly reversed under a CO atmosphere.[136b]

Under forcing conditions, more complicated transformations do occur, which

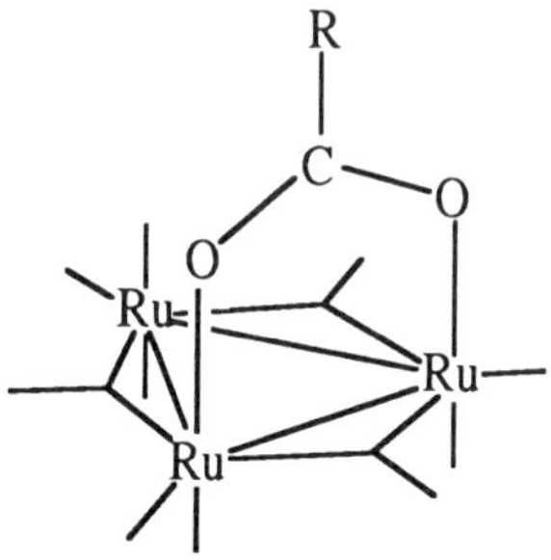

[89c]

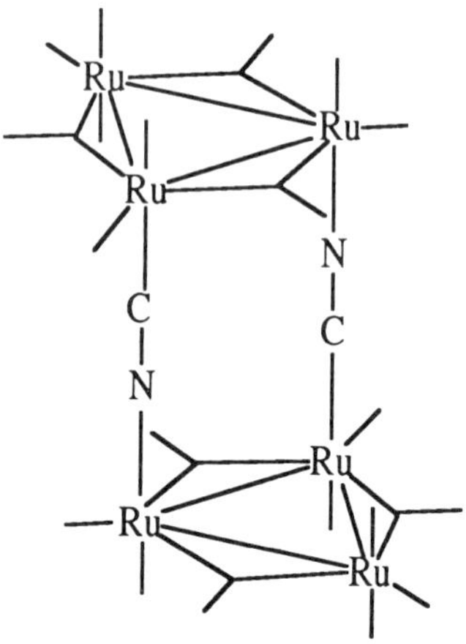

[91c]$^{2-}$

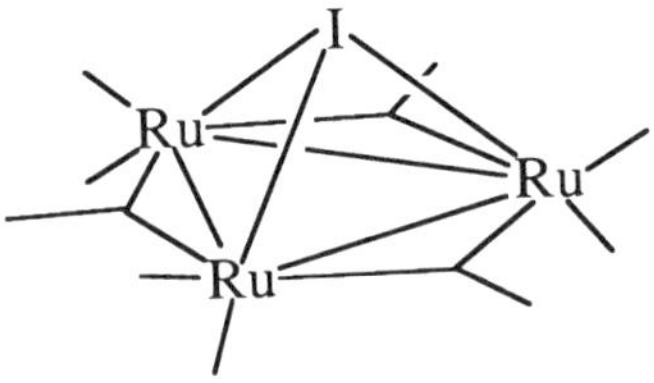

[90d]

may involve solvent participation, as exemplified by the formation of $Ru_4(\mu\text{-}Cl)(\mu_3\text{-}OCH_2CH_3)_2(CO)_{10}$ (93) in a prolonged reaction of (1) with [PPN][Cl] in ethanol.[137]

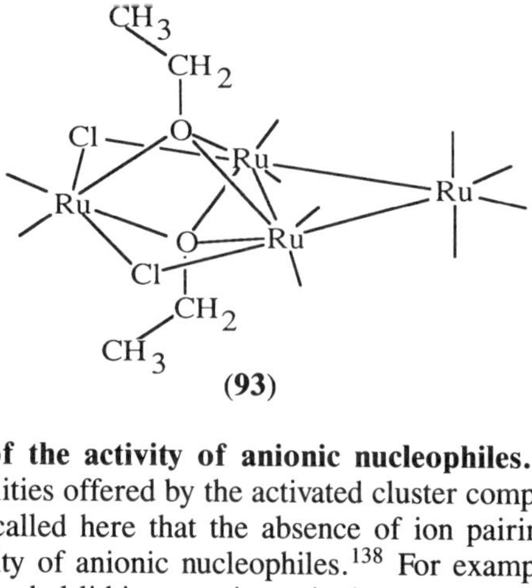

(93)

Enhancement of the activity of anionic nucleophiles. Before considering the attractive possibilities offered by the activated cluster complexes listed in Table 5.1, it should be recalled here that the absence of ion pairing is often required to enhance the activity of anionic nucleophiles.[138] For example, in the treatment of $Os_3(CO)_{12}$ with methyl lithium to give anionic acyl derivatives, Kaesz and co-workers observed an acceleration of CO evolution upon addition of Kryptate.[119] Similarly, Alper and co-workers[139] noted that addition of Crown ether to potassium fluoride, or direct use of quaternary ammonium fluoride led to a "naked fluoride ion" capable of associative reaction with $Fe_3(CO)_{12}$ (**94**) to give an adduct which was tentatively formulated as $[Fe_3(CO)_{11}\{C(O)F\}]^-$ [**95**].

In this respect, a simple comparison of two alternate synthetic routes to the anion $[Ru_3(\mu\text{-}Cl)(CO)_{10}]^-$ is also illustrative of the importance of these effects.

$$Ru_3(CO)_{12} + LiCl + 2Me_3NO \xrightarrow{THF,0°C} [Li][Ru_3(\mu\text{-}Cl)(CO)_{10}] + 2CO_2 \quad (5.6)$$

$$Ru_3(CO)_{12} + [PPN][Cl]^* \xrightarrow{THF,25°C} [PPN][Ru_3(Cl)(CO)_{11}] + CO \quad (5.7a)$$

$$[PPN][Ru_3(Cl)(CO)_{11}] \xrightarrow[\text{or vacuum}]{\text{nitrogen flow,}} [PPN][Ru_3(\mu\text{-}Cl)(CO)_{10}] + CO \quad (5.7b)$$

dissolved in the minimum amount of CH_2Cl_2.

In reaction (5.6), trimethylamine N-oxide is required to oxidize CO to CO_2, favoring further coordination of the halide.[90] In reaction (5.7), such a reagent is not required. The "naked" halide ion in [PPN][Cl] is sufficiently nucleophilic to penetrate the ligand shell under mild conditions. The rate of the reaction is limited only by the poor solubility of the salt in THF. Adduct formation is instantaneous if the salt is added in the minimum amount of CH_2Cl_2, and the subsequent reaction step (5.7b) is quantitative when the solution is degassed under vacuum for a few minutes.[131a]

Direct addition of a highly dissociated salt to $Ru_3(CO)_{12}$ (according to type 5.7a reaction) provides a simple and direct route to various adducts of anionic nucleophiles with $Ru_3(CO)_{12}$;[131a] in particular, it appears to be the simplest way to synthesize $[PPN][Ru_3(\mu\text{-}H)(CO)_{11}]$ [**85b**] quantitatively within a few minutes, equation (5.8).[140] Noticeably, such a reaction will take hours when carried out in dichloromethane.[141]

$$Ru_3(CO)_{12} + [PPN][BH_4]^* \xrightarrow{THF,25°C,1\ min} [PPN][Ru_3(\mu\text{-}H)(CO)_{11}] + CO \quad (5.8)$$

dissolved in the minimum amount of CH_2Cl_2.

From stoichiometric to catalytic activation. Acidification of type B and C anions reported in Table 5.1 produces edge double-bridged species $Ru_3(\mu\text{-}H)(\mu\text{-}C(O)Nu)(CO)_{10}$ (Nu = R, OR, NR_2) or $Ru_3(\mu\text{-}H)(\mu\text{-}Nu)(CO)_{10}$ (Nu = X)[90] that are still highly reactive and undergo stereospecific substitutions at 25°C. The labilizing effect of bridging acyl or carboxamido groups is approximately of the same magnitude as that of bridging halides.[120,142] The recent extension of such reactions to organic ligands is exemplified here by the spectacular example of a side-on coordination of ethylene in the acyl cluster complex $Os_3(\mu\text{-}H)(\mu\text{-}C(O)R)(CO)_9(\eta^2\text{-}H_2CCH_2)$ (**96**), where the ligand occupies a *cis* position relative to the acyl oxygen.[143a] An η^3 methallyl group derived from But-2-yne also coordinates at the same site in $Ru_3(\eta^3\text{-}CH_2CHCHCH_3)(\mu\text{-}O=CNMe_2)(\mu\text{-}CO)(CO)_8$.[143b]

(96)

The reports by Darensbourg of ^{13}C enrichment of $Ru_3(CO)_{12}$[126] catalyzed by OR^-, and by Ford of a stoichiometric synthesis of the neutral complex $Ru_3(CO)_{11}PR_3$ from the methoxycarbonyl adduct $[Ru_3(\mu\text{-}C(O)OR)(CO)_{11}]^-$ [86a][127,88b] provided the first indications that nucleophilic anions may participate in a catalytic activation of $Ru_3(CO)_{12}$. This was subsequently demonstrated for a series of nucleophilic anions[131a] (reaction 5.9, type a catalyst) and recently extended to the case of H^- as a nucleophile (reaction 5.9, type b catalyst).[140]

$$Ru_3(CO)_{12} + nPR_3 \xrightarrow{\text{Catalyst, THF, } 25°C} Ru_3(CO)_{12-n}(PR_3) + nCO \quad (n = 1, 2) \quad (5.9)$$

Catalysts precursors:
a) [PPN][Nu]:[131a] $Nu = CN^-$, CH_3COO^-, F^-, Cl^-, Br^-, I^-
b) Hydride donors:[140] K-Selectride, [PPN][HRu(CO)_4],
[PPN][HRu_3(CO)_{11}], [PPN][HRu_3(CO)_{10}PR_3] under CO

The efficiency of these systems is matching that of the BPK catalyst developed by Michael Bruce (see Section 5.2.2), with the additional advantage that both PPN salts and K-Selectride are catalysts that can be kept in a bottle.[131a-e] In the promotion of reaction (5.9) by (a) or (b) precursors, the catalysis is supposed to involve type A adducts (Table 5.1) as transfer agents for the nucleophilic anion. For example, when a hydride donor is used as a catalyst precursor, the rates for substitution show a marked dependence on the hydride donating properties of the salt. A fast zero-order reaction takes place with K-Selectride as a catalyst (turnover $\approx$ 20 min^{-1}), while the observation of an induction period upon initiation by catalytic amounts of [PPN][HRu_3(CO)_{11}] [85b] as well as the accelerating effect of CO in reactions initiated by [PPN][HRu_3(CO)_{10}PR_3] [97] are consistent with a mechanism based on "[Ru_3(CO)_{12}H]" [85a] as the effective hydride transfer agent.[140] A view of the proposed mechanism based on a formyl intermediate is provided in Scheme 5.22.

The catalytic cycle in Scheme 5.22 is reminiscent of earlier observations on the hydride transfer properties of [HRu_3(CO)_{11}]$^-$ [124,144] having dramatic implications in the water-gas shift reaction,[116,124,145] or in the synthesis of ethyleneglycol via reduction of carbon monoxide[146] (see Chapter 7).

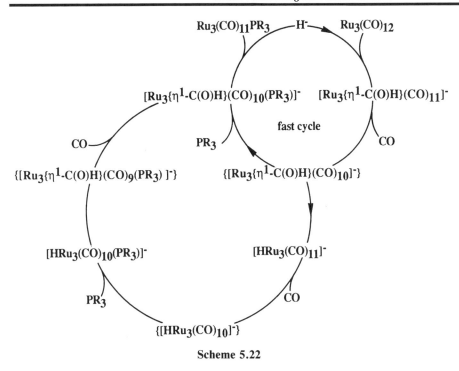

Scheme 5.22

Extension to ligands and organic substrates other than phosphines. The possibility to extend the catalytic substitutions to organic substrates would be a priori attractive. The doped cluster anions $[Ru_3(CO)_{12-n}\{Nu\}]$ react readily under ambient conditions with organic substrates L to give substituted cluster anions $[Ru_3(CO)_{12-n'}L\{Nu\}]$, but, as shown later, the latter species do not spontaneously expel Nu^-, particularly if L is not basic enough. In fact, this is not a disadvantage, since the presence of Nu^- favors the occurrence of further transformations of the incoming ligand on the cluster core. Furthermore, according to the observed solvent effects discussed previously, there is still a possibility to control the activity of Nu^- by a modification of the aprotic character of the medium. These concepts are illustrated in various examples of nucleophile promoted reactions provided in the following paragraphs.

Activation of hydrogen under mild conditions. Even better than other categories of activated species, clusters that are doped by nucleophilic anion are prone to activate hydrogen under mild conditions. The mechanism of such a reaction has been investigated in detail in the case of methoxycarbonyl adducts $[Ru_3(CO)_{11}(CO_2CH_3)]^-$;[147] it involves reversible CO dissociation followed by rate-limiting H_2 addition:

$$[Ru_3(CO_2CH_3)(CO)_{11}]^- \rightleftarrows [Ru_3(CO_2CH_3)(CO)_{10}]^- + CO \qquad (5.10)$$

$$[Ru_3(CO_2CH_3)(CO)_{10}]^- + H_2 + CO \rightarrow [HRu_3(CO)_{11}]^- + HCO_2CH_3 \qquad (5.11)$$

The complicated transformation (5.11) is believed to involve "$[H_2Ru_3(CO_2CH_3)(CO)_{10}]^-$" which would release methyl formate to give "$[HRu_3(CO)_{10}]^-$," the latter then scavenging CO to give $[HRu_3(CO)_{11}]^-$. This proposal is reasonable, since cluster anions of general formula $[H_2Os_3\{Nu\}(CO)_{10}]^-$ [14] have been isolated from the reaction of $H_2Os_3(CO)_{10}$ with a variety of anionic nucleophiles.[148] Futhermore, a reaction sequence of the type (5.10)–(5.11) is also observable for other anionic nucleophiles, though the mechanism has not been established in such cases: $[Ru_3(Cl)(CO)_{11}]^-$ reacts within 10 minutes with hydrogen in THF to give $[HRu_3(CO)_{11}]^-$ as the principal product, while "HCl" is released; $[HRu_3(CO)_{11}]^-$ is also instantaneously obtained from the reaction of the halide adduct with potassium selectride at 25°C.[149]

The facile reaction of $[Ru_3(X)(CO)_{11}]^-$ with hydrogen accounts for the formation of the active mixture of complexes $\{[HRu_3(CO)_{11}]^- + [Ru(CO)_3I_3]^-\}$ in Dombek's procedure for the synthesis of ethylene glycol by hydrogenation of CO from $Ru_3(CO)_{12}$ in the presence of iodide promoters.[146a]

Hydrogenation of olefins. The doped cluster anion $[Ru_3\{NCO\}(CO)_{11}]^-$ [87a] has been shown to function as a catalyst for the hydrogenation of alkenes.[150] Model studies based on the corresponding osmium complexes (and maleic anhydride as the substrate) have been carried out.[151] The mechanism, which is discussed in detail by Gladfelter in Chapter 7, rests on the observation that NCO⁻ functions both as a labilizing group and a versatile lightly bridging ligand favoring the coordination of both hydrogen and an olefin prior to their combination on cluster core. The key step where maleic anhydride inserts into a metal-hydride bond to give a terminal alkyl group has been characterized in the case of osmium, and the X-ray structure of $[PPN][Os_3(\mu-H)\{\mu-NCO\}(CO)_9(\eta^1-CHCH_2C(O)OC(O))]$ [98] has been reported.[151]

[98]

Halide-promoted migratory insertion and its relevance to the hydroformylation of alkenes. Few years ago, Kaesz and co-workers reported the reaction of the edge-double bridged species $Ru_3(\mu-H)(\mu-Cl)(CO)_{10}$ (99) with ethylene and CO at very mild conditions providing the μ-propionyl derivative $Ru_3(\mu-O-C(CH_2CH_3))(\mu-Cl)(CO)_{10}$ (100), Scheme 5.23.[152]

An unobserved alkyl intermediate "$Ru_3(\eta^1-CH_2CH_3)(\mu-Cl)(CO)_{10}$" resulting from the alkene insertion into a metal hydride bond was postulated. Further support to this proposal came from the isolation of $Os_3(CH_3)(\mu-I)(CO)_{10}$ (102) (by protonation of $[Os_3(\mu-CH_2)(\mu-I)(CO)_{10}]^-$ [101]), shown to undergo rapid reaction

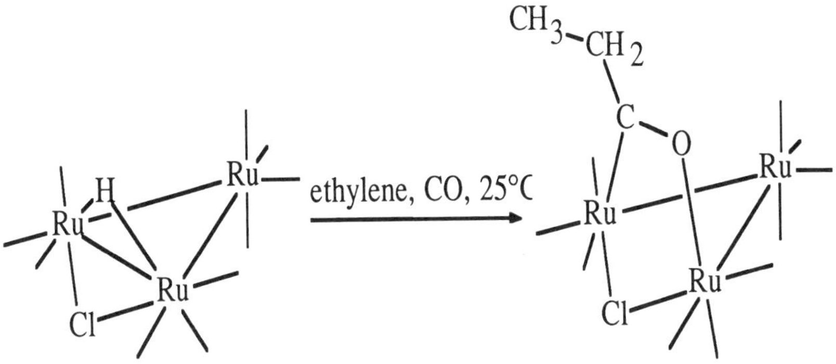

Scheme 5.23

with CO to provide the acetyl derivatives $Os_3(\eta^1\text{-}C(O)CH_3)(\mu\text{-}I)(CO)_{11}$ (**103**) and $Os_3(\mu\text{-}C(O)CH_3)(\mu\text{-}I)(CO)_{10}$ (**104**).[153]

In light of the unifying view of the activity of anionic nucleophiles discussed previously, it is significant that the anionic complex $[HRu_3(CO)_{11}]^-$ also undergoes fast reaction with ethylene under CO atmosphere to provide the acyl derivative $[Ru_3(\mu\text{-}O\text{—}C(CH_2CH_3))(CO)_{10}]^-$ [**105a**],[152a] thus modeling a key intermediate in the hydroformylation of alkenes catalyzed by this cluster anion.[154,155] The parallel reaction of $[HFe_3(CO)_{11}]^-$ with ethylene leads to a related species $[Fe_3(\mu_3\text{-}\eta^2\text{-}O\text{—}C(CH_2CH_3))(CO)_9]^-$ [**252a**] involving a face-bridging acyl,[152b] the structure of which has been determined (see the drawing in Scheme 5.49).

Halide-promoted coupling of a methylene fragment with carbon monoxide. An important effect of halide promoters in the ruthenium-catalyzed hydrogenation of CO is to shift the product selectivity from C_1 to C_2 products, principally ethyleneglycol.[146] A dramatic example of halide promoted coupling of a methylene fragment with carbon monoxide has been reported (Scheme 5.24).

Coupling of a methylene group with a coordinated carbon monoxide ligand from $Os_3(\mu\text{-}CH_2)(\mu\text{-}CO)(CO)_{10}$ (**105**) is induced by reaction with carbon monoxide, leading to the slow formation of the ketene cluster $Os_3(\mu\text{-}CH_2CO)(CO)_{12}$ (**106**).[156] The activated species $[PPN][Os_3(\mu\text{-}CH_2)(\mu\text{-}X)(CO)_{10}]$ [**107**] derived by addition of [PPN][X] to (**105**) (where X is a halide or a pseudo-halide, like NCO)[157] undergoes the same coupling reaction 100 times faster to give $[PPN][Os_3(\mu\text{-}CH_2CO)(\mu\text{-}X)(CO)_{10}]$ [**108**]. Further transformations of the coordinated ketene ligand are observed upon reaction with electrophiles or nucleophiles.[158] Of particular interest is the observation that reaction of (**108**) with methanol under CO in dichloromethane leads to the enolate cluster species $[PPN][Os_3(\eta^1\text{-}CH_2C\{O\}CH_3)(CO)_{10}$ [**109**] via nucleophilic attack at the ketenyl carbon and removal of the halide as "HX."[158]

Halide promoted carbonylation of nitroaromatics. $Fe_3(CO)_{12}$ or $Ru_3(CO)_{12}$ are currently used as catalyst precursors for the carbonylation of nitroaromatics to produce isocyanates, carbamates, and ureas. The use of halide promoters in such reactions has been shown to improve the selectivity to carbamates.[159,160] Mechanistic suggestions for these reactions were nicely modeled

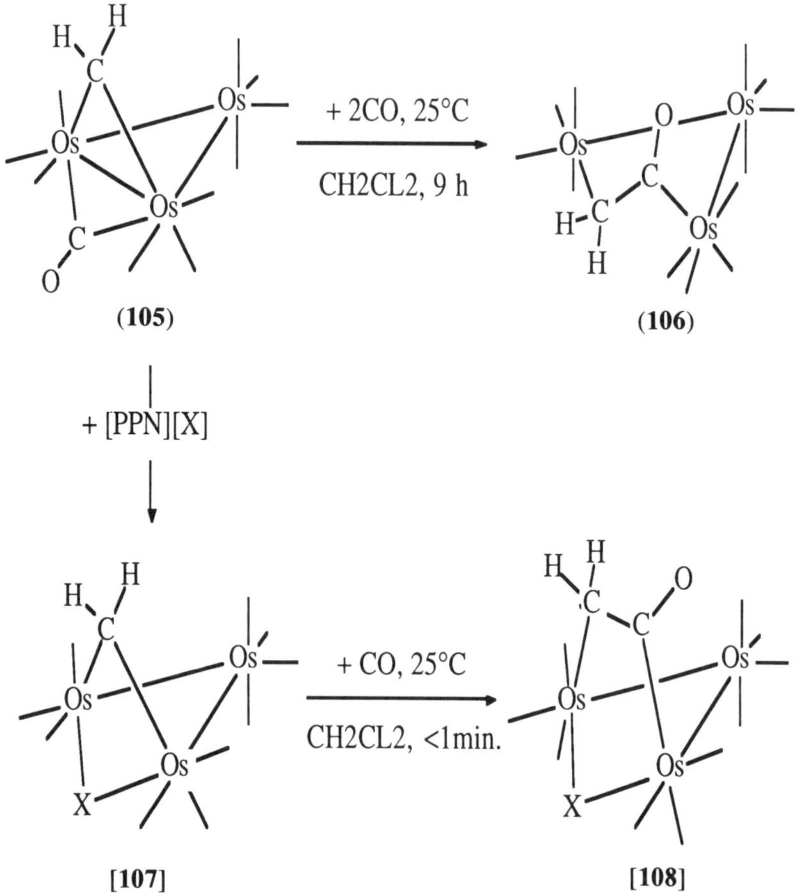

Scheme 5.24

from $Fe_3(\mu_3\text{-}NPh)_2(CO)_9$,[160] but the production of carbamates from this precursor was only stoichiometric, and currently concomitant with cluster decomposition. Dramatic progress in such model studies was recently made by direct use of the halide adducts $[PPN][Ru_3(\mu\text{-}X)(CO)_{10}]$ **[90c]** (X = Cl, Br, I) (Scheme 5.25). Unlike $Ru_3(CO)_{12}$, they react rapidly with PhNO under ambient conditions to yield $[PPN][Ru_3(\eta^1\text{-}X)(\mu_3\text{-}NPh)(CO)_8]$ **[110]** (X = Cl, Br, I).[161] The halide promoting ability (Cl $\approx$ Br > I) is just that previously noted for phosphine substitution. Reaction of the latter species with CO releases PhNCO, while the halide adduct **[90c]** is recovered.

The important implication of this reaction sequence is that the halide not only promotes the activation of PhNO to give a nitrene, but it also subsequently favors the labilization of Ru—N bonds, and the coupling of this fragment with carbon monoxide to eliminate the modified substrate PhNCO. Such a coupling reaction is interpreted as a result of the supersaturation induced by reformation of the

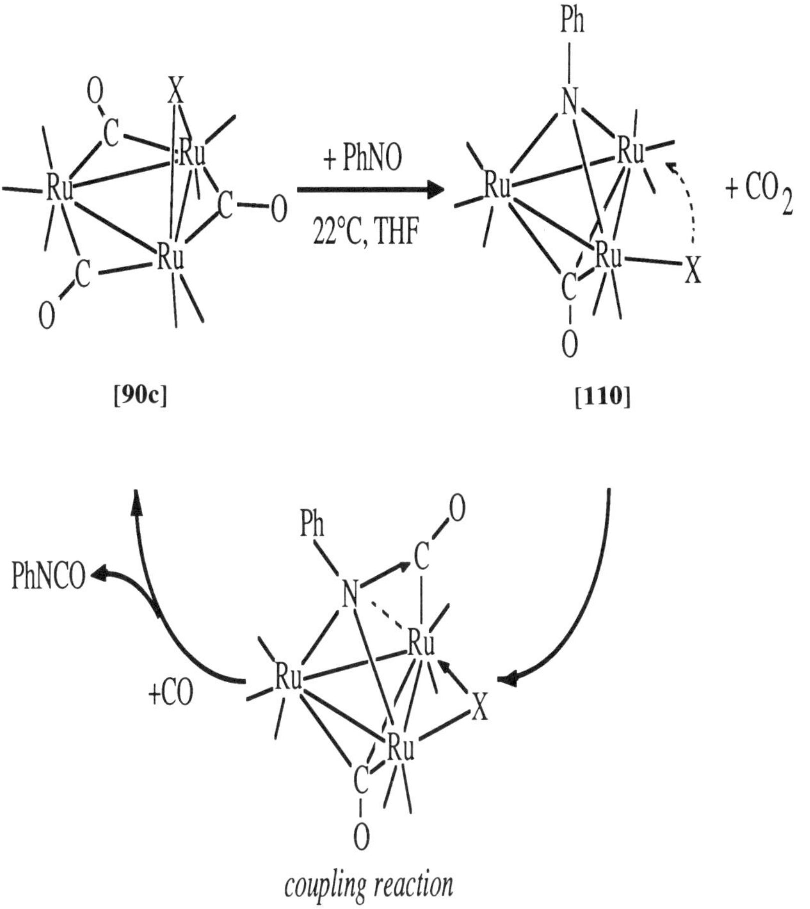

coupling reaction

Scheme 5.25

halide bridge (the inability of the cyanide anion to promote such a reaction is thus consistent with its reluctance to form intramolecular bridges, see earlier).

Let us recall here that the elimination of a stable nitrene bridge was previously found to be a serious obstacle to the closure of a catalytic cycle (see introduction and Scheme 5.1). Additional support for the proposed intermediate in Scheme 5.25 comes from earlier observations by Deeming (Scheme 5.7) as well as from a recent report on the X-ray structure of the anion [HRu$_3$(CO)$_9$(PhNCO)] [**111**].[162]

Promoter effect of anionic nucleophiles on the activation of alkynes. Thermal reactions of alkynes with simple binary carbonyl metal clusters like M$_3$(CO)$_{12}$ are essentially nonselective, and yield a number of stable products that are usually obtained in very low yields.[14,163] By contrast, the doped species [PPN][Ru$_3$(μ-Cl)(CO)$_{10}$] [**90c**] reacts within 2–3 minutes in THF with alkynes to produce selectively and quantitatively the substituted species [PPN][Ru$_3$(μ-Cl)(μ − RCCR′)(CO)$_9$] [**112**] (R = Ph or Me; R′ = Ph, Me, or H) (Scheme 5.26).[164]

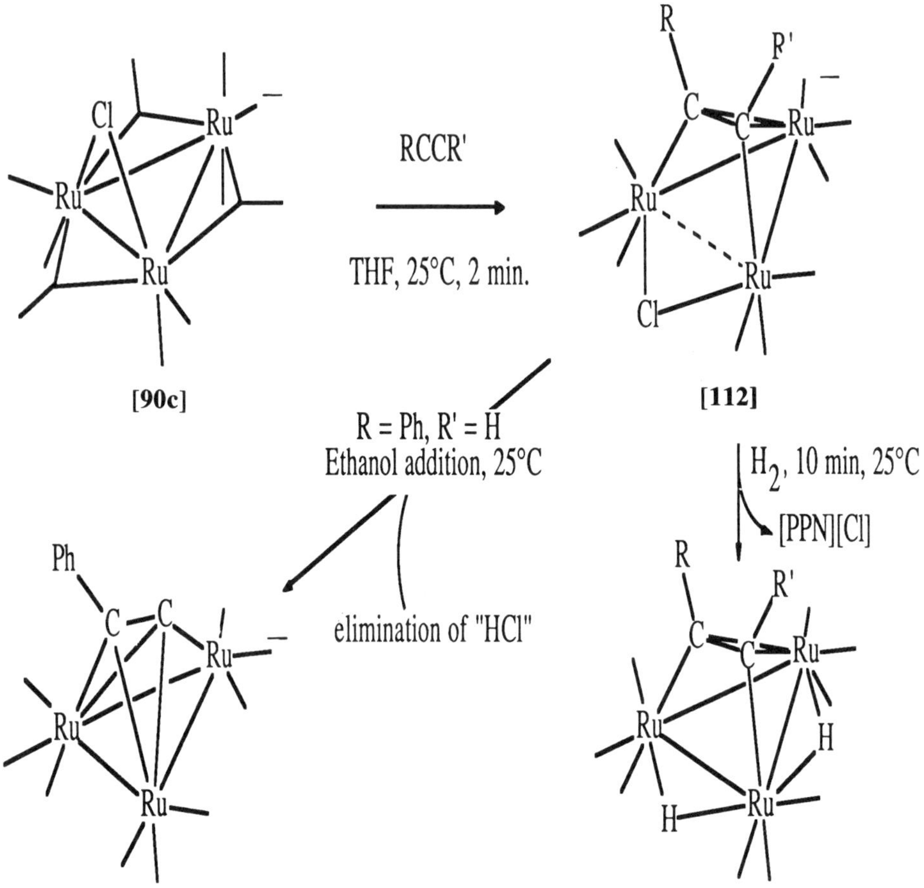

Scheme 5.26

When $R' = H$, simple addition of a protic solvent like ethanol reduces the interaction of the halide with the cluster. The resulting unsaturation promotes the oxidative addition of the C—H bond to the metal, while reductive elimination of "HCl" (deprotonation of the cluster) gives $[PPN][Ru_3(\mu\text{-}CCR)(CO)_9]$ [113]. The complex $[PPN][Ru_3(\mu\text{-}Cl)(\mu - RCCR')(CO)_9]$ [112] reacts within 10 minutes with hydrogen at 25°C in dichloromethane to give the neutral hydrido cluster complex $Ru_3(\mu\text{-}H)_2(\mu - RCCR')(CO)_9$ (114) as the principal reaction product. In alcohol solution, deprotonation of the latter species by the released $[PPN][Cl]$ yields the cluster anion $[PPN][Ru_3(\mu\text{-}H)(\mu\text{-}RCCR')(CO)_9]$ [115].[164]

Besides these observations, there are indications that anionic nucleophiles will also promote various transformations of coordinated alkynes. For example, the reaction of the stable vinyl hydride cluster $Os_3(\mu\text{-}H)(\mu\text{-}CF_3CCHCF_3)(CO)_{10}$ (116) with halides or pseudo-halides[165] promotes a carbon-hydrogen coupling reaction

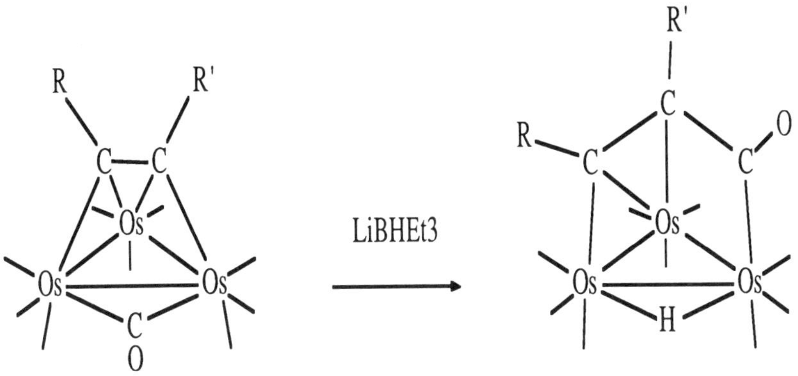

Scheme 5.27

to give the new complex [PPN][Os$_3$(η^2-CF$_3$CHCHCF$_3$)(CO)$_9$(Br)] [117] where the alkene is coordinated to only one metal center, illustrating an important step in the hydrogenation of alkynes to alkenes by a metal cluster.[166]

Also of interest is the observation that low temperature reaction of the alkyne cluster Os$_3$(μ − RCCR')(CO)$_{10}$ (118) with H$^-$ as a nucleophilic anion induces carbon-carbon coupling (in competition with CO loss) to give the complex Os$_3$(μ-H)(μ − RCCR'CH)(CO)$_{10}$ (120) via the intermediacy of [Os$_3$(μ-H)(μ − RCCR'CO)(CO)$_{10}$] [119], (Scheme 5.27).[167] The connection with other coupling reactions discussed earlier is obvious.

This and related observations discussed previously illustrate a general principle that also governs a number of reactions presented in the following pages: the supersaturation of a carbonyl cluster induced by a nucleophile is generally balanced by reductive coupling reactions unless a CO loss occurs. The effect of anionic nucleophiles is thus maximized under CO atmosphere.

Prospects on possible extension to other transition metals. The principal doped anionic species discussed earlier are found in the iron triad, and concern ruthenium in particular. Significantly, there is also a parallel growing number of applications based on ruthenium cluster precursors and halide promoters.[146,155,159,160,168] Although Os$_3$(CO)$_{12}$ is reactive only toward strong anionic nucleophiles (hydride, or strongly basic amines), some of its derivatives, like Os$_3$(μ-CH$_2$)(μ-CO)(CO)$_{10}$ or [Os$_3$(η^5-C$_5$H$_5$)(CO)$_{10}$][BF$_4$] [121]$^+$ (containing the electron rich carbocyclic ligand C$_5$H$_5$),[169] become susceptible to nucleophilic attack by milder nucleophilic anions such as halides.

There are also some indications that extension to Group 8 transition metals would be possible: anionic nucleophiles do react with Ir$_4$(CO)$_{12}$ (122) to give [Ir$_4$(CO)$_{11}$C(O)Nu]$^-$ [123] (Nu = OR$^-$),[170] or [Ir$_4$(CO)$_{11}$(Nu)]$^-$ [124] (Nu = halides or pseudo-halides).[171] While thermally induced substitution reactions within the parent cluster (122) are unselective, the intermediacy of the anionic species [NEt$_4$][Ir$_4$(CO)$_{11}$Br] [124a] provides a mild path for the synthesis of neutral substituted derivatives Ir$_4$(CO)$_{11}$L (125).[172]

The nucleophilic activation of ligand-stabilized cluster complexes is also certainly worthy of further investigations in the future; for example, nucleophilic addition of H^- to the carbonyl ligands has been observed for the stabilized tetracobalt clusters $Co_4(\mu_4\text{-}PPh_2)(CO)_{10}$ (126), but has not been examined in terms of cluster activation[173] (see Section 5.7). However, it appears that in such studies, one should always keep in mind that the modification of a carbonyl cluster complex by a stabilizing group is also susceptible to modify the site of attack of the nucleophile. Let us recall here that hydride attack on the phosphinidene cluster complex $Fe_3(\mu_3\text{-}PPh)(CO)_9$ (8a) occurs exclusively at the phosphinidene ligand[47c] without any detectable transient formyl species (see Section 5.3).[160] Also significant is the observation that $M_3(\mu_3\text{-}S)_2(CO)_9$ (127a-c) (M = Fe, Ru, Os),[174a] undergoes attack of $HNMe_2$ either at the metal or at the carbon of a CO ligand depending on the nature of the metal. Besides, addition of $HNMe_2$ to $Os_4(\mu_3\text{-}S)(CO)_{12}$ (128) occurs via opening of the metal atom tetrahedron to give a butterfly adduct.[174b]

There is no doubt that more thorough investigations will be necessary in the future to provide a full understanding of the systems discussed here. Indeed, a number of points remain presently obscure: for example, let us recall that $Co_4(CO)_{12}$ (129) reacts with CH_3^- to give the anion $[Co_4(CO)_{11}(\eta^1\text{-}C(O)CH_3)]^-$ [130].[175] Yet, the latter adduct is stable; it has been crystallized, and an X-ray structure has been reported. It is intriguing that the terminal acyl group here exerts no labilizing effect on adjacent carbonyls!

5.2.9. Overview on Cluster Activation

Though the simple classification adopted in the previous presentation is convenient as a first approach to the problem of cluster activation, it may be rather artificial for a thorough investigation of specific cases. This is illustrated here by an additional example taken from the chemistry of borohydride cluster complexes.[176] Typically, the anionic cluster complex $[Fe_3(\mu\text{-}H)(CO)_9(BH_2R)]^-$ [131] should be regarded as an activated species due to its ability to form readily adducts $[Fe_3(\mu\text{-}H)(CO)_9(BH_2R)L]^-$ [131+L] in the presence of a variety of incoming substrates L. Though it does not clearly fall into one of the categories distinguished earlier (it might be eventually regarded as a modified BH_4^- adduct of $Fe_3(CO)_{12}$, and might thus be connected with anion promoted systems discussed in Section 5.2.8), it combines some of their individual properties. Indeed, the labile adduct species [131+L] whose structure is still unknown is predisposed to competing cleavage of metal-metal or metal-boron bonds. The balance between these paths is determined by (i) the nature of the substrate L, that is, its relative affinity for boron or iron, (ii) the substrate concentration, (iii) the nature of boron substituents.

Some observed reaction paths taken from this complicated system are given in the following: substitution via H_2 displacement is observed for L = CO [equation (5.12), also observable when L = PMe_2Ph at low concentrations]; this supports the important idea that reductive elimination of small molecules may also provide a low energy path for the coordination of substrates.

$$[Fe_3(\mu\text{-}H)(CO)_9BH_3]^- + CO \rightarrow [Fe_3(CO)_9(\mu\text{-}CO)BH_2]^- + H_2$$
$$\text{[131a]} \qquad\qquad\qquad\qquad \text{[132a]} \qquad\qquad\qquad (5.12)$$

By contrast, reaction of (131a) with H_2O, equation (5.13), a poor Lewis base with respect to iron, results in a removal of the borane cap; the unsaturated trimetal unit then scavenges CO to give $[Fe_3(\mu\text{-}H)(CO)_{11}]^-$ [133].

$$[Fe_3(\mu\text{-}H)(CO)_9BH_3]^- + H_2O \rightarrow [(\mu\text{-}H)Fe_3(CO)_{11}]^- + B(OH)_3 \qquad (5.13)$$

[131a]   [133]

In the case of PMe_2Ph, not shown here, the product distribution reflects the dual affinity of this strong base for boron and metal, and also reveals the occurrence of concurrent cluster fragmentation.

This example, as well as others discussed in Sections 5.2.5 through 5.2.8, are illustrative of a growing attention to new categories of cluster complexes that are formally electronically saturated, but whose activity currently exceeds that of truly "unsaturated" species (Section 5.2.3). In general, these derivatives are obtained by modifying simple binary carbonyl cluster complexes upon addition of appropriate inorganic main group elements[23] or inorganic fragments which combine with the metal within the cluster core. The diversity of possible associations of this type offers numerous unexplored ways for the future design of novel cluster systems with enhanced activity.[177]

Specific Transformations

5.3. Transformations of Phosphorus-Containing Ligands

Evidence for the ability of a metal cluster to transform a coordinated phosphine by activation of C—H and C—P bonds was first obtained in 1972 by Nyholm and co-workers in the course of a prolonged thermal reaction of $Os_3(CO)_{12}$ (2) with triphenylphosphine.[178] Extended observations on PMe_2Ph, $AsMe_2Ph$ and tri-alkylphosphines were made by Deeming,[179] while parallel ligand transformations on $Ru_3(CO)_{12}$ (1) were reported by Stone.[180] Following these pioneering studies, there have been numerous detailed investigations on cluster-assisted degradations of phosphine ligands. Such reactions have been reviewed,[2,26,181] and their relevance to homogeneous catalyst deactivation has been stressed,[181a] suggesting that phosphines may be inappropriate as ancillary ligands in cluster complexes when these are used as catalyst precursors.

Yet, recent studies have indicated that controlled transformations of these ligands on cluster faces are of interest in several instances. First, as mentioned in Section 5.2.6 of this chapter, the phosphorus-containing fragments (phosphido, phosphinidene, "naked" phosphorus[182]) derived from a phosphane may be used as stabilizing groups for polynuclear metal ensembles.[27] Furthermore, these fragments are chemically reactive and may participate in the transformation of various organic substrates that become coordinated to the cluster.

5.3.1. Elementary Steps

There are no mechanistic studies available on cluster-assisted transformations of phosphines, phosphites, and related ligands. Thus, the present state of knowledge of such reactions rests on the isolation of intermediates which have provided in-

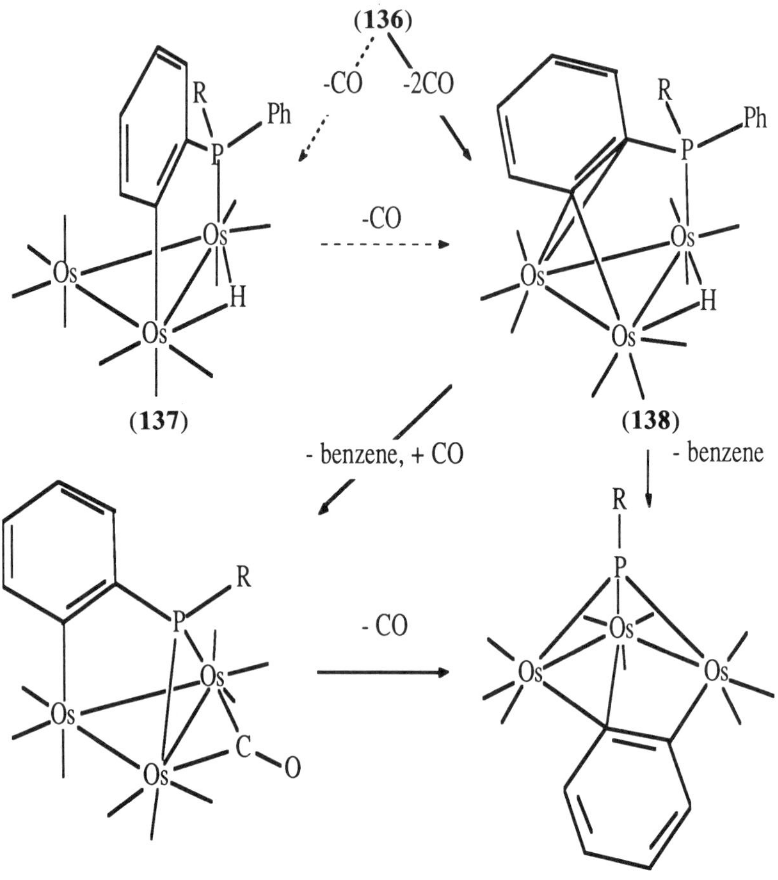

Scheme 5.28

sight into plausible reaction pathways. For triangular clusters of the iron triad, monosubstituted derivatives $M_3(CO)_{11}PR_3$ are ideal candidates for tracing the transformation of PR_3 given that dissociative loss of CO from such complexes is much easier than for polysubstituted species.[183] Typically, diphenylpyridylphosphine does not undergo any transformation upon prolonged thermolysis of the trisubstituted derivative $Ru_3(CO)_9((P(C_6H_5)_2(C_5H_4N))_3$ (**134**); cluster fragmentation is then the only observable reaction.[184] By contrast, activation of this ligand via P—C bond cleavage occurs spontaneously at 25°C from the monosubstituted derivative $Ru_3(CO)_{11}((P(C_6H_5)_2(C_5H_4N))$ (**135**) (see below).[185]

Activation of C—H bonds on phosphorus substituents; orthometallation. For aryl phosphines and related ligands, orthometallation is commonly the initial process. This is illustrated in Scheme 5.28 for the species $Os_3(CO)_{11}(PPh_2R)$ (**136**) (R = Ph or Me).[186,187]

Thermally induced loss of CO from (**136**) provides a vacant coordination site which is easily trapped by activation of a C—H bond to give $Os_3(\mu\text{-H})(\mu_3\text{-}$ $P(C_6H_4)PhR)(CO)_9$ (**138**) where metallation of two carbon atoms of the C_6H_4 group is observable (described here as a σ bond to one metal center and a two-electron η^2 interaction between C=C double bond and the adjacent metal center). The probable intermediate $Os_3(\mu\text{-H})(\mu\text{-}P(C_6H_4)PhR)(CO)_{10}$ (**137**) (classic orthometallation through a terminal σ bond) was not seen here, though such a step has been well characterized in other cluster complexes.[178,188] Such an interaction is also found in the complex $Os_3(\mu\text{-}P(C_6H_4)R)(\mu\text{-CO})(CO)_9$ (**139**) appearing here, though the latter does not lie on the main route to the final product $Os_3(\mu_3\text{-PR})(\mu_3\text{-}$ $C_6H_4)(CO)_9$ (**140**).[186,187]

The reversibility of orthometallation is currently observable.[189] Thermolysis of $Os_3(CO)_{10}(dppm)$ (**141**) provides the 46-e unsaturated orthometallated species $Os_3(\mu\text{-H})(\mu\text{-}P(C_6H_5)_2CH_2P(C_6H_5)(C_6H_4))(CO)_8$ (**142**) which may in turn add 2 carbonyl groups sequentially to regenerate the parent complex. Besides, hydrogenolysis of the metal carbon bonds of (**142**) yields the 46-e cluster $Os_3(\mu\text{-}$ $H)_2(CO)_8(dppm)$ (**143**).[189b]

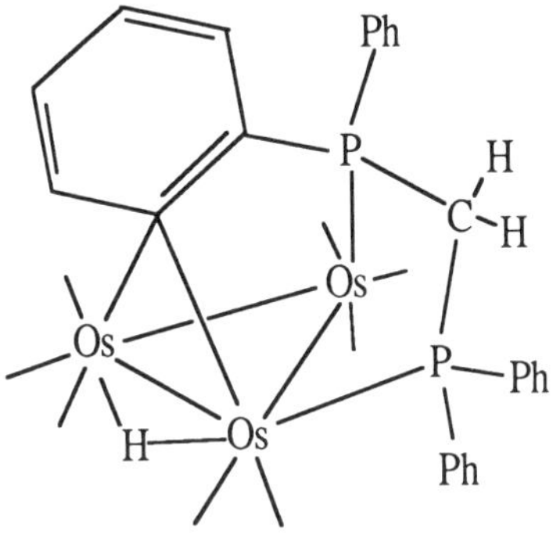

(**142**)

Cluster complexes modeling intermediate stages in P-C bond cleavage. The phosphido-bridged species $Ru_3(\mu\text{-H})(\mu\text{-}P(C_6H_5)_2)(CO)_9$ (**44**)[89,190] (see Scheme 5.13 in Section 5.2.5) involves the weak interaction of a P-C(phenyl) bond with the unique ruthenium atom, thus reflecting the need of this metal to relieve its unsaturation. Such an interaction is prone to favor direct cleavage of the corresponding P-C bond, observable under thermal activation, and leading to $Ru_4(\mu\text{-}P(C_6H_5))(CO)_{13}$ (**144**), or by reaction with hydrogen to give $Ru_3(\mu\text{-}$ $H)_2(\mu\text{-}P(C_6H_5))(CO)_9$ (**145**) in 90% yield via loss of benzene. This suggests that orthometallation is not a prerequisite for the cleavage of a P-C bond.

Direct interaction of a P—C bond with a metal center is also observable during the thermally induced degradation of dppm on the face of $Ru_3(CO)_8(dppm)_2$ (**12**) (Scheme 5.29).[191a–b]

The complex $Ru_3(\mu\text{-H})(\mu\text{-}P(C_6H_5)CHP(C_6H_5)(C_6H_4))(CO)_7(dppm)$ (**146**) is seen at intermediate stage: partial degradation of a coordinated dppm molecule has provided the face-bridging organic fragment $\mu\text{-}P(C_6H_5)CHP(C_6H_5)(C_6H_4)$. The X-ray structure of (**146**) indicates that the phosphorus atom of the bridging

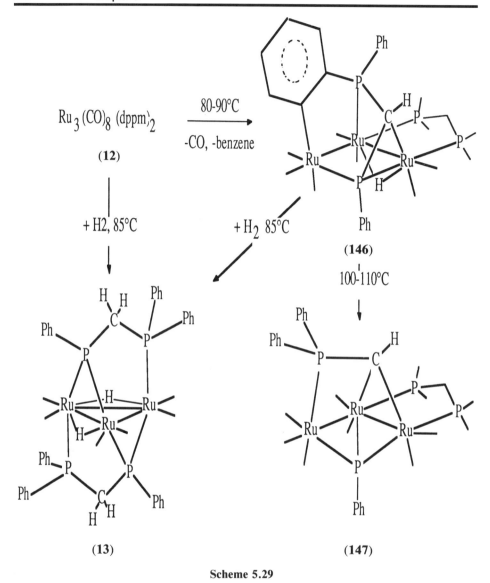

Scheme 5.29

phosphido group and the adjacent carbon (methylene) are bound to the same metal. Further scission of this "activated" bond is seen in the final reaction step leading to the isomeric complex $Ru_3(\mu_3\text{-}P(C_6H_5))(CHP(C_6H_5)_2)(CO)_7(dppm)$ (**147**): the resulting phosphinidene group has moved toward the opposite face, while the other fragment, a phosphinocarbene group, has rearranged itself on the metal triangle through an ortho-demetallation process. In the presence of hydrogen, the reaction sequence is modified to provide the new complex $Ru_3(\mu\text{-}H)_2(\mu_3\text{-}P(C_6H_5)CH_2P(C_6H_5)_2)(CO)_6$ (**13**) as the main product. Both dppm molecules

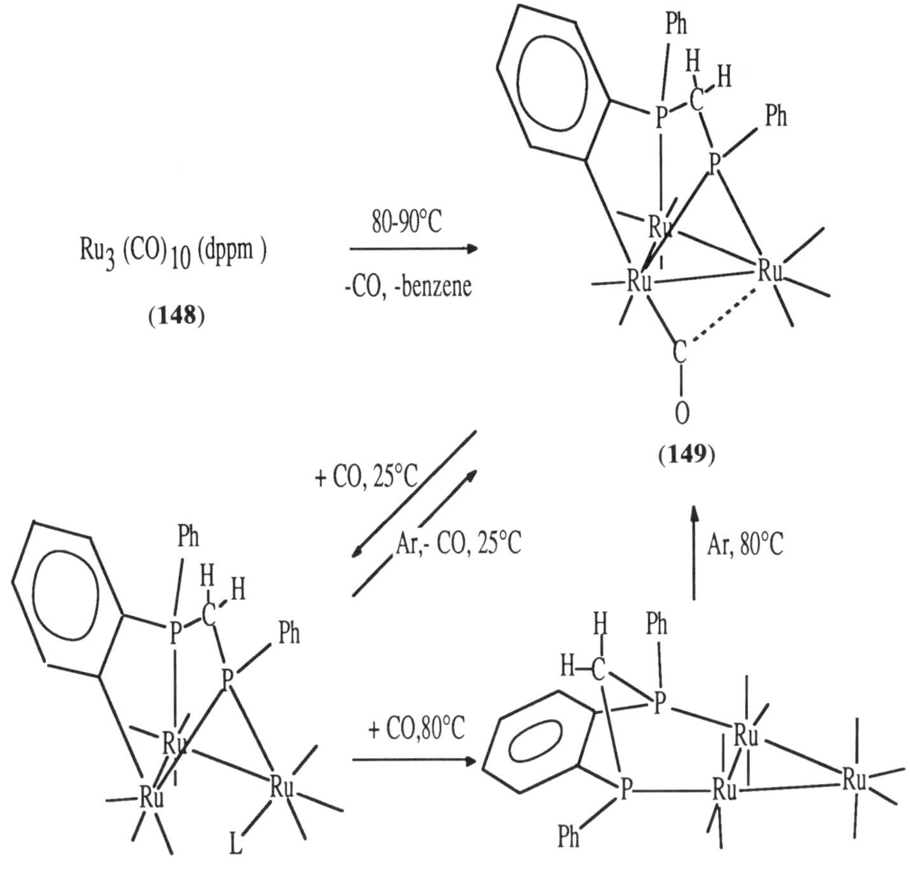

Scheme 5.30

have been transformed in this case.[61,191a−b] Interestingly, a modified sequence is observed when bis(dimethylphosphino)methane replaces dppm. In this case, activation of the C—H bond of the methylene group is preferred over P—C bond cleavage.[191c,d]

Conversion of bis(diphenylphosphino)methane into a new bidentate phosphine. The transformation of dppm on the face of $Ru_3(CO)_{10}$(dppm) (**148**) has been examined in detail by several research groups;[107,192,193] only the principal results of these studies are discussed here (Scheme 5.30).

Thermally induced loss of CO from (**148**) results in the formation of the new species $Ru_3(\mu_3\text{-}P(C_6H_5)CH_2P(C_6H_5)(C_6H_4))(CO)_8$ (**149**).[192] Direct P—C bond cleavage at two metal centers has likely occurred to give the bridging phosphido group, while orthometallation of a phenyl ring has provided the hydrogen atom required for the elimination of benzene. The resulting complex (**149**) reacts easily with CO or phosphines under ambient conditions to give the open 50-e cluster adduct $Ru_3(\mu_3\text{-}P(C_6H_5)CH_2P(C_6H_5)(C_6H_4))(CO)_8L$ (**150a-b; a**, $L = CO$; **b**, $L = PPh_3$).[107] When (**150a**) is heated under CO atmosphere, the resulting "supersaturation" is balanced by a reductive coupling between the metallated phenyl ring and the phosphido group to give $Ru_3(\mu\text{-}P(C_6H_5)CH_2P(C_6H_5)(C_6H_4))(CO)_{10}$ (**151**). This interesting conversion may be regarded as the cluster-assisted "synthesis" of a new bidentate phosphine ligand.[107,192] By extension, one may expect that coupling of a bridging phosphido group with any adjacent coordinated alkyl group may be favored under CO atmosphere. This is effectively what happens for related phosphido-bridged species under hydroformylation conditions, where alkenes are converted into transient alkyl groups (see later) {the same type of coupling reaction must also account for the transformation of the tripod ligand $P(C_6H_5)_2)_3CH$ in the thermal conversion of $Ru_3(\mu\text{-}(P(C_6H_5)_2)_3CH)(CO)_9$ (**152**) into $Ru_3(\mu\text{-}P_3(C_6H_5)_5CH)(CO)_9$ (**153**)[194]}. These carbon-phosphorus coupling reactions are generally prevented under hydrogen atmosphere, due to competition with more favorable C—H coupling. This has been a general observation in studies of the stepwise degradation of dppm in trinuclear clusters (**13**) (Scheme 5.29)[191] and (**148**)[192,193] as well as in the case of the tetranuclear species $Ru_4(\mu\text{-}H)_4(CO)_{10}(dppm)$ (**154**).[191,193]

Versatile behavior of aryl groups derived from the cleavage of P—C bonds. As evidenced from the previous examples, aryl groups are currently eliminated as aromatics, assuming that hydrido ligands are available for such reductive coupling reactions. Otherwise, these groups may either remain coordinated to the cluster or undergo further transformations as examined in the following.

Direct η^1 coordination of a phenyl group to a metal center is seen in $Pt_3(\mu\text{-}PPh_2)_3(PPh_3)_2(Ph)$ (**155**)[195,196] or in $Ir_3(\mu_3\text{-}PPh)(\mu\text{-}PPh_2CH_2PPh_2)(\eta^1\text{-}C_6H_4)(CO)_6$ (**156**)[197] [note that the source of phosphinidene, dppm and aryl groups in (**156**) is the tripod ligand $HC(P(C_6H_5)_2)_3$].

(155)   (156)

A metallated phenyl group may experience further C—H bond activation leading to C_6H_4 (see Scheme 5.28, for example). Progressive encapsulation of such a group within a cluster frame may also occur under forcing conditions. This is seen during the pyrolytic decomposition of $Ru_3(CO)_{11}(PPh_3)$ (**157**) leading to the complexes $Ru_4(\mu_4\text{-PPh})(\mu_4\text{-}\eta^4\text{-}C_6H_4)(CO)_{11}$ (**158**) and $Ru_5(\mu_5\text{-PPh})(\mu_4\text{-}\eta^6\text{-}C_6H_4)(CO)_{13}$ (**159**); these provide attractive models for the dissociative chemisorption of benzene on metal surfaces.[198]

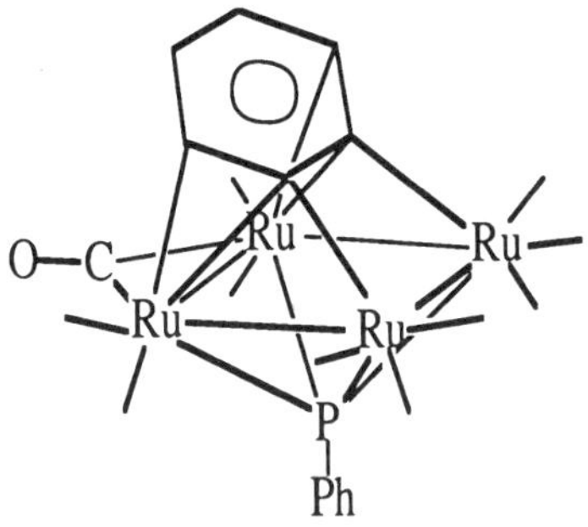

(**158**) 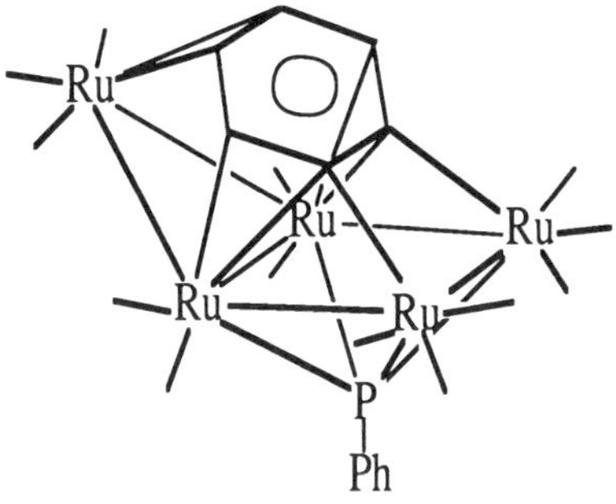   (**159**)

Under mild conditions, η^1 coordinated phenyl groups may alternately undergo migratory CO insertion,[185] as originally observed in a bimetallic species[199] (in specific cases, migration to an inorganic heteroatom (boron),[200a] or to a coordinated organic fragment[200b] may also occur). For example, as noted at the beginning of this section, spontaneous transformation of the monosubstituted complex $Ru_3(CO)_{11}(P(C_6H_5)_2(C_5H_4N))$ (**135**) occurs at 25°C on a silicagel column to provide the acyl complex $Ru_3(\mu\text{-}C(O)(C_6H_5))(\mu_3\text{-}P(C_6H_5)(C_5H_4N))(CO)_8$ (**160**) quantitatively.[185]

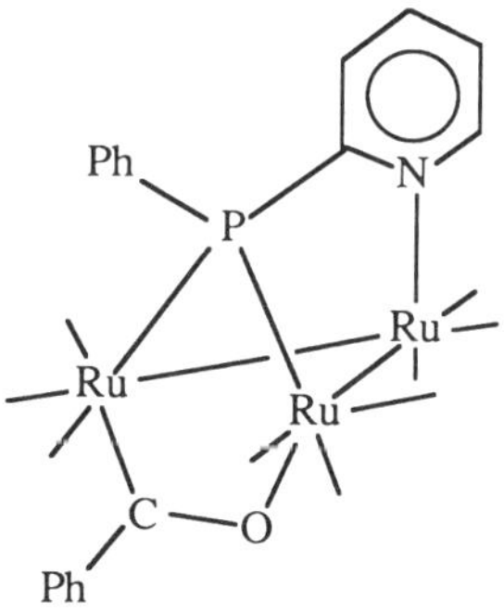

(**160**)

Interestingly, reaction of (**160**) with hydrogen produces benzene, not benzaldehyde, and yields the hydrido cluster species $Ru_3(\mu\text{-}H)(\mu_3\text{-}P(C_6H_5)(C_5H_4N))(CO)_9$ (**161**). By contrast, benzaldehyde is released in reaction of (**160**) with H^-; the mild conditions of the latter reaction avoid de-insertion of the acyl group.[106]

PR_2H, PRH_2, PH_3 and related bidentate ligands PRH—CH_2—PRH as precursors for stabilizing groups in cluster complexes. Given that oxidative addition of P—H bonds to a metal center is favored over P—C bond activation, the

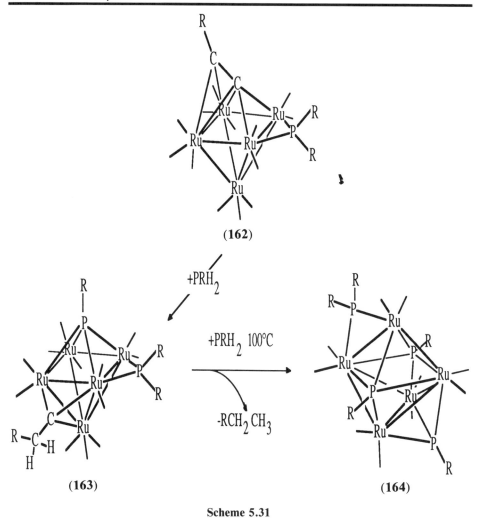

Scheme 5.31

ligands just discussed are ideal sources for the selective introduction of phosphido or phosphinidene groups which may then be used as building blocks for a variety of cluster complexes[27,201] (see Scheme 5.31 and Chapter 3).

Reduction of coordinated organic substrates by H transfer from primary and secondary phosphines. A further interesting application of primary and secondary phosphines is the possibility to transfer their hydrogen atoms to coordinated organic substrates, thus releasing the corresponding reduced organic products.

Typically, reduction of a coordinated acetylide to a free alkane was originally achieved by sequential addition of a primary phosphine to the cluster $Ru_5(CO)_{13}(\mu_4\text{-}\eta^2\text{-}CCR)(\mu\text{-}P(C_6H_5)_2)$ (**162**), leading to the complex $(H)(Ru_5(CO)_{10}(\mu\text{-}P(C_6H_5)_2)(\mu_3\text{-}P(C_6H_5))(\mu_4\text{-}P(C_6H_5))_2$ (**164**) via the intermediacy of $Ru_5(CO)_{12}(\mu_4\text{-}P(C_6H_5))(\mu_3\text{-}CCH_2R)$ (**163**) (Scheme 5.31).[202]

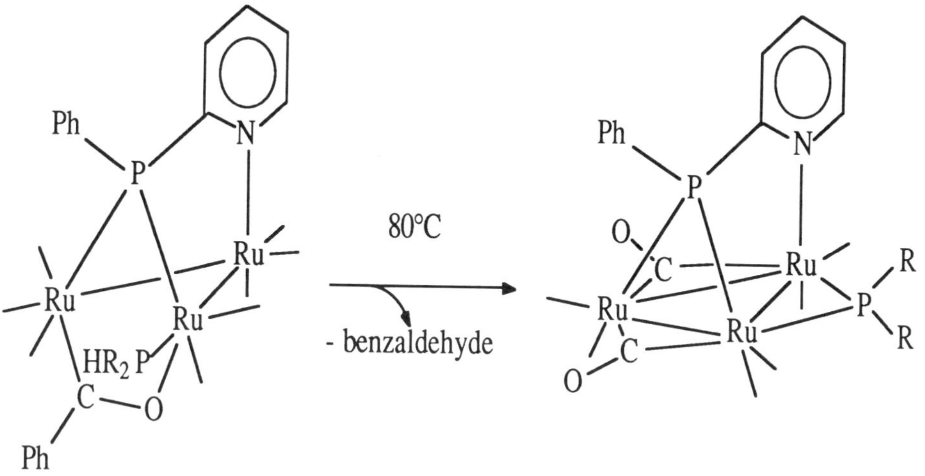

Scheme 5.32

Partial reduction of a face-bridging alkylidyne by PR_2H, followed by migration of the resulting alkyl group to a coordinated CO has been observed by Jeffery and co-workers.[203]

Finally, in the thermally induced transformation of the acyl cluster complex $Ru_3(\mu\text{-}C(O)(C_6H_5))(\mu_3\text{-}P(C_6H_5)(C_5H_4N))(CO)_8(P(C_6H_5)H)$ (165) [substituted analog of (160), see earlier] into the phosphido-bridged species $Ru_3(\mu_3\text{-}P(C_6H_5)(C_5H_4N))(\mu\text{-}P(C_6H_5)_2)(CO)_8$ (64) (Scheme 5.32), the source of hydrogen-releasing benzaldehyde is the coordinated phosphine $P(C_6H_5)_2H$.[106]

Clearly, the stoichiometric H transfer observed here could be of genuine interest for catalytic purposes if the initial phosphine could be regenerated by some means from the bridging phosphido group. In fact, experiments discussed in Section 5.2.6 of this chapter (Scheme 5.17)[106] have provided evidence for a hydrogen-assisted opening of a phosphido bridge leading to $P(C_6H_5)_2H$.

5.3.2. Coupling Reactions Between Phosphido or Phosphinidene Groups and Other Substrates

Early evidences for the chemical reactivity of these groups. Examples of $P-C$[105,107] and $P-H$[106] coupling reactions occurring in cluster complexes have been already mentioned, respectively in Schemes 5.16, 5.17, and 5.30. An important background for such bridge elimination reactions is found in the original independent observations of Carty,[204] Geoffroy,[205] Wojcicki,[206] and Kyba[207] in studies of binuclear complexes (see selected examples following).

Metal-mediated transformations of phosphorus ligands under catalytic conditions. In the course of a hydroformylation of 1-hexene, equation (5.14), using the oligomeric complex $[Co(\mu\text{-}P(C_6H_5)_2)(CO)_3]_x$ (166) as a catalyst precursor, Geoffroy and co-workers[205a] noted the irreversible formation of $P(C_6H_5)_2(hexyl)$

via a bridge-opening reaction leading to $Co_2(CO)_6(P(C_6H_5)_2(hexyl))_2$ (**167**), equation (5.15).

$$1\text{-hexene} + CO + H_2 \xrightarrow[\substack{\text{(166) as catalyst, } 110^\circ C, \\ 1250 \text{ psi, toluene}}]{} C_7 \text{ aldehydes} \qquad (5.14)$$

$$[Co(\mu\text{-}P(C_6H_5)_2)(CO)_3]_x + 1\text{-hexene} + H_2$$
$$(\mathbf{166})$$

$$\rightarrow (x/2)\ Co_2(CO)_6(P(C_6H_5)_2(hexyl))_2$$
$$(\mathbf{167}) \qquad\qquad (5.15)$$

A related bridge elimination was observed in the presence of ethanol under forcing conditions [110°C, 8h, 1000 psi, CO/H_2, equation (5.16)].

$$[Co(\mu\text{-}P(C_6H_5)_2)(CO)_3]_x + 2\ \text{EtOH} \rightarrow (x/2)\ Co_2(CO)_6(P(C_6H_5)_2(OEt))_2$$
$$(\mathbf{166}) \qquad\qquad\qquad\qquad\qquad (\mathbf{168})$$
$$(5.16)$$

More recently, phosphido-bridged rhodium[208] and cobalt[209] complexes were also expected to account for the observed aryl group scrambling between aryl phosphines under the typical conditions of the hydrogenation or the hydroformylation of alkenes. The products of metal-mediated phosphorus bond cleavage of various aryl phosphines were found to be benzene derivatives (hydrogenolysis), aldehydes and alcohols (carbonylation), and biphenyl derivatives (via coupling reactions),[209] in full agreement with the diverse possibilities just discussed.

Chemical reactivity of bridging phosphido groups. In addition to the cases noted previously, this topic is well documented by studies in bimetallic derivatives: coupling reactions with hydrides, alkyls, carbenes,[205-207] alkynes,[210a] oxygen,[210b] sulfur,[210b] vinyl groups,[210c] or phosphorus ligands[210d] have been reported.

Though bimetallic complexes are out of the topic of this chapter, the mechanism of the hydride-promoted opening of a phosphido bridge in $Fe_2(\mu\text{-}PPh_2)_2(CO)_6$ (**169**) is given in Scheme 5.33 as reported in the original work of Wojcicki.[205a] The paths for this reaction have been traced at low temperature: (i) Initial hydride attack at CO gives the anionic formyl complex $[Fe_2(\mu\text{-}PPh_2)_2(CO)_5(CHO)]^-$ [**170**]; (ii) subsequent de-insertion of the formyl group occurs at the expense of a metal-metal bond to give the planar hydrido anion $[Fe_2(\mu\text{-}PPh_2)_2(CO)_6(H)]^-$ [**171**]; (iii) the terminal hydride ligand couples with the bridging phosphido to provide a terminal PR_2H ligand in the final complex $[Fe_2(\mu\text{-}PPh_2)(\mu\text{-}CO)(CO)_5(PR_2H)]^-$ [**172**].

Changes in the nature of the bridging phosphido groups may direct the initial nucleophilic attack directly at phosphorus.[207]

Chemical reactivity of phosphinidene groups; conversion into phosphido groups. Huttner and co-workers reported the first example of a reversible acetylene insertion into a metal phosphinidene bond following its coordination to the metal via a metal-metal bond cleavage process (see Scheme 5.16 in Section 5.2.6).[105]

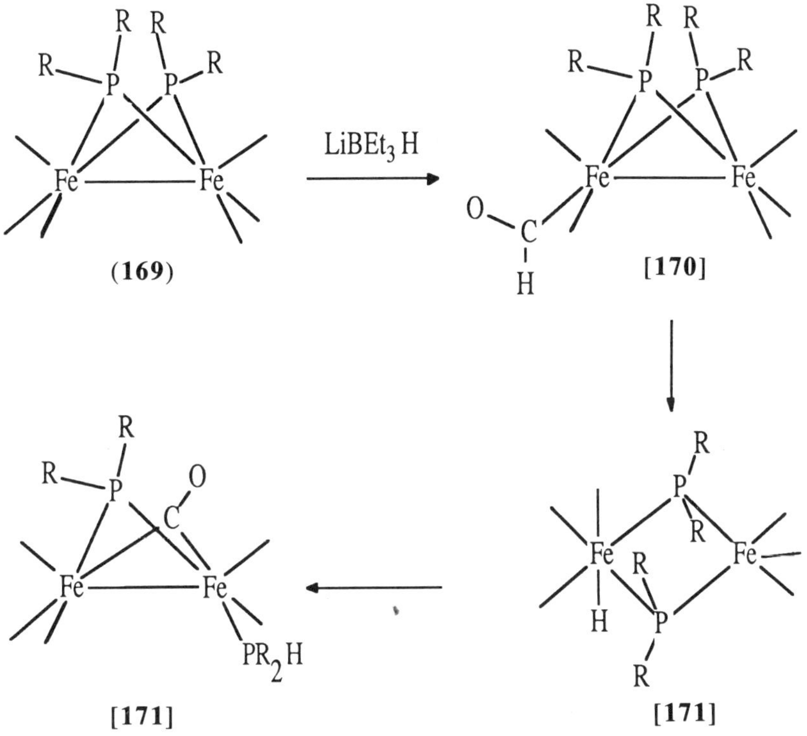

Scheme 5.33

A number of related phosphinidene-acetylene coupling reactions have now been observed;[211-213] one example is provided in Scheme 5.34, showing the UV promoted addition of diphenylacetylene to the well-known *bis*-phosphinidene species $Fe_3(\mu-P(C_6H_4-OCH_3))_2(CO)_9$ (**8e**).[212] In the adduct species, the acetylene is inserted across the P atoms and is π-bound to the metal and σ-bound to both phosphorus atoms.

A nice stepwise conversion of a phosphinidene into a phosphido group is seen in Scheme 5.35.[214] The di-hydrido phosphinidene cluster complex $Fe_3(\mu-H)_2(\mu_3-P-C_6H_4-OCH_3)(CO)_9$ (**174**) undergoes stepwise reduction to a deprotonated dianion $[Fe_3(\mu_3-P-C_6H_4-OCH_3)(CO)_9]^{2-}$ [**176**] upon treatment with $NaNH_2$ in refluxing THF (the intermediate mono-anionic species $[Fe_3(\mu-H)(\mu_3-P-C_6H_4-OCH_3)(CO)_9]^-$ [**175**] may be trapped under ambient conditions); further reaction of (**176**) with CH_2I_2 results in a phosphorus-methylene coupling leading to the neutral complex $Fe_3(\mu-H)_2(\mu_3-P(CH_2)(C_6H_4-OCH_3))(\mu-CO)(CO)_9$ (**177**). This phospha-alkene complex is then subsequently hydrogenated through a sequence H^-/H^+ leading to the phosphido-bridged species $Fe_3(\mu-H)_2(\mu_3-P(CH_3)(C_6H_4-OCH_3))(CO)_9$ (**178**) which is approximately structurally related to the ruthenium complex (**44**) (Sections 5.2.5 and 5.3; an additional feature here is that a C—C bond of the C_6H_4—OCH_3 group participates in the coordination to the metal) and exhibits a comparable chemical reactivity.[214]

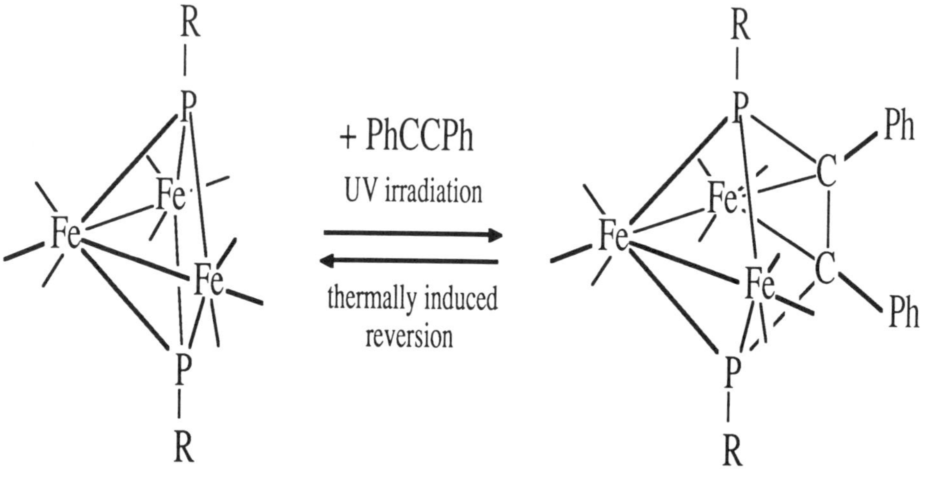

Scheme 5.34

While the example just given illustrates the nucleophilic character of a bridging phosphinidene ligand in a di-anionic cluster complex, there is also evidence for its electrophilic character in neutral species as shown in the two following examples.[47c,160] The neutral bis-phosphinidene cluster species $Fe_3(\mu_3\text{-}P(C_6H_5))_2(CO)_9$ (**8a**) is attacked by H^- directly at phosphorus to give the anion $[Fe_3(\mu_3\text{-}P(C_6H_5))(\mu_2\text{-}P(H)(C_6H_5))(CO)_9]^-$ (**179**).[47c]

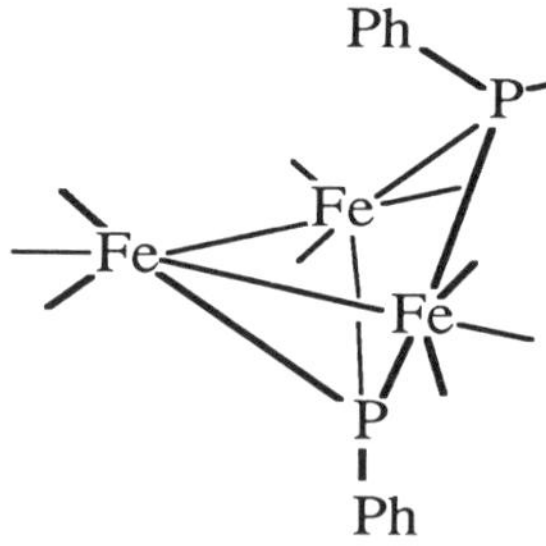

[**179**]

A more complex, but fully characterized reaction sequence is observed upon sequential treatment of (**8a**) with R^- and R^+ (Scheme 5.36).[160] Nucleophilic attack by phenyl-lithium generates the anionic benzoyl cluster $[Fe_3(\mu_3\text{-}PPh)_2(CO)_8(\eta^1\text{-}C\{O\}Ph)]^-$ [**180**]; further alkylation with $EtOSO_2CF_3$ gives the unstable carbene complex $Fe_3(\mu_3\text{-}PPh)_2(\eta^1\text{-}C\{OEt\}Ph)(CO)_8$ (**181**) which finally rearranges via a phosphinidene-carbene coupling to give $Fe_3(\mu_3\text{-}PPh)(\mu_3\text{-}PhPC(OEt)R)(CO)_9$ (**182**). The latter species bears some analogies with the related phospha-alkene complex (**177**) presented in Scheme 5.35.

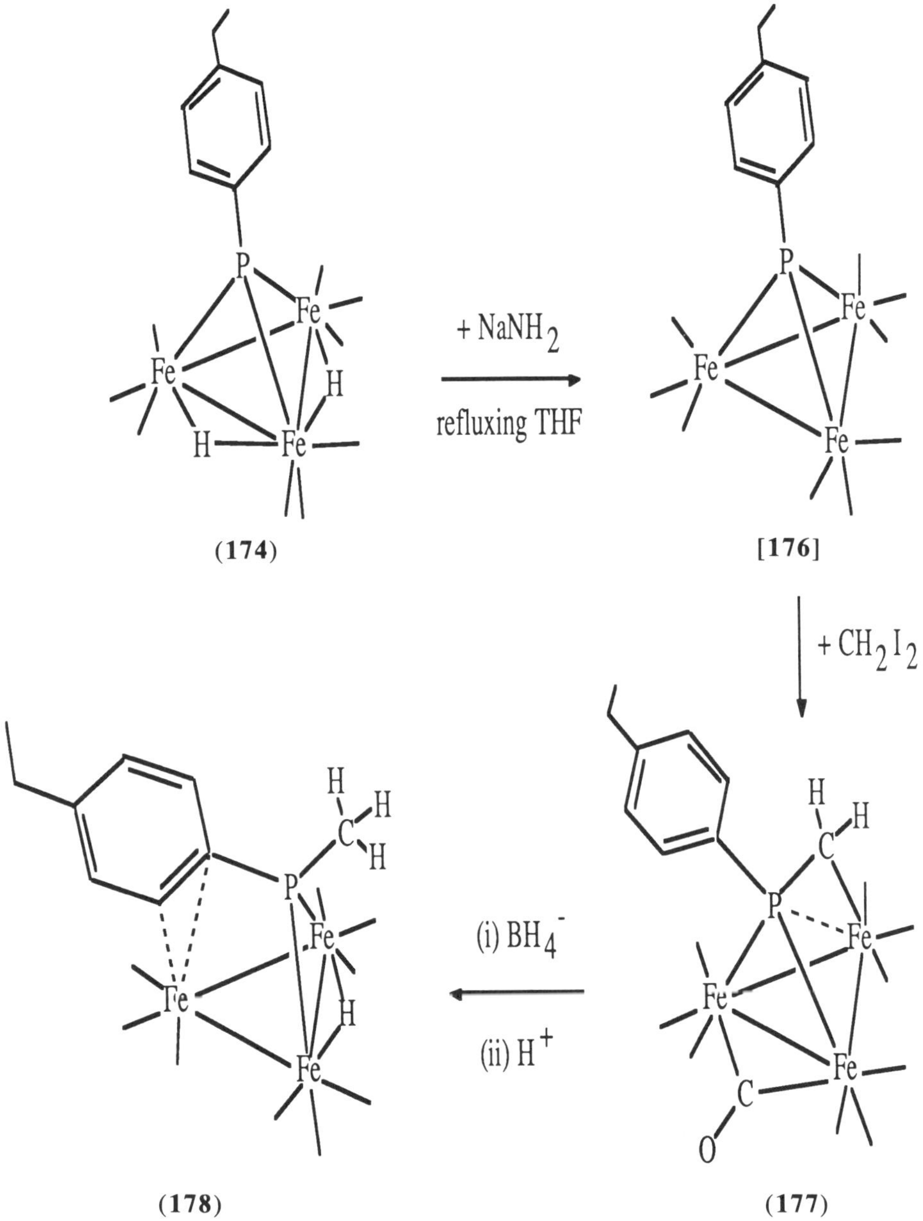

(174)

+ NaNH$_2$

refluxing THF

[176]

+ CH$_2$I$_2$

(i) BH$_4^-$

(ii) H$^+$

(178)

(177)

Scheme 5.35

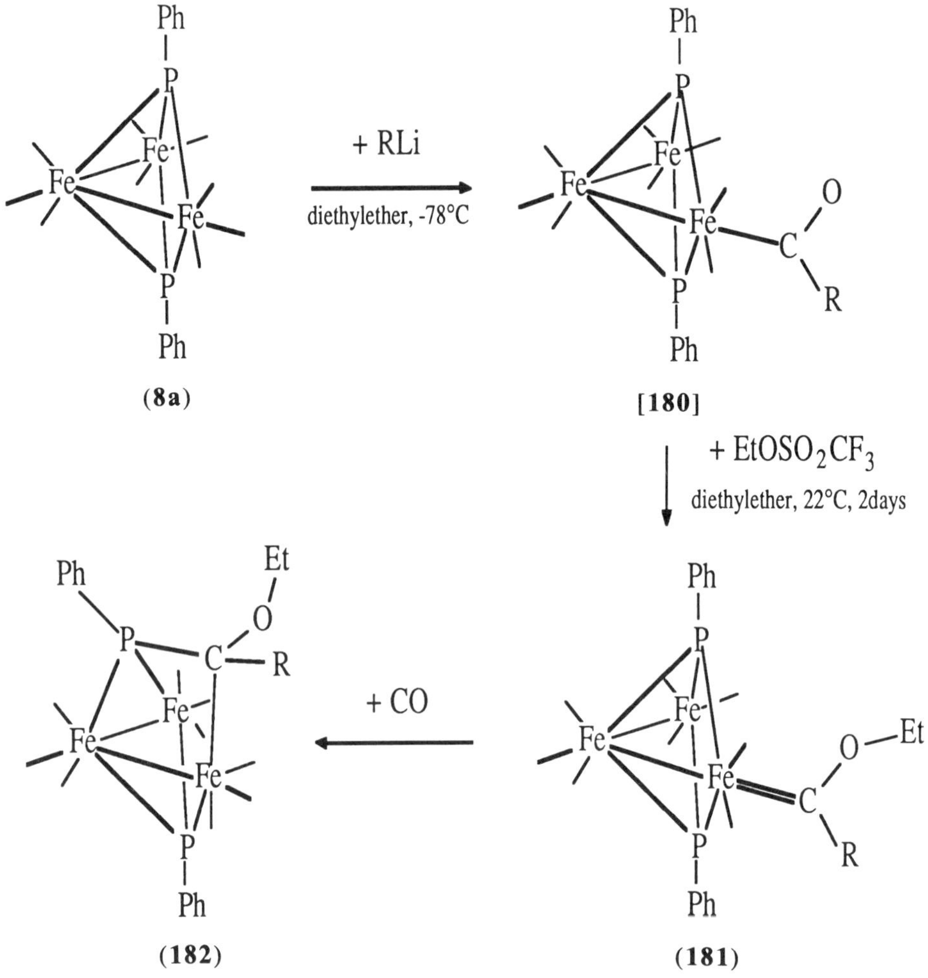

Scheme 5.36

5.4. Transformations of Sulfur-Containing Ligands

In the early reports of Professor Hieber and co-workers on reactions of thiols with iron carbonyls,[215] mercaptobenzothiazole was found to behave in an anomalous way, leading to a product which was also obtained later by King from cyclohexene episulfide and $Fe_3(CO)_{12}$, and was finally identified as $Fe_3(\mu_3\text{-}S)_2(CO)_9$ (183).[216] This provided an early evidence for the ease of cluster-promoted S—C bond cleavage and initiated numerous investigations in the important field of sulfido cluster complexes which is now well represented by important review articles.[20,217]

Following the pioneering studies, intermediate complexes resulting from the oxidative addition of S—H bonds to $M_3(CO)_{12}$, like $M_3(\mu\text{-}H)(\mu\text{-}SR)(CO)_{10}$ (M = Ru, Os) or $M_3(\mu\text{-}H)(\mu_3\text{-}SR)(CO)_9$ (M = Fe, Ru)[218] were subsequently isolated, though in many cases concurrent formation of mono, dinuclear, or polymeric complexes was currently observable.

Studies of such thiolato cluster complexes have been oriented toward model studies of surface reactions. For example, the linkage of mercaptobenzothiazole in $Ru_3(\mu\text{-H})(\mu\text{-S}_2NC_7H_4)(CO)_9$ (**184**) provides a reasonable model for the coating of a metal surface by this efficient corrosion inhibitor.[219]

(184)

More recently, the transformations of sulfur-containing ligands on cluster faces have been examined in detail with the aim to understand processes like the desulfurization of fossil fuels,[220] or the universal poisonous effects of sulfur on heterogeneous catalysts.[221] The elucidation of the mechanisms which govern S—C bond cleavage have also led investigators to design rational syntheses of sulfido-bridged cluster complexes. Selected examples given later suggest that the reaction paths ending at a bridging sulfido group are parallel with those leading from phosphines to phosphinidene groups (see Section 5.3), an additional complicating factor (not extensively discussed in this chapter) being that sulfur may donate up to 6 electrons, thereby favoring aggregation of metal atoms and formation of higher nuclearity species.[20,222] Finally, recent developments aimed to use sulfido-bridged cluster complexes as catalyst precursors have emphasized the noninnocency of bridging sulfido ligands and have highlighted some of their versatile effects in the transformation of other substrates.

5.4.1. Stepwise Transformations

Activation of sulfur-containing ligands by unsaturated and lightly stabilized complexes. Among sulfur compounds, only SO_2 undergoes simple adduct formation with $Os_3(\mu\text{-H})_2(CO)_{10}$ (**10**), leading to $Os_3(\mu\text{-SO}_2)(\mu\text{-H})_2(CO)_{10}$ (**14b**).[223] By contrast, the initial adduct is not seen in the case of CS_2 which interacts with two independent cluster molecules and is directly reduced to a bridging methanedithiolate group, giving the di-cluster complex $(\mu\text{-S}_2CH_2)[Os_3(\mu\text{-H})(CO)_{10}]_2$ (**185**).[224] Such an intermolecular association is prevented when the starting cluster is the PMe_2Ph-substituted analog of (**10**), $Os_3(\mu\text{-H})_2(CO)_9(PMe_2Ph)$ (**20**): in this case, the dithioformato complex $Os_3(\mu\text{-H})(\mu\text{-S}_2CH)(CO)_9(PMe_2Ph)$ (**186**) and the thioformaldehyde complex $Os_3(\mu_3\text{-S})(\mu\text{-SCH}_2)(CO)_9(PMe_2Ph)$ (**187**) are then isolated as the principal products from the reaction mixture. Further migration of the thio-formaldehyde from its edge-bridging position in (187) toward a face-bridging position is also observable under forcing conditions.[224]

(186)   (187)

A comparable transformation is seen when an isothiocyanate RN=C=S is reacted with $Os_3(\mu\text{-}H)_2(CO)_{10}$ (10) (Scheme 5.37):[96] There is incorporation of the ligand into the cluster as a thioformamido group RN=CH—S to give $Os_3(\mu\text{-}H)(\mu\text{-}SC(H)N\text{-}p\text{-}C_6H_4F)(CO)_{10}$ (188) in 86% yield; the compound loses CO under UV irradiation to give $Os_3(\mu\text{-}H)(\mu_3\text{-}SC(H)N\text{-}p\text{-}C_6H_4F)(CO)_9$ (51). Upon refluxing for 15 minutes, S—C cleavage occurs to give the open cluster $Os_3(\mu\text{-}H)(\mu_3\text{-}S)(\mu\text{-}HC=N\text{-}p\text{-}C_6H_4F)(CO)_9$ (189) (62% yield).

The same sequence is also observed upon reaction of various thioamides with the lightly stabilized complex $Os_3(CO)_{10}(CH_3CN)_2$ (37a).[225]

The coordinatively unsaturated cationic platinum cluster $[Pt_3(\mu_3\text{-}CO)(\mu\text{-}dppm)_3]^+$ (190) has also been used to model the poisonous effect of H_2S on a platinum 111 surface.[226]

Activation of coordinated arene-thiolato ligands. The sequence S—C cleavage/arene elimination is now well established for $M_3(\mu\text{-}H)(\mu\text{-}SR)(CO)_{10}$ (191) (M = Os),[227] (192), (M = Ru).[228] Though orthometallation may be observed (see following), it does not necessarily lie on the pathway to S—C cleavage, as unambiguously demonstrated by the synthesis of sulfido-osmium derivatives from $Os_3(\mu\text{-}H)(\mu\text{-}S(C_6F_5)(CO)_{10}$ (191a).[229]

The course of these reactions may be modified if other substrates are coordinated to the cluster.[230,231] For example,[231] conversion of a terminal carbene into a π-complexed iminium ligand via phenyl transfer from an orthometallated thiolato group is seen in the thermally induced transformation of $Os_3(\mu\text{-}H)_2(\mu_3\text{-}S\text{-}C_6H_4)(\eta^1\text{-}CHNMe_2)(CO)_8$ (193) into $Os_3(\mu_3\text{-}S)(\mu\text{-}H)(\eta^2\text{-}CPhH=NMe_2)(CO)_8$ (194) (2 h, refluxing $CHCl_3$) (Scheme 5.38). In refluxing hexane, the iminium ligand undergoes further C—H activation at two metal centers to regenerate a phenyl(dimethylamino)carbene in $Os_3(\mu\text{-}H)_2(\mu_3\text{-}S)(\eta^1\text{-}C(C_6H_4)(NMe_2)(CO)_8$ (195).[231]

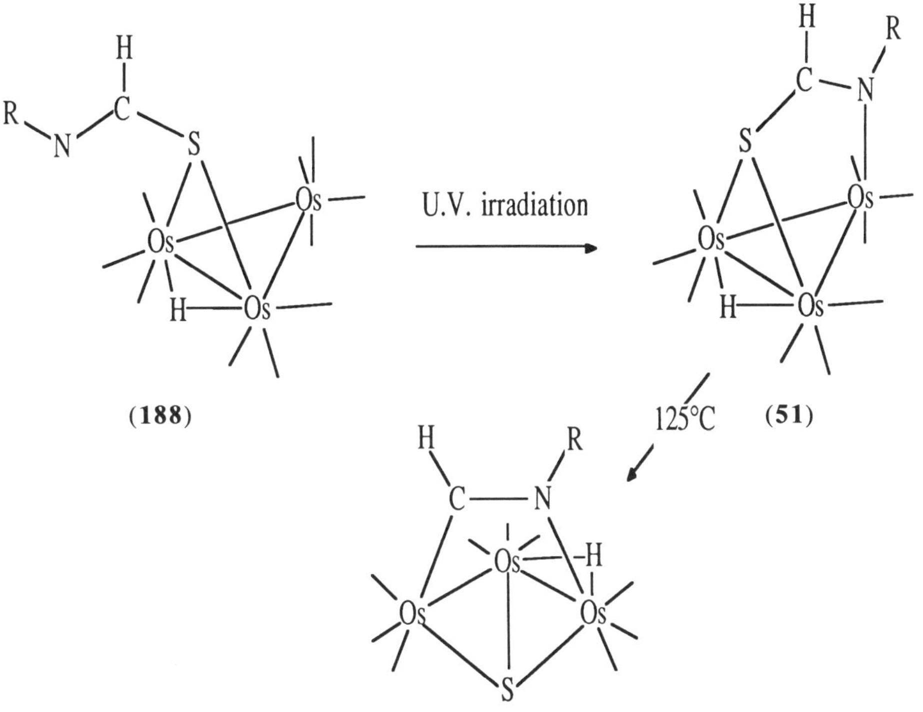

U.V. irradiation

(188)

(51)

125°C

(189)

Scheme 5.37

5.4.2. Coupling Reactions Between Bridging Sulfido Groups and Other Coordinated Substrates

Coupling with acetylenes. The cluster $Os_4(\mu_3\text{-S})(CO)_{12}$ (**196**) reacts with HCCR in refluxing hexane over 12 hours to give two products, one of which, $Os_4(\mu_4\text{-}\eta^3\text{-}SC(R)=CH)(CO)_{12}$ (**197**) (obtained in ca. 30% yield), is the result of a coupling reaction between the acetylene and the bridging sulfido group (Scheme 5.39).[232]

In refluxing octane, the latter species undergoes subsequent transformations[233a] involving (i) a cleavage of the S—C bond leading to $Os_4(\mu_3\text{-S})(\mu_3\text{-HCCR})(CO)_{12}$ (**198**), followed by (ii) a rearrangement of the initial butterfly metal framework into a chain of metal atoms in $Os_4(\mu_3\text{-S})(\mu_4\text{-HCCR})(CO)_{12}$ (**199**), (iii) a cyclization induced by loss of CO and leading to the rhomboidal cluster $Os_4(\mu_4\text{-}S)(\mu_4\text{-HCCR})(CO)_{11}$ (**200**). The overall sequence provides a detailed insight into the steps which govern the migration of an alkyne ligand on the surface of a sulfido-bridged cluster species.

The final species (**200**) is unsaturated; $Os_4(\mu_4\text{-S})(\mu_4\text{-RCCR})(CO)_{11}$ (**200b**) exhibits enhanced reactivity toward hydrogen,[68] or alkynes through a "ligand-assisted" addition where the initial interaction between the alkyne and the cluster complex is expected to take place at the sulfur atom.[233b] Noticeably, (**197**) and

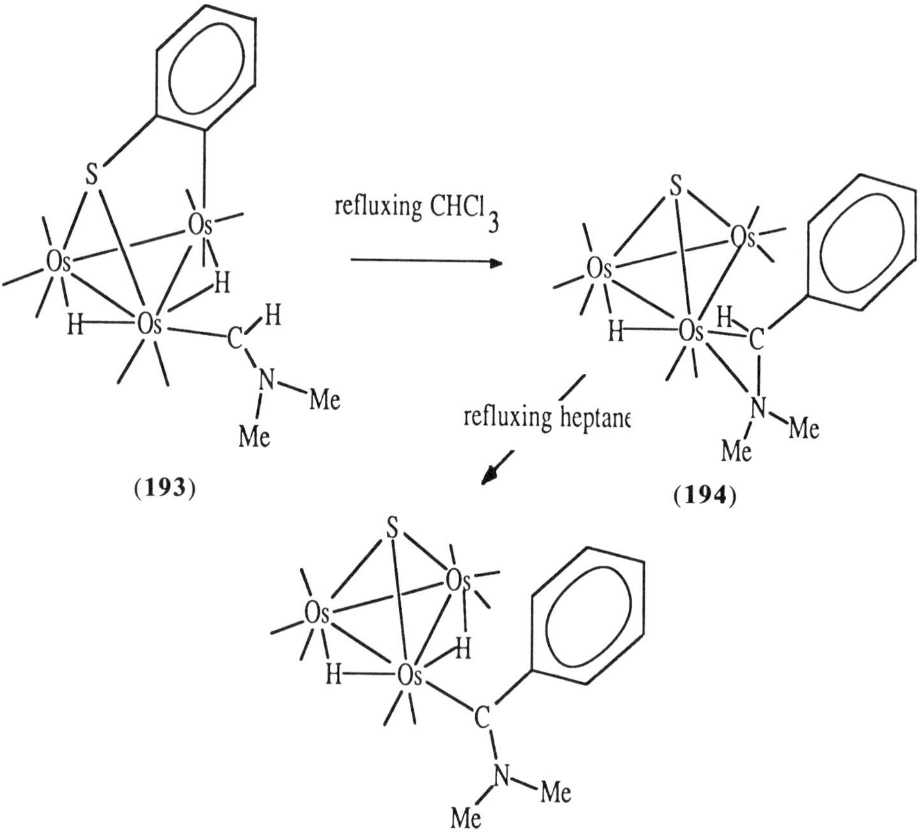

(193)   refluxing CHCl$_3$ (194)

                          refluxing heptane

(195)

Scheme 5.38

(200) are structurally related to other species[105,211] derived from phosphinidene complexes.

Poisoning effect of sulfur on the transformation of hydrocarbon fragments. A nice illustration of the ability of sulfur ligands to quench the transformation of a methylene group is provided in the set of interconversions shown in Scheme 5.40.[234]

Let us recall that the complex $Os_3(\mu\text{-}CH_2)(\mu\text{-}CO)(CO)_{10}$ (105) has been used as a model for tracing the coupling of a bridging methylene group with CO to give a ketene (see Scheme 5.24) which may be subsequently reduced as CH_3COOH or CH_3COOCH_3 upon reaction with H_2O and CH_3OH.[156] Reaction of (105) with ethylene—or cyclohexene—sulfide gives the thioformaldehyde complex $Os_3(\mu\text{-}SCH_2)(CO)_{11}$ (201) as a result of sulfur insertion into a metal-methylene bond;[234] thermally induced CO loss from the latter results in migration of the thioformaldehyde group in face-bridging position in the complex $Os_3(\mu\text{-}SCH_2)(CO)_{10}$ (202), followed by C—H activation leading to the thioformyl com-

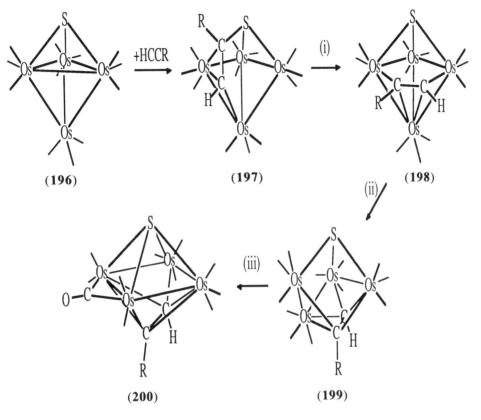

Scheme 5.39

plex $Os_3(\mu\text{-H})(\mu\text{-SCH})(CO)_9$ (**203**). Both the thioformaldehyde and the thioformyl group can be reduced under hydrogen to give the methane-thiolato complex $Os_3(\mu\text{-H})(\mu\text{-SCH}_3)(CO)_{10}$ (**191b**) as the end product in this sequence. More drastic conditions will be required to release methane from (**191b**), and to give the sulfido osmium cluster $Os_3(\mu\text{-H})_2(\mu_3\text{-S})(CO)_9$ (**205**).

A further example relevant to the poisoning effect of sulfur is available from the work of Keister and co-workers (Scheme 5.41):[235] the cluster $Ru_3(\mu\text{-H})_3(\mu_3\text{-CSEt})(CO)_9$ (**206**) rearranges to $Ru_3(\mu\text{-H})(\mu\text{-}\eta^2\text{-CH}_2SEt)(CO)_9$ (**207**) at 50–60°C via two C—H reductive elimination steps, while sulfur traps the two vacant coordination sites thus created and prevents complete removal of the organic sulfide.

(Note: Scheme 5.54 in Section 5.7 provides an example of ligand desulfurization.)

Concluding remark on sulfido-bridged cluster complexes. Besides evidences presented earlier that sulfido ligands are chemically reactive, there are well-established examples of sulfido trimetal clusters which are remarkably stable, and yet active in promoting ligand transformations such as the stoichiometric oligomerization of alkynes[39] (see Scheme 5.56 in Section 5.7) or the catalytic

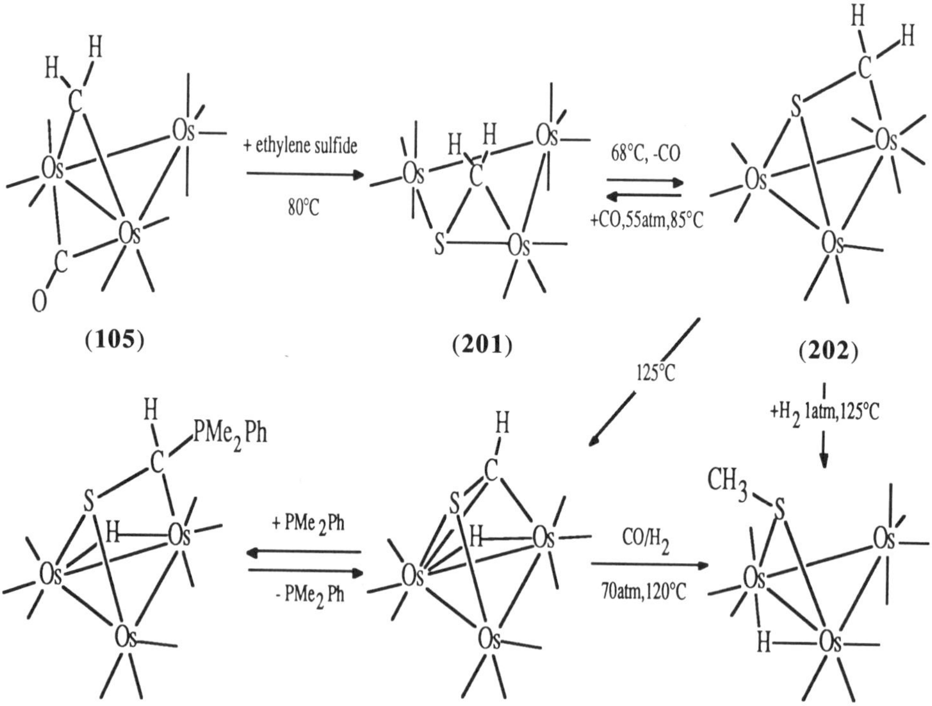

Scheme 5.40

Scheme 5.41

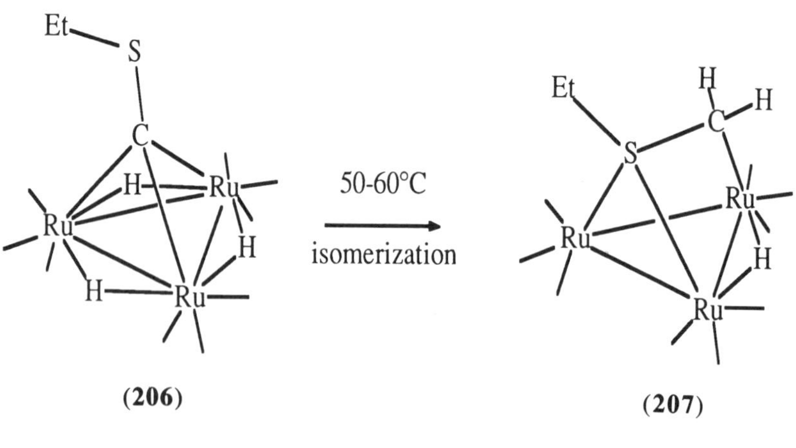

transalkylation of tertiary amines[236] (see the full details in Chapter 7). In such complexes, the bridging sulfur is apparently inert and serves as an efficient stabilizing group for the metal framework; whether or not the incoming substrate has in fact interacted reversibly with sulfur at an intermediate step is still an open question.

5.5. Transformations of Oxygen-Containing Ligands; Activation of Oxygen

Stability of alkoxo groups in cluster complexes. While thiols are convenient sources for bridging sulfido groups in cluster complexes, alcohols cannot be used as precursors for bridging oxo groups. Direct reaction of alcohols with electronically saturated carbonyl cluster complexes is not currently observable, and at least requires forcing conditions.[237-239] Thus, cluster activation by various means,[75,57,66d,240] or direct use of OR^- (as extensively discussed in Section 5.2.8) is often necessary to promote the formation of alkoxo cluster complexes. For example, the recently designed oxygen-stabilized cluster $Ru_3(\mu\text{-}OC_6H_4OMe)_2$ $(CO)_8$ (**208**) has been obtained in good yield by reaction of $2(MeO)C_6H_4OH$ with $Ru_3(CO)_{12}$ in the presence of Me_3NO.[240] This species nicely models an oxide-grafted metal ensemble.

[208]

Let us also recall here a rare example where an alkoxo group is derived from the reduction of acetone by the unsaturated cluster complex $[Re_3(\mu\text{-}H)_4(CO)_{10}]^-$ [22] (see Scheme 5.9).[66c]

In general, bridging alkoxo groups do not undergo further metal-mediated degradation, which makes them attractive candidates as ancillary ligands in cluster complexes when these are used as catalyst precursors[97] (see Section 5.2.5).

A μ-oxo-bridged metal cluster derived from an acyl complex. While the reduction of CO or NO bonds is achieved by metal cluster complexes, oxygen is generally released as CO_2 or H_2O in these reactions (see Sections 5.6 and 5.7; note: there is one example where the cleavage of NO produces a nitrido cluster

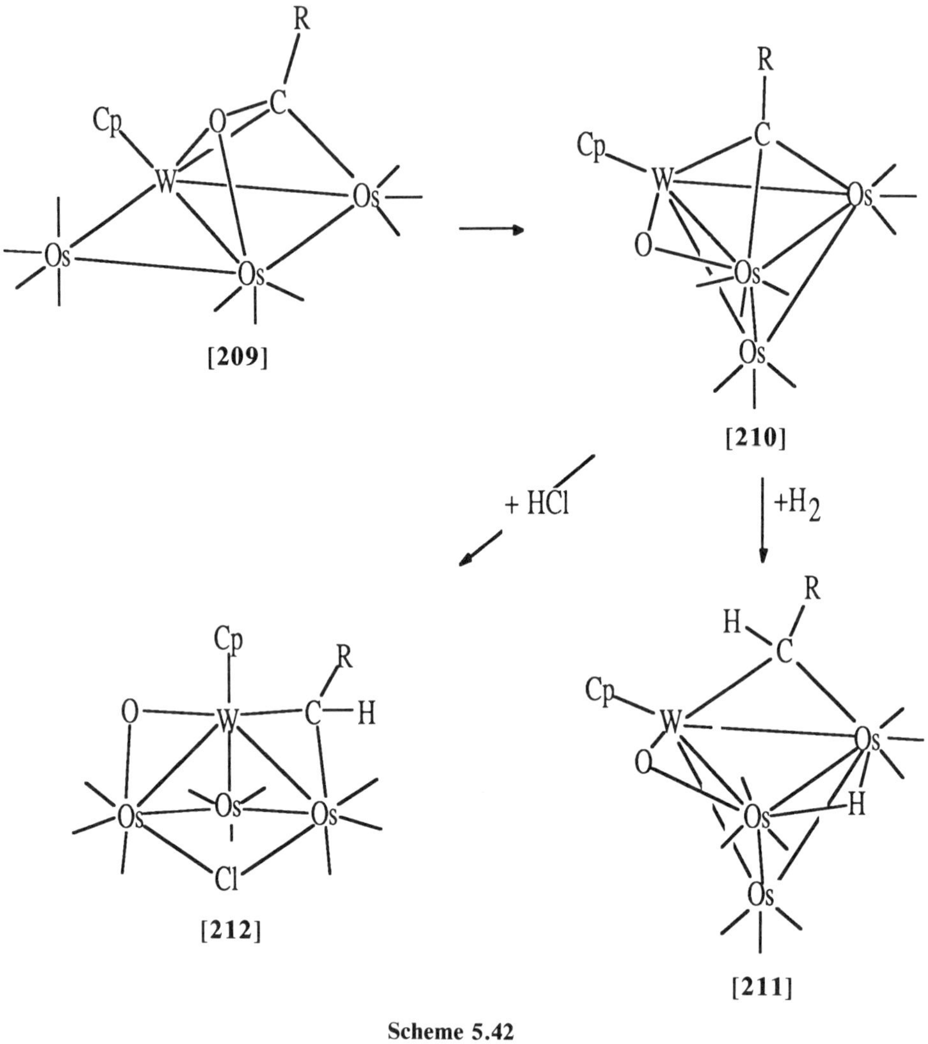

[209]

[210]

+ HCl

+H₂

[212]

[211]

Scheme 5.42

complex containing a terminal oxo ligand, see compound (**241**) in 5.6; however, this oxo ligand is not derived from NO).

Yet, retention of oxygen is observed in the thermally induced scission of the acyl CO bond in the complex $Os_3WCp(\mu_3-\eta^2-C(O)CH_2R)(CO)_{11}$ (**209**) which leads to the oxo complex $Os_3WCp(\mu_2-O)(\mu_3-CCH_2R)(CO)_9$ (**210**) (Scheme 5.42).[241]

The edge-bridging oxo ligand here acts as a 4-*e* donor. Its stability in the present case may be related to the oxophilic character of tungsten. Interestingly, the alkylidyne ligand in (**210**) can be subsequently hydrogenated. Though the oxo group is unchanged in the final product $Os_3WCp(\mu-H)(\mu_2-O)(\mu-CHCH_2R)(CO)_9$ (**211**), it has been suggested that the transient formation of a hydrogen adduct here might reflect the ability of the oxo ligand to move reversibly in a terminal position at intermediate step.[241a] Furthermore, an adduct of **(210)** with HCl, formulated as $Os_3WCp(\mu\text{-}Cl)(\mu_2\text{-}O)(\mu\text{-}CHCH_2R)(CO)_9$ **(212)**, has been isolated at $25°C$.[241b] Stereoselective substitution within this compound has been interpreted in terms of the *cis*-labilizing properties of oxygen previously demonstrated by Kaesz for acyl compounds and by Darensbourg for acetate compounds, as discussed in Section 5.2.8.

Activation of oxygen by metal cluster complexes. Though numerous carbonyl cluster complexes are destroyed in contact with O_2, there are few cases where a clean reaction is observed.[242−246] For example, the bis(diphenylphosphino)methane substituted complex $Ru_3(CO)_8(dppm)_2$ **(12a)** reacts with oxygen at $85°C$ in ethoxyethanol solution to produce the oxo-bridged complex $Ru_3(\mu_3\text{-}O)(\mu_3\text{-}CO)(CO)_5(dppm)_2$ **(213)** in 65% yield (parallel reaction is also observed with the bis(diphenylarsino)methane derivative **12b**).[242a−b]

[213]

It is noteworthy that the presence of the face-bridging oxo ligand in **(213)** inhibits the metal-mediated transformation of dppm which proved to be a facile process for the antecedent species **(12)** (Scheme 5.29). The bridging CO ligand can be displaced by H_2 to give the reactive di-hydrido cluster complex $Ru_3(\mu_3\text{-}O)(\mu\text{-}H)_2(CO)_5(dppm)_2$ **(214)** (88% yield).[242b] This strongly stabilized complex has been used as a catalyst precursor for the hydrogenation of alkenes. Catalysis by the intact cluster has been claimed on the basis of a kinetic study.[242c]

Related species where the μ-oxo ligand is derived from the reaction of a carbonyl cluster with oxygen also include the beautiful raft species $Os_6(\mu_3\text{-}O)(CO)_{15}(P(OCH_3)_3)_4$ **(215)**[243] and the di-anion $[Fe_3(\mu_3\text{-}O)(CO)_9]^{2-}$ **[216]**.[244] The latter reacts cleanly with $[Mn(CO)_3(CH_3CN)_3][PF_6]$ to give the butterfly complex $[Fe_3Mn(\mu_4\text{-}O)(CO)_{12}]^-$ **[217]**.[245]

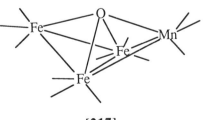

[217]

Finally, photolysis of an O_2-saturated toluene solution of $Fe_2(CO)_9$ and $Mo_2(\eta^5\text{-}C_5Me_5)_2(CO)_4$ produces the complex $FeMo_2(\mu_3\text{-}O)(C_5Me_5)_2(CO)_7$ $(218)^{246a}$ where it appears that oxygen has nicely functioned as a building block for cluster construction.

(218)

There is a hint here that a development of the chemistry of oxo-cluster complexes in the future could result in unusual reactivity patterns. Current interest in this area is well represented by a recent review article.[246b]

5.6. Transformations of Nitrogen-Containing Ligands

Some aspects of the chemistry of nitrogen-containing ligands have been outlined earlier in several paragraphs of Section 5.2. We have discussed in particular the important promoter effect of nitrogen bases and nucleophilic anions (NR_2^-, N_3^-, and NO_2^-) on reactions of metal clusters (see Section 5.2.8). Some other relevant challenging problems that have received particular attention in recent years are discussed in the following. The important field of nitrosyl and nitrido cluster complexes is only very briefly outlined here since it has been recently covered by Gladfelter in an excellent review.[18]

Clusters are implicated as catalyst precursors in a variety of important transformations of nitrogen-containing ligands, for example, in the reduction of nitroaromatics to amines and carbamates (see Section 5.2.8),[159,160] the transalkylation of amines[247,236] the reductive coupling of alkylisocyanates,[248] the carbonylation of amines,[249] the transfer hydrogenation of benzylideneaniline,[250] etc. (see Chapter 7 for full details). Yet, the mechanism of most of these reactions remains presently unclear. For example, mechanistic studies of the transalkylation of amines have been partially hindered by the lack of observable intermediates. Besides, a major impediment in model studies of the transformations of various nitrogen-containing ligands is also the recurrent formation of robust cluster-bound nitrene fragments μ_3-NR which cannot be easily released from the metal framework. This dramatic problem has been stressed by several authors[33-36,251] (see Section 5.1 and Scheme 5.1). It has been recently solved in some instances,[160] in particular by the use of labilizing groups[161] (see following, Scheme 5.25, and Section 5.2.8).

Reduction of CN multiple bonds in nitriles and isocyanides. The early report of a catalytic hydrogenation of isocyanides to secondary amines by $Ni_4(RNC)_7$ $(219)^{252}$ has stimulated numerous investigations on cluster-assisted reductions

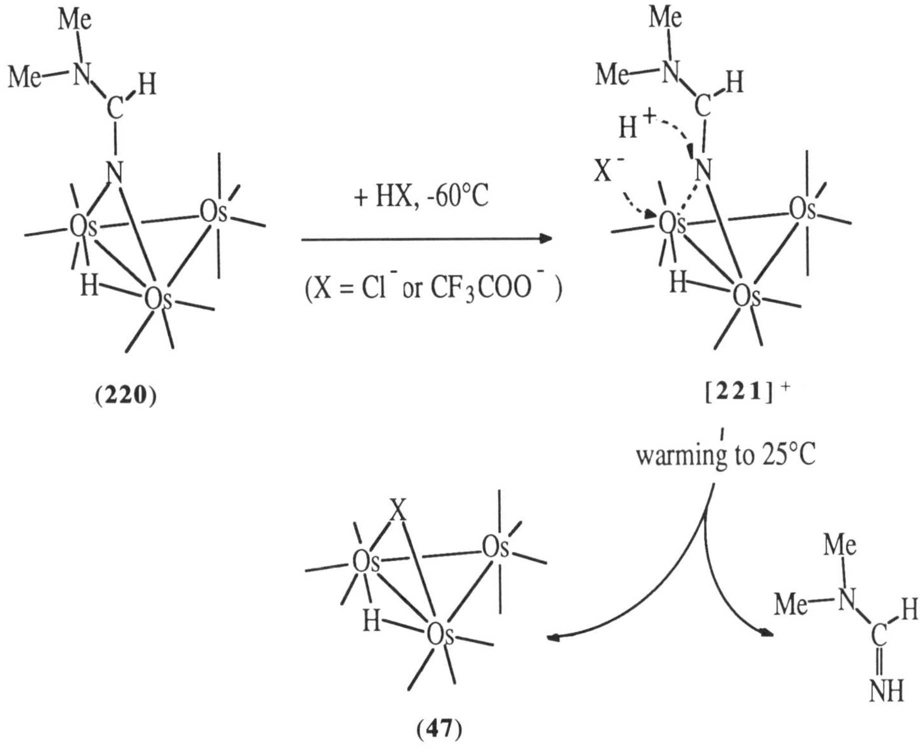

Scheme 5.43

of CN multiple bonds in nitriles (see Scheme 5.1 for example[33,34])[35,36,253] or isocyanides.[254,255] Since these important reactions are now classic, only two of the most recent reports are discussed here.

Example 1: Cyanodimethylamine reacts with $Os_3(\mu\text{-H})_2(CO)_{10}$ (**10**) to give the classic adduct $Os_3(\mu\text{-H})_2(CO)_{10}(NCNMe_2)$ (**14**) which is subsequently converted into the single product $Os_3(\mu\text{-H})(\mu\text{-NCHNMe}_2)(CO)_{10}$ (**220**) by hydrogen transfer to the carbon atom of the ligand (Scheme 5.43).[253] Protonation of (**220**) at low temperature by strong acids HX, like HCl or CF_3COOH, occurs at nitrogen to give the transient cationic derivative $[Os_3(\mu\text{-H})(\mu\text{-NHCHNMe}_2)(CO)_{10}]^+$ [**221**]. On warming to room temperature, subsequent nucleophilic attack of the anion X^- (Cl^- or CF_3COO^-) at the metal releases the modified substrate $NHCHNMe_2$, while the complex $Os_3(\mu\text{-H})(\mu\text{-X})(CO)_{10}$ (**47**) is obtained in high yield. The relevance of this reaction to the effects of nucleophilic anions discussed in Section 5.2.8 is obvious. It should also be noted that treatment of (**220**) with hydrogen leads to the recovery of (**10**), suggesting that hydrogenation and reductive elimination of amine has been achieved.

Example 2: The catalytic hydrogenation of isocyanides to secondary amines mediated by the bimetallic species $Rh_2(\mu\text{-H})_2(P(O\text{-}i\text{-}Pr)_3)_4$ (**222**) has been observed, and a catalytic cycle based principally on the three intermediates (**223**), (**224**), and (**225**) has been suggested.[255] Under 1 atm of hydrogen, the triple bond of the coordinated isocyanide in $Rh_2(\mu\text{-}H)_2(\mu\text{-}CNR)(P(O\text{-}i\text{-}Pr)_3)_4$ (**223**) is slowly reduced to a single bond under mild conditions (20°C, 2 days) with formation of $Rh_2(\mu\text{-}H)(\mu\text{-}CH_3NR)(P(o\text{-}i\text{-}Pr)_3)_4$ (**225**). Monitoring the reaction allows the detection of the formimidoyl intermediate $Rh_2H(\mu\text{-}H)(\mu\text{-}HC{=}NR)(P(O\text{-}i\text{-}Pr)_3)_4$ (**224**). The free amine CH_3NHR is finally released slowly from (**225**) to give $Rh_2(\mu\text{-}H)_2(P(O\text{-}i\text{-}Pr)_3)_4$ (**222**).[255] Unfortunately, the viability of this catalytic cycle is limited in particular by side reactions of these intermediates with excess of isocyanide leading to substituted products with loss of phosphite.

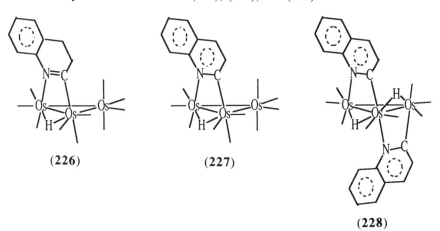

(**223**)   (**224**)   (**225**)

Stability of nitrogen heterocycles in their reactions with metal clusters. Reactions of aliphatic or aromatic nitrogen heterocycles with trinuclear osmium,[74,256–258] or ruthenium clusters[82,257,259–264] occurring with retention of the metal framework are now well documented. A common feature of the interaction of such ligands with metal clusters is that coordination of nitrogen activates the adjacent carbon position toward reaction with the metal via oxidative addition of the C—H bond. For example,[257] dehydrogenation of tetrahydroquinoline to quinoline by $Os_3(CO)_{12}$ has been observed; however, the reaction is poorly catalytic, due to the stability of the intermediates (**226**), (**227**), and (**228**).

(**226**)   (**227**)

(**228**)

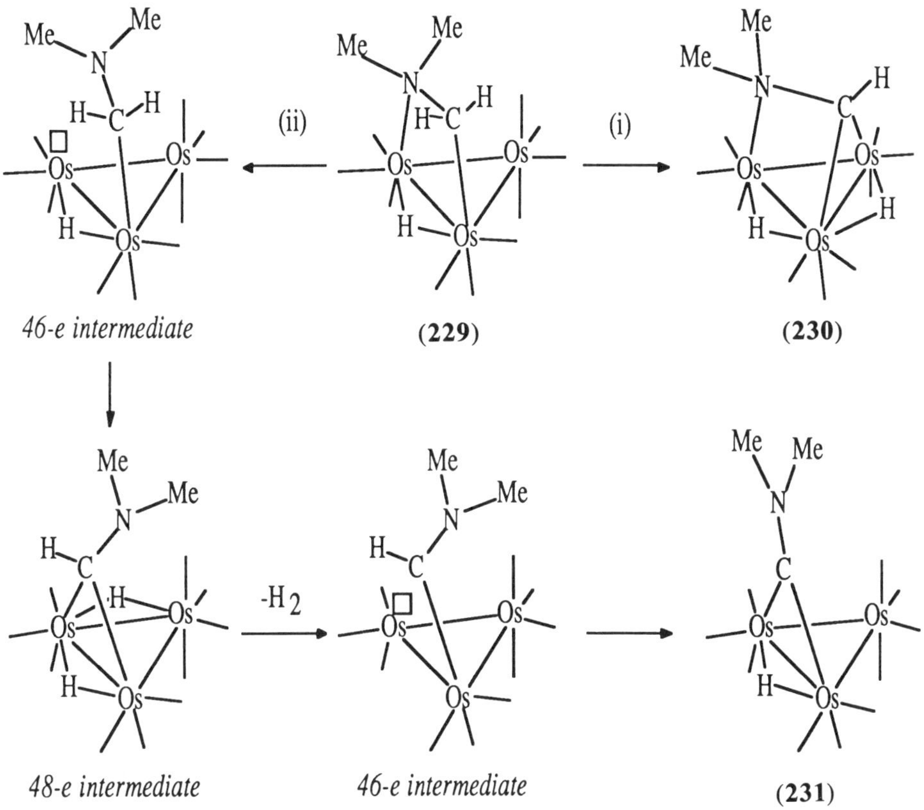

Scheme 5.44

When there is a methyl substituent instead of an H atom in α position of a nitrogen heterocycle, activation of the C—H bonds of this group is seen to occur at very mild conditions.[258]

Though it has been suggested that clusters might be regarded as potential models for the active site of hydrodenitrogenation catalysts,[257] no C—N cleavage has been so far observed in the reaction of clusters with nitrogen heterocycles.[256-264]

Facile cleavage of a C—N bond in *bis*(dialkylamino)methane and transformations of the resulting dimethyliminium ligand. The cleavage of CN bonds is rarely observed in reactions of amines with metal cluster complexes,[58] though it must occur in transalkylation reactions. Yet, the interaction of the diamine $CH_2(NMe_2)_2$ with $Os_3(\mu-H)_2(CO)_{10}$ proceeds directly by cleavage of the C—N bond to produce the complex $Os_3(\mu-H)(\mu-\eta^2-H_2CNMe_2)(CO)_{10}$ (**229**) containing an edge-bridging dimethyliminium ligand $\mu-\eta^2-CH_2NMe_2$ (Scheme 5.44).[265]

Upon thermal activation of (**229**), loss of CO (path i in Scheme 5.44) occurs in competition with de-coordination of the nitrogen atom (path ii). These parallel paths lead to different products. In the former one, C—H cleavage at two metal centers converts the dimethyliminium ligand into a face-bridging dimethylaminocarbene group $\mu_3-\eta^2-CHNMe_2$ to produce the complex $Os_3(\mu-H)_2(\mu_3-\eta^2-$

HCNMe$_2$)(CO)$_9$ (**230**). In the alternate path proposed by the authors, C—H activation produces an intermediate di-hydrido complex containing an edge-bridging methylene group. Loss of hydrogen from the latter species favors further C-H activation leading to the final product Os$_3$(μ-H)(μ-CNMe$_2$)(CO)$_{10}$ (**231**).[265] The preceding transformations are relevant to those observed for trialkylamines. Indeed, (**231**) was isolated earlier by Deeming from the reaction of trimethylamine with Os$_3$(CO)$_{12}$.[266]

Cluster promoted cleavage of NN double bond in azoalkanes and azoarenes. The relative inertness of nitrene ligands makes them attractive as stabilizing groups for trinuclear clusters when these are used as catalyst precursors (see Chapter 7). The metal-mediated cleavage of azo compounds provides one of the possible routes to these precursors. For example, the *bis*(arylimido)triruthenium cluster Ru$_3$(μ_3-NAr)$_2$(CO)$_9$ (**232a**) (analogous to the iron derivative **8b**) can be obtained in moderate 15–20% yields by direct thermal reaction of azoarenes ArNNAr with Ru$_3$(CO)$_{12}$ under carbon monoxide,[267] while the unsymmetric analog Ru$_3$(μ_3-NAr)(μ_3-NAr$'$)(CO)$_9$ (**232b**) is obtained selectively from Ru$_3$(μ_3-NAr)(CO)$_{10}$ (**233**) through reaction (5.17),[268] which involves both an NN cleavage and a C—N coupling. Under N$_2$, metallation of the aryl group of the azoarene reduces the yield of the cleavage product:

$$Ru_3(\mu_3\text{-NAr})(CO)_{10} + Ar'NNAr'$$

$$\xrightarrow[\text{CO atmosphere. 6 h}]{\text{refluxing heptane,}} Ru_3\ (\mu_3\text{-NAr})(\mu_3\text{-NAr}')(CO)_9 + Ar'NCO \qquad (5.17)$$

In the two reactions just considered, there is no trappable intermediate showing transient coordination of the azoarene ligand. However, evidence for such a derivative has been obtained in iron chemistry.[269] Indeed, the complex Fe$_3$(μ_3-η^2-EtN=NEt)(CO)$_9$ (**233**) contains a face-bridging azoalkane ligand which acts as a 6-*e* donor. NN cleavage occurs upon prolonged thermolysis of this species (ligroin, 120°C, 11 h) to produce the known nitrene complex Fe$_3$(μ_3-NEt)$_2$(CO)$_9$ (**8b$'$**) in 75% yield.[269] Since there is no loss of CO in the overall reaction, one may reasonably suggest that the splitting of the N=N bond occurs at the expense of a metal-metal bond in a transition state where the ligand has moved toward an edge of the metal triangle, in the same way as do alkynes (Section 5.7).

Formation of CN bonds. *a) Coupling reactions involving nitrene derivatives.* Geoffroy and co-workers have recently reported a detailed comparative study of the reactivity of phosphinidene and nitrene derivatives.[160] While the *bis*-nitrene derivative Fe$_3$(μ_3-NPh)$_2$(CO)$_9$ (**8b**) proved to be much more stable than the phosphinidene analog (**8a**), complete removal of the capping nitrene group could be achieved through the reaction sequence shown in Scheme 5.45 (to be compared with that shown in Scheme 5.36). The carbene group generated here couples with the face-bridging nitrene fragment to produce N-phenylcarbamate along with the mono-nitrene derivative Fe$_3$(μ_3-NR)(CO)$_{10}$ (**236**).

Though the preceding reaction is only stoichiometric, it may be relevant to the cluster-assisted conversion of nitrobenzene into carbamates.[159] Furthermore, the important role of halide promoters in the coupling of cluster-bound nitrenes with carbon monoxide has been demonstrated (Scheme 5.25 and relevant discussion).[161]

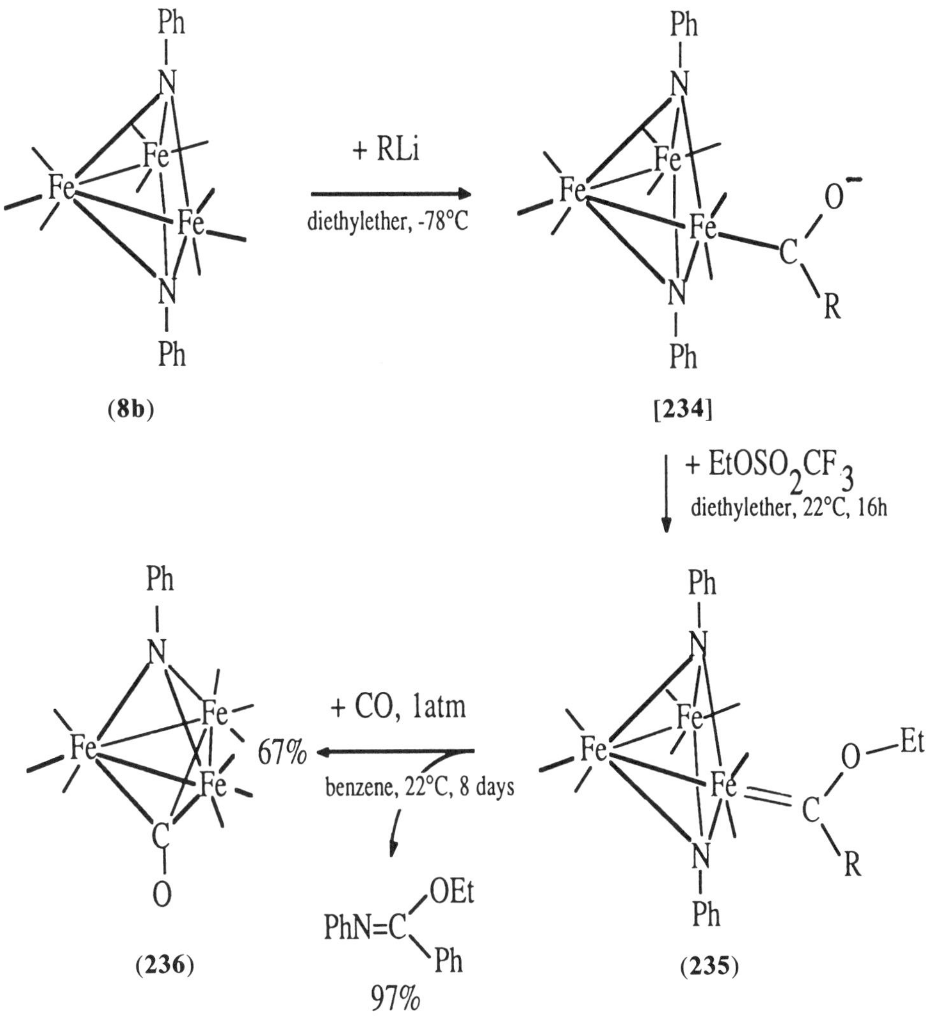

Scheme 5.45

b) reversible NO⁺ insertion into a metal-carbon bond. [115] The *bis*-alkylidyne cluster $Co_3Cp_3(\mu_3\text{-}CR)(\mu_3\text{-}CR')$ (**74**) reacts smoothly with NO^+ to give the cationic adduct $[Co_3Cp_3(\mu_3\text{-}RCNO)(\mu_3\text{-}CR')]$ [**237**] in which it appears that NO^+ has inserted regiospecifically into the more electron rich M—C bond (Scheme 5.46).

The resulting cluster-bound alkanenitrileoxide ligand possesses an interesting reactivity. First, de-insertion of the nitrosyl ligand promoted by $NaOCH_3$ induces the coupling of the two alkylidyne moieties at very mild conditions to give $[Co_3Cp_3(\mu_3\text{-}RCCR')(\mu\text{-}NO)]$ [**238**]. Second, NO cleavage within this ligand is observed under 10 atm of CO and produces the complex $[Co_3Cp_3(\mu_3\text{-}RCN)(\mu_3\text{-}CR')]$

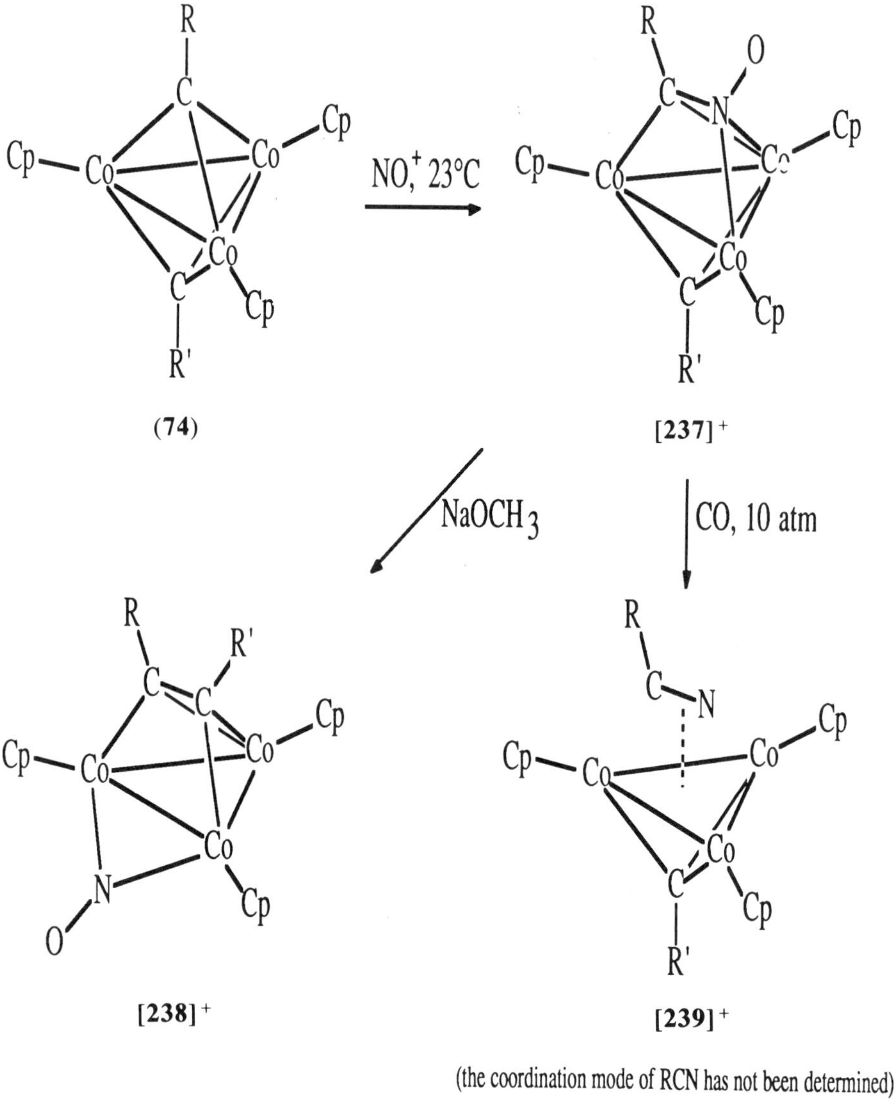

(the coordination mode of RCN has not been determined)

Scheme 5.46

[239]. The formation of a cluster bound acetonitrile obtained through a comparable coupling reaction has been simultaneously reported by Mathieu and co-workers.[270]

NO bond cleavage and formation of nitrido cluster complexes. An extreme form of the cluster-assisted transformation of nitrogen-containing ligands is the formation of nitrido cluster complexes. These are obtained in particular by cleavage of NO bonds in nitrosyl cluster complexes.[18] This is illustrated here by the quantitative conversion of $[FeRu_3(CO)_{12}(NO)]^-$ (**240**) into $[FeRu_3N(CO)_{12}]^-$ (**69b**). One of the two possible mechanistic paths proposed by the authors is shown in Scheme 5.47.[271]

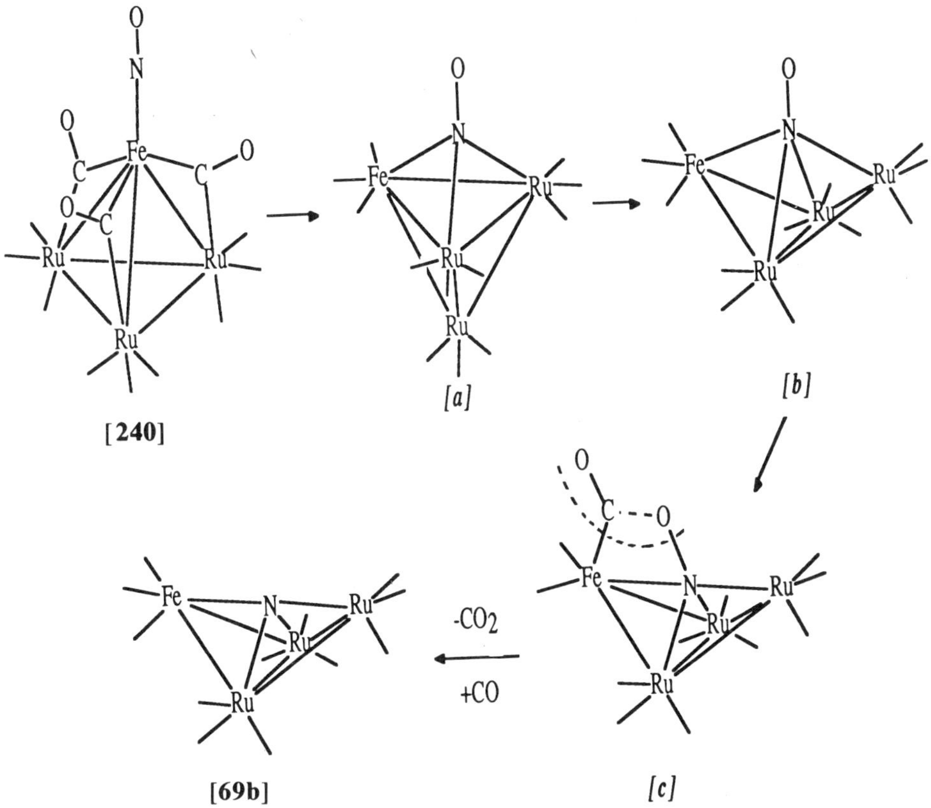

Scheme 5.47

Nitrido cluster complexes are believed to be intermediates in the reduction of coordinated NO by hydrogen to produce cluster bound NH and NH_2 fragments.[18]

Unlike carbido ligands, which are too reactive to be stabilized by a trinuclear metal atom polyhedron (Section 5.7), nitrido ligands can be trapped in a three-metal-atom environment, as observed for the well characterized cluster complex $Mo_3(\mu_3\text{-N})(Cp)_3(CO)_4$ (**241**) and related mixed-metal Mo/W species.[272]

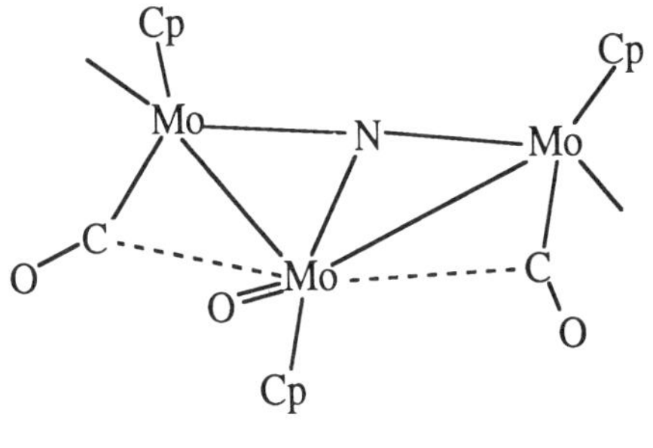

(241)

5.7. Transformations of Simple Carbon-Containing Ligands: CO, Carbides, and Hydrocarbon Fragments

Studies of the reactivity of the simplest cluster-bound carbon-containing fragments are central to the development of organometallic cluster chemistry.[13,17,273] In particular, they have established fundamental concepts which may be valuable for metal ensembles in general. Typically, the stepwise transformations of carbon monoxide on molecular clusters provide realistic models for various mechanistic schemes proposed for the surface catalyzed CO reduction occurring in the Fischer-Tropsch process.[30,274]

5.7.1. From Carbon Monoxide to Hydrocarbon Fragments

Original observation of a proton-induced reduction of CO to methane on a butterfly cluster complex.

The dramatic pioneering work of Shriver and co-workers on the stepwise proton-induced reduction of CO to methane from $[Fe_4(CO)_{13}]^{2-}$ [242] has emphasized the role of multicenter interactions on the CO cleavage process (Scheme 5.48).[17,275] In this transformation, the initial opening of the tetrahedral metal framework of (242) to a butterfly favors the coordination of a CO in a $\mu\text{-}\eta^2$ fashion.

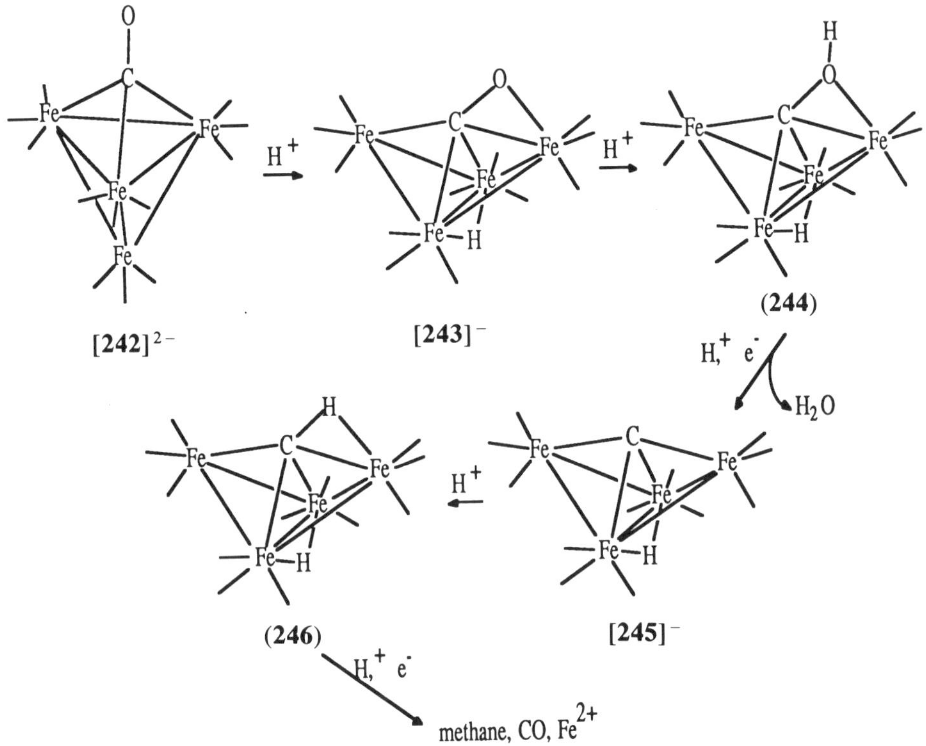

Scheme 5.48

The resulting reduction of the C—O bond order permits further proton-induced cleavage of this bond to yield an intermediate carbido ligand which is subsequently protonated. In the presence of reducing agents, up to one mole of CH_4 per mole of cluster is finally evolved.[275] The only step which remains presently unclear is perhaps the final desorption of methane which appears to be concomitant with a degradation of the metal cluster. However, detailed information on the pathways for the reductive elimination of hydrocarbons from trimetallic species is available from the important work of Keister[276a,b] and Shapley[276c,d] (see Scheme 5.6) as well as Fehlner's studies based on isolobal BH_4 ligands.[276e,f]

The intermediacy of an exposed carbido-ligand in the cluster-promoted formation of methane has motivated numerous investigations on the reactivity of carbido-cluster complexes. These have been reviewed in detail by Bradley[13a] and Muetterties.[13b] Recent years have seen an interesting trend in studies of carbido-cluster complexes: attempts to generate highly exposed carbido ligands in trinuclear species have led to the isolation of cluster-bound ketenylidene ligands which display a fascinating carbide-like reactivity.[17b] Their chemistry is discussed in the final pages of this section.

In account of the preceding observations, attachment of a carbonyl oxygen to a metal center seems to be the driving force for the reduction of carbon monoxide.[17] Such an interaction is rarely observable in trimetallic species.[277] Larger metal ensembles (essentially tetranuclear)[17a,278] or intermolecular association of cluster-bound CO ligands with oxophilic metal centers[279] are required to observe a reduction of the C—O bond order. Yet, as shown in the following, CO reduction at three metal centers can be achieved by sequential treatment with appropriate nucleophilic and electrophilic reagents.

Reduction of CO to a methylene group via a formyl intermediate. (See also Section 5.2.8.) Treatment of $Os_3(CO)_{12}$ (**2**) by potassium Selectride at 0°C gives the formyl complex $[Os_3(CHO)(CO)_{11}]^-$ **[247]** which is subsequently treated with acid to give the methylene complex $Os_3(CH_2)(\mu\text{-}CO)(CO)_{10}$ (**105**).[134] Labeling experiments have demonstrated that the two hydrogen atoms of the methylene group are derived from the initial hydride donor. This is consistent with the proposed reaction sequence shown in equations (5.18)–(5.20) which is fully consistent with (i) the observed production of $Os_3(CO)_{12}$ and (ii) the improved yield of (**105**) upon slow acidification: the hydroxymethylene complex generated at intermediate step reacts rapidly with H^- provided by intermolecular hydride transfer from unreacted amounts of the initial formyl complex.

$$[Os_3(CDO)(CO)_{11}]^- \xrightarrow{H^+} Os_3(CDOH)(CO)_{11} \qquad (5.18)$$

$$Os_3(CDOH)(CO)_{11} + [Os_3(CDO)(CO)_{11}]^-$$
$$\rightarrow [Os_3(CD_2OH)(CO)_{11}]^- + Os_3(CO)_{12} \qquad (5.19)$$

$$[Os_3(CD_2OH)(CO)_{11}]^- + H^+ \rightarrow Os_3(\mu\text{-}CD_2)(CO)_{11} + H_2O \qquad (5.20)$$

The methylene group in (**105**) is readily engaged in a number of coupling reactions discussed earlier in this chapter (Scheme 5.24 and the relevant discussion in Section 5.2.8; see also Scheme 5.40)[156–158,234] Dramatic new reports on the reactivity of this group in other cluster complexes have recently appeared.[280]

A formyl intermediate is also involved in the fascinating stepwise CO reduction to methanol occurring on the face of $[Re_3(\mu\text{-}H)_4(CO)_{10}]^-$ [22][66b] (Scheme 5.8). In that case, a slightly different sequence $CHO \rightarrow \mu_3\text{-}CH_2O \rightarrow \mu_3\text{-}CH_2OH \rightarrow CH_3OH$ has been identified. Reductive elimination of methanol in the final step is preferred over C—O bond cleavage.

Reduction of CO via an alkoxymethylidyne intermediate; formation of methylidyne, benzylidyne, or methoxycarbene ligands at three metal centers. The alkylidyne cluster $Os_3(\mu\text{-}H)(\mu\text{-}COCH_3)(CO)_{10}$ (**6b**) (derived from $Os_3(CO)_{12}$ through the classic sequence H^-/CH_3^+)[281] is attacked by H^- at the electrophilic carbyne center to produce the trappable anion $[Os_3(\mu\text{-}H)(\mu\text{-}CHOCH_3)(CO)_{10}]^-$ [248] which next undergoes C-O cleavage upon acidification to produce the complex $Os_3(\mu\text{-}H)(\mu_3\text{-}CH)(CO)_{10}$ (**249**), equations (5.21)–(5.22).[282]

(**249**)

The complex (**249**) involves an sp^2 hybridized semi-triply bridging methylidyne ligand. The weak stabilizing interaction of the unique metal center with the C-H moiety reflects the electrophilic character of this group. Displacement of this interaction is indeed observed upon reaction with nucleophiles such as methylpyridine.[282]

$$Os_3(\mu\text{-}H)(\mu\text{-}COCH_3)(CO)_{10} \xrightarrow{H^-} [Os_3(\mu\text{-}H)(\mu\text{-}CHOCH_3)(CO)_{10}]^- \quad (5.21)$$

$$[Os_3(\mu\text{-}H)(\mu\text{-}CHOCH_3)(CO)_{10}]^- \xrightarrow{H^+} Os_3(\mu\text{-}H)(\mu_3\text{-}CH)(CO)_{10} + \text{``}CH_3OH\text{''}$$

$$(5.22)$$

A closely related two-step procedure based on sequential addition of the reagents LiPh and $MeOSO_2CF_3$ to (**6b**) results in substitution of the methoxy group by a phenyl group, leading to the benzylidyne species $Os_3(\mu\text{-}H)(\mu_3\text{-}CPh)(CO)_{10}$ (**250**) being structurally related to (**249**).[283] However, slight changes in the reaction conditions lead to the production of the new carbene-carbyne cluster complex $Os_3(\mu\text{-}H)(\mu_3\text{-}CPh)(\eta^1\text{-}C(OMe)_2)(CO)_9$ (**251**).[284] The formation of this species may be reasonably accounted for by the reaction sequence shown in Scheme 5.48, involving (i) nucleophilic attack of Ph^- at a CO ligand (occurring in competition with direct attack at the carbyne center), (ii) nucleophilic attack of the resulting

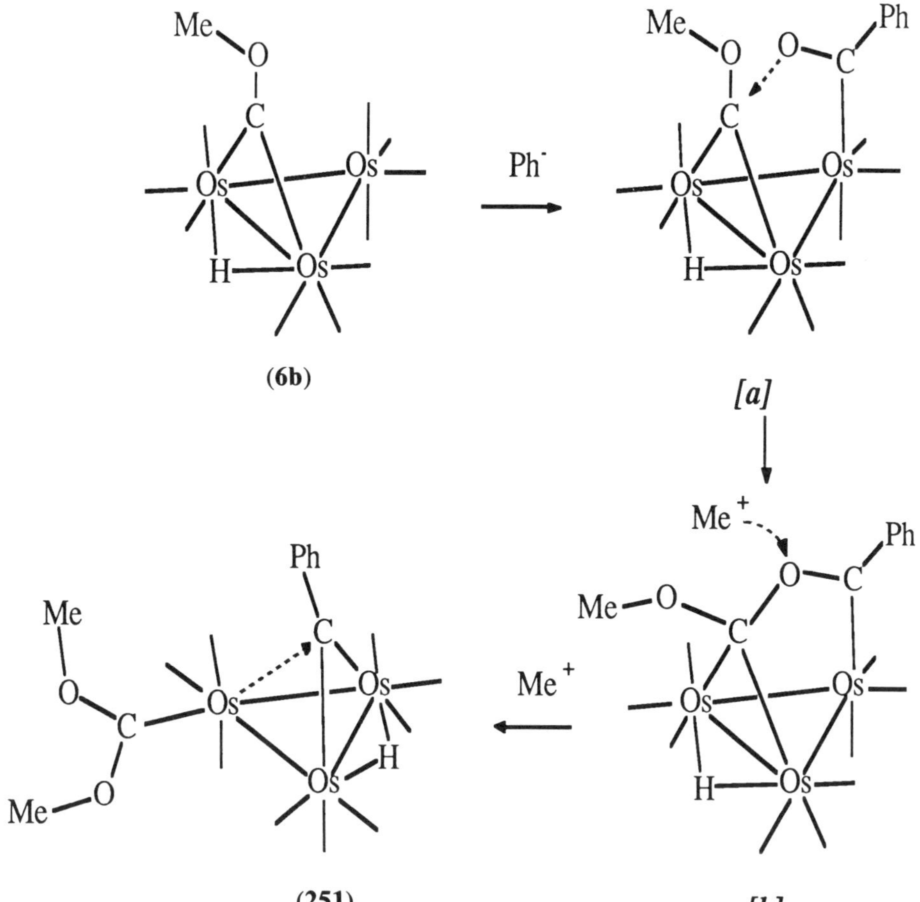

Scheme 5.48

acyl oxygen at the electrophilic carbyne center, and (iii) oxygen transfer from the acyl group to the carbyne center in the presence of the methylating agent to produce the terminal dimethoxycarbene ligand.

Reduction of CO via bridging acyl intermediates. An example of thermally induced C—O bond cleavage within a bridging acyl ligand providing oxo and alkylidyne groups has been presented in Scheme 5.42.[241] Besides, electrophilic attack at the oxygen of a bridging acyl is also prone to induce a disruption of the C—O linkage to produce coordinated μ_3-OR and μ_3-CR ligands, as evidenced by the following transformation, Scheme 5.49.[285]

Reduction of CO to a Fischer carbene; original observations. Terminal η^1-acyl groups are expected to behave in a different way than bridging ones in the presence of alkylating agents. In particular, they are prone to provide Fischer type carbenes which are well known in mononuclear complexes.[286] Following unsuccessful attempts to alkylate the acyl oxygen atom of [Li][Os$_3$(η^1-

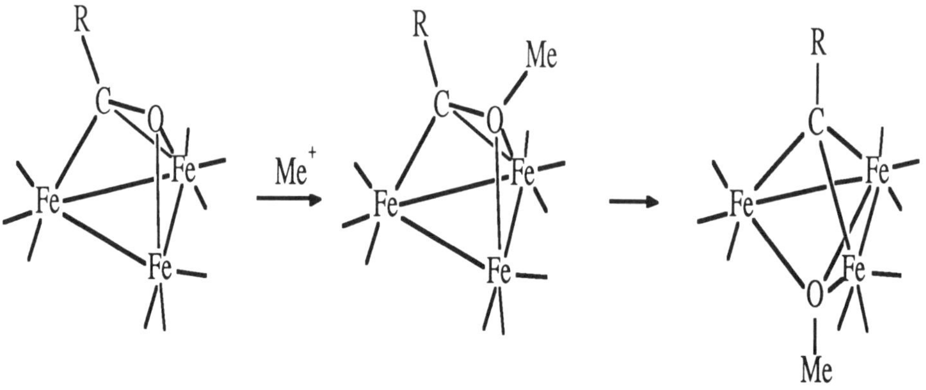

[252]   [253]

Scheme 5.49

C(O)CH$_3$)(CO)$_{11}$] [92] (alkylation of this anion is slow as compared with the rate of formation of a bridging acyl), Kaesz and co-workers were able to perform a complete Fischer reaction sequence on the neutral species Os$_3$(μ-H)(μ-O-CCH$_3$)(CO)$_{10}$ (7b) (Scheme 5.50).[135,287,288] Titration of (7b) with methyl lithium in diethylether at $-30°$C led to the *bis*-acyl derivative [Li][Os$_3$(μ-H)(η^1-C(O)CH$_3$)

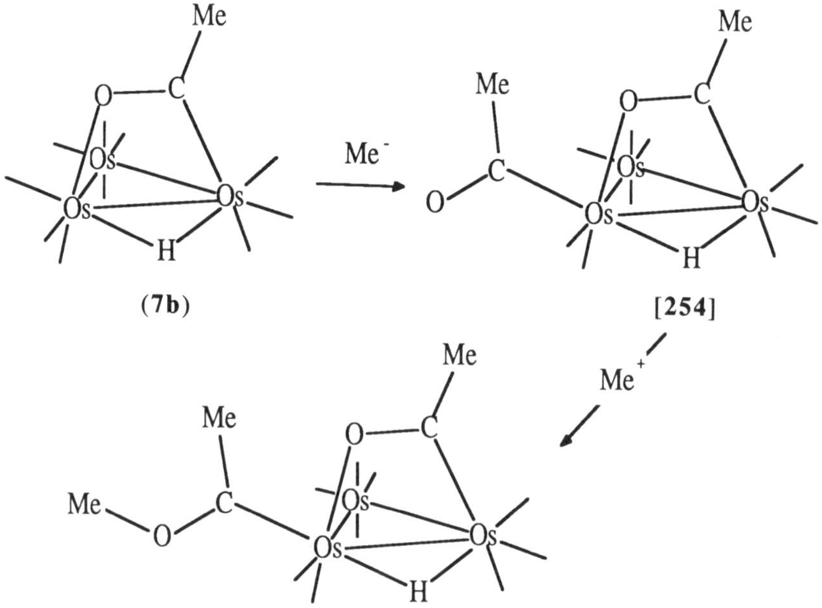

(7b)   [254]

(255)

Scheme 5.50

(μ-O—CCH$_3$)(CO)$_9$] [254]. Subsequent alkylation of this anion with a slight excess of CH$_3$OSO$_2$CF$_3$ provided the neutral methoxy carbene derivative Os$_3$(μ-H)(η^1-C(OCH$_3$)CH$_3$)(μ-O—CCH$_3$)(CO)$_9$ (255) in 70% yield after 36 h. The same, but more labile species was intercepted in the case of ruthenium.[288,289] Spontaneous reductive elimination of aldehyde from this intermediate was found to trigger double C—H bond activation within the methyl substituents of the carbene group at unprecedented mild conditions.

Terminal carbenes are now becoming well-established ligands in cluster chemistry (Scheme 5.48, for example). They are known to undergo facile coupling reactions with bridging ligands like phosphinidenes (Scheme 5.36)[160] or nitrenes (Scheme 5.45).[160] Alternately, they also show a tendency to move in bridging position.[173] Furthermore, there is presently a growing attention on the reactivity of aminocarbenes (Scheme 5.38).[290]

5.7.2. Reactivity of Cluster-Bound Hydrocarbon Fragments: Cleavage and Formation of Carbon–Carbon Bonds

Original reports on the cluster assisted cleavage of alkynes. The first evidence for a cluster-promoted scission of a coordinated alkyne providing alkylidyne fragments was obtained by Shapley from the observation of a thermally induced conversion of the tetranuclear mixed-metal complex Os$_3$WCp(H)(μ_3-RCCR′)(CO)$_{10}$ (256) into the *bis*(alkylidyne) complex Os$_3$WCp(H)(μ_3-CR)(μ_3-CR′)(CO)$_9$ (257).[291] Experimental evidence for a closely related scission occurring at three metal centers was subsequently obtained upon flash vacuum pyrolysis of the alkyne complexes (MCp)$_3$(μ_3-RCCR′)(μ_3-CO) (258a-b) (a, M = Rh; b, M = Ir).[292] These were shown to be intermediates in the known reaction of the mononuclear species MCp(CO)$_2$ with alkynes leading to *bis* alkylidyne derivatives (MCp)$_3$(μ_3-CR)(μ_3-CR′) (259). A theoretical analysis by extended Hückel calculations based on the model complex M$_3$Cp(μ_3-RCCR′)(μ_3-CO) (258c) (c, M = Co, R = H) led these authors to propose the now classic "edge pathway" sequence for alkyne scission shown in Scheme 5.51.

Rotation of the alkyne from its initial "parallel" (μ_3-η^2-//) coordination mode in (258) to a perpendicular mode is required to allow migration of this ligand to the edge of the cluster. Subsequent CO loss from this intermediate triggers the C—C bond cleavage.[292] In parallel to this report, a simultaneous important study by Wollhardt and co-workers on related cobalt complexes established that the cleavage process can be reversible.[293]

These pioneering discoveries have motivated numerous studies aimed at understanding the electronic features which govern the acetylene rotation process.[294] Concurrently, dramatic progress has been made in the control of carbon—carbon cleavage and formation.

Evidences for reversible CO mediated alkyne scission/alkylidyne-alkylidyne coupling under mild conditions. (See also Schemes 5.20, 5.58, 5.59, and relevant discussions.) Since coordinative unsaturation appears to be the driving force for alkyne scission, such a reaction should be more easily controlled for first row transition metal clusters which are prone to lose or gain CO under mild conditions. This has been demonstrated by Mathieu and co-workers in studies of the reactivity of the anionic alkylidyne complex [Fe$_3$(μ_3-CCH$_3$)(μ-CO)(CO)$_9$]$^-$

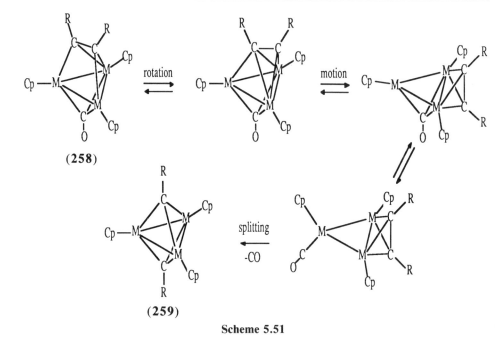

Scheme 5.51

[261],[295a] available in good yield from the reaction of $[Fe_3(\mu\text{-H})(CO)_{11}]^-$ [260] with acetylene, equation (5.23)[295b]

$$[Fe_3(\mu\text{-H})(CO)_{11}]^- + HCCH \xrightarrow{\text{5 h, acetone, r.t.}} [Fe_3(\mu_3\text{-CCH}_3)(CO)_{10}]^- \quad (5.23)$$

Alkylation of the anion (261) with $C_2H_5^+$ gives the reactive neutral *bis*-alkylidyne derivative $Fe_3(\mu_3\text{-CCH}_3)(\mu_3\text{-COC}_2H_5)(CO)_9$ (262a). Coupling of the two alkylidyne moieties within this species is induced by reaction with CO (20 atm, r.t., 48 h), leading to the alkyne complex $Fe_3(\mu_3\text{-}\eta^2\text{-CH}_3CCOC_2H_5)(CO)_{10}$ (263) (Scheme 5.52). The latter slowly reverts to the *bis*-alkylidyne derivative

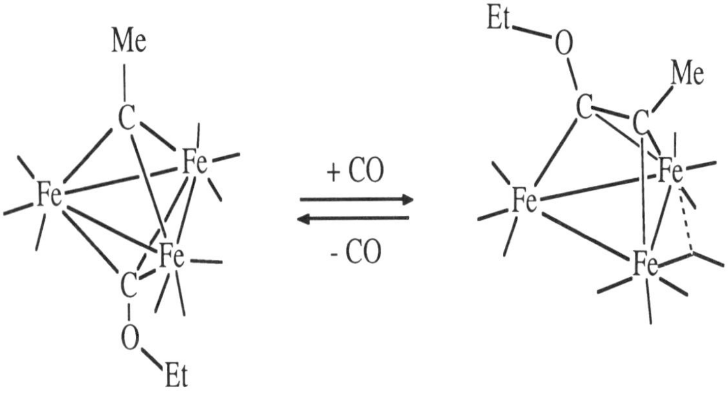

(262)   **(263)**

Scheme 5.52

under ambient conditions.[295a] (Note: the molecular geometry shown for (**263**) in Scheme 5.52 is that found for its phosphine substituted analog.)

Influence of the nature of metal atoms on the cleavage process. While there is no observable C—C bond cleavage for the alkyne-substituted triosmium cluster $Os_3(\mu_3\text{-RCCR})(CO)_{10}$ (**264**) even under forcing conditions, the mixed-metal derivative $OsW_2Cp_2(\mu_3\text{-}\eta^2\text{-RCCR})(CO)_7$ (**265**) undergoes scission of the alkyne induced by loss of two CO ligands to give $OsW_2Cp_2(\mu_3\text{-CR})(\mu\text{-CR})(CO)_5$ (**266**) [refluxing methylcyclohexane (101°C), 20 min., 88-95% yield].[296]

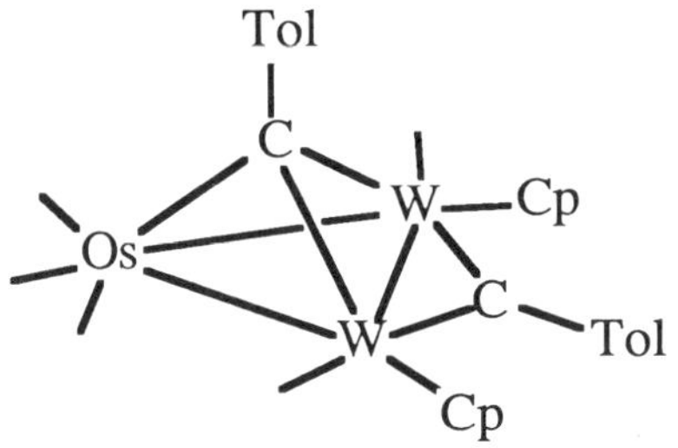

(**266**)

The formation of strong W—C bonds in the forward reaction is believed to facilitate the cleavage process. The reaction is cleanly reversed under carbon monoxide (1 atm, 25°C, 5 min., 95% yield). It is noteworthy that hydrogen reacts with (**266**), but does not cause carbon-carbon coupling.[296]

Electron induced carbon-carbon bond formation. A nice illustration of this general principle is found in the following sequences, Scheme 5.53.[297]

Electrochemical 1-e reduction of the alkylidyne cluster complex $[Fe_3(\mu_3\text{-}CCH_3)(\mu_3\text{-CO})(CO)_9]^-$ [**261**] results in a supersaturation which is released by coupling of the alkylidyne ligand with CO to give a propynolate ligand CH_3—CC—O$^-$ which binds to the metal triangle in a classic $\mu_3\text{-}\eta^2//$ fashion in the complex $[Fe_3(\mu_3\text{-}\eta^2\text{-CH}_3CCO)(CO)_9]^{2-}$ [**267**]. Subsequent protonation at oxygen by methanol or weak acids produces the acetylide complex $[Fe_3(\mu_3\text{-}\eta^2\text{-CCCH}_3)(CO)_9]^-$ [**268**].[297]

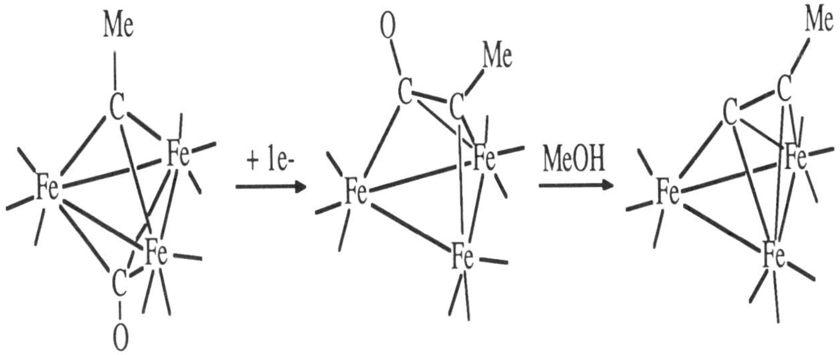

$[261]^-$ $[267]^{2-}$ $[268]^-$

Scheme 5.53

It is noteworthy that a transformation which is essentially the reverse of the previous one, that is, the conversion of an acetylide to a methylidyne via a co-ordinated acetylenic ligand, has been observed by Deeming in the chemistry of osmium.[298]

A comparable electron-induced coupling of two alkylidyne units is also seen in the sequential treatment of the *bis*-alkylidyne cluster $Os_3(\mu\text{-C-Ph})(\mu\text{-COMe})(CO)_9$ (**269**) with Na/benzophenone and acid to give $Os_3(\mu\text{-H})(\mu\text{-CCPh})(CO)_9$ (**270**).[299] Unlike the case mentioned for (**266**), hydrogen will promote carbon-carbon formation from (**269**), leading to the alkyne bridged derivative $Os_3(\mu\text{-H})_2(\mu\text{-PhCCOMe})(CO)_9$ (**271**).

Finally a 2-*e* reduction procedure based on $[Mn(CO)_5]^-$ as the reducing agent has been recently applied to the case of the *bis*-alkylidyne derivative $Fe_3(\mu_3\text{-CCH}_2R)(\mu_3\text{-COC}_2H_5)(CO)_9$ (**262b**). The course of this reaction is influenced by the nature of the R group: coupling of the two alkylidyne units produces the intermediate face-bridging ligand $RCH_2CCOC_2H_5$ which either gives the corresponding anionic acetylide complex (in parallel to the sequence shown in Scheme 5.53) or rearranges to a cluster-bound allenyl ligand.[300]

Alkyne-induced carbyne-carbyne coupling and related reactions; carbon-carbon chain growth. The insertion of alkynes into the M—C bonds of triply bridging alkylidyne ligands is well documented for ruthenium and osmium clusters.[276a] For example, the reaction of alkynes $RCCR'$ with either $Ru_3(\mu\text{-H})(\mu\text{-CX})(CO)_{10}$ (**6**) (X = OMe, or SEt), or $Ru_3(\mu\text{-H})_3(\mu_3\text{-CX})(CO)_9$ (**42**) (X = SEt) results in alkyne insertion into a metal-carbon bond of the alkylidyne group to produce the complex $Ru_3(\mu\text{-H})(\mu_3\text{-XC—CR—CR'})(CO)_9$ (**272**) containing a 1-3-dimetalloallyl ligand (Scheme 5.54).[301] Upon reaction with hydrogen, (**272**) is converted into the alkylidyne complex $Ru_3(\mu\text{-H})_3(\mu_3\text{-C—CHR—CH}_2R)(CO)_9$ (**274**). Labeling experiments have demonstrated that the hydride is transferred to the ligand prior to the addition of hydrogen. The isolation of the trappable intermediate complex $Ru_3(\mu\text{-X})(\mu_3\text{-}\eta^3\text{-C—CR—CHR'})(CO)_9$ (**273**) when X = SEt, R = R' = Ph reveals that the initial isomerization process involves a transfer of the S-Et group to the metal. This group is subsequently released in the final hydrogenation step.[276a,302] The whole sequence provides a remarkable example of the ability of alkylidyne clusters to promote carbon-carbon chain growth.

Alkylidyne-alkyne coupling also occurs in the parallel reaction of alkynes with the iron complex $Fe_3(\mu\text{-H})(\mu\text{-CR})(CO)_{10}$ (**276**) though in this case, the nature of the oligomeric products is highly dependent on the nature of the alkynes.[303]

A different reaction occurs with the *bis*-alkylidyne derivative (**262a**), Scheme 5.55:[304] alkynes $RCCR'$ are seen to promote the formation of an oligomeric chain to produce the new species $Fe_3(\mu\text{-CMe—COEt—CR—CR'})(\mu\text{-CO})(CO)_6$ (**277**). Five isomeric forms of this complex have been isolated in relative abundance depending on the nature of the R substituents of the alkyne. They differ in the position of these substituents along the oligomeric chain: for example, direct alkylidyne-alkylidyne coupling produces (**277a**), while alkyne insertion into the two carbyne units leads to (**277b**). Among other isomers, not shown in Scheme 5.55, one includes the sequence in which CR and CR' groups are not adjacent.[304]

Related examples of alkyne oligomerization in metal cluster complexes have been reported.[305] In particular, the stoichiometric oligomerization of phenyl-acetylene to 1-3-5-triphenylbenzene has been achieved with the mixed-metal

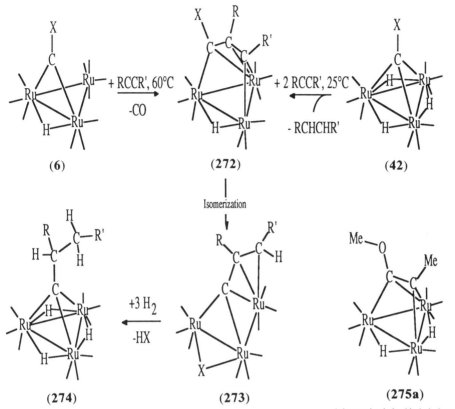

(6)   (272)   (42)

+ RCCR', 60°C
-CO

+ 2 RCCR', 25°C
- RCHCHR'

Isomerization

(274)   (273)   (275a)

+3 H₂
-HX

(minor product isolated in the hydrogenation
of 272 when X = OMe, and R = R' = H)

Scheme 5.54

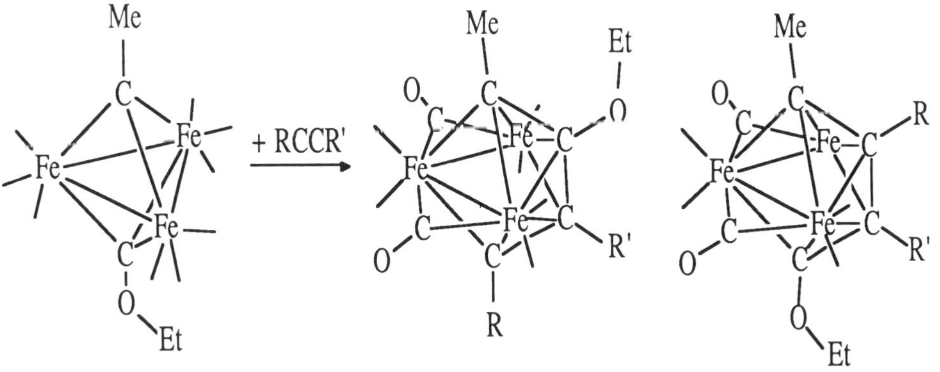

(262a)   (277a)   (277b)

+ RCCR'

Scheme 5.55

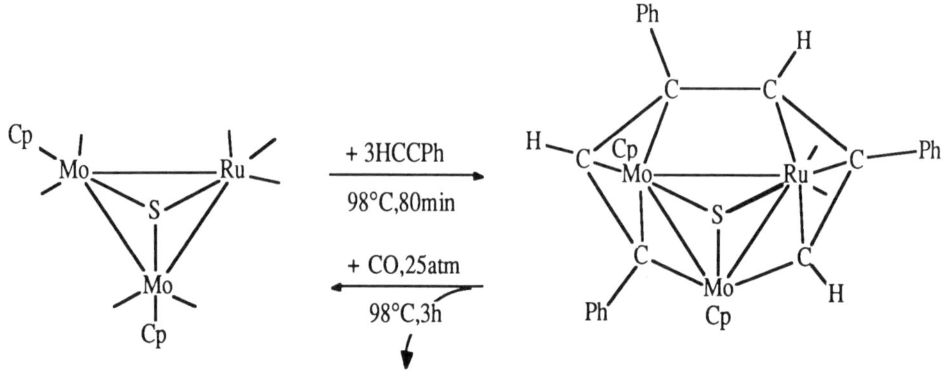

(278)   1,3,5 triphenylbenzene (74%)   **(279)** (yield,15%)

Scheme 5.56

complex $RuMo_2Cp_2(\mu_3\text{-}S)(CO)_7$ (**278**) through the intermediacy of the complex $RuMo_2Cp_2(\mu\text{-}C(Ph)C(H)C(Ph)C(H)C(Ph)C(H))(CO)_2$ (**279**) (Scheme 5.56).[39]

Though binuclear complexes are out of the topic of this review, let us recall that reactions of alkynes at two metal centers are now well controlled and have proved to be a valuable source of cyclic organic compounds. A representative example is found in the recent report by Knox on the synthesis of tropone by reaction of a bimetallic complex with acetylene and carbon monoxide.[306]

Other coupling reactions. Various additional means to induce coupling reactions from cluster-bound alkylidyne fragments are known.[307] Let us cite in particular the UV-initiated intermolecular association of $Fe_3(\mu_3\text{-}CF)_2(CO)_9$ (**280**) with $[Cp^*Co(CO)_2]$ leading to the formation of the heterometallic butterfly complex $Fe_3CoCp^*(\mu_3\text{-}\eta^2\text{-}FCCF)(CO)_9$ (**281**) which contains a difluoroethyne moiety.[308]

Interactions between cluster bound alkylidyne and alkylidene fragments. Such interactions are observable for $Fe_2MnCp^*Cp(\mu_3\text{-}COMe)(\mu\text{-}C(H)Me)(CO)_5$ (**282a**), a unique cluster complex containing both a methoxycarbyne group and an ethylidene group (Scheme 5.57).[309]

Upon standing several days at ambient temperature, this complex rearranges via rotation of the ethylidene group to produce the more stable diastereomeric complex (**282b**). Two other products are isolated under these conditions: one, formulated as $Fe_2MnCp^*Cp(\mu_3\text{-}CMe)(\mu\text{-}C(H)OMe)(CO)_5$ (**283**), is the result of an intramolecular hydrogen migration from the ethylidene group to the methoxycarbyne group. The second one, available in low yield, is the binuclear methoxyvinyl complex (**284**) resulting from a carbyne-ethylidene coupling.

5.7.3. From Carbides and Ketenylidenes to Hydrocarbon Fragments and Organic Substrates

An extreme form of the cluster-assisted "degradation" of CO or hydrocarbon fragments is the encapsulation of the carbon element as a carbide ligand within the metal-atom polyhedron.[13,310] The most reactive carbido cluster complexes are indeed those having an exposed carbide atom.[13,311,312] Though MO calculations

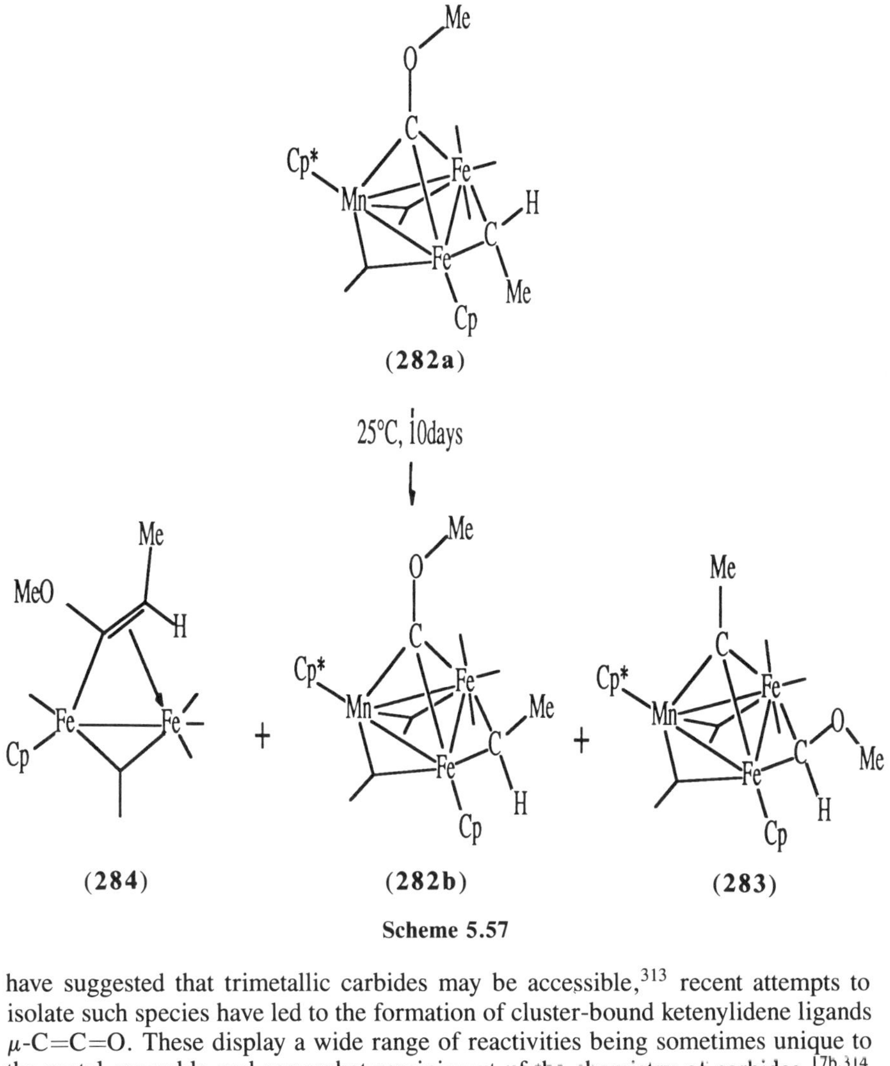

(**282a**)

25°C, 10days

(**284**)   +   (**282b**)   +   (**283**)

Scheme 5.57

have suggested that trimetallic carbides may be accessible,[313] recent attempts to isolate such species have led to the formation of cluster-bound ketenylidene ligands μ-C=C=O. These display a wide range of reactivities being sometimes unique to the metal ensemble and somewhat reminiscent of the chemistry of carbides.[17b,314] In other words, the α carbon of the ketenylidene group could be regarded as a carbide atom being (lightly) stabilized by a carbonyl group.

Formation of ketenylidene group. The first ketenylidenes were isolated by halide abstraction from μ—C—Cl groups in trimetallic cobalt cluster complexes.[315] More recently, thermally induced activation of the methylene group in $Os_3(\mu\text{-}CH_2)(\mu\text{-}CO)(CO)_{10}$ (**105**) was found to produce $Os_3(\mu\text{-}H)_2(\mu\text{-}CCO)(CO)_9$ (**285**).[316] This volatile complex could also be obtained even more readily by rearrangement of solid samples of the methyne complex $Os_3(\mu\text{-}CH)(CO)_{10}$ (**249**) in a sublimation apparatus.[317] In parallel to these studies, the general process which proved successful for the synthesis of tetranuclear butterfly carbides (O-acylation followed by reductive cleavage) was applied to Fe_3 systems, in this case leading to the di-anionic ketenylidene $[PPN]_2[Fe_3(\mu_3\text{-CCO})(CO)_9]$ **[288a]**, equations (5.24)–(5.25).[318,319]

$$(5.24)$$

$$[PPN]_2[Fe_3(CO)_{11}] + CH_3C(O)Cl \rightarrow [PPN][Fe_3(\mu_3\text{-COC(O)CH}_3)(CO)_{10}]$$
$$\mathbf{[286a]^{2-}} \qquad\qquad\qquad \mathbf{[287a]^{-}}$$

$$[PPN][Fe_3(\mu\text{-COC(O)CH}_3)(CO)_{10}] + Na/Ph_2CO$$
$$\mathbf{[287a]^{-}}$$

$$\rightarrow [PPN]_2[Fe_3(\mu_3\text{-CCO})(CO)_9] + OCH_3{}^{-}$$
$$\mathbf{[288a]^{2-}} \qquad\qquad\qquad\qquad (5.25)$$

This procedure was subsequently applied to the preparation of the analogous ruthenium complex $[PPN]_2[Ru_3(\mu_3\text{-CCO})(\mu\text{-CO})_3(CO)_6]$ **[288b]**[320,321] and finally extended to the osmium derivative $[PPN]_2[Os_3(\mu_3\text{-CCO})(CO)_9$ **[288c]**.[322]

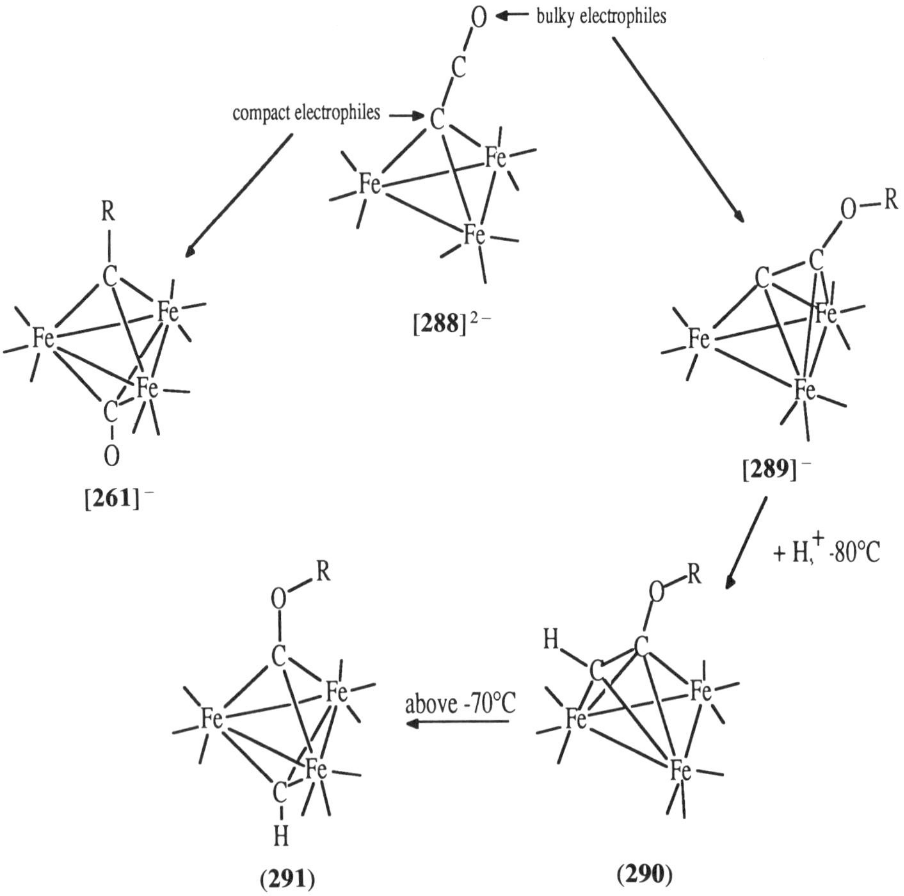

Scheme 5.58

Metal ensemble effects in the chemistry of anionic ketenylidenes [PPN]$_2$[M$_3$(μ_3-CCO)(CO)$_9$] (M = Fe, Ru, Os). The reaction of [Fe$_3$(μ_3-CCO)(CO)$_9$]$^{2-}$ [288a] with electrophilic reagents follows two alternate paths, depending on the steric bulk of these reagents (Scheme 5.58).[318,319]

Compact electrophiles, like H$^+$ or Me$^+$, attack at the α carbon position, with concomitant shift of CO to the metal to produce the known methylidyne or alkylidyne species [Fe$_3$(μ-CR)(μ-CO)(CO)$_9$]$^-$ [261] (R = H or CH$_3$$^+$)[318] which can also be prepared by another route, see equation (5.23). By contrast, more bulky groups like ethyl triflate or acetyl chloride react directly at the oxygen of the ketenylidene to produce the acetylide complex [Fe$_3$($\mu_3\eta^2$-CCOR)(CO)$_9$]$^-$ [289].[319] Upon reaction with fluorosulfonic acid at low temperature, the latter species protonates at the α position to give the unstable alkyne complex Fe$_3$(μ_3-η^2-HCCOR)(CO)$_9$ (290). This species is electronically unsaturated and the ethoxyalkyne ligand adopts the unusual μ_3-η^2 perpendicular mode. This configuration favors a cleavage of the carbon-carbon bond, which is effectively observable above $-70°$C, and leads to the di-alkylidyne species Fe$_3$(μ_3-CH)(μ_3-COR)(CO)$_9$ (291), methylidyne analog of (262a).

The occurrence of an alkyne complex along the path leading to (261) has been suggested to explain the Cα-C-β cleavage induced by compact electrophiles. Further evidence for such a species has been obtained in the reaction of CH$_3$$^+$ with the di-anionic osmium ketenylidene [PPN]$_2$[Os$_3$(μ_3-CCO)(CO)$_9$] [288c] which also proceeds via initial attack at the α carbon atom (by contrast, protonation occurs at the metal in this case and also for ruthenium).[322] The direction of the reaction sequence shown in Scheme 5.59 is controlled by carbon monoxide. Indeed, C-C bond cleavage within the presumed intermediate alkyne species is prevented under CO and in the presence of two equivalents of CH$_3$$^+$, leading to the neutral acetylene complex Os$_3$(μ_3-η^2-MeCCOMe)(CO)$_{10}$ (263c). C-C bond cleavage occurs in the absence of carbon monoxide, while O-alkylation of the resulting alkylidyne complex gives the *bis*-alkylidyne derivative Os$_3$(μ_3-CMe)(μ_3-COMe)(CO)$_9$ (262c). Clearly, the 2-e oxidation induced by the addition of two equivalents of CH$_3$$^+$ is balanced either by ligand addition or by C-C bond cleavage. In contrast to the case of iron, however, (Scheme 5.52) the complexes obtained through these parallel paths are not interconvertible.[322]

Surprisingly, the ruthenium ketenylidene [PPN]$_2$[Ru$_3$(μ_3-CCO)(μ-CO)$_3$(CO)$_6$] [288b] exhibits a different behavior in its reaction with electrophiles (Scheme 5.60).[320,321] Both H$^+$ and CH$_3$$^+$ attack at the metal. Alkylation under CO atmosphere leads to the anionic acylmethylidyne complex [Ru$_3$(μ_3-η^2-CC(O)CH$_3$)(μ_3-CO)(CO)$_9$]$^-$ [292].[13]C labeling experiments have established the following sequence for this reaction: (i) alkylation at the metal, (ii) migratory CO insertion to give a metal-bound acyl, (iii) acyl migration to the α carbon of the ketenylidene ligand with concomitant shift of the carbonyl group of the ketenylidene down to the metal. The acylmethylidyne complex (292) can be subsequently converted into the neutral vinyl derivative Ru$_3$(μ_3-η^2-C=C(OCH$_3$)CH$_3$)(μ_3-CO)(CO)$_9$ (293) upon addition of methyl triflate.

The different reactivity of the ruthenium ketenylidene as compared with iron and osmium derivatives has been interpreted on the basis of extended Hückel molecular orbital calculations and structural evidence.[322] Unlike the iron and osmium ketenylidene ligands, which are tilted away from the axial position by 33°

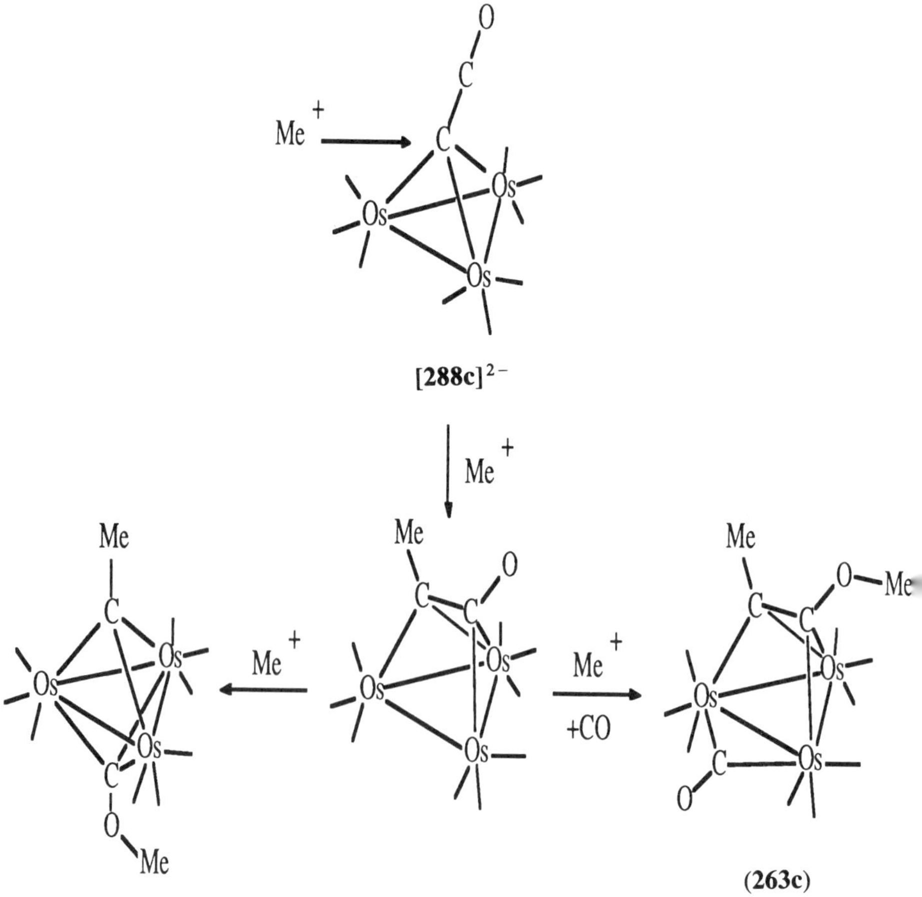

Scheme 5.59

and 26°, respectively, the deviation of the ruthenium ketenylidene is only 12°
This geometry reduces the accessibility of the α carbon atom. Furthermore, the
exposed metal region is located at the highest electron population of its HOMO
thus favoring direct attack of electrophiles at the metal.[322]

The acylmethylidyne complex [Ru$_3$(μ_3-η^2-CC(O)CH$_3$)(μ_3-CO)(CO)$_9$]$^-$ [292
synthesized in the previous reaction exhibits the typical behavior of activate
complexes which have been previously examined in Section 5.2. For example
this complex reacts reversibly with CO under mild conditions to give the adduc
[Ru$_3$(μ_3-η^2-CH$_3$C(O)CCO)(μ-CO)$_3$(CO)$_7$]$^-$ [294] (Scheme 5.61).[323] Labeling ex
periments indicate that the incorporation of the incoming ligand into the pool o
metal-bound carbonyls triggers the migration of another CO to the α carbon c
the acylmethylidyne. The acetyl group participates in the CO insertion proces
by entering into a bonding interaction with ruthenium. A closely related pro
cess is seen in the hydrogenation reaction of the complex (292) which is mad

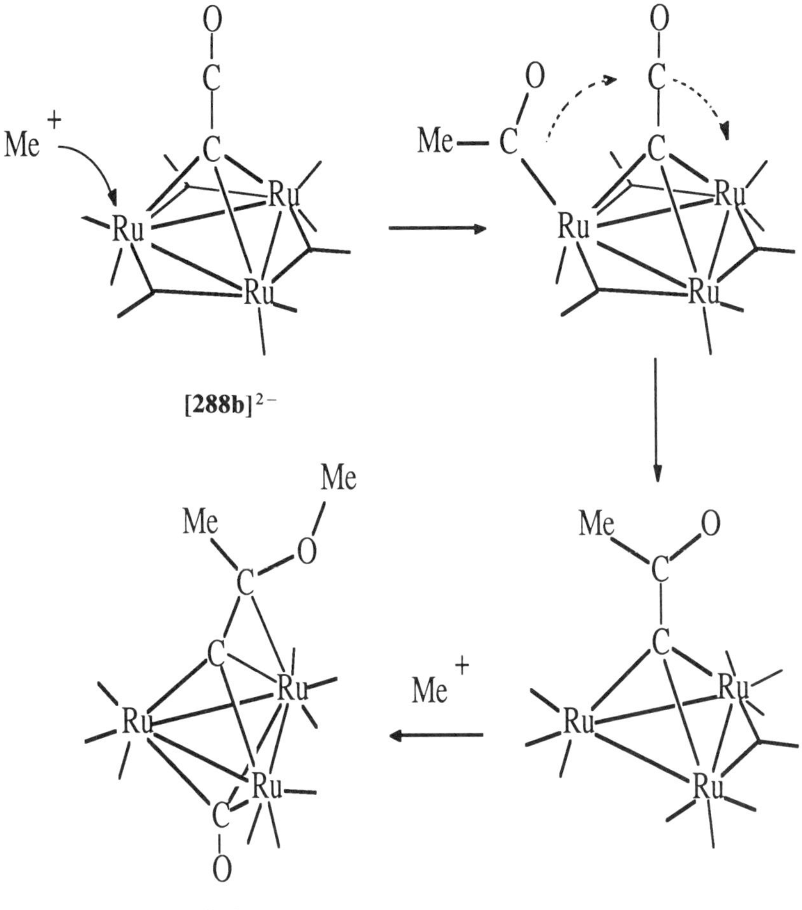

Scheme 5.60

to occur at very mild conditions and leads to the new species $[Ru_3(\mu\text{-}H)(\mu_3\text{-}\eta^2\text{-} CHC(O)CH_3)(CO)_9]^-$ [295]. Interestingly, reductive elimination of acetone from this complex is induced by reaction with hydrochloric acid. We find it significant here that the halide anion is necessary to labilize the metal-ligand bonds and to release the modified substrate from the metal framework.

5.8. Summary of Ligand Transformations

A number of cluster-assisted ligand transformations have been highlighted from the literature of recent years. The scope of this chapter has been limited to selected reactions involving transition metal carbonyl clusters and the following ligand categories: (i) functionalized ligands containing respectively hetero-atoms

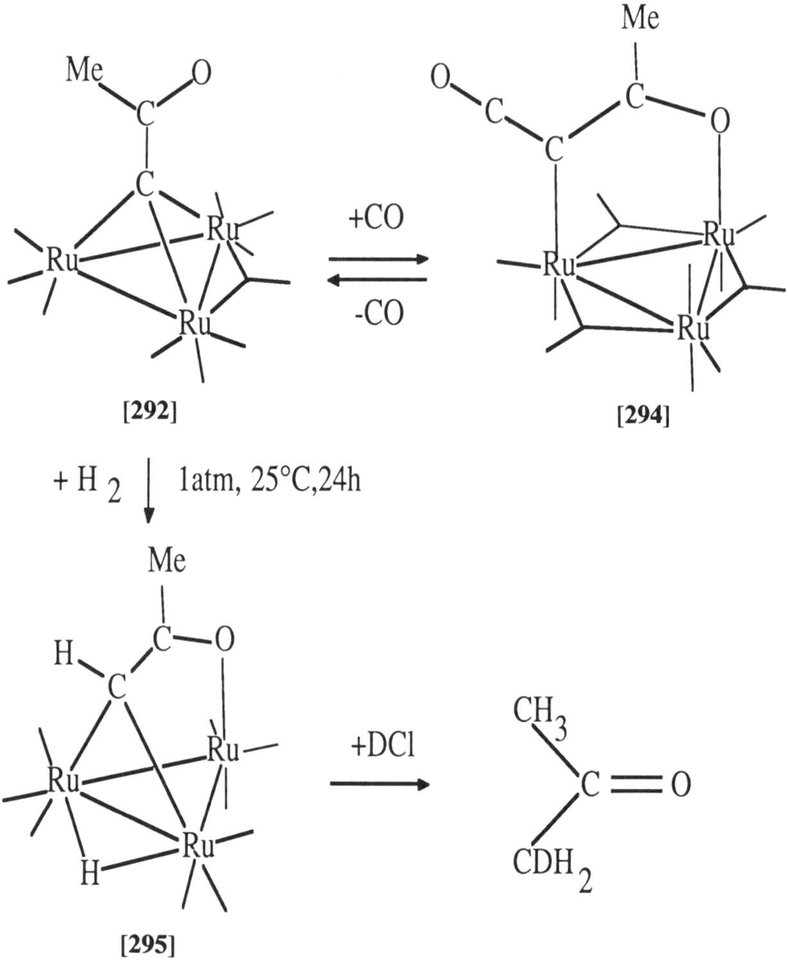

Scheme 5.61

like phosphorus, sulfur, oxygen, or nitrogen, and (ii) simple cluster-bound carbon-containing fragments, obtained either by reduction of carbon monoxide or by activation of unsaturated olefins and organic substrates. A brief summary of this presentation is provided.

Phosphorus-containing ligands. Metal-mediated transformations of coordinated phosphanes are typical reactions that are facilitated by a cooperative effect of contiguous metal centers. They proceed through sequential oxidative additions (direct cleavage of phosphorus-element bonds P—C, P—H,. . .and/or activation of the C—H bonds of the phosphorus substituents) and reductive eliminations (possibly involving migration of the phosphorus substituents to other coordinated substrates) generally ending with the stabilization of bridging phosphido or phosphinidene groups. These transformations can be made to occur at very mild conditions and can be eventually reversed in specific cases. Phosphido and phosphinidene groups also experience facile and reversible coupling reactions with a variety of incoming substrates. For example, a reversible hydrogen-promoted conversion of a bridging phosphido group into the corresponding secondary phosphine has been recently reported.

Sulfur-containing ligands. Parallel, and even more facile, transformations are observed for thiols, thioamides, and related sulfur-containing ligands, thereby leading to the encapsulation of a bridging sulfido group within a metal atom polyhedron. For sulfido bridged cluster complexes, coupling reactions between the sulfur atom and alkynes or hydrocarbon fragments have also been recently observed; they are helpful to understand the poisoning effects of sulfur in surface reactions. Evidences have been presented that some sulfido bridged cluster species are stable, and yet active in promoting stoichiometric or catalytic ligand transformations.

Oxygen-containing ligands. Cluster complexes containing oxygen donor ligands provide valuable models for oxide grafted species, and in some cases, they display a comparable chemical reactivity. Alkoxo groups are of particular interest as ancillary ligands due to the stability of their carbon-oxygen bond. Furthermore, the intrinsic properties of coordinated oxygen (*cis*-labilizing effect, variable hapticity...) are known to facilitate the activation of various ligands including unsaturated hydrocarbons. Oxo cluster complexes have been synthesized, generally by direct activation of molecular oxygen. At the present stage of current studies, little is known about the chemical reactivity of the oxygen atom in such species.

Nitrogen-containing ligands. The challenge of important applications of industrial relevance, such as the reduction of nitroaromatics to amines and carbamates using iron and ruthenium clusters as catalyst precursors, has motivated much of the recent work on nitrogen-containing ligands. While the triply bridging nitrene ligand was thought for a long time to be chemically inert, its stepwise conversion into a carbamate has been recently achieved. Besides, dramatic progress has also been made on the knowledge of fundamental reactions like the reduction of CN multiple bonds, and the cleavage and formation of CN, NN, and NO bonds.

Simple carbon-containing ligands. Following the original observation of a stepwise reduction of CO to methane on a butterfly tetrahedral cluster complex, various means to convert coordinated carbon monoxide into cluster-bound hydrocarbon fragments have been reported for trinuclear complexes. Related carbon-containing fragments can also be obtained from acetylenes by cluster-mediated cleavage of the carbon-carbon triple bond. This reaction and its reverse, carbon-carbon formation, are now well controlled. In specific cases, carbon-carbon splitting can be achieved at three-metal centers far below ambient conditions (the best record is around −50°C). Conversely, dramatic examples of carbon-carbon chain growth on metal clusters provide valuable models for surface reactions occurring in the Fischer Tropsch process. The simplest cluster-bound organic fragment, the carbide ligand, possesses a rich chemistry in low-nuclearity complexes where it is highly exposed. In trinuclear species, it stabilizes itself by scavenging a carbonyl group to give a ketenylidene ligand which displays a fascinating carbide-like reactivity. Coupling reactions based on this simple fragment are prone to produce a variety of different organic molecules.

Through this chapter, it appears that an important outgrowth of recent studies on cluster complexes has been to provide more rational means to tailor organic substrates. Though numerous cluster-assisted ligand transformations were observed in the early pioneering work, they usually lead to a deactivation of organic or inorganic fragments concomitant with their trapping in polymetallic environments. From such reactions, however, scientists have learned the attractive possibilities offered by molecular metal ensembles, in particular for the cleavage of some high energy chemical bonds. Then they have found the means to control these reactions and to gain more insight into their mechanism. Finally, they are presently at the point to perform the reverse ones, that is, to construct a variety of elaborated organic molecules from simple cluster-bound fragments. This is indeed the way to organic synthesis and catalysis, even if, from this point of view, cluster chemistry is still at the exploratory stage. Thus, it is hoped that conjugated efforts on the design of new reactive homometallic or heterometallic cluster complexes, new ancillary ligands, and efficient supports will make it possible to take advantage of the rich chemistry of molecular metal ensembles for the synthesis of valuable chemicals.

References

1. H. Vahrenkamp, *Struct. Bonding*, 1977, **32**, 1 and earlier reviews cited therein.
2. A. P. Humphries and H. D. Kaesz, *Progr. Inorg. Chem.*, 1979, **25**, 145.
3. A. J. Deeming, in *Transition metal clusters*, B. F. G. Johnson (Ed.). Chichester: Wiley, 1980, p. 391.
4. (a) E. L. Muetterties, *J. Organomet. Chem.*, 1980, **200**, 177; (b) E. L. Muetterties, R. R. Burch and A. M. Stolzenberg, *Ann. Rev. Phys. Chem.*, 1982, **33**, 89.
5. B. F. G. Johnson and J. Lewis, *Adv. Inorg. Chem. Radiochem.*, 1981, **24**, 225.
6. H. Vahrenkamp, *Adv. Organomet. Chem.*, 1983, **22**, 169.
7. R. D. Adams and I. T. Horvàth, *Progr. Inorg. Chem.*, 1985, **33**, 127.
8. G. Lavigne and H. D. Kaesz, in *Metal clusters in catalysis*, B. C. Gates, L. Gucz and H. Knözinger (Eds.). Amsterdam: Elsevier, 1986, Ch. IV, p. 43.
9. P. Braunstein, *Nouv. J. Chim.*, 1986, **10**, 365.
10. J. S. Bradley, in *Metal clusters*, M. Moskovits (Ed.). New York: Wiley-Interscience 1986, Ch. V, p. 105.
11. P. Chini, G. Longoni and V. G. Albano, *Adv. Organomet. Chem.*, 1976, **14**, 285.
12. W. L. Gladfelter and G. L. Geoffroy, *Adv. Organomet. Chem.*, 1980, **18**, 207.
13. (a) J. S. Bradley, *Adv. Organomet. Chem.*, 1983, **22**, 1; (b) M. Tachikawa and E L. Muetterties, *Progr. Inorg. Chem.*, 1981, **28**, 203.
14. E. Sappa, A. Tiripicchio and P. Braunstein, *Chem. Rev.*, 1983, **83**, 203.
15. K. Burgess, *Polyhedron*, 1984, **3**, 1175.
16. N. J. Nicholls, *Polyhedron*, 1984, **3**, 1307.
17. (a) C. P. Horwitz and D. F. Shriver, *Adv. Organomet. Chem.*, 1984, **23**, 219; (b D. F. Shriver and M. J. Sailor, *Acc. Chem. Res.*, 1988, **21**, 374.
18. W. L. Gladfelter, *Adv. Organomet. Chem.*, 1985, **24**, 41.
19. P. R. Raithby and M. J. Rosales, *Adv. Inorg. Chem. Radiochem.*, 1985, **29**, 169
20. R. D. Adams, *Polyhedron*, 1985, **4**, 2003.
21. W. E. Geiger and N. G. Connelly, *Adv. Organomet. Chem.*, 1985, **24**, 87.
22. M. O. Albers, D. J. Robinson and N. J. Coville, *Coord. Chem. Rev.*, 1986, **69** 127.
23. (a) W. A. Herrmann, *Angew. Chem. Int. Ed. Engl.*, 1986, **25**, 56; (b) D. Fenske J. Ohmer, J. Hachgenei and K. Merzweiler, *Angew. Chem. Int. Ed. Engl.*, 1988 **27**, 1277.
24. M. D. Vargas and J. N. Nicholls, *Adv. Inorg. Chem. Radiochem.*, 1986, **30**, 12?

25. A. J. Deeming, *Adv. Organomet. Chem.*, 1986, **26**, 1.
26. M. I. Bruce, *Coord. Chem. Rev.*, 1987, **76**, 1.
27. G. Huttner and K. Knoll, *Angew. Chem. Int. Ed. Engl.*, 1987, **26**, 743.
28. C. E. Housecroft, *Polyhedron*, 1987, **6**, 1935.
29. (a) *Advanced inorganic chemistry*, F. A. Cotton and G. Wilkinson (Eds.). New York: Wiley-Interscience, 1980, Ch. 26, p. 1080; (b) *Comprehensive organometallic chemistry*, G. Wilkinson, F. G. A. Stone and E. W. Abel (Eds.). Oxford: Pergamon, 1982. Specific citations within this work are made in the following pages; (c) *Comprehensive coordination chemistry*, G. Wilkinson, R. D. Gillard and J. A. McCleverty (Eds.). Oxford: Pergamon, 1987.
30. (a) E. L. Muetterties, T. N. Rhodin, E. Band, C. F. Brucker and W. R. Pretzer, *Chem. Rev.*, 1979, **79**, 91; (b) E. L. Muetterties and J. Stein, *Chem. Rev.*, 1979, **79**, 479.
31. A. Ceriotti, A. Fait, G. Longoni, G. Piro, F. Demartin, M. Manassero, N. Masciocchi and M. Sansoni, *J. Am. Chem. Soc.*, 1986, **108**, 8091.
32. (a) R. Ugo, *Catal. Rev.*, 1975, **11**, 225; (b) A. K. Smith and J. M. Basset, *J. Mol. Catal.*, 1977, **2**, 229; (c) R. Whyman, in *Transition metal clusters*, B. F. G. Johnson (Ed.). Chichester: Wiley, 1980, p. 545; (d) R. M. Laine, *J. Mol. Catal.*, 1982, **14**, 137; (e) E. L. Muetterties and M. J. Krause, *Angew. Chem. Int. Ed. Engl.*, 1983, **22**, 135; (f) J. Zwart and R. Snel, *J. Mol. Catal.*, 1985, **30**, 305; (g) L. Markò and A. Vizi-Orosz, in *Metal clusters in catalysis*, B. C. Gates, L. Guczi and H. Knözinger (Eds.). Amsterdam: Elsevier, 1986, Ch. V, p. 89; (h) P. Braunstein and J. Rosé, in *Stereochemistry of organometallic and inorganic compounds*, I. Bernal (Ed.). Amsterdam: Elsevier, 1988, Vol. 3, in press; (i) see also W. L. Gladfelter in Chapter 7 of this book. (j) G. Süss-Fink and F. Neumann, in The Chemistry of the Metal-Carbon Bond, F. R. Hartley (Ed.). New York: Wiley, 1989, Ch. 7, p. 231.
33. M. A. Andrews and H. D. Kaesz, *J. Am. Chem. Soc.*, 1979, **101**, 7255.
34. H. D. Kaesz, C. B. Knobler, M. A. Andrews, G. van Burskirk, R. Stostak, C. E. Strouse, Y. C. Lin and A. Mayr, *Pure Appl. Chem.*, 1982, **54**, 131.
35. Z. Dawoodi, M. J. Mays and K. Henrick, *J. Chem. Soc. Dalton Trans.*, 1984, 433.
36. W. Bernhard and H. Vahrenkamp, *Angew. Chem. Int. Ed. Engl.*, 1984, **23**, 381.
37. B. C. Gates, in *Metal clusters in catalysis*, B. C. Gates, L. Guczi and H. Knözinger (Eds.). Amsterdam: Elsevier, 1986, Ch. IX, p. 415.
38. W. Bernhardt, C. von Schnering and H. Vahrenkamp, *Angew. Chem. Int. Ed. Engl.*, 1986, **25**, 279.
39. R. D. Adams, J. E. Babin, M. Tasi and J.-G. Wang, *Organometallics*, 1988, **7**, 755.
40. (a) M. R. Desrosiers, D. A. Wink, R. Trautman, A. E. Friedman and P. C. Ford, *J. Am. Chem. Soc.*, 1986, **108**, 1917 and references therein. (b) For photochemical reactions of surface supported $Ru_3(CO)_{12}$, see: T. Dieter and H. D. Gafney, *Inorg. Chem.*, 1988, **27**, 1730.
41. J. G. Bentsen and M. S. Wrighton, *J. Am. Chem. Soc.*, 1987, **109**, 4530.
42. A. J. Poë and C. V. Sekhar, *J. Am. Chem. Soc.*, 1986, **108**, 3673, and references therein.
43. J. G. Bentsen and M. S. Wrighton, *J. Am. Chem. Soc.*, 1987, **109**, 4518.
44. A. E. Friedman and P. C. Ford, *J. Am. Chem. Soc.*, 1986, **108**, 7851.
45. G. J. Bezems, P. H. Rieger and S. Visco, *J. Chem. Soc. Chem. Commun.*, 1981, 265.
46. (a) J. K. Kochi, *J. Organomet. Chem.*, 1986, **300**, 139. (b) P. Lemoine, *Coord. Chem. Rev.*, 1988, **83**, 169.
47. (a) H. H. Ohst and J. K. Kochi, *J. Chem. Soc. Chem. Commun.*, 1986, 121. (b) H. H. Ohst and J. K. Kochi, *J. Am. Chem. Soc.*, 1986, **108**, 2897. (c) H. H. Ohst and J. K. Kochi, *Inorg. Chem.*, 1986, **25**, 2066.

48. T. M. Bockman and J. K. Kochi, *J. Am. Chem. Soc.*, 1987, **109**, 7725.
49. J. C. Cyr, J. A. DeGray, D. K. Gosser, E. S. Lee and P. H. Rieger, *Organometallics*, 1985, **4**, 950 and references therein.
50. A. J. Downward, B. H. Robinson, J. Simpson and A. M. Bond, *J. Organomet. Chem.*, 1987, **320**, 363.
51. (a) M. I. Bruce, D. C. Kehoe, J. G. Matisons, B. K. Nicholson, P. H. Rieger and M. L. Williams, *J. Chem. Soc. Chem. Commun.*, 1982, 442. (b) M. I. Bruce, B. K. Nicholson and M. L. Williams, *Inorg. Synth.*, Vol XXV, in press.
52. A. A. Bhattacharyya, C. C. Nagel and S. G. Shore, *Organometallics*, 1983, **2**, 1187.
53. N. J. Coville, M. O. Albers and E. Singleton, *J. Chem. Soc. Dalton Trans.*, 1983, 947.
54. M. O. Albers, N. J. Coville and E. Singleton, *J. Organomet. Chem.*, 1987, **326**, 229.
55. A. E. Stiegman, A. S. Goldman, D. B. Leslie and D. R. Tyler, *J. Chem. Soc. Chem. Commun.*, 1984, 632.
56. S. Aime, M. Botta, R. Gobetto and D. Osella, *Organometallics*, 1985, **4**, 1475.
57. S. Aime, M. Botta, R. Gobetto, D. Osella and F. Padovan, *J. Chem. Soc. Dalton Trans.*, 1987, 253.
58. S. Aime, R. Gobetto, F. Padovan, M. Botta, E. Rosenberg and R. W. Gellert, *Organometallics*, 1987, **6**, 2074.
59. R. D. Adams and J. P. Selegue, in *Comprehensive organometallic chemistry*, G. Wilkinson, F. G. A. Stone and E. W. Abel (Eds.). Oxford: Pergamon, 1982, Vol. IV, Ch. 33, p. 968.
60. S. A. R. Knox, J. W. Koepke, M. A. Andrews and H. D. Kaesz, *J. Am. Chem. Soc.*, 1975, **97**, 3942.
61. G. Lavigne, N. Lugan and J.-J. Bonnet, *Organometallics*, 1982, **1**, 1040.
62. (a) J. R. Shapley, J. B. Keister, M. R. Churchill and B. G. de Boer, *J. Am. Chem. Soc.*, 1975, **97**, 4145; (b) M. R. Churchill and B. G. de Boer, *Inorg. Chem.*, 1977, **16**, 878; (c) *ibid.*, 1977, **16**, 2397; (d) J. B. Keister and J. R. Shapley, *Inorg. Chem.*, 1982, **21**, 3304.
63. A. J. Deeming, S. Donovan-Mtunzi, S. E. Kabir, A. J. Arce and Y. De Sanctis, *J. Chem. Soc. Chem. Commun.*, 1987, 1457.
64. (a) R. B. Calvert and J. R. Shapley, *J. Am. Chem. Soc.*, 1977, **99**, 5225; (b) R. B. Calvert, J. R. Shapley, A. J. Schultz, J. M. Williams, S. L. Suib and G. D. Stucky, *J. Am. Chem. Soc.*, 1978, **100**, 6240; (c) R. B. Calvert and J. R. Shapley, *J. Am. Chem. Soc.*, 1978, **100**, 7726; (d) R. L. Keiter, D. S. Strickland, S. R. Wilson and J. R. Shapley, *J. Am. Chem. Soc.*, 1986, **108**, 3846.
65. A. J. Deeming, Y. Fuchita, K. Hardcastle, K. Henrick and M. McPartlin, *J. Chem. Soc. Dalton Trans.*, 1986, 2259.
66. (a) T. Beringhelli, G. Ciani, G. D'Alfonso, H. Molinari and A. Sironi, *Inorg. Chem.*, 1985, **24**, 2666; (b) T. Beringhelli, G. D'Alfonso, G. Ciani and H. Molinari, *Organometallics*, 1987, **6**, 194; (c) T. Beringhelli, G. D'Alfonso, M. Freni, G. Ciani, M. Moret and A. Sironi, *J. Organomet. Chem.*, 1988, **339**, 323. (d) T. Beringhelli, G. D'Alfonso, M. Freni, G. Ciani, A. Sironi and H. Molinari, *J. Chem. Soc. Dalton Trans.*, 1986, 2691.
67. H. J. Haupt, P. Balsaa and U. Flörke, *Angew. Chem. Int. Ed. Engl.*, 1988, **27**, 263.
68. R. D. Adams and S. Wang, *Organometallics*, 1986, **5**, 1272.
69. (a) L. J. Farrugia, M. Green, D. R. Hankey, A. G. Orpen and F. G. A. Stone, *J. Chem. Soc. Chem. Commun.*, 1983, 310; (b) L. J. Farrugia, M. Green, D. R. Hankey, M. Murray, A. G. Orpen and F. G. A. Stone, *J. Chem. Soc. Dalton Trans.*, 1985, 177.

70. A. C. Bray, M. Green, D. R. Hankey, J. A. K. Howard, O. Johnson and F. G. A. Stone, *J. Organomet. Chem.*, 1985, **281**, C12.
71. E. G. Brian, B. F. G. Johnson, J. W. Kelland, J. Lewis and M. McPartlin, *J. Chem. Soc. Chem. Commun.*, 1976, 254.
72. M. Tachikawa and J. R. Shapley, *J. Organomet. Chem.*, 1977, **124**, C19.
73. S. Winstein, H. D. Kaesz, C. G. Kreiter and E. C. Friedrich, *J. Am. Chem. Soc.*, 1965, **87**, 3267.
74. (a) B. F. G. Johnson, J. Lewis and D. A. Pippard, *J. Chem. Soc. Dalton Trans.*, 1981, 407; (b) B. F. G. Johnson, J. Lewis, T. I. Odiaka and P. R. Raithby, *J. Organomet. Chem.*, 1981, **216**, C56.
75. E. G. Brian, B. F. G. Johnson and J. Lewis, *J. Chem. Soc. Dalton Trans.*, 1977, 1328.
76. G. Süss Fink, L. Khan and P. R. Raithby, *J. Organomet. Chem.*, 1982, **228**, 179.
77. (a) J.-K. Shen, Y.-L. Shi, Y.-C. Gao, Q.-Z. Shi and F. Basolo, *J. Am. Chem. Soc.*, 1988, **110**, 2414; (b) T. Y. Luh, *Coord. Chem. Rev.*, 1984, **60**, 255.
78. (a) B. F. G. Johnson, J. Lewis, P. R. Raithby and C. Zuccaro, *J. Chem. Soc. Chem. Commun.*, 1979, 916; (b) B. F. G. Johnson, J. Lewis and T. I. Odiaka, *J. Organomet. Chem.*, 1986, **307**, 61; (c) R. D. Adams, J. E. Babin and H. S. Kim, *Inorg. Chem.*, 1986, **25**, 4319; (d) M. Hidai, H. Matsuzaka, Y. Koyasu and Y. Uchida, *J. Chem. Soc. Chem. Commun.*, 1986, 1451.
79. (a) T. Beringhelli, G. D'alfonso, M. Freni and H. Molinari, *J. Organomet. Chem.*, 1986, **311**, 177; (b) R. D. Adams, J. E. Babin and H. S. Kim, *Inorg. Chem.*, 1986, **25**, 1122.
80. K. Dahlinger, A. J. Poë, P. K. Sayal and V. K. Sekhar, *J. Chem. Soc. Dalton Trans.*, 1986, 2145.
81. G. A. Foulds, B. F. G. Johnson and J. Lewis, *J. Organomet. Chem.*, 1985, **294**, 123.
82. G. A. Foulds, B. F. G. Johnson and J. Lewis, *J. Organomet. Chem.*, 1985, **296**, 147.
83. S. Aime and A. J. Deeming, *J. Chem. Soc. Dalton Trans.*, 1983, 1807.
84. L. M. Bavaro, P. Montangero and J. B. Keister, *J. Am. Chem. Soc.*, 1983, **105**, 4977.
85. D. M. Dalton, D. J. Barnett, T. P. Duggan, J. B. Keister, P. T. Malik, S. P. Modi, M. R. Shaffer and S. A. Smesko, *Organometallics*, 1985, **4**, 1854.
86. J. C. Vites and T. P. Fehlner, *Organometallics*, 1984, **3**, 491.
87. (a) R. Colton and C. J. Commons, *Aust. J. Chem.*, 1975, **28**, 1673; (b) D. M. Curtis, K. R. Han and W. M. Bultler, *Inorg. Chem.*, 1980, **19**, 2096.
88. (a) D. J. Taube and P. C. Ford, *Organometallics*, 1986, **5**, 99; (b) D. J. Taube, R. van Eldik and P. C. Ford, *Organometallics*, 1987, **6**, 125.
89. S. A. MacLaughlin, N. J. Taylor and A. J. Carty, 1984, **3**, 392.
90. C. E. Kampe, N. M. Boag, C. B. Knobler and H. D. Kaesz, *Inorg. Chem.*, 1984, **23**, 1390.
91. B. F. G. Johnson, J. Lewis, W. J. H. Nelson, N. J. Nicholls, M. D. Vargas, D. Braga, K. Henrick and M. McPartlin, *J. Chem. Soc. Dalton Trans.*, 1984, 1809.
92. R. J. Goudsmit, P. J. Jackson, B. F. G. Johnson, J. Lewis, W. J. H. Nelson, J. Puga, M. D. Vargas, D. Braga, K. Henrick, M. McPartlin and A. Sironi, *J. Chem. Soc. Dalton Trans.*, 1985, 1795.
93. M. A. Gallop, B. F. G. Johnson, J. Lewis and P. R. Raithby, *J. Chem. Soc. Chem. Commun.*, 1986, 706.
94. J. Puga, R. Sanchez-Delgado, A. Andriollo, J. Ascanio and D. Braga, *Organometallics*, 1985, **4**, 2064.
95. (a) A. J. Deeming, R. Peters, M. B. Hursthouse and J. D. Backer-Dirks, *J. Chem.*

Soc. Dalton Trans., 1982, 1205; (b) A. J. Deeming and R. Peters, *J. Organomet. Chem.*, 1982.

96. R. D. Adams, Z. Dawoodi, D. F. Foust and B. E. Segmüller, *Organometallics*, 1983, **2**, 315.

97. (a) A. Choplin, B. Besson, L. D'Ornelas, R. Sanchez Delgado and J. M. Basset, *J. Am. Chem. Soc.*, 1988, **110**, 2783; (b) L. D'Ornelas, A. Choplin, J. M. Basset, L. Y. Hsu and S. G. Shore, *Nouv. J. Chim.*, 1985, **9**, 155; (c) for related alumina-supported species $Os_3(\mu\text{-}H)(CO)_{10}\{OAl\}$, see: F. B. M. Duivenvoorden, D. C. Koningsberger, Y. S. Uh and B. C. Gates; (d) see also: T. H. Walker, G. R. Frauenhoff, J. R. Shapley and E. Oldfield, *Inorg. Chem.*, 1988, **27**, 2563.

98. G. Huttner, J. Schneider, H. D. Müller, G. Mohr, J. von Seyerl and L. Wohlfahrt, *Angew. Chem. Int. Ed. Engl.*, 1979, **18**, 76.

99. A. J. Carty, S. A. Mclaughlin and N. J. Tailor, *J. Organomet. Chem.*, 1981, **204**, C27.

100. F. Richter and H. Vahrenkamp, *Organometallics*, 1982, **1**, 756.

101. K. Knoll, G. Huttner, L. Zsolnai, I. Jibril and M. Wasiucionek, *J. Organomet. Chem.*, 1985, **294**, 91.

102. J. Schneider, M. Minelli and G. Huttner, *J. Organomet. Chem.*, 1985, **294**, 75.

103. R. P. Planap and H. Vahrenkamp, *Organometallics*, 1987, **6**, 492.

104. (a) D. Mali and H. Vahrenkamp, *J. Mol. Catal.*, 1985, **29**, 305; (b) C. U. Pittman, M. Richmond, M. Absi-Halabi, H. Beurich, F. Richter and H. Vahrenkamp, *Angew. Chem. Int. Ed. Engl.*, 1982, **21**, 780; (c) M. Müller and H. Vahrenkamp, *Chem. Ber.*, 1983, **116**, 2748; d) K. A. Sutin, J. W. Kolis, M. Mlekuz, P. Bougeard, B. G. Sayer, M. A. Quilliam, R. Faggiani, C. J. L. Lock, M. J. McGlinchey and G. Jaouen, *Organometallics*, 1987, **6**, 439.

105. (a) K. Knoll, G. Huttner, L. Zsolnai and O. Orama, *Angew. Chem. Int. Ed. Engl.*, 1986, **25**, 1119; (b) K. Knoll, O. Orama and G. Huttner, *Angew. Chem. Int. Ed. Engl.*, 1984, **23**, 976; (c) K. Knoll, G. Huttner, T. Fässler and L. Zsolnai, *J. Organomet. Chem.*, 1987, **327**, 255; (d) K. Knoll, T. Fässler and G. Huttner, *J. Organomet. Chem.*, 1987, **332**, 309.

106. (a) N. Lugan, G. Lavigne, J. J. Bonnet, R. Réau, D. Neibecker and I. Tkatchenko, *J. Am. Chem. Soc.*, 1988, **110**, 5369; (b) a comparable phosphido bridge elimination induced by reaction with hydrogen has been recently observed in a bimetallic species: see A. M. Arif, D. J. Chandler and R. A. Jones, *Inorg. Chem.*, 1987, **26**, 1780; (c) H_2 addition to the metal phosphorus bond of a coordinated dangling phosphido group has now been observed in a mononuclear complex (L. Dahlenburg, personal communication); (d) for reversible activation of a P—H bond in a bimetallic species, see also: R. Baker, J. C. Calabrese and T. E. Glassman, *Organometallics*, 1988, **7**, 1889.

107. N. Lugan, J. J. Bonnet and J. A. Ibers, *Organometallics*, 1988, **7**, 1538.

108. (a) B. F. G. Johnson, J. Lewis, D. A. Pippard and P. R. Raithby, *J. Chem. Soc. Chem. Commun.*, 1978, 551; (b) B. F. G. Johnson, J. Lewis and D. A. Pippard, *J. Organomet. Chem.*, 1978, **160**, 263; (c) *ibid.*, 1981, **213**, 249; (d) B. F. G. Johnson, J. Lewis, D. A. Pippard, and P. R. Raithby, *Acta Cryst.*, 1980, **B36**, 703.

109. R. E. Stevens and W. L. Gladfelter, *J. Am. Chem. Soc.*, 1982, **104**, 6454.

110. (a) M. L. Blohm, D. E. Fjare and W. L. Gladfelter, *J. Am. Chem. Soc.*, 1986, **108**, 2301; (b) M. L. Blohm and W. L. Gladfelter, *Organometallics*, 1986, **5**, 1049.

111. (a) T. K. Dutta, J. C. Vites and T. P. Fehlner, *Organometallics*, 1986, **5**, 385; (b) T. K. Dutta, X. Meng, J. C. Vites and T. P. Fehlner, *Organometallics*, 1987, **6**, 2191.

112. J. W. Kolis, E. M. Holt and D. F. Shriver, *J. Am. Chem. Soc.*, 1983, **105**, 7307.

113. J. C. Vites, C. E. Housecroft, G. B. Jacobsen and T. P. Fehlner, *Organometallics*, 1984, **3**, 1591.

114. K. P. Vollhardt and M. Wolfgruber, *Angew. Chem. Int. Ed. Engl*, 1986, **25**, 929.

115. A. Goldhaber, K. P. C. Vollhardt, E. C. Walborsky and M. Wolfgruber, *J. Am. Chem. Soc.*, 1986, **108**, 516.

116. P. C. Ford and A. Rokicki, *Adv. Organomet. Chem.*, 1988, **28**, 139.

117. P. Chini, S. Martinengo and G. Giordano, *Gazz. Chim. Ital.*, 1972, **102**, 330.

118. R. Szostak, C. E. Strouse and H. D. Kaesz, *J. Organomet. Chem.*, 1980, **191**, 243.

119. A. Mayr, Y. C. Lin, N. M. Boag and H. D. Kaesz, *Inorg. Chem.*, 1982, **21**, 1704.

120. A. Mayr, Y. C. Lin, N. M. Boag, C. E. Kampe, C. B. Knobler and H. D. Kaesz, *Inorg. Chem.*, 1984, **23**, 4640.

121. (a) D. E. Morris and F. Basolo, *J. Am. Chem. Soc.*, 1968, **90**, 2536; (b) J. D. Atwood and T. L. Brown, *J. Am. Chem. Soc.*, 1975, **97**, 3380; (c) J. D. Atwood and T. L. Brown, *J. Am. Chem. Soc.*, 1976, **98**, 3155; (d) J. D. Atwood and T. L. Brown, *J. Am. Chem. Soc.*, 1976, **98**, 3160; (e) M. A. Cohen and T. L. Brown, *Inorg. Chem.*, 1976, **15**, 1417; (f) D. L. Lichtenberger and T. L. Brown, *J. Am. Chem. Soc.*, 1978, **100**, 366; (g) T. L. Brown and P. A. Bellus, *Inorg. Chem.*, 1978, **17**, 3726; (h) R. J. Angelici, *Acc. Chem. Res.*, 1972, **5**, 335.

122. K. A. Azam, C. C. Yin and A. J. Deeming, *J. Chem. Soc. Dalton Trans.*, 1978, 1201.

123. (a) R. C. Schoening, J. L. Vidal and R. A. Fiato, *J. Organomet. Chem.*, 1981, **206**, C43; (b) J. A. Partin and M. G. Richmond, *J. Organomet. Chem.*, 1988, **353**, C13.

124. (a) J. C. Bricker, C. C. Nagel and S. G. Shore, *J. Am. Chem. Soc.*, 1985, **107**, 377; (b) M. W. Payne, D. L. Leussing and S. G. Shore, *J. Am. Chem. Soc.*, 1987, **109**, 617.

125. B. F. G. Johnson, J. Lewis, P. R. Raithby and G. Süss, *J. Chem. Soc. Dalton Trans.*, 1979, 1356.

126. D. L. Darensbourg, R. L. Gray and M. Pala, *Organometallics*, 1984, **3**, 1928.

127. (a) M. Anstock, D. Taube, D. C. Cross and P. C. Ford, *J. Am. Chem. Soc.*, 1984, **106**, 3696. (b) D. J. Taube, A. Rokicki and P. C. Ford, *Inorg. Chem.*, 1987, **26**, 526.

128. D. E. Fjare, J. A. Jensen and W. L. Gladfelter, *Inorg. Chem*, 1983, **22**, 1774.

129. R. E. Stevens and W. L. Gladfelter, *Inorg. Chem.*, 1983, **22**, 2034.

130. D. L. Darensbourg, M. Pala and J. Waller, *Organometallics*, 1983, **2**, 1285.

131. (a) G. Lavigne and H. D. Kaesz, *J. Am. Chem. Soc.*, 1984, **106**, 4647; for recent examples of the use of PPN salts as catalysts for substitution reactions in cluster complexes, see the following references: (b) B. Fontal, C. C. Santini, J. Orlewski and J. M. Basset, *Inorg. Chem.*, 1986, **24**, 4321; (c) G. Süss-Fink and H. Jungbluth, *J. Organomet. Chem.*, 1988, **352**, 185; (d) M. I. Bruce, M. L. Williams, B. W. Skelton and A. H. White, *J. Organomet. Chem.*, 1986, **306**, 115; (e) M. Pizzotti, F. Porta, S. Cenini and F. Demartin, *J. Organomet. Chem.*, 1988, **356**, 105; (f) see also references 106a, 140, 185.

132. G. Lavigne, N. Lugan and J.-J. Bonnet, *J. Chem. Soc. Chem. Commun.*, 1987, 957.

133. G. R. Steinmetz, A. D. Harley and G. L. Geoffroy, *Inorg. Chem.*, 1980, **19**, 2985.

134. G. R. Steinmetz, E. D. Morrison and G. L. Geoffroy, *J. Am. Chem. Soc.*, 1984, **106**, 2559.

135. C. M. Jensen, C. B. Knobler and H. D. Kaesz, *J. Am. Chem. Soc.*, 1984, **106**, 5926.

136. (a) G. Lavigne and H. D. Kaesz, unpublished observations; (b) S. H. Han, G. L. Geoffroy, B. D. Dombek and A. L. Rheingold, *Inorg. Chem.*, 1988, **27**, 4355.

137. B. F. G. Johnson, J. Lewis, J. M. Mace, P. R. Raithby and M. D. Vargas, *J. Organomet. Chem.*, 1987, **321**, 409.

138. M. Y. Darensbourg, *Progr. Inorg. Chem.*, 1985, **33**, 221.

139. H. Alper and L. C. Damude, *Organometallics*, 1982, **1**, 579.

140. G. Lavigne, N. Lugan and J.-J. Bonnet, *Inorg. Chem.*, 1987, **26**, 2345.
141. D. H. Gibson, F. U. Ahmed and K. R. Phillips, *J. Organomet. Chem.*, 1981, **218**, 325.
142. C. E. Kampe and H. D. Kaesz, *Inorg. Chem.*, 1984, **23**, 4646.
143. (a) Y. J. Chen, C. B. Knobler and H. D. Kaesz, *Polyhedron*, 1988, **7**, 1891; (b) N. M. Boag, W. J. Sieber, C. E. Kampe, C. B. Knobler and H. D. Kaesz, *J. Organomet. Chem.*, 1988, **355**, 385.
144. D. S. Barratt and D. J. Cole-Hamilton, *J. Chem. Soc. Chem. Commun.*, 1985, 1559.
145. R. M. Laine and E. J. Crawford, *J. Mol. Catal.*, 1988, **44**, 357.
146. (a) B. D. Dombek, *J. Am. Chem. Soc.*, 1980, **102**, 6855; B. D. Dombek, *J. Am. Chem. Soc.*, 1981, **103**, 6508; B. D. Dombek, *J. Organomet. Chem.*, 1983, **250**, 467; B. K. Warren and B. D. Dombek, *J. Catal.*, 1983, **79**, 334; B. D. Dombek, *Organometallics*, 1985, **4**, 1707. (b) J. F. Knifton, *J. Am. Chem. Soc.*, 1981, **103**, 3959; J. F. Knifton, *J. Chem. Soc. Chem. Commun.*, 1981, 188; J. F. Knifton, *J. Mol. Catal.*, 1981, **11**, 91; J. F. Knifton, *J. Catal.*, 1982, **76**, 101; J. F. Knifton, R. A. Grigsby, Jr. and J. J. Lin, *Organometallics*, 1984, **3**, 62. (c) J. F. Knifton in *Aspects of homogeneous catalysis*, R. Ugo (Ed.). Reidel Publishing Company, 1988, **6**, 1. (d) B. D. Dombek, *J. Organomet. Chem.*, 1989, **372**, 151.
147. D. J. Taube, A. Rokicki, M. Anstock and P. C. Ford, *Inorg. Chem.*, 1987, **26**, 526.
148. S. Kennedy, J. J. Alexander and S. G. Shore, *J. Organomet. Chem.*, 1981, **219**, 385.
149. G. Lavigne, N. Lugan and J. J. Bonnet, in preparation.
150. J. L. Zuffa, M. L. Blohm and W. L. Gladfelter, *J. Am. Chem. Soc.*, 1986, **108**, 552.
151. J. L. Zuffa and W. L. Gladfelter, *J. Am. Chem. Soc.*, 1986, **108**, 4669.
152. (a) C. E. Kampe, N. M. Boag and H. D. Kaesz, *J. Am. Chem. Soc.*, 1983, **105**, 2896; (b) M. Lourdichi, R. Pince, F. Dahan and R. Mathieu, *Organometallics*, 1983, **2**, 1417.
153. E. D. Morrison, S. L. Bassner and G. L. Geoffroy, *Organometallics*, 1986, **5**, 408.
154. (a) G. Süss Fink and G. Herrman, *J. Chem. Soc. Chem. Commun.*, 1985, 735; (b) G. Süss Fink and J. Reiner, *J. Mol. Catal.*, 1982, **16**, 231; (c) G. Süss Fink and G. F. Schmidt, *J. Mol. Catal.*, 1987, **42**, 361.
155. (a) J. Knifton, *J. Mol. Catal.*, 1987, **43**, 65; (b) J. Knifton, *J. Mol. Catal.*, 1988, **47**, 99.
156. (a) E. D. Morrison, G. R. Steinmetz, G. L. Geoffroy, W. C. Fultz and A. L. Rheingold, *J. Am. Chem. Soc.*, 1984, **106**, 4783; (b) S. L. Bassner, G. L. Geoffroy and A. L. Rheingold, *Polyhedron*, 1988, **7**, 791.
157. (a) E. D. Morrison and G. L. Geoffroy, *J. Am. Chem. Soc.*, 1985, **107**, 3541; (b) E. D. Morrison, G. L. Geoffroy, A. L. Rheingold and W. C. Fultz, *Organometallics*, 1985, **4**, 1413.
158. S. L. Bassner, E. D. Morrison, G. L. Geoffroy and A. L. Rheingold, *Organometallics*, 1987, **6**, 2207.
159. (a) S. Cenini, M. Pizzotti and C. Crotti in *Aspects of homogeneous catalysis*, R. Ugo (Ed.). Reidel Publishing Company, 1988, **6**, 97; (b) S. Cenini, M. Pizzotti, C. Crotti, F. Porta and G. La Monica, *J. Chem. Soc. Chem. Commun.*, 1984, 1286; Italian Patent 21591 A/83, June 7, 1983; (c) S. Cenini, C. Crotti, M. Pizzotti and F. Porta, *J. Org. Chem.* 1988, **53**, 1243; (d) H. Alper and K. E. Hashem, *J. Am. Chem. Soc.*, 1981, **103**, 6514; (e) H. des Abbayes and H. Alper, *J. Am. Chem. Soc.*, 1977, **99**, 98.
160. G. D. Williams, R. R. Whittle, G. L. Geoffroy and A. L. Rheingold, *J. Am. Chem. Soc.*, 1987, **109**, 3936.
161. S.-H. Han, G. L. Geoffroy and A. L. Rheingold, *Inorg. Chem.*, 1987, **26**, 3426.

162. S. Bhaduri, H. Khwaja and P. G. Jones, *J. Chem. Soc. Chem. Commun.*, 1988, 194.

163. M. I. Bruce, in *Comprehensive organometallic chemistry*, G. Wilkinson, F. G. A. Stone and E. W. Abel (Eds.). Oxford: Pergamon, 1982, Volume IV.

164. S. Rivomanana, G. Lavigne, N. Lugan, J. J. Bonnet, R. Yanez and R. Mathieu, *J. Am. Chem. Soc.* 1989, **111**, 8959.

165. Z. Dawoodi, M. J. Mays, P. R. Raithby and K. Henrick, *J. Chem. Soc. Dalton Trans.*, 1980, 641.

166. Z. Dawoodi, K. Henrick and M. J. Mays, *J. Chem. Soc. Chem. Commun.*, 1982, 696.

167. A. J. Deeming and P. J. Manning, *Phil. Trans. R. Soc. Lond.*, 1982, **A308**, 59.

168. (a) S.-I. Yoshido, S. Mori, H. Kinoshita and Y. Watanabe, *J. Mol. Catal.*, 1987, **42**, 215; (b) M. Hidai, Y. Koyasu, K. Chikanari and Y. Uchida, *J. Mol. Catal.*, 1987, **40**, 243; (c) Y. Kiso, M. Tanaka, H. Nakamura, T. Yamasaki and K. Saeki, *J. Organomet. Chem.*, 1986, **312**, 357; (d) J. F. Knifton, *J. Chem. Soc. Chem. Commun.*, 1985, 1412; (e) M. Hidai, Y. Koyasu, K. Chikanari and Y. Uchida, *J. Mol. Catal.*, 1987, **40**, 243.

169. M. A. Gallop, B. F. G. Johnson, J. Lewis and P. R. Raithby, *J. Chem. Soc. Chem. Commun.*, 1986, 707.

170. L. Garlaschelli, S. Martinengo, P. Chini, F. Canziani and R. Bau, *J. Organomet. Chem.*, 1981, **213**, 379.

171. (a) P. Chini, G. Ciani, L. Garlaschelli, M. Manassero, S. Martinengo, A. Sironi and F. Canziani, *J. Organomet. Chem.*, 1978, **152**, C35; (b) nucleophilic attack of NaOMe at CO in $Ir_6(CO)_{16}$ has been recently shown to give $Na[Ir_6(CO)_{15}CO_2Me]$; see: L. Garlashelli, M. C. Malatesta, S. Martinengo, F. Demartin, M. Manassero and M. Sansoni, *J. Chem. Soc. Dalton Trans.*, 1986, 777.

172. (a) R. Ros, A. Scrivanti, V. G. Albano, D. Braga and L. Garlaschelli, *J. Chem. Soc. Dalton Trans.*, 1986, 2411; (b) R. Ros, A. Scrivanti and R. Roulet, *J. Organomet. Chem.*, 1986, **303**, 273; (c) J. N. Nicholls, P. R. Raithby and M. D. Vargas, *J. Chem. Soc. Chem. Commun.*, 1986, 1617.

173. M. G. Richmond and J. K. Kochi, *Organometallics*, 1987, **6**, 777.

174. (a) R. D. Adams and J. E. Babin, *Inorg. Chem.*, 1986, **25**, 4010; (b) R. D. Adams and S. Wang, *Inorg. Chem.*, 1986, **25**, 2534.

175. M. J. Went, C. P. Brock and D. F. Shriver, *Organometallics*, 1986, **5**, 755.

176. C. E. Housecroft and T. P. Fehlner, *J. Am. Chem. Soc.*, 1986, **108**, 4867.

177. While this work was reviewed, dramatic new reports bearing relevance to the field of cluster activation have appeared: (a) J. L. Zuffa, S. J. Kivi and W. L. Gladfelter, *Inorg. Chem.*, 1989, **28**, 1888; (b) S. R. Drake, B. F. G. Johnson and J. Lewis, *J. Chem. Soc. Chem. Commun.*, 1988, 1033; (c) A. Darchen, H. Mousser and H. Patin, *J. Chem. Soc. Chem. Commun.*, 1988, 968; (d) S.-J. Wang and R. J. Angelici, *Inorg. Chem.*, 1988, **27**, 3233; (e) A. M. Arif, T. A. Bright and R. A. Jones, *J. Am. Chem. Soc.*, 1988, **110**, 6894; (f) T. S. Janik, M. R. Churchill, T. P. Duggan and J. B. Keister, *J. Organomet. Chem.*, 1988, **353**, 343; (g) D. S. Dumond and M. G. Richmond, *J. Am. Chem. Soc.*, 1988, **110**, 7547; (h) T. Chin-Choy, W. T. Harrison, G. D. Stucky, N. Keder, and P. C. Ford, *Inorg. Chem.* 1989, **28**, 2028.

178. (a) C. W. Bradford and R. S. Nyholm, *J. Chem. Soc. Dalton Trans.*, 1973, 529; (b) G. J. Gainsford, J. M. Guss, P. R. Ireland, R. Mason, C. W. Bradford and R. S. Nyholm, *J. Organomet. Chem.*, 1972, **40**, C70.

179. (a) A. J. Deeming, R. E. Kimber and M. Underhill, *J. Chem. Soc. Dalton Trans.*, 1973, 2589; (b) A. J. Deeming and M. Underhill, *J. Chem. Soc. Dalton Trans.*, 1973, 2727; (c) A. J. Deeming, I. P. Rothwell, M. B. Hursthouse and J. D. Backer-Dirks, *J. Chem. Soc. Dalton Trans.*, 1981, 1879.

180. M. I. Bruce, G. Shaw and F. G. A. Stone, *J. Chem. Soc. Dalton Trans.*, 1972, 2094.

181. (a) P. E. Garrou, *Chem. Rev.*, 1985, **85**, 171; (b) Y. Jeannin, *Trans. Met. Chem.*, 1986, **11**, 426.

182. (a) P. Chini, G. Ciani, S. Martinengo, A. Sironi, L. Longhetti and B. T. Heaton, *J. Chem. Soc. Chem. Commun.*, 1979, 129; (b) J. L. Vidal, W. E. Walker, R. L. Pruett and R. C. Schoening, *Inorg. Chem.*, 1979, **18**, 129; (c) J. L. Vidal, *Inorg. Chem.*, 1981, **20**, 243.

183. N. Brodie, A. Poë and V. J. Sekhar, *J. Chem. Soc. Chem. Commun.*, 1985, 1090 and references therein.

184. A. Maisonnat, J. P. Farr, M. M. Olmstead, C. Hunt and A. L. Balch, *Inorg. Chem.*, 1982, **21**, 3961.

185. N. Lugan, G. Lavigne and J. J. Bonnet, *Inorg. Chem.*, 1987, **26**, 585.

186. A. J. Deeming, S. E. Kabir, N. I. Powell, P. A. Bates and M. B. Hursthouse, *J. Chem. Soc. Dalton Trans.*, 1987, 1529.

187. S. C. Brown, J. Evans and L. Smart, *J. Chem. Soc. Chem. Commun.*, 1980, 1021.

188. V. G. Albano, D. Braga, R. Ros and A. Scrivanti, *J. Chem. Soc. Chem. Commun.*, 1985, 866.

189. (a) J. A. Clucas, D. F. Foster, M. M. Harding and A. K. Smith, *J. Chem. Soc. Chem. Commun.*, 1984, 949; (b) J. A. Clucas, M. M. Harding and A. K. Smith, *J. Chem. Soc. Chem. Commun.*, 1985, 1280.

190. (a) S. A. MacLaughlin, A. J. Carty and N. J. Taylor, *Canad. J. Chem.*, 1982, **60**, 87; (b) A. J. Carty, *Pure Appl. Chem.*, 1982, **54**, 113; (c) V. D. Patel, N. J. Taylor and A. J. Carty, *J. Chem. Soc. Chem. Commun.*, 1984, 99; (d) A. J. Carty, S. A. MacLaughlin and N. J. Taylor, *J. Organomet. Chem.*, 1981, **204**, C27; (e) F. Van Gastel, S. A. MacLaughlin, M. Linch, A. J. Carty, E. Sappa, A. Tiripicchio and M. Tiripicchio-Camellini.

191. (a) C. Bergounhou, J.-J. Bonnet, P. Fompeyrine, G. Lavigne, N. Lugan and F. Mansilla, *Organometallics*, 1986, **5**, 60; (b) G. Lavigne and J.-J. Bonnet, *Inorg. Chem.*, 1981, **20**, 2713; (c) for contrasting transformations of *bis*(dimethylphosphino)methane in related complexes, see: J. A. Clucas, D. F. Foster, M. H. Harding and A. K. Smith, *J. Chem. Soc. Dalton Trans.*, 1987, 277; see also: (d) L. Manojlovic-Muir, D. A. Brandes and R. J. Puddephatt, *J. Organomet. Chem.*, 1987, **332**, 201.

192. N. Lugan, J. A. Ibers and J.-J. Bonnet, *J. Am. Chem. Soc.*, 1985, **107**, 4484.

193. M. I. Bruce, E. Horn, O. B. Shawkataly, M. R. Snow, E. R. T. Tiekink and M. L. Williams, *J. Organomet. Chem.*, 1986, **316**, 187.

194. (a) M. H. Harding, B. S. Nicholls and A. K. Smith, *J. Organomet. Chem.*, 1982, **226**, C17; (b) J. J. deBoer, J. A. van Doorn and C. Masters, *J. Chem. Soc. Chem. Commun.*, 1978, 1005.

195. N. J. Taylor, P. C. Chieh and A. J. Carty, *J. Chem. Soc. Chem. Commun.*, 1975, 448.

196. R. Bender, P. Braunstein, A. Tiripicchio and M. Tiripicchio Camellini, *Angew. Chem. Int. Ed.*, 1985, **24**, 861.

197. M. M. Harding, B. S. Nicholls and A. K. Smith, *J. Chem. Soc. Dalton Trans.*, 1983, 1479.

198. S. A. R. Knox, B. R. Lloyd, A. G. Orpen, J. M. Vinas and M. Weber, *J. Chem. Soc. Chem. Commun.*, 1987, 1498.

199. (a) J. R. Bliskensderfer, C. B. Knobler and H. D. Kaesz, *J. Am. Chem. Soc.*, 1975, **97**, 2681; (b) *ibid*, 1975, **97**, 2686; (c) G. R. Doel, N. D. Feasey, S. A. R. Knox, A. G. Orpen and J. Webster, *J. Chem. Soc. Chem. Commun.*, 1986, 542.

200. (a) J. Feilong, T. P. Fehlner and A. L. Rheingold, *Angew. Chem. Int. Ed. Engl.*, 1988, **27**, 424; (b) J. C. Daran, Y. Jeannin and O. Kristiansson, *Organometallics*, 1985, **4**, 1882.

201. (a) H. Vahrenkamp and E. Wucherer, *Angew. Chem. Int. Ed. Engl.*, 1981, **20**, 680;

(b) K. Natarajan, O. Sheidsteger and G. Huttner, *J. Organomet. Chem.*, 1981, **221**, 301; (c) J. S. Field, R. J. Haines and D. N. Smit, *J. Organomet. Chem.*, 1982, **221**, 301; (d) J. S. Field, R. J. Haines and D. N. Smit, *J. Organomet. Chem.*, 1986, **304**, C17; (e) J. S. Field, R. J. Haines and D. N. Smit, *J. Chem. Soc. Dalton Trans.*, 1988, 1315; (f) S. B. Colbran, B. F. G. Johnson, J. Lewis and R. M. Sorrel, *J. Organomet. Chem.*, 1985, **296**, C1; (g) V. D. Patel, A. A. Cherkas, D. Nucciarone, N. J. Taylor and A. J. Carty, *Organometallics*, 1985, **4**, 1792; (h) S. B. Colbran, B. F. G. Johnson, J. Lewis and R. M. Sorrel, *J. Chem. Soc. Chem. Commun.*, 1986, 525; (i) A. M. Arif, D. E. Heaton, R. A. Jones, K. B. Kidd, T. C. Wright, B. R. Whittlesey, J. L. Atwood, W. E. Hunter and H. Zhang, *Inorg. Chem.*, 1987, **26**, 4065.

202. K. Kwek, N. J. Taylor and A. J. Carty, *J. Am. Chem. Soc.*, 1984, **106**, 4636.
203. J. C. Jeffery and J. G. Lawrence-Smith, *J. Chem. Soc. Chem. Commun.*, 1985, 275.
204. (a) W. F. Smith, N. J. Tailor and A. J. Carty, *J. Chem. Soc. Chem. Commun.*, 1976, 896; (b) A. J. Carty, *Adv. Chem. Ser.*, 1982, **196**, 163.
205. (a) A. D. Harley, G. J. Guskey and G. L. Geoffroy, *Organometallics*, 1983, **2**, 53; (b) G. L. Geoffroy, S. Rosenberg, P. M. Shulman and R. R. Whittle, *J. Am. Chem. Soc.*, 1984, **106**, 1519; (c) S. Rosenberg, R. R. Whittle and G. L. Geoffroy, *J. Am. Chem. Soc.*, 1984, **106**, 5934.
206. (a) Y.-F. Yu, J. Gallucci and A. Wojcicki, *J. Am. Chem. Soc.*, 1983, **105**, 4826; (b) Y.-F. Yu, C. N. Chau, A. Wojcicki, M. Calligaris, G. Nardin and G. Balducci, *J. Am. Chem. Soc.*, 1984, **106**, 3704; (c) S. G. Shyu and A. Wojcicki, *Organometallics*, 1985, **4**, 1457; (d) Y.-F. Yu, A. Wojcicki, M. Calligaris and G. Nardin, *Organometallics*, 1986, **5**, 47; (e) S. G. Shyu, M. Calligaris, G. Nardin and A. Wojcicki, *J. Am. Chem. Soc.*, 1987, **109**, 3617.
207. E. P. Kyba, R. E. Davis, C. N. Clubb, S.-T. Liu, H. O. A. Palacios and J. McKennis, *Organometallics*, 1986, **5**, 869.
208. (a) A. G. Abatjoglou, E. Billig and D. R. Bryant, *Organometallics*, 1984, **3**, 923; (b) A. G. Abatjoglou and D. R. Bryant, *Organometallics*, 1984, **3**, 932.
209. (a) R. A. Dubois, P. E. Garrou, K. D. Lavin and H. R. Allcock, *Organometallics*, 1986, **5**, 460; (b) R. E. Dubois and P. E. Garrou, *Organometallics*, 1986, **5**, 466.
210. (a) R. Regragui, P. H. Dixneuf, N. J. Taylor and A. J. Carty, *Organometallics*, 1984, **3**, 814; (see also ref. 205a); (b) B. Klingert and H. Werner, *J. Organomet. Chem.*, 1983, **252**, C47; (c) K. Henrick, J. A. Iggo, M. J. Mays and P. R. Raithby, *J. Chem. Soc. Chem. Commun.*, 1984, 209; (d) H. Vahrenkamp and D. Wolters, *Angew. Chem. Int. Ed. Engl.*, 1983, **22**, 154.
211. J. Lunniss, S. A. MacLaughlin, N. J. Taylor, A. J. Carty and E. Sappa, *Organometallics*, 1985, **4**, 2066.
212. K. Knoll, G. Huttner and L. Zsolnai, *J. Organomet. Chem.*, 1986, **307**, 237.
213. J. S. Field, R. J. Haines, E. Minshall and D. N. Smit, *J. Organomet. Chem.*, 1986, **310**, C69.
214. (a) K. Knoll, G. Huttner, M. Wasiucionek and L. Zsolnai, *Angew. Chem. Int. Ed. Engl.*, 1984, **23**, 739; (b) K. Knoll, G. Huttner, L. Zsolnai, O. Orama and M. Wasiucionek, *J. Organomet. Chem.*, 1986, **310**, 225.
215. (a) W. Hieber and P. Spacu, *Z. Anorg. Allgem. Chem.*, 1937, **233**, 353; (b) W. Hieber and C. Scharfenberg, *Ber.*, 1940, **73**, 1012.
216. (a) R. B. King, *Inorg. Chem.*, 1963, **2**, 326; (b) L. F. Dahl and P. W. Sutton, *Inorg. Chem.*, 1963, **2**, 1067; (c) R. Havlin and G. R. Knox, *J. Organomet. Chem.*, 1965, **4**, 247.
217. (a) H. Vahrenkamp, *Angew. Chem. Int. Ed. Engl.*, 1975, **14**, 322; (b) P. Zanello, *Coord. Chem. Rev.*, 1988, **87**, 1.
218. (a) G. R. Crooks, B. F. G. Johnson and J. Lewis, *J. Chem. Soc. A*, 1969, 797; (b) J. A. de Beer and R. J. Haines, *J. Chem. Soc. Chem. Commun.*, 1970, 288; (c)

R. Bau, B. Don, R. Greatrex, R. J. Haines, R. A. Love and R. D. Wilson, *Inorg. Chem.*, 1975, **14**, 3021; (d) T. A. Cresswell, J. A. K. Howard, F. G. Kennedy, S. A. R. Knox and H. Wadepohl, *J. Chem. Soc. Dalton Trans.*, 1981, 2220.

219. S. Jeannin, Y. Jeannin and G. Lavigne, *Inorg. Chem.*, 1978, **17**, 2103.

220. (a) S. C. Schuman and H. Shalit, *Catal. Rev.*, 1970, **4**, 245; (b) R. Angelici, *Acc. Chem. Res.*, 1988, **21**, 387 and references therein; (c) C. M. Friend and J. T. Roberts, *Acc. Chem. Res.*, 1988, **21**, 394 and references therein.

221. (a) L. L. Hegedus and R. W. McCabe, *Catalyst poisoning*, Marcel Decker (Ed.). New York, 1984; (b) C. H. Bartholomew, P. K. Agrawal and J. R. Katzer, *Adv. Catal.*, 1982, **31**, 135; (c) J. Oudar, *J. Catal. Rev. Sci. Eng.*, 1980, **22**, 171.

222. (a) D. Fenske, J. Hachgenei and J. Ohmer, *Angew. Chem. Int. Ed. Engl.*, 1985, **24**, 706; (b) D. Fenske, J. Ohmer and J. Hachgenei, *Angew. Chem. Int. Ed. Engl.*, 1985, **24**, 993; (c) D. Fenske and J. Ohmer, *Angew. Chem. Int. Ed. Engl.*, 1987, **26**, 148.

223. G. D. Jarvinen and R. R. Ryan, *Organometallics*, 1984, **3**, 1434.

224. R. D. Adams, N. M. Golembeski and J. P. Selegue, *J. Am. Chem. Soc.*, 1981, **103**, 546.

225. A. M. Brodie, H. D. Holden, J. Lewis and M. J. Taylor, *J. Chem. Soc. Dalton Trans.*, 1986, 633.

226. M. C. Jennings, N. C. Payne and R. J. Puddephatt, *J. Chem. Soc. Chem. Commun.*, 1986, 1809.

227. (a) R. D. Adams and L. W. Wang, *J. Am. Chem. Soc.*, 1982, **104**, 4115; (b) R. D. Adams, I. T. Horvàth, B. E. Segmuller and L. W. Wang, *Organometallics*, 1983, **2**, 1301; (c) R. D. Adams, I. T. Horvàth and H.-S. Kim, *Organometallics*, 1984, **3**, 548.

228. R. D. Adams, J. E. Babin and M. Tasi, *Inorg. Chem.*, 1986, **25**, 4514.

229. R. D. Adams and L.-W. Yang, *J. Am. Chem. Soc.*, 1983, **105**, 235.

230. R. D. Adams, J. E. Babin and H.-S. Kim, *J. Am. Chem. Soc.*, 1987, **109**, 1414.

231. R. D. Adams and J. E. Babin, *J. Am. Chem. Soc.*, 1987, **109**, 6872.

232. R. D. Adams and S. Wang, *Organometallics*, 1985, **4**, 1902.

233. (a) R. D. Adams and S. Wang, *J. Am. Chem. Soc.*, 1987, **109**, 924; R. D. Adams and S. Wang, *Organometallics*, 1987, **6**, 739.

234. R. D. Adams, J. E. Babin and M. Tasi, *Organometallics*, 1987, **6**, 1717.

235. M. R. Churchill, J. W. Ziller, D. M. Dalton and J. B. Keister, *Organometallics*, 1987, **6**, 806.

236. R. D. Adams, H.-S. Kim and S. Wang, *J. Am. Chem. Soc.*, 1985, **107**, 6107.

237. B. F. G. Johnson, P. A. Kilty and J. Lewis, *J. Chem. Soc. Chem. Commun.*, 1968, 180.

238. K. A. Azam, A. J. Deeming, R. E. Kimber and P. R. Shukla, *J. Chem. Soc. Dalton Trans.*, 1976, 1853.

239. For a recent example, see: S. Bhaduri, K. Sharma and P. G. Jones, *J. Chem. Soc. Chem. Commun.*, 1987, 1769.

240. C. C. Santini, J.-M. Basset, B. Fontal, J. Krause, S. Shore and C. Charrier, *J. Chem. Soc. Chem. Commun.*, 1987, 512.

241. (a) J. R. Shapley and J. T. Park, *J. Am. Chem. Soc.*, 1984, **106**, 1144; (b) Y. Chi, J. R. Shapley, J. W. Ziller and M. R. Churchill, *Organometallics*, 1987, **6**, 301.

242. (a) G. Lavigne, N. Lugan and J. J. Bonnet, *Nouv. J. Chim.*, 1981, **5**, 423; (b) A. Colombie, J. J. Bonnet, P. Fompeyrine, G. Lavigne and S. Sunshine, *Organometallics*, 1986, **5**, 1154; (c) P. Fompeyrine, C. Bergounhou, G. Commenges and J. J. Bonnet, *J. Mol. Catal.*, 1988, **48**, 285.

243. R. J. Goudsmit, B. F. G. Johnson, J. Lewis, P. R. Raithby and K. H. Whitmire, *J. Chem. Soc. Chem. Commun.*, 1983, 246.

244. A. Ceriotti, L. Resconi, F. Demartin, G. Longoni and M. Manassero, *J. Organomet. Chem.*, 1983, **249**, C35.

245. C. K. Schauer and D. F. Shriver, *Angew. Chem. Int. Ed. Engl.*, 1987, **26**, 255.

246. (a) C. P. Gibson, J.-S. Huang and L. F. Dahl, *Organometallics*, 1986, **5**, 1676; (b) F. Bottomley and L. Sutin, *Adv. Organomet. Chem.*, 1988, **28**, 339.

247. R. B. Wilson, Jr. and R. M. Laine, *J. Am. Chem. Soc.*, 1985, **107**, 361.

248. G. Süss Fink and G. Herrmann, *Angew. Chem. Int. Ed. Engl.*, 1986, **25**, 570.

249. Y. Tsuji, T. Oshumi, T. Kondo and Y. Watanabe, *J. Organomet. Chem.*, 1986, **309**, 333.

250. A. Basu, S. Bhaduri, K. Sharma and P. G. Jones, *J. Chem. Soc. Chem. Commun.*, 1987, 1126.

251. (a) J. A. Smieja and W. L. Gladfelter, *J. Organomet. Chem.*, 1985, **297**, 349; (b) see also reference 268b.

252. E. L. Muetterties, E. Band and W. R. Pretzer, *J. Am. Chem. Soc.*, 1977, **99**, 7380.

253. J. Banford, M. J. Mays and P. R. Raithby, *J. Chem. Soc. Dalton Trans.*, 1985, 1355.

254. R. D. Adams and N. M. Golembeski, *J. Am. Chem. Soc.*, 1979, **101**, 2579.

255. S. T. McKenna, R. A. Andersen and E. L. Muetterties, *Organometallics*, 1986, **5**, 2233.

256. C. C. Yin and A. J. Deeming, *J. Chem. Soc. Dalton Trans.*, 1975, 2091.

257. A. Eisenstadt, C. M. Giandomenico, M. F. Frederick and R. M. Laine, *Organometallics*, 1985, **4**, 2033.

258. R. Zoet, G. van Koten, K. Vrieze, J. Jansen, K. Goubitz and C. H. Stam, *Organometallics*, 1988, **7**, 1565.

259. F. A. Cotton, B. E. Hanson and J. D. Jamerson, *J. Am. Chem. Soc.*, 1977, **99**, 6588.

260. P. Mastropasqua, P. Lahuerta, K. Hildenbrand and H. Kisch, *J. Organomet. Chem.*, 1979, **172**, 57.

261. T. Venäläinen, J. Pursiainen and T. A. Pakkanen, *J. Chem. Soc. Chem. Commun.*, 1985, 1348.

262. M. I. Bruce, M. G. Humphrey, M. R. Snow, E. R. T. Tiekink and R. C. Wallis, *J. Organomet. Chem.*, 1986, **314**, 311.

263. R. H. Fish, Tae-Jeong Kim, J. L. Stewart, J. H. Bushweller, R. K. Rosen and J. W. Dupon, *Organometallics*, 1986, **5**, 2193.

264. J. A. Cabeza, L. Oro, A. Tiripicchio and M. Tiripicchio-Camellini, *J. Chem. Soc. Dalton Trans.*, 1988, 1437.

265. R. D. Adams and J. E. Babin, *Organometallics*, 1988, **7**, 963.

266. Y. C. Yin and A. J. Deeming, *J. Organomet. Chem.*, 1977, **133**, 123.

267. (a) M. I. Bruce, M. G. Humphrey, O. B. Shawkataly, M. R. Snow and E. R. T. Tiekink, *J. Organomet. Chem.*, 1986, **315**, C51; (b) M. I. Bruce, M. G. Humphrey, O. B. Shawkataly, M. R. Snow and F. R. T. Tiekink, *J. Organomet. Chem.*, 1987, **336**, 199.

268. (a) J. A. Smieja, J. E. Gozum and W. L. Gladfelter, *Organometallics*, 1986, **5**, 2154; (b) J. A. Smieja, J. E. Gozum and W. L. Gladfelter, *Organometallics*, 1987, **6**, 1311.

269. E. J. Wucherer and H. Vahrenkamp, *Angew. Chem. Int. Ed. Engl.*, 1987, **26**, 355.

270. D. Nuel and R. Mathieu, *J. Organomet. Chem.*, 1986, **307**, C5.

271. D. E. Fjare and W. L. Gladfelter, *J. Am. Chem. Soc.*, 1984, **106**, 4799.

272. (a) N. D. Feasey, S. A. R. Knox and A. G. Orpen, *J. Chem. Soc. Chem. Commun.*, 1982, 75; (b) N. D. Feasey and S. A. R. Knox, *J. Chem. Soc. Chem. Commun.*, 1982, 1062.

273. (a) W. A. Herrmann, *Adv. Organomet. Chem.*, 1982, **20**, 160 and references therein; (b) S. A. R. Knox, *Pure Appl. Chem.*, 1984, **56**, 81 and references

therein; (c) J. E. Hahn, *Progr. Inorg. Chem.*, 1984, **31**, 205; (d) D. Seyferth, *Adv. Organomet. Chem.*, 1976, **14**, 97; (e) A. J. Carty, *Pure Appl. Chem.*, 1982, **54**, 113.

274. (a) W. A. Herrmann, *Angew. Chem. Int. Ed. Engl.*, 1982, **21**, 117; (b) R. B. Anderson, *The Fischer-Tropsch synthesis*, Orlando: Academic Press, 1987; (c) H. Schulz, C_1 *Mol. Chem.*, 1985, **1**, 231.

275. (a) K. Withmire and D. F. Shriver, *J. Am. Chem. Soc.*, 1980, **102**, 1456; (b) M. A. Drezdon and D. F. Shriver, *J. Mol. Catal.*, 1983, **21**, 81; (c) C. P. Horwitz, E. M. Holt, C. P. Brock and D. F. Shriver, *J. Am. Chem. Soc.*, 1985, **107**, 8136; (d) C. P. Horwitz and D. F. Shriver, *J. Am. Chem. Soc.*, 1985, **107**, 8147.

276. (a) J. B. Keister, *Polyhedron*, 1988, **7**, 847 and references therein; (b) T. P. Duggan, D. J. Barnett, M. J. Muscatella and J. B. Keister, *J. Am. Chem. Soc.*, 1986, **108**, 6076; (b) M. Cree-Uchiyama, J. R. Shapley and G. M. St-George, *J. Am. Chem. Soc.*, 1986, **108**, 1316; (d) W-Y. Yeh, H.-J. Kneuper and J. R. Shapley, *Polyhedron*, 1988, **7**, 961 and references therein; (e) J. Vites, C. E. Housecroft, C. Eigenbrot, M. Buhl, G. J. Long and T. P. Fehlner, *J. Am. Chem. Soc.*, 1986, **108**, 3304; (f) T. P. Fehlner, *New J. Chem.*, 1988, **12**, 307 and references therein.

277. W. A. Herrmann, M. L. Ziegler, K. Weidenhammer and H. Biersack, *Angew. Chem. Int. Ed. Engl.*, 1979, **18**, 960.

278. (a) C. P. Gibson and L. F. Dahl, *Organometallics*, 1988, **7**, 535 and references therein; (b) R. D. Adams, J. E. Babin and M. Tasi, *Angew. Chem. Int. Ed. Engl.*, 1987, **26**, 685.

279. (a) S. Gambarotta, S. Stella, C. Floriani, A. Chiesi-Villa and C. Guastini, *Angew. Chem. Int. Ed. Engl.*, 1986, **25**, 254 and references therein; (b) D. H. Berry and J. E. Bercaw, *Polyhedron*, 1988, **7**, 759.

280. (a) J. S. Holmgren, J. R. Shapley, S. R. Wilson and W. T. Pennington, *J. Am. Chem. Soc.*, 1986, **108**, 508; (b) D. Nucciarone, N. J. Taylor, A. J. Carty, A. Tiripicchio, M. Marisa Camellini and E. Sappa, *Organometallics*, 1988, **7**, 118 and numerous references therein.

281. J. B. Keister, *J. Chem. Soc. Chem. Commun.*, 1979, 214.

282. J. R. Shapley, M. E. Cree-Uchiyama, G. M. St.-George, M. R. Churchill and C. Bueno, *J. Am. Chem. Soc.*, 1983, **105**, 140.

283. W. Y. Yeh, J. R. Shapley, Y.-J. Li and M. R. Churchill, *Organometallics*, 1985, **4**, 767.

284. (a) J. R. Shapley, W. Y. Yeh, M. R. Churchill and Y.-J. Li, *Organometallics*, 1985, **4**, 1898; (b) W. Y. Yeh, J. R. Shapley, J. W. Ziller and M. R. Churchill, *Organometallics*, 1987, **6**, 1; (c) M. R. Churchill, J. W. Ziller, J. W. Shapley and W. Y. Yeh, *J. Organomet. Chem.*, 1988, **353**, 103.

285. W. K. Wong, K. W. Chiu, G. Wilkinson, A. M. R. Galas, M. Thornton-Pett and M. B. Hursthouse, *J. Chem. Soc. Dalton Trans.*, 1983, 1557.

286. E. O. Fischer, *Adv. Organomet. Chem.*, 1976, **14**, 1.

287. C. M. Jensen, T. J. Lynch, C. B. Knobler and H. D. Kaesz, *J. Am. Chem. Soc.*, 1982, **104**, 4679.

288. H. D. Kaesz and C. M. Jensen, *Polyhedron*, 1988, **7**, 1035.

289. (a) C. M. Jensen and H. D. Kaesz, *J. Am. Chem. Soc.*, 1983, **105**, 6969; (b) C. M. Jensen and H. D. Kaesz, *J. Organomet. Chem.*, 1987, **330**, 133.

290. R. D. Adams, J. E. Babin and H.-S. Kim, *Polyhedron*, 1988, **7**, 967.

291. J. T. Park, J. R. Shapley, M. R. Churchill and C. Bueno, *J. Am. Chem. Soc.*, 1983, **105**, 6182.

292. A. D. Clauss, J. R. Shapley, C. N. Wilker and R. Hoffmann, *Organometallics*, 1984, **3**, 619 and references therein.

293. N. T. Allison, J. R. Fritch, K. P. C. Vollhardt and E. C. Walborsky, *J. Am. Chem. Soc.*, 1983, **105**, 1384.

294. For recent leading references from different authors, see (a) B. E. R. Shilling and R. Hoffmann, *J. Am. Chem. Soc.*, 1979, **101**, 3456; (b) J.-F. Halet, J.-Y. Saillard, R. Lissilour, M. J. McGlinchey and G. Jaouen, *Inorg. Chem.*, 1985, **24**, 218; (c) G. Douglas, L. Manojlovic-Muir, K. W. Muir, M. Rashidi, C. M. Anderson and R. J. Puddephatt, *J. Am. Chem. Soc.*, 1987, **109**, 6527; (d) C. E. Housecroft and S. M. Owen, *J. Organomet. Chem.*, 1988, **339**, 139; (e) D. Osella, R. Gobetto, P. Montangero, P. Zanello and A. Cinquantini, *Organometallics*, 1986, **5**, 1247; (f) S. Aime, R. Bertoncello, V. Busetti, R. Gobetto, G. Granozzi and D. Osella, *Inorg. Chem.*, 1986, **25**, 4004; (g) M. Mlekuz, P. Bougeard, B. G. Sayer, S. Peng, M. J. McGlinchey, A. Marinetti, J.-Y. Saillard, J. B. Naceur, B. Mentzen and J. Jaouen, *Organometallics*, 1985, **4**, 1123; (h) J. A. Clucas, P. A. Dolby, M. M. Harding and A. K. Smith, *J. Chem. Soc. Chem. Commun.*, 1987, 1829.

295. (a) D. Nuel, F. Dahan and R. Mathieu, *Organometallics*, 1985, **4**, 1436; (b) M. Lourdichi and R. Mathieu, *Nouv. J. Chim.*, 1982, **6**, 231; (c) M. Lourdichi and R. Mathieu, *Organometallics*, 1986, **5**, 2067; (d) J. Suades and R. Mathieu, *J. Organomet. Chem.*, 1986, **312**, 335.

296. Y. Chi and J. R. Shapley, *Organometallics*, 1985, **4**, 1900.

297. (a) F. Dahan and R. Mathieu, *J. Chem. Soc. Chem. Commun.*, 1984, 432; (b) D. de Montauzon and R. Mathieu, *J. Organomet. Chem.*, 1983, **252**, C83.

298. E. Boyar, A. J. Deeming and S. E. Kabir, *J. Chem. Soc. Chem. Commun.*, 1986, 577.

299. W. Y. Yeh and J. R. Shapley, *J. Organomet. Chem.*, 1986, **315**, C29.

300. J. Suades, F. Dahan and R. Mathieu, *Organometallics*, 1988, **7**, 47.

301. (a) L. R. Beanan, Z. A. Rahman and J. B. Keister, *Organometallics*, 1983, **2**, 1062; (b) L. R. Beanan and J. B. Keister, *Organometallics*, 1985, **4**, 1713; (b) M. R. Churchill, J. C. Fettinger, J. B. Keister, R. F. See and J. F. Ziller, *Organometallics*, 1985, **4**, 2112.

302. J. W. Ziller, D. K. Bower, D. M. Dalton, J. B. Keister and M. R. Churchill, *Organometallics*, 1989, **8**, 492.

303. D. Nuel and R. Mathieu, *Organometallics*, 1988, **7**, 16.

304. D. Nuel, F. Dahan and R. Mathieu, *J. Am. Chem. Soc.*, 1985, **107**, 1658.

305. (a) D. Lentz and H. Michael, *Chem. Ber.*, 1988, **121**, 1413; (b) B. F. G. Johnson, J. Lewis, R. Khattar, F. J. Lahoz, J. Lewis and P. R. Raithby, *J. Organomet. Chem.*, 1987, **319**, C51 and references therein; (c) E. Cabrera, J. C. Daran, Y. Jeannin and O. Kristianson, *J. Organomet. Chem.*, 1986, **310**, 367.

306. G. H. Hogarth, F. Kayser, S. A. R. Knox, D. A. V. Morton, A. G. Orpen and M. L. Turner, *J. Chem. Soc. Chem. Commun.*, 1988, 358.

307. (a) K. C. P. Wollhardt and E. C. Walborsky, *J. Am. Chem. Soc.*, 1983, **105**, 5507; (b) D. Nuel, F. Dahan and R. Mathieu, *Organometallics*, 1986, **5**, 1278.

308. D. Lentz and H. Michael, *Angew. Chem. Int. Ed. Engl.*, 1988, **27**, 845.

309. (a) R. H. Fong and W. H. Hersch, *J. Am. Chem. Soc.*, 1987, **109**, 2843; (b) R. H. Fong and W. H. Hersch, *Organometallics*, 1988, **7**, 794.

310. (a) D. L. Davies, J. C. Jeffery, D. Miguel, P. Sherwood and F. G. A. Stone, *J. Chem. Soc. Chem. Commun.*, 1987, 454 and references therein; (b) L. J. Farrugia, A. D. Miles and F. G. A. Stone, *J. Chem. Soc. Dalton Trans.*, 1985, 2437.

311. For recent leading references, see (a) J. S. Bradley, S. Harris, J. M. Newsam, E. W. Hill, S. Leta and M. A. Modrick, *Organometallics*, 1987, **6**, 2060 and references therein; (b) P. L. Bogdan, C. Woodcock and D. F. Shriver, *Organometallics*, 1987, **6**, 1377.

312. S. D. Wijeyesekera, R. Hoffmann and C. N. Wilker, *Organometallics*, 1984, **3**, 962.

313. J. W. Kolis, F. Basolo and D. F. Shriver, *J. Am. Chem. Soc.*, 1982, **104**, 5626.

314. G. L. Geoffroy and S. L. Bassner, *Adv. Organomet. Chem.*, 1988, **28**, 1.

315. D. Seiferth, G. H. Williams and C. L. Nievert, *Inorg. Chem.*, 1977, **16**, 758.

316. A. C. Sievert, D. S. Strickland, J. R. Shapley, G. R. Steinmetz and G. L. Geoffroy, *Organometallics*, 1982, **1**, 214.
317. J. R. Shapley, D. S. Strickland, G. M. St.-George, M. R. Churchill and C. F. Bueno, *Organometallics*, 1983, **2**, 185.
318. J. W. Kolis, E. M. Holt and D. F. Shriver, *J. Am. Chem. Soc.*, 1983, **105**, 7307.
319. J. A. Hriljac and D. F. Shriver, *J. Am. Chem. Soc.*, 1987, **109**, 6010.
320. M. J. Sailor and D. F. Shriver, *Organometallics*, 1985, **4**, 1476.
321. M. J. Sailor, C. P. Brock and D. F. Shriver, *J. Am. Chem. Soc.*, 1987, **109**, 6015.
322. M. J. West, M. J. Sailor, P. L. Bogdan, C. P. Brock and D. F. Shriver, *J. Am. Chem. Soc.*, 1987, **109**, 6023.
323. M. J. Sailor, M. Sabat and D. F. Shriver, *Organometallics*, 1988, **7**, 728.

Polyhedral Rearrangements and Fragmentation Reactions in Cluster Complexes

Brian F. G. Johnson and Alison Rodgers

6.1. Introduction

A feature of metal cluster compounds is their ability to undergo molecular re-arrangement and fragmentation. These two processes are intimately related and the factors that control rearrangement also control fragmentation. A rearrange-ment may be classified according to the energy required for the process and it is customary to define two categories:

  (i) fluxional behavior
  (ii) isomerization.

A fluxional rearrangement is a low energy process with an activation energy which is simply defined by the time scale of the method of investigation—usually NMR—and falls within the range $\sim 20\text{--}80$ kJ mol^{-1}. Isomerization, which includes fluxional behavior, is used to describe processes which occur on longer than NMR timescale and hence have higher activation energies than fluxional processes. For fragmentation even higher energics are generally involved.

The molecular rearrangement of clusters is not a simple process. Convention-ally it has been taken to involve the interconversion of ligand positions about a fixed, rigid, central metal cluster core, and in the most widely studied systems, such as the cluster carbonyls, it is usually described in terms of carbonyl migration. This is seldom the case. Motion of the ligands usually also involves the motion of the metal nuclei. This movement of metal nuclei may vary from a relatively sim-ple perturbation of the overall metal cluster shape to a complete rearrangement. Irrespective of the extent of the movement, however, the motions of ligands and metal atoms are interdependent and cannot be divorced one from another. The reason for this follows simply from consideration of a reaction. A reaction can be viewed as a series of steps, each of which proceeds from a locally stable point,

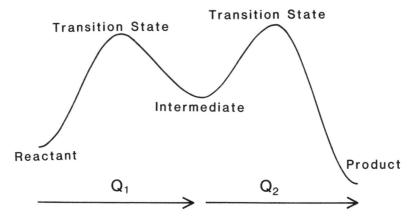

Figure 6.1 ▪ Schematic illustration of the successive steps of a reaction path, each initiated along a normal mode of the system Q_i.

via a saddle point transition state, to another locally stable point on a potential energy surface,[1] Figure 6.1. The motion which leads to the reaction is along a single normal mode of the reacting system, with metal atoms and ligands moving in concert in a special symmetry adapted manner.[2]

6.2. Normal Modes of a Cluster

The normal modes of a cluster, which can be at least partly determined from symmetry theory, provide a clear systematic beginning to the study of rearrangement reactions in metal clusters. Some of the modes will be largely ligand motion and some largely metal motion, but most will involve at least limited coupling of both. Take as an example $Os_3(CO)_{12}$ which has D_{3h} symmetry. The Os_3 system in isolation has a_1' and e' vibrations, a_2' and e'' rotations, and a_2'' and e' translations. The ligand system in isolation also has vibrations, rotations, and translations. Motions of the two polyhedra which have the same symmetry transformation properties then couple together to make symmetry adapted normal modes of the combined cluster system. Three of the normal modes will be rotations, three translations, and the rest vibrations. In this example, the metal polyhedron has vibrations belonging to all irreducible representations except a_1'', so all cluster vibrations of a_1', a_2', e', a_2'', and e'' symmetries will involve at least limited motion of both M_m and L_l. Any vibration of a_1'' symmetry, however, can only involve ligand motion. An important example of an a_1'' vibration of $Os_3(CO)_{12}$ is the vibration which converts the ligand polyhedron from an icosahedron to a cube-octahedron.

The most important conclusion to be drawn about rearrangements in clusters which follows immediately from this discussion is that ligand rearrangements in clusters are not random motions of ligands about a metallic core, M_m, but precisely defined motions which will usually involve a (perhaps limited) amount of M_m motion of the same symmetry. It is however often convenient in studying rearrangement mechanisms of a cluster compound to consider first the symmetry adapted motions of the separate metal and ligand polyhedra, and then consider the

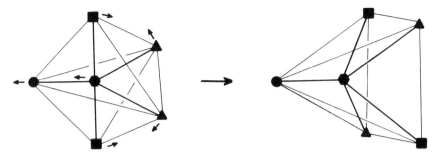

Figure 6.2 ▪ E' normal mode of a trigonal bipyramidal metal unit results in a square pyramidal structure provided the amplitude of vibration is sufficiently large.

coupled motions. In this way the symmetry allowed rearrangements of, say, M_m can be determined as was done in reference 3. The concomitant symmetry adapted ligand motion must then be included to determine the relative energetics of the symmetry allowed metal polyhedron rearrangement pathways within the cluster.

Usually vibration along a particular normal mode, which may lead to rearrangement or fragmentation, is simply an oscillation about a stable geometry of the cluster. The nature of these vibrations can be examined by conventional spectroscopic methods and fall in the low frequency region of the spectrum. As the energy of the system increases, the amplitude of a vibration may increase until it eventually is sufficiently large to surmount a potential energy barrier and to lead to a change in polyhedral geometry. For example, one can envisage the E' normal mode of a trigonal bipyramidal metal unit which, provided the amplitude of vibration is sufficiently large, results in a square pyramidal geometry (Figure 6.2). It is important to understand that molecular rearrangements and fragmentations take place by the same type of process—a vibration of the system, and that there is no fundamental difference in motion leading to fluxional behavior (nuclei exchange) or motion leading to fragmentation.

The normal modes of a whole cluster involve a motion of the central metal polyhedron, M_m, which is coupled to a motion of the ligand polyhedron, L_l, both of which transform according to the same irreducible representation of the point group of the system. The metal polyhedron (M_m) motions of a normal mode can be classified into two types: (i) those which in the absence of ligands would be rotations (or perhaps translations) of M_m and (ii) those which in the absence of ligands would be proper vibrations of M_m. These two types of motion are of course coupled to some extent, but it is nonetheless a helpful division. The vibrations of "rotation parentage" are of particular relevance for relative rearrangements of the metal polyhedron and the ligand polyhedron where both M_m and L_l retain their own geometry. For example, oscillation of the Fe_3 triangle within the icosahedron of CO ligands in $Fe_3(CO)_{12}$ accounts for the observed fluxional behavior in the solid.[4] These rotation parentage vibrations are the cluster analogue of "librations" in crystalline structures, Figure 6.3. Librations are "soft" vibrations, that is, they show a strong dependence on temperature. These are usually low frequency modes and theoretically should be detectable by monitoring the way in which they change as the temperature is increased. In experimental terms one simply expects to see a

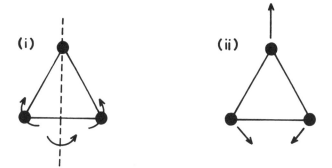

Figure 6.3 ▪ Schematic illustration of (i) a libration and (ii) a typical vibration of vibration parentage.

band in the infrared or Raman spectrum which changes its form with temperature. Care must be taken here, however, since metal-ligand modes also often show pronounced temperature dependence.

Librations cause the two polyhedra—ligand and metal—to undergo motion with respect to each other. If, for convenience, we imagine the peripheral ligand polyhedra to be fixed, then this motion may be visualized as a small motion of the internal metal polyhedron which changes the relative disposition of the two polyhedron. At low temperature the amplitude of this motion will be small and will not induce net change of ligand positions. However, as the temperature is raised and the amplitude increases, this motion—or libration—may lead to a change of ligand positions with respect to the metal polyhedron. The ligands have maintained the same relative dispositions one-to-another, and only appear to have undergone an exchange process. This type of motion will occur under all circumstances and in any phase. Its significance will, however, be very phase dependent. In the solid, where intermolecular forces (ligand-ligand) dominate, the ligands might be expected to resist large movements or migrations and thus libration will be more apparent.[4] To some extent, the same might be true in solution where ligand-solvent interactions will be important but, in general, it is safe to assume that since the cluster is no longer rigidly constrained this effect will comparatively be less significant. Other types of vibrations of the cluster system result in products where not only are the two polyhedra rearranged with respect to one another, but they are also internally rearranged or even have different component parts.

Unfortunately, although for very simple systems normal modes are not too difficult to establish, for more complicated systems (and yet in cluster terms, still very simple systems), it is an extremely difficult and time-consuming procedure. For $Fe_3(CO)_{12}$, for example, a classic among fluxional systems, the normal modes have yet to be established. The main computational problem is the determination of the extent of mixing within each set of symmetry adapted metal and ligand motions. For high symmetry systems such as $Os_3(CO)_{12}$, approximate normal modes can often be determined from a combination of symmetry theory and chemical intuition; for lower symmetry systems such an approach is less useful. Our basis of understanding of rearrangement reactions is therefore currently limited to what can be deduced independently about the motions of the ligand envelope and the internal metal polyhedral unit.

6.3. Bonding and Energetics of a Cluster

When one envisages a molecular rearrangement one generally considers bonds to be broken and bonds to be formed. However, for a cluster rearrangement the picture is not quite so simple since the standard idea of a 2-electron bond is not always applicable. It is tempting to say that each edge or nearest neighbor M—M link in the metal polyhedron corresponds to a chemical bond, but this is not necessarily the case for a cluster system. Although polyhedral edges are frequently considered to correspond to a directional bond, the bond in clusters is such that, in general, the parameterization of the overall binding energy within this cluster system in terms of either edges or faces is not satisfactory. It may, of course, under certain circumstances be convenient to do so, and to some extent we shall choose to follow this course here, but in reality bonds may not be localized on either edge or faces. If one were to separate the components of the overall chemical glue holding this cluster unit together into edge bonds, then most frequently these bonds would have bond orders of less than one. Consider, for example $Rh_6(CO)_{16}$, which according to simple electron-counting theory[5] has 22 electrons available for M—M bonding and so each polyhedral edge within this Rh_6 octahedral unit (12 edges) has a bond order of 11/12.

Despite the many deficiencies of electron-counting schemes, they form a helpful starting point for the consideration of transition metal cluster bonding. We will therefore proceed by exploring them in some detail. The first step is to establish the number, x, of electrons each atom requires in its valence shell for maximum stability. Experience tells us that for hydrogen $x = 2$, and that for first row main group systems $n = 8$. By analogy one would expect $x = 18$ for transition metals since the valence atomic orbitals are nine in number: $4s$, $4p$, $3d$. The first applications of the principles of electron counting which we will consider are some simple hydrocarbons.

Ethane has a total of 14 valence electrons. H has $x = 2$, so 12 electrons must be shared between C's and H's to give the H's stability. The remaining 2 electrons must be shared by the 2 carbon atoms to make them up to octets, resulting in a single C—C bond. Ethene has a total of 12 valence electrons, 8 of which are shared between C's and H's, so the remaining 4 must be shared by the 2 carbon atoms, resulting in a double C—C bond. Ethyne possesses 10 valence electrons. Each C—H bond employs 2, leaving 6 for C—C bonding. All 6 must be involved in C—C bonding to complete the C octets, hence a triple bond. Similarly, C_4H_6 has 22 valence electrons, 12 of which are shared between C's and H's. The remaining 10 electrons must be assigned to satisfy the octets of the 4 C atoms, which requires each of the 10 electrons to be shared by two different C's. C_4H_6 therefore has 5 C—C bonds, so 1 single and 2 doubles, or 2 singles and 1 triple.

The number of valence electrons in transition metal clusters make the problem more difficult, but the same principles apply. It is most important to ensure 18 electrons per metal atom. Each CO contributes 2 electrons to the metal valence electron count. $Mn_2(CO)_{10}$ therefore has 34 electrons in the metals' valence shells. To complete the Mn's 18 electron count per atom, there must be a single Mn—Mn bond whereby the 2 metal atoms share 2 electrons. This argument correctly deduces the Mn—Mn bond order of one.

$Os_3(CO)_{12}$ and $Fe_3(CO)_{12}$ similarly both have 48 metal valence electrons. To complete the metal 18-electron count there must be 3 M—M bonds providing 6 shared electrons. Thus the metals form a triangle.

Other clusters can be treated in an analogous manner. $Os_5(CO)_{16}$ requires 9 Os—Os bonds, which results in a trigonal bipyramidal structure. Note that a square-based pyramidal arrangement of the 5 osmium atoms with 8 edges is not a reasonable structure on these grounds. The dihydrido cluster $H_2Os_3(CO)_{10}$ requires 4 Os—Os bonds to complete the 18 electrons on each Os; hence 3 single and 1 double. Finally, $H_4Re_4(CO)_{12}$ requires 8 Re—Re bonds, so 2 double bonds and 4 single bonds in the tetrahedral metal polyhedron. We will return to this discussion in Section 6.5.

For some systems, usually those containing 5 or less metal atoms, there is a direct correspondence between the electron count and the number of polyhedral edges. However, for most systems we must consider alternative ways of describing the bonding. A bonding description which differs from the 2-electron bond used earlier has been developed for the formally electron-deficient boron hydrides and extended to include transition metal clusters. Thus, a clear analogy exists between the $Os(\mu_2\text{-}H)_2Os$ bridge in $H_2Os_3(CO)_{10}$ and the $B(\mu_2\text{-}H)_2B$ bridge in B_2H_6, and between $H_4Re_4(CO)_{12}$ with face-centered H and B_4Cl_4 with face-centered Cl.

The idea of electron deficiency works well for a large number of transition metal clusters and instead of the simple 2-electron directional bond approach adopted previously, an alternative molecular orbital (m.o.) scheme (using a basis of valence atomic orbitals) offers a good bonding picture. According to this scheme, delocalized bonds, including multicenter bonds, provide a satisfactory approach. Good accounts of this scheme appear elsewhere.[5] In essence the m.o. picture describes the cluster unit as bonded by $n + 1$ bonding electron pairs (where n is the number of metal atoms), and not λ (the number of edges) as required by the simplistic model employed earlier. (It is interesting to note that an analogous argument when applied to main group systems, for example, an m.o. argument where all bonding orbitals in an atomic orbital basis set are occupied and all the antibonding orbitals are unoccupied, results in the octet rule.) The advantage of such a scheme over the electron counting scheme just presented is illustrated by $Rh_6(CO)_{16}$. Thirty-two electrons from the carbon monoxide plus the 54 rhodium valence electrons cannot provide each Rh with 18 electrons using directional 2-center bonds. Whereas according to the m.o. approach 7 bonding electron pairs $(n + 1)$ define the octahedron. However, acceptance of the electron deficiency scheme leads to problems of relating bonds to polyhedral edges and, for that matter, faces. There is no direct correlation of bonds with direct metal-metal contacts. This scheme has the advantage of allowing us to understand the electron counts of very many clusters; however, it destroys the simple relationship between M—M distance (or polyhedral edge) and the chemical bond. It is possible to parameterize this problem and associate given amounts of electron density with edges, but in reality this is of little use.

A third possibility is suggested when the energy of a transition metal cluster, $M_\mu L_l$, is symbolically written as the sum of metal–metal (M—M) interactions plus metal-ligand (M—L) interactions plus ligand–ligand (L—L) interactions,[6] for example

$$E_{\text{cluster}} = \Sigma M\text{—}M + \Sigma M\text{—}L + \Sigma L\text{—}L \qquad (6.1)$$

Transition metals have s, p, and d electrons available for bonding; some of these will be involved with bonding to ligands and some to other metal atoms. If we remove the electrons (more strictly the electron density) required for M—L bonding from our initial consideration, the remaining s, p, and d electrons bind the metal atoms together. Not all of the d electrons are involved in M—L bonding, so the M—M bonding might be expected to reflect the bonding characteristics of a small fragment of bulk transition metal and so the energy of M_m can be written as[7]

$$E_{M-M} = E_{rep}(s, p) + E_{attr}(d) \qquad (6.2)$$

$E_{rep}(s, p)$ is positive and due to the repulsion of valence s and p electrons by cores of adjacent transition metal atoms, it is thus short range. $E_{attr}(d)$ is negative and due to the attraction of the metallic-type bonding of the d electrons. The form for the cohesive energy of bulk metal where each atom has less than 10 d electrons has been shown by Woolley to be an adequate description of $E_{attr}(d)$ when account is taken of the reduced d electron density in a cluster due to M—L bonding. Thus we can write[8]

$$E_{M-M} \approx (R_{M-M})^{-5}(Z_M) \dot{A} \qquad (6.3)$$

where R_{M-M} is the nearest neighbor distance between metal atoms, Z_M is the number of M's nearest neighbors, and A is a constant determined by the number of d electrons and the details of the atomic potential at each site. Summation over metal atoms is implied in equation (6.3) which ignores the interaction between metal atoms which are not nearest neighbors. Broadly speaking the (Z_M) is a function of the polyhedron structure which M_m adopts; R_{M-M} reflects the size of the system; and A varies both as a function of the metal involved, and also of the ligand system to the extent that the ligand system determines the number of electrons available for M—M bonding. The justification of equation (6.3) lies in the methods of solid-state physics, for example chemical pseudo potential and Xα methods.[9]

For a given M_mL_l system consideration of only the M_m cohesive energy of equation (6.3) would suggest that M_m will have the structure which maximizes the magnitude of the cohesive energy, for example, tetrahedral for $m = 4$, trigonal bipyramidal for $m = 5$, bicapped tetrahedron or octahedron for $m = 6$, tricapped tetrahedron or pentagonal bipyramidal for $m = 7$ etc.,[10] since A will be approximately constant for the different possible structures. For the larger systems, $m \geq 7$, perhaps one might expect to see variations in structure since cohesive energies vary so little (0.2% difference in cohesive energy between the pentagonal bipyramid and the capped octahedron). In practice, a variety of M_m structures are observed for all m. This reflects the large (possibly dominant) contribution to the total energy made by the M—L interactions. A metal polyhedron which does not maximize the cohesive energy may be observed because this M_m structure gives rise to more favorable M—L interactions than the most stable metal polyhedron that is possible.

The second two contributions to the total energy of a metal cluster are those due to M—L bonding and L—L interactions. There is currently no entirely satisfactory account of M—L bonding in metal complexes. However, consideration of M—L and L—L interactions in complexes can help our understanding of the same interactions in cluster compounds. The additional metal atoms and the possibilities of bridging as well as terminal ligands affect the details rather than the principles of the M—L and L—L interactions. As in complexes, we might expect a range of M—L coordination numbers to be observed in clusters, depending on the identities of the metal atoms and the ligands. In a cluster changing the identity or number of metal atoms or changing the metal polyhedron structure can alter the relative magnitudes of the contribution of Σ M—M and Σ M—L to the total energy, and so may cause completely different structures to be found.

Stone[11] showed that the broad features of bonding and antibonding m.o.'s in a cluster follow from symmetry considerations. His analysis suggests that the detailed geometry of the ligands relative to the metal is not usually due to M—L bonding effects. Some time ago it was recognized that the ligands in cluster systems organized themselves into regular or semiregular polyhedral forms.[12] The factors which control the shape the ligands adopt were visualized as being exactly the same as those which govern molecular shape in coordination compounds, namely, relatively weak ligand-ligand forces. Simple calculations using a point on a sphere model allowed a range of polyhedra to be produced for a range of ligand numbers from six to eighteen. As might be expected, the lowest energy geometries obtained were generally fully triangulated polyhedra since it is here that ligand-ligand repulsive forces are minimized and ligand-ligand attractive forces are maximized. The structure of the cluster was then derived initially by simply placing one polyhedron (the metal) inside the other (the ligand). In many examples this ligand envelope does not correspond to this low(est) energy polyhedral form, presumably because the low energy form corresponds to a structure with relatively poor M—L bonding. This usually occurs for systems in which the symmetry of the idealized metal polyhedron and that of the idealized ligand polyhedron are not immediately compatible. In this case each polyhedron will adjust until a common symmetry is found. Thus, the Co_6 unit in $Co_6(CO)_{14}^{4-}$ has O_h symmetry and the ligand polyhedron—an omnicapped cube—is exactly compatible; hence a regular, highly symmetric cluster. In contrast, in $Co_6(CO)_{15}^{2-}$, the difference in symmetries between the Co_6 unit and the $(CO)_{15}$ unit leads each to distort.

In conclusion to the consideration of structure according to equation (6.1) we can say that the bonding in metal clusters can be understood as an interplay between the desire to (i) maximize the magnitude of the cohesive energy of the metal polyhedron, (ii) maximize M—L bonding energy, and (iii) not cause steric crowding of the ligands. The subtleties of this discussion of transition metal cluster energetics need not concern us here. But, let us consider the rearrangements of a cluster system in these terms. A cluster reaction involves some change in the metal-metal interactions, the metal-ligand interactions, and ligand-ligand interactions. In detecting whether a rearrangement has taken place, then, we must consider whether the geometry of the system has adopted a new equilibrium polyhedron (in a labeled atom sense) rather than considering only formal bonds which may not have sufficient meaning in a cluster.

6.4. Fluxional Behavior and Isomerization

In the previous section we outlined the principles governing molecular rearrangement leading to fluxional behavior and isomerization. We emphasized that the symmetry principles governing these rearrangements are the same and, being based on the normal modes of the system, are in theory predictable. However, although it is a relatively simple matter to carry out a full vibrational analysis of simple polyhedra, for example, the tetrahedron or trigonal bipyramid in isolation, this is not the case for complicated many-atom molecules such as carbonyl clusters. Until computational methods are sufficiently well established to be applied to these systems we must proceed using the deductions that can be made from experiments (see Section 6.2). The emphasis of our discussion will be on fluxional behavior, for which there is the most experimental data available.

The reactant structure is the starting point for most studies of rearrangement processes. However, for a transition metal cluster it is not necessarily a straightforward matter to determine the reactant structures in solution. The term "ground-state structure" is usually understood to refer to the structure in the solid state-crystal—as determined by X-ray crystallography. A species in the environment of a crystalline lattice experiences quite large external packing forces, which are not present in solution and may have a major effect on the structure of the molecule. Effects of this kind are emphasized in crystals of ionic compounds and there are many such compounds in carbonyl cluster chemistry. In ionic materials the major bonding force is the lattice energy, and variations in "structure" of a carbonyl anion as the counter ion is changed are to be expected, although this aspect of cluster chemistry has not been explored. There are examples, however. The anion $[H_3Os_4(CO)_{12}]^-$ shows either C_s symmetry or C_{3v} symmetry depending on the cation. In addition, extensive vibration and libration already operate under these conditions, and structural studies are limited by disorder arising from these motions or simply by the random orientations of molecules within the crystalline state.[13] Despite these considerations there is a tendency among chemists to compare structures of closely related anions without consideration of the cation involved, and to assume that the crystal structure is also (at least approximately) the solution structure. The constraints imposed by crystallographic symmetry are extremely important and should not be ignored, both for consideration of fluxionality and isomerization in the solid state and for deductions about solution structure from solid-state data.

For crystalline samples studies are largely restricted to X-ray diffraction methods, although in a limited number of cases neutron diffraction methods have been employed. X-ray diffraction studies have provided excellent detail of the gross molecular structures of many cluster systems, but there is room for more detailed attention to M—M and M—L bond and angle parameters. For many cluster carbonyls the data is (understandably) poor and few studies have been made at temperatures other than ~ ambient. Under these conditions the molecule may be undergoing motion. Let us consider this aspect in more detail.

A value of 10^{-18} s is often quoted as the time scale associated with X-ray diffraction studies. However, it must be stressed that this value has no meaning for a diffraction experiment. In fact a measure of a single X-ray observation ("a reflection") takes an average of 100–500 s, implying a "snap shot" of ca. 10^{20} superimposed pictures of each atom position. This procedure is repeated a great number of times during data collection. The average, over time and space, of this extremely large number of pictures of the atomic positions (or, better, of the electron density centroids) represents what can be observed in an X-ray experiment with no indication whatsoever of the time required for the photon-atom interaction. With this in mind the question of motions in the solid state may be stated more precisely. The problem is no longer that of the time required for the process—because many kinds of molecular motions (vibrations, librations, rotations, or rearrangements) take place at rates greater than 10^2 s—but that of the "number of changes" between consecutive positions occurring during reflection measurements. If the number of changes is small (i.e., the energy barrier is high) no motions will be detected by the X-ray experiment and the atoms will be distributed between their extreme positions. On the other hand if the energy barrier is low then the "number of jumps" will be large and the rearranging atoms will be detected in intermediate positions also. In the extreme case of free rotation, diffused (unresolved) electron density distributions will appear in the electron density map.

In some cases an indication of atomic movements of low energy rearrangement processes may be provided indirectly by an analysis of the atomic displacement amplitudes (thermal parameters[14]) obtained from X-ray and neutron diffraction data. Methods based on this approach have been used recently to investigate the relationship between solid-state data and CO-migration pathways found by multinuclear NMR techniques in solution[15] and the occurrence of dynamic Jahn-Teller distortions in solid Cu(II) and Fc(III) complexes.[16] More important to us in this chapter are the variable temperature X-ray studies on organometallic (and organic) species which have shown that the temperature dependence of the atomic displacement parameters has physical significance and contains information on true atomic positions.[17]

In solution a cluster structure may differ from its crystal structure due to the absence of packing forces. In addition there is clear evidence to show that in solution the molecular structures can be perturbed by molecule-solvent interaction, which can be substantial. The dielectric constant (i.e., polarity) is an important influence. The effects of these interactions may be reflected in a simple shift of $\nu(CO)$ in the infrared spectrum by a few wave numbers or, and this is not uncommon, by a structural change. For example, $Co_2(CO)_8$,[18] which has two bridging carbonyls in the solid, has been shown by infrared spectroscopy to exist as a mixture of bridged and nonbridged (less polar) isomers in hydrocarbon solvents. Similarly, $Fe_3(CO)_{12}$, which has C_s symmetry in the solid, appears to exist as a C_{2v} or D_3 form in solution, or a mixture of both.[19]

Structural studies in solution are limited to NMR and vibrational spectroscopic methods. In infrared spectroscopy a typical terminally bonded carbonyl exhibits a C—O stretch at 2000 cm^{-1} (6.0×10^{13} Hz) and an edge-bridging carbonyl at 1800 cm^{-1} (5.4×10^{13} Hz). To be indistinguishable in an infrared experiment these two groups must undergo site exchange at a rate greater than the difference between the two frequencies, 6×10^{12} Hz. In other words, for carbonyl clusters the infrared timescale is of the order of 1.6×10^{-13} second. This is too short to permit site exchange for virtually all carbonyls. Hence, the infrared spectrum gives information about the "ground-state" structure in solution (or for that matter in the solid).

If the rate law for the process exchanging the carbonyl ligands obeys the Arrhenius equation

$$A = A_0 e^{-\Delta E/(kT)} \tag{6.4}$$

then we can show that for a rearrangement to occur on the infrared timescale, the activation energy must be <10 kJ mol^{-1}, for a typical pre-exponential factor

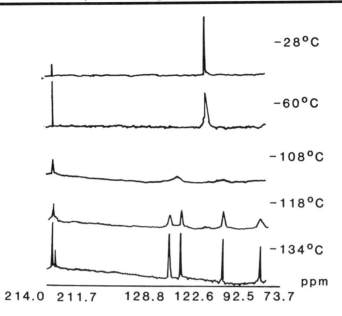

Figure 6.4 ▪ Illustration of coalescence of NMR spectrum as temperature increases.[20]

(for a simple, unimolecular first order reaction) of 10^{15} s^{-1} and typical rate A of 230 s^{-1} at 250 K. For NMR, on the other hand, the activation energy is about 60 kJ mol^{-1}. This corresponds to the activation energy of cluster rearrangements in many carbonyls. Thus, the ^{13}C NMR spectra of many metal carbonyls are temperature dependent in the accessible temperature range 100 K to 400 K.

In an NMR experiment, magnetic nuclei placed in a magnetic field absorb radio frequency radiation and are excited into higher quantum states. The differences in absorption frequency between nuclei in different chemical environments are very small, only a few points per million (ppm) of the operating frequency [usually 0–10 ppm downfield from Si(CH$_3$)$_4$ for ^{1}H NMR and 150–250 ppm downfield from Si(^{13}CH$_3$)$_4$ for ^{13}CO in metal carbonyls].

If the ^{13}C chemical shift difference between the inequivalent CO groups in a molecule is 10 ppm the difference in absorption frequency between the two nuclei at a typical operating frequency of 23 MHz is 230 Hz (i.e., 230 s^{-1}). If the two carbonyls undergo site exchange at a rate faster than this, they are not distinguishable by the NMR experiment, and a single ^{13}C NMR signal is observed; this is the "fast exchange limit" and the molecule is termed fluxional (see introduction). If the exchange is slower than this and the two independent signals are observed then we refer to the "slow exchange limit." For exchange rates at about 230 s^{-1} a broad complicated lineshape occurs; the signals are coalescing and the situation is midway between the two limits, Figure 6.4.

There is now a vast amount of NMR data available on a multitude of cluster systems. However, information is largely restricted to organometallic compounds because they contain or can be enriched with easily examinable nuclei such as ^{1}H, ^{13}C, and ^{17}O. Recent advances in experimental methods have also permitted xamination of various metal nuclei, for example ^{103}Rh, ^{195}Pt, and so on.[21] Thus, for many molecules it is now possible to examine not only the motion of the ligands about the metal cluster unit but also of the cluster unit itself.

In addition to the ligand envelope and the metal polyhedron there is now emerging a class of cluster which contains interstitially bonded atoms such as H, C, N, P, and on many occasions metal ions. Examples include $[Rh_{13}(CO)_{24}H_3]^{2-}$ and $[Au_{12}(P\phi_3)_8SCN_3]$. Certain of these internal atoms may themselves migrate throughout the metal polyhedron, migrate to the surface, or even exchange with external ligands. In general this behavior is only commonly observed for H, although there is some evidence to suggest that C and N may undergo "surface" $\leftrightarrow$ "internal site" migrations. Such behavior is clearly a complicated issue and although migration of, for example, H through a cluster of metal atoms (e.g., Rh_{13}) may be considered as being independent of, at least, surface ligand motion, this, for the reason mentioned in Section 6.2, cannot strictly be the case. The motion will be governed by precisely the same symmetry rules that governed all other molecular motion. Fluxional behavior of all kinds is a totally concerted motion.

This is not the place to restate vast quantities of experimental data. There are many reviews and articles[22] devoted to this topic and the reader is referred to them. Rather we shall attempt to bring together the various types of fluxional behavior that have been described and assess their viability. To begin with, the earliest attempts to understand the motion ligands undergo around central cluster units were based on localized migration pathways. The central unit was regarded as a fixed nonparticipating block. Consideration was also restricted—because of the lack of appropriate experimental facilities—to studies in solution. Essentially two types of CO migration were postulated:

(i) Migration from one metal atom to another
(ii) Site interchange about the same metal atom.

The former idea stemmed from observations on simple dimeric systems such as $Co_2(CO)_8$ in the ground-state structure, that is, the structure established in the crystalline state at about room temperature—and herein lies potential danger. There will usually be a difference in symmetry between the crystalline "ground static geometry" and the solution structure (see earlier). This is nicely illustrated by $Os_3(CO)_{12}$.[23] In solution the ^{13}CO NMR spectrum at room temperature exhibits two chemical shift values as expected from a structure with D_{3h} symmetry. In the solid, however, a total of twelve independent values are observed in accord with the lower symmetry imposed by the crystallographic lattice. In this example the structure approximates to the same form independent of phase. This is not always the case. There are examples of molecules which show structures markedly dependent on environment, solid or solution. An example is $Fe_3(CO)_{12}$. Here is clear spectroscopic evidence to indicate different structural forms in solid and solution (possibly the bridged C_{2v} structure illustrated in Figure 6.5 and the unbridged D_3 analogue).[24] The true ground-state structure of this molecule is clearly difficult to establish, although in fairness it is possible to get a very good idea from X-ray studies of the solid state.

To return to CO migration, infrared studies of $Co_2(CO)_8$ clearly reveal the existence of several isomeric forms,[25] Figure 6.6. Interconversion of (1) and (2) may be simply viewed as the consequence of edge-bridge opening and closing,

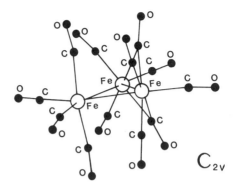

Figure 6.5 ▪ C_{2V} bridged structure of $Fe_3(CO)_{12}$.

Figure 6.7. This provides a perfectly reasonable and straightforward explanation of CO fluxionality. In this case the mechanism involves the migration of CO ligands from one cobalt atom to another. It also leads to the site exchange about an individual cobalt atom. These two processes cannot be divorced from one another.

Now consider $Os_3(CO)_{12}$. In the solid this possesses a D_{3h} geometry. The ^{13}C NMR shows two peaks of equal intensity below 60°C and one signal at higher temperatures. On the basis of Os—CO coupling, the probable explanation of this observation is that the equatorial and axial CO ligands on each osmium atom undergo exchange, that is, there is site exchange about the same metal atom at temperatures above 60°C.

The same idea also provides an understanding of the fluxional behavior of $Rh_4(CO)_{12}$. In this case, the ground-state structure has C_{3v} symmetry (3) with three CO ligands spanning the basal plane.[26] Fluxional behavior here may be understood to correspond to edge-bridge opening to give a geometry of T_d symmetry—hence all CO's are now equivalent. Re-formation of three bridges along the edges of any one of the four equivalent triangular faces in this T_d intermediate will lead to the "scrambling" of COs.

All fluxional behavior in cluster carbonyls may be described in this manner, although of course there may be several processes of type (i) or (ii) or any combination of them. The behavior of the substituted derivatives $Ir_4(CO)_{11}(PPh_2Me)$ are of this type.[27]

We have stressed that each step of any reaction must proceed along a normal mode of the system. Thus each step usually involves both ligand and metal motion. This is clearly illustrated by the reaction of $[(t\text{-}BuP)Fe_3(CO)_{10}]$ with diphenyl acetylene reported by Knoll et al.[28] The situation for rearrangement reactions, es-

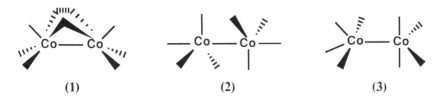

Figure 6.6 ▪ Isomeric forms of $Co_2(CO)_8$.

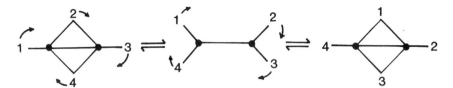

Figure 6.7 ■ Proposed mechanism for interconversion of two isomeric forms of $Co_2(CO)_8$.

pecially of the metal polyhedron, is often simpler than this statement implies, as the vibrational energies of an isolated metal polyhedron are generally of significantly lower energy than those of an isolated ligand polyhedron, so the ligand-metal vibrational coupling is smaller than the intermetal or interligand couplings. Thus to a first approximation we can determine mechanisms for rearrangement reactions within a metal polyhedron by studying it in isolation. The ligand system will then slightly modify the vibrations and perhaps (significantly) affect the relative energies of the proposed mechanisms. We therefore require a means of determining the metal polyhedron vibrations which can lead to energetically feasible rearrangements. There exists a wide range of normal modes and hence polyhedral rearrangements within cluster units. They range from the rather trivial scissoring mode of the Fe_3 triangle in $Fe_3(CO)_{12}$ to the more substantial rearrangement found, for example, in $C_2B_{10}H_{12}$. It is apparent that the energies for such rearrangements vary considerably and that they are not governed by the same considerations as the rearrangements of ligand polyhedra.

For a cluster unit the shape is governed by strong attractive bonding forces between the constituent metal atoms, whereas the ligand shape is determined by relatively small ligand-ligand interactions. A measure of the attractive forces in a cluster unit is the cohesive energy of equation (6.3) which is proportional to the square root of the connectivity. Substantial differences in cohesive energy are found for apparently closely related polyhedra, for example, an octahedron and trigonal prism; these differences arise from the changes in connectivity within the M_m unit (each atom has four nearest neighbors in an octahedron and only three in a trigonal prism, so the ratio of their cohesive energies is $2/\sqrt{3}$). As a consequence, for any polyhedral rearrangement in M_m one might reasonably expect a pathway in which the change in cohesive energy is kept to a minimum;[10] in other words one might expect a rearrangement to proceed by successive cleavages of single M—M contacts, each cleavage being followed by the formation of a new contact. Thus a mechanism such as the rearrangement of an octahedron via a trigonal twist which involves simultaneous cleavage of three M—M contacts is not expected, though an analogous mechanism proceeding by successive break/link steps is possible.[3] This approach to the rearrangement reactions of metal polyhedra has been followed to derive symmetry allowed energetically feasible mechanisms for the most common structures for $m = 5$ to 12. The same principles can be used to treat other systems. Energetic considerations (or equivalently orbital symmetry arguments) of the whole cluster then determine which of the postulated mechanisms is most probable.

In some cases, the interversion may occur via the same route as that proposed for the rearrangement of the ligand system in the corresponding coordination compound. This is the case for a trigonal bipyramidal structure where the two concerted symmetry allowed mechanisms[29] for a metal complex are also appropriate for an M_5 metal polyhedron. However, the reasoning which suggests that the mechanisms are energetically feasible in the two different types of systems is completely different.

6.5. Some Case Histories

The polynuclear carbonyls $Fe_3(CO)_{12}$, $Co_4(CO)_{12}$, and $Rh_4(CO)_{12}$ are among the most systematically investigated clusters. Yet they have proven to be the most difficult systems to understand. Only recently would it be fair to state that a real appreciation of their structure and the rearrangements they undergo has been achieved.

Triiron dodecacarbonyl has been shown to be statistically disordered (i.e., the ligand and metal polyhedra have two relative orientations) in the solid state with the molecule placed around a crystallographic inversion center which generates a second image of the Fe_3 triangle and of the twelve CO groups (Figure 6.8).[30] The carbonyl groups are in asymmetric bridging positions along one triangular edge which is significantly shorter than the other two [2.558(1) Å as opposed to 2.677(2) Å and 2.683(1) Å]. The molecule possesses approximate C_2 symmetry with the pseudo twofold axis passing through the middle of the bridged Fe—Fe bond and the opposite Fe atom. It is important to note that the almost superposable C- and O-atom images in the two different $Fe_3(CO)_{12}$ geometries could be distinguished in the more recent and precise of the two independent structural determinations allowing recognition of $O\cdots O$ and $C\cdots C$ atom pairs, separated on average by 0.43 and 0.50 Å, respectively. The disorder was explained in terms of a simple static model due to the high regularity of the outer, (virtually) icosahedral, peripheral polyhedron described by the CO groups which does not appreciably differ from one molecular orientation to the other.

In solution there is a problem. First the structure appears to be solvent dependent. For solutions in nonpolar solvents the infrared spectrum is consistent (more or less) with C_{2v} symmetry.[24b] Thus, both terminal and bridging CO absorptions

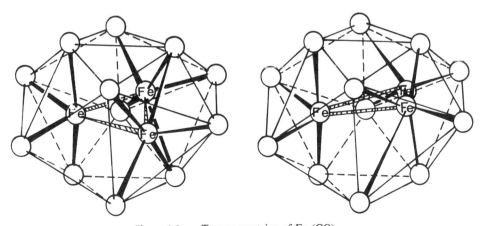

Figure 6.8 ▪ Two geometries of $Fe_3(CO)_{12}$.

are observed in line with prediction. In more polar solvents there is a dramatic change. Bands associated with the CO bridges decrease significantly in intensity and a different set of terminal bonds are apparent. This change was originally believed to be brought about by the conversion of the C_{2v} form into the D_3 form illustrated earlier. This idea was appealing because the homologous $Ru_3(CO)_{12}$ and $Os_3(CO)_{12}$ have the D_3 structure in the solid. It appeared that $Fe_3(CO)_{12}$ existed in two isomeric forms in solution. However, the ^{13}C NMR for enriched samples shows that all carbonyls are equivalent at $-150°C$. Thus, the activation energy for the C_{2v}/D_3 rearrangement is less than 20 kJ mol^{-1}.

Cotton proposed that in $Fe_3(CO)_{12}$ fluxionality in solution occurred by a concerted bridge-terminal pairwise exchange through the D_3 form and onto a "new" C_{2v} structure. This mechanism will operate about all three edges of the iron triangle and necessarily involved a "scissoring" motion of this triangle to bring about the equilibration of the three iron atoms. This corresponds to an equilibration of metal-metal distances of 2.558 Å, 2.677 Å, and 2.683 Å and is of interest in connection with our comments about the value of metal-metal distances in metal clusters (see earlier).

Although this explanation is attractive, it is not the only explanation of the infrared and NMR data. As mentioned previously the structure of $Fe_3(CO)_{12}$ corresponds to an icosahedron (slightly flattened) of carbonyl groups containing the triangle of iron atoms. Examination of this arrangement reveals that there are three possible orientations of the metal triangle within the icosahedron: one with C_{2v} symmetry and two edge-bridging CO groups (as observed in the solid), one with D_3 symmetry, and, finally, one with C_{2v} symmetry but with two face-centered CO groups. Conversion of one form to another in the sequence

$$C_{2v} \leftrightarrow D_3 \leftrightarrow C'_{2v} \leftrightarrow D_3 \leftrightarrow C_{2v}$$

may occur by a libration which is simply a tilt (a very low energy process) of the triangle about any one of its three twofold axes. The D_3 form contains no CO bridges and is consistent with the observed infrared spectrum at low temperature. Repeated interchange between the C_{2v} and D_3 forms leads to the equilibrium of all carbonyls. This scheme is attractive because unlike Cotton's mechanism it offers a good explanation of the isomers and fluxional behavior of the compound.

The alternative explanation of the infrared data is given support by recently reported magic-angle spinning ^{13}C NMR data for solid $Fe_3(CO)_{12}$. At low temperatures ($<-95°C$) the spectrum is consistent with the C_s symmetry observed in X-ray crystal structures, that is, twelve NMR resonances. As the temperature is raised the spectrum changes and six signals of intensities 2:2:2:2:2:2 are observed. None of these resonances can be attributed to bridging or semibridging CO groups. This change is best explained by the libration motion described earlier to account for the solution infrared data. In the slow exchange limit the crystallographic symmetry (C_s) gives rise to twelve CO resonances—not five as required by C_{2v} molecular symmetry. As the temperature is raised, libration of the Fe_3 triangle between the D_3 and C_s forms leads to the expected six signals in the observed intensity ratios. As the temperature is raised further, total equilibration would be expected. It is important to note that this is not the same sequence as expected for $Fe_3(CO)_{12}$ in solution.

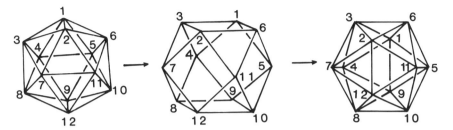

Figure 6.9 ▪ Icosahedra-cuboctahedra-icosahedra interconversion.

This mechanism which may operate in the solid or solution—although it may appear different because of the imposed crystal symmetry—involves the libration of the Fe_3 triangle within the CO icosahedron with the relative disposition of the CO groups remaining constant. Given the intermolecular CO···CO interactions expected in the solid this is entirely reasonable. That is not to say that carbonyls cannot undergo positional interchange. It simply means that the activation energy for libration is lower than that for CO interchange.

Carbonyl exchange certainly will occur and will do so easily in solution. This exchange may occur by a concerted mechanism in which the icosahedral CO envelope rearranges to a cube-octahedral transition state and then onto a "new" icosahedron. This breathing motion will occur in concert with the Fe_3 scissoring movement.

These ideas are not restricted to $Fe_3(CO)_{12}$. Precisely the same methods may now be applied to $Co_4(CO)_{12}$. Like $Fe_3(CO)_{12}$, $Co_4(CO)_{12}$ is also disordered in the solid. Again this disorder reflects the different orientations of the metal poly-hedron with the CO-icosahedron from molecule to molecule in the solid lattice. But remember all molecules possess the same C_{3v} symmetry although the crystal symmetry is lower. In this compound, structural analysis (X-ray) reveals that one cobalt atom differs from the other three in that it is bonded to three terminal CO ligands (Figure 6.9). For this structure there are three equivalent *pseudo-C_3* axes passing through the basal cobalt atoms and one unique C_3 axis passing through the apical cobalt atom. In the solid, libration about any one of the three pseudo axes leads to terminal-bridge interchange and limited carbonyl equilibration. At higher temperatures libration about all four C_3 axes leads to further—but not complete—equilibration of the CO ligands in the solid. In solution this will lead to total equilibration. Just as with $Fe_3(CO)_{12}$ this motion will be accompanied by a breathing motion of the carbonyl icosahedron towards a cube-octahedral transition state, Figure 6.9. As the temperature is raised this will lead, eventually, to a com-plete icosahedral ⇔ cube-octahedral interchange and the complete equilibration of all carbonyl ligands by CO exchange.

Placement of the Co_4 tetrahedron within the icosahedron has several possibil-ities. We shall consider the three most obvious, Figure 6.10. First, it is possible to achieve a T_d form in which all carbonyls are terminal. Rotation of the tetrahedron by 15° about any one of the four equivalent C_3 axes generates the observed C_{3v} form. Alternatively rotation about any one of the four C_2 axes generates a second T_d form in which four $Co(CO)_2$ units are linked by four face-centered carbonyl bridges. Of course libration between these two forms accounts for the fluxional

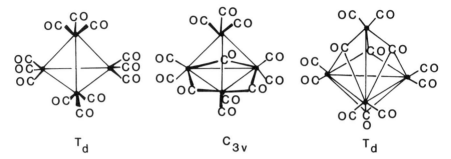

Figure 6.10 ▪ Three potential isomers of $Co_4(CO)_{12}$.

behavior in the solid state. However, unlike $Fe_3(CO)_{12}$, no evidence for this alternative isomer (or any other) has been found although low temperature infrared studies for crystalline samples indicate that some structural change does occur.

6.6. Fragmentation

Strictly speaking, a fragmentation reaction of a cluster is the reaction whereby a cluster unit breaks up into smaller subunits. However, we will, to a certain extent, include in our discussion the reaction steps subsequent to the fragmentation step. The reason for this is that at least some of the subunits formed from a fragmentation reaction are usually highly reactive species and so cannot be isolated. The identity of all the products from the fragmentation step can often only be inferred from the products of the subsequent, low activation energy, steps. Thus the fragmentation of clusters is frequently observed but the processes by which it occurs have not been examined in any detail. In general, work has been mainly restricted to organometallic or more specifically carbonyl clusters and we will therefore restrict our attention to these.

Fragmentation of carbonyl clusters occurs because they are thermodynamically unstable with regard to their monometal or possibly bimetal counterparts. This statement is of little use for determining whether or not a cluster may fragment since, in contrast to normal molecular structures, thermodynamic bond energies are not readily available. Some effort[31] has been made in the establishment of values for M—CO in its various bonding modes, that is, terminal or bridging. As might be expected from the fluxional nature of transition metal cluster compounds, there is often little difference in the overall value Σ M—CO for different modifications (structures) of this same molecule. However, absolute values of E_{M-C} are difficult to establish. Certainly there is a systematic increase in value on descending a transition-metal series. The tendency for carbide formation on electron impact which increases in the order third row $>$ second row $>$ first row almost certainly reflects this. But quoted bond energy values must be regarded with some caution. There is no good reason why a mononuclear species with five M—CO bonds should have an E_{M-C} value which is the same as the E_{M-C} value for a cluster $M_3(CO)_{12}$ just as E_{P-Cl} in PCl_3 is different from E_{P-Cl} in PCl_5. We expect M—CO to change according to the nuclearity of the cluster and the number of M—CO bonds involved.

The establishment of E_{M-M} values is even more problematic and one must consider whether such a value has any meaning. For relatively simple systems, for example $Os_3(CO)_{12}$, it is not unreasonable to assume three Os—Os direct bonds corresponding to triangular edges. It is less reasonable to assume edge bonds in most other metallic polyhedra. We have discussed this problem in Section 6.3 of this chapter. The difficulty is then in obtaining reliable estimates for interactions in a whole range of different metal polyhedra in which both the coordination number of the metal atom and the M—M distances involved vary. The problem is compounded by our restricted view of the nature of this metal-metal bond. Views of bonding developed for normal main group compounds must be reconsidered before application to transition metal systems. In order to illustrate this particular aspect we will consider the compounds formed by carbon and compare the bonding with that between transition metals. Carbon may form at least six types of C—C single bonds. These may be viewed in the language of hybridization simply as

   (i) an sp^3-sp^3 combination as in H_3C-CH_3
   (ii) an sp^3-sp^2 combination as in $H_3C-CH=CH_2$
   (iii) an sp^3-sp combination as in $H_3C-C{\equiv}CH$
   (iv) an sp^2-sp^2 combination as in $H_2C=CH-CH=CH_2$
   (v) an sp^2-sp combination as in $H_2C=CH-CH{\equiv}CH$
   (vi) an $sp-sp$ combination as in $HC{\equiv}CH-CH{\equiv}CH$

These C—C "single" bonds are clearly different, and one might reasonably expect a difference in both C—C bond energy and bond distance from (i) to (vi). In fact, this distance is remarkably constant ($\sim 5\%$ variation), which allows C—C distances or bond energies to be considered as transferable parameters for a whole variety of different organic molecules, and as a consequence firm predictions of stability and reaction mechanisms are possible. This is not the case for polymetallic clusters.

Transition metal atoms or ions in clusters contribute a wide range of coordination number, have different types of bonding and all the complexities introduced by d electrons. They have available at least nine atomic orbitals for chemical bonding not only in the formation of metal-metal links but also for metal-ligand bonds. Thus, if we now examine the orbital combinations which may lead to metal-metal bond formation we are obliged to consider a far more comprehensive range of (for simplicity) hybridized states (assuming such a description has any validity), for example sp^3, dsp^3, dsp^2, d^2sp^3, etc. It is possible, just as with carbon, that these different combinations, for example sp^3-sp^3 or dsp^2-sp^3, that might arise will not lead to much variation in either bond length or bond energy. But this is unlikely given the difference between d electrons, and s and p electrons, and is borne out by experimental observation. There is a wide range of metal-metal distances recorded for different combinations of the same metal in clusters (Table 6.1).

This problem is not restricted to single bonds. The whole concept of bond multiplicity, at least as applied to cluster systems, is problematic. In carbon chemistry, there is good evidence to support the concept of bond multiplicity. The values of C—C bond distances show the expected decrease $C-C > C=C > C{\equiv}C$ and the chemistry of C_2H_6, C_2H_4, and C_2H_2 is fully in accord with this idea of bond multiplicity. However, in transition metal clusters the situation is different. First, there can be no definitive value for a metal-metal "single" bond in clusters because, as we argued previously, different types of single bonds are possible,

Table 6.1 ▪ Some Metal-Metal Distances in Transition Metal Clusters

Cluster	M—M Distances in Å					
$Os_3(CO)_{12}$	2.886	2.873	2.884			
$H_2Os_3(CO)_{11}$	2.989	2.91	2.857			
$Os_5(CO)_{16}$	2.738	2.889	2.749	2.866	2.764	
$Os_6(CO)_{18}$	2.780	2.829	2.816	2.757	2.808	2.802
	2.732	2.806	2.789	2.800	2.836	2.806
$H_2Re_2(CO)_8$	2.90					
$H_2Re_3(CO)_{12}{}^-$	3.173	3.181	3.035			
$H_3Re_3(CO)_{10}{}^{2-}$	3.031	3.031	2.797			
$HRe_3(CO)_{12}{}^{2-}$	3.00	3.00	3.14			
$Re_4(CO)_{16}{}^{2-}$	2.956	2.982	3.024			

even if one accepts that there is such a thing as a single M—M bond. Obviously the problem becomes more acute when one attempts to examine double bonds or bonds of greater multiplicity. That is not to say they do not exist, but the definition of a multiple bond is even more difficult than a single bond. The problem is deciding whether or not a multiple M—M bond is present. Bond distance cannot be a good criterion, since, as we have already explained and which is obvious from a consideration of Table 6.1, this may vary widely even for a so-called single bond. Usually the decision is made on the basis of the electron-counting arguments (which were outlined in Section 6.3), despite their limitations.

In $H_2Os_3(CO)_{10}$ which we deduced in Section 6.3 to have four Os—Os bonds, i.e. one double and two singles, one triangular edge is substantially shorter than the remaining two:[32] some evidence in support of a double bond. But, it is worth noting that in $Fe_3(CO)_{12}$, for which no multiple bonds are predicted, one triangular edge is substantially shorter than the other two,[24a] suggesting the restricted application of bond distance as a criterion of bond multiplicity or perhaps the inapplicability of the concept of bonds, single or multiple. In $H_4Re_4(CO)_{12}$ the six Re—Re tetrahedral edges are about the same length,[33] providing no evidence of double character despite the conclusions from electron-counting arguments that it has eight Re—Re bonds.

Thus, the problem of finding good E_{M-C} and E_{M-M} values is enormous both practically and conceptually. Strictly speaking we should consider only total system energies of reactant and potential products. However, as discussed in Section 6.3, it is also meaningful to consider total M—M bonding energy (cohesive energy), and M—L and L—L interaction energies. There are some general comments that can be made:

(i) M—C bond energies increase down a triad
(ii) M—M bond energies increase down a triad
(iii) The rate of increase in E_{M-C} is less than that of E_{M-M}.

In other words, the stability sequence, first row clusters < second row clusters < third row clusters holds.

Having established that it is difficult to be sure of the thermodynamic driving force in cluster systems we should remember that in any consideration of stability kinetic factors (i.e., the energy difference between reactant and transition state) play the dominant role. Thus, the apparent ease of decomposition of $Fe_3(CO)_{12}$ compared to that of $Os_3(CO)_{12}$[34] may be due more to the mechanism of decomposition, and the energies of the transition states, than the varying bond energies of reactant and products from the two systems. Apparently similar systems may favor different pathways for reasons that are not obvious.

The thermal decomposition of the carbonyls follows different pathways according to the metal involved. Tri-iron dodecacarbonyl, for example, yields $Fe(CO)_5$ and ultimately iron metal[34]

$$Fe_3(CO)_{12} = Fe(CO)_5 + \text{``}Fe_2(CO)_7\text{''}$$

$$Fe(CO)_5 = Fe + 5CO$$

$$\text{``}Fe_2(CO)_7\text{''} = 2Fe + 7CO$$

with the fragmentation reaction only being the first and rate-determining step. In contrast, $Ru_3(CO)_{12}$ yields $Ru_6C(CO)_{17}$, and $Os_3(CO)_{12}$, $Os_6(CO)_{18}$.[36] In neither of these cases has the mechanism of decomposition been established although it has been postulated that the first step involves the same process,[34]

$$M_3(CO)_{12} = M(CO)_5 + \text{``}M_2(CO)_7\text{''}$$

the driving force being provided by the stability of the $M(CO)_5$ species. The second unconfirmed product $M_2(CO)_7$ would be highly unsaturated and expected to undergo reaction rapidly. One such reaction might be dimerization:

$$2\text{``}M_2(CO)_7\text{''} = M_4(CO)_{14}$$

The new dimer in turn might undergo similar fragmentation:

$$M_4(CO)_{14} = M(CO)_5 + \text{``}M_3(CO)_9\text{''}$$

Again dimerization of the highly unsaturated second product would be expected:

$$2\text{``}M_3(CO)_9\text{''} = M_6(CO)_{18}$$

In a complex thermal reaction other products would be expected, for example,

$$M_2(CO)_7 + M_3(CO)_9 = M_5(CO)_{16}$$

This scheme conveniently "fits" the products observed from the degradation of $Os_3(CO)_{12}$ but not that of Fe or Ru.[34] For ruthenium the formation of carbide must involve the following process:

$$2CO = \text{``}C\text{''} + CO_2$$

which must be a metal-mediated process and clearly illustrates that the delicate balance of transition state energies dictates the sort of products observed. In other series the problem is less complex. For example, it would appear that all three dodecacarbonyls of the cobalt triad follow the same course:[34]

$$M_2(CO)_8 = M_4(CO)_{12} \rightarrow M_6(CO)_{16}$$

In this series the initial unsaturated product may be formed by simple CO dissociation:

$$M_2(CO)_8 = \text{``}M_2(CO)_7\text{''} + CO$$

Although it is of interest to speculate on decomposition or fragmentation pathways, and certainly they may give some guidance to the nature of expected products, it will be exceedingly difficult to cstablish the nature of the reactive intermediates. On occasion it may be possible to rule out potentially active species. Thus, for a time, there was a generally held view that polymerization reactions proceeded via a radical mechanism. Certainly there is good evidence for the formation of radicals from both $Co_2(CO)_8$ and $Mn_2(CO)_{10}$:[35]

$$Co_2(CO)_8 = 2 \cdot Co(CO)_4$$

$$Mn_2(CO)_{10} = 2 \cdot Mn(CO)_5$$

However, in the case of $Os_3(CO)_{12}$, polymerization which is rapid at moderate temperatures is not initiated by irradiation. Certainly irradiation brings about the formation of active mononuclear species, probably an $Os(CO)_4$ diradical, since this may be trapped by a range of substrates, but polymerization does not occur.

$$Os_3(CO)_{12} + Os(CO)_4$$

These views lead us to the complex and vexing question of substitution reactions which forms the converse side of the fragmentation question. The reactions of mononuclear carbonyls have been shown to take place via a dissociative mechanism,[36] for example

$$Ni(CO)_4 = Ni(CO)_3 + CO$$

$$Ni(CO)_3 + L = Ni(CO)_3L$$

This ties in nicely with our views on bonding. A fully saturated system is not likely to undergo association to produce an electron-rich (20-electron) system, although this is not an absolute criterion as 20-selectron systems do exist, for example $(C_5H_5)_2Ni$.

Of course this process must also be available to polynuclear systems but the relative bond energies M—CO and M—M should be remembered and it has been argued that substitution reactions of $Mn_2(CO)_{10}$ proceeds by ligand dissociation at low temperatures and fragmentation at higher temperatures:[36]

$$Mn_2(CO)_{10} = 2Mn(CO)_5$$

$$Mn(CO)_5 + L = Mn(CO)_4L + CO$$

$$Mn(CO)_4L + Mn(CO)_5 = Mn_2(CO)_9$$

or

$$2Mn(CO)_4L = Mn_2(CO)_8L_2$$

For many systems, for example $Ru_3(CO)_{12}$, it would appear that both mechanisms may operate. Bond dissociation may occur to produce a highly active intermediate in which the nuclearity of the system is retained but the molecule is held together by a combination of M—M bonds and bridging groups at lower temperature; at higher temperatures M—CO bond dissociation may also occur. Much further work is necessary in this area and a greater range of molecules of increasing nuclearity should be studied.

6.7. Summary

In this chapter we have addressed three important facets of cluster chemistry—fluxional behavior, isomerization, and fragmentation. We have stressed that these phenomena are directly related and theoretically may be explored by symmetry considerations via the normal modes of the system. In reality, as we have emphasized, this application of symmetry theory to cluster molecules is not easy, and until more sophisticated computational methods are available even the simplest clusters containing three metal atoms—such as $Fe_3(CO)_{12}$—cannot be explicitly explored.

An important and natural consideration of any of these processes must involve a detailed understanding of the energies of the system involved. This means an appreciation of the various bond energies, in most cases $E_{metal\text{-}metal}$ and $E'_{metal-CO}$ (or more generally $E_{metal\text{-}ligand}$). At present this is a poorly understood area. There is a paucity of experimental data and the familiar concept of the direct chemical bond is difficult to apply. This being the case, attempts to predict chemical reactivity or reaction pathways are difficult. In this account an attempt to surmount this problem has been considered. This involves the use of "cohesive energy" which works well for metals and their alloys and may be extended to clusters and their derivatives. Cohesive energy, together with the symmetry considerations mentioned earlier, may lead to a firmer understanding of molecular rearrangement and fragmentation in these complex molecules.

Clusters may undergo any one of the three processes in any phase. Irrespective of the phase under consideration the processes involved will follow the same, symmetry-controlled laws. But, it must be remembered that in the solid there are strong intermolecular forces and the constraints of the crystalline lattice are the dominating influences rather than simple molecular symmetry and intramolecular forces. To some extent this is reflected in the changes in structure that many clusters undergo as they move from phase to phase. Nevertheless fluxional behavior, for example, apparently follows the same general pathways in all phases, except that the activation energies of the process will be different—although the differences will generally be quite small.

References

1. R. G. Pearson, *Symmetry rules for chemical reactions*, New York: John Wiley and Sons, 1976.
2. A. Rodger and P. E. Schipper, *Chem. Phys.*, 1986, **107**, 329.
3. A. Rodger and B. F. G. Johnson, *Polyhedron*, 1988, **7**, 1107.
4. C. E. Anson, R. E. Benfield, A. W. Bott, B. F. G. Johnson, D. Braga and E. A. Marseglia, *J. Chem. Soc. Chem. Comm.*, 1988, 889.
5. K. Wade, in *Transition metal clusters*, B. F. G. Johnson (Ed.). New York: John Wiley and Sons, 1980, Ch. 3 and references therein.
6. B. F. G. Johnson and A. Rodger, *Inorg. Chim. Acta*, 1988, **145**, 71.
7. D. G. Pettifor, in *Physical metallurgy*, R. W. Cahn and P. Haasen (Eds.). Amsterdam: Elsevier, 1983, Chap. 3 and references therein.
8. R. G. Woolley, in *Transition metal clusters*, B. F. G. Johnson (Ed.). New York: John Wiley and Sons, 1980, Chap. 9 and references therein.
9. R. G. Woolley, *Inorg. Chem.*, 1985, **24**, 3519.
10. B. F. G. Johnson, *J. Chem. Soc. Chem. Commun.*, 1986, 29.
11. A. J. Stone, *Inorg. Chem.*, 1981, **20**, 563.
12. See e.g. R. E. Benfield and B. F. G. Johnson, *Trans. Met. Chem.*, 1981, **6**, 131 and references therein.
13. D. Benfield, D. Braga and B. F. G. Johnson, *Polyhedron*, 1988, **7**, 2549.
14. B. T. M. Willis and A. W. Pryor, *Thermal vibrations in crystallography*, London: Cambridge University Press, 1975.
15. D. Braga and B. J. Heaton, *J. Chem. Soc. Chem. Commun.*, 1987, 608.
16. J. H. Ammeter, H. B. Burgi, E. Camp, V. Meyer-Sandrin and W. P. Jensen, *Inorg. Chem.*, 1979, **18**, 733; A. Chandrasekhar and H. B. Burgi, *Acta Cryst.*, 1984, **B40**, 387.
17. C. P. Brock and J. D. Dunitz, *Acta Cryst.*, 1968, **B24**, 63; A. Kvick, W. M. Canning, T. F. Koetzle and G. J. B. Williams, *Acta Cryst.*, 1980, **B36**, 115; P. Seiler and J. D. Dunitz, *Acta Cryst.*, 1979, **B35**, 2020; ibid, 1980, **B36**, 2946.
18. G. G. Sumner, H. P. Klug and L. E. Alexander, *Acta Cryst*, 1964, **17**, 732.
19. F. A. Cotton and J. M. Troup, *J. Am. Chem. Soc.*, 1974, **96**, 4155.
20. S. Aime and L. Milone, *Progress in NMR Spectroscopy*, 1977, **11**, 183.
21. J. K. M. Sanders and B. K. Hunter, *Modern NMR spectroscopy*, Oxford University Press, 1987, p. 47.
22. See e.g. E. Bond and E. L. Muetterties, *Chem. Rev.*, 1978, **78**, 639.
23. (a) S. Aime, O. Gambino, L. Milone, E. Sappa and E. Rosenberg, *Inorg. Chim. Acta*, 1975, **15**, 53; (b) A. Forster, B. F. G. Johnson, J. Lewis, T. W. Matheson, B. H. Robinson and W. G. Jackson, *J. Chem. Soc. Chem. Commun.*, 1974, 1042.
24. (a) F. A. Cotton and D. L. Hunter, *Inorg. Chim. Acta*, 1974, **11**, L9; (b) B. F. G. Johnson, *J. Chem. Soc. Chem. Commun.*, 1976, 703.
25. (a) J. R. Boehm and A. L. Balch, *Inorg. Chem.*, 1977, **16**, 778; (b) J. P. Jesson and P. Meakin, *J. Am. Chem. Soc.*, 1974, **96**, 5760.

26. C. H. Wei, G. R. Wilkes and L. F. Dahl, *J. Am. Chem. Soc.*, 1967, **89**, 4792.
27. G. F. Stuntz and J. R. Shapley, *J. Am. Chem. Soc.*, 1977, **99**, 607.
28. K. Knoll, G. Huttner, L. Zsolnai and O. Orama, *Angew. Chem. Int. Ed. Engl.*, 1986, **25**, 1119.
29. A. Rodger and P. E. Schipper, *Inorg. Chem.*, 1988, **27**, 458.
30. C. J. Wei and L. F. Dahl, *J. Am. Chem. Soc.*, 1969, **91**, 1351; F. A. Cotton and J. M. Troup, *J. Am. Chem. Soc.*, 1974, **96**, 4155.
31. M. Poliakoff and J. Turner, *J. Chem. Soc. Chem. Commun.*, 1970, 1005 and references therein.
32. A. G. Orpen, A. V. Rivera, E. G. Bryan, D. Pippard, G. M. Sheldrick and K. D. Rouse, *J. Chem. Soc. Chem. Commun.*, 1978, 723.
33. R. Bau, S. W. Kirtley, T. N. Sorrell and S. Winarko, *J. Am. Chem. Soc.*, 1974, **96**, 998.
34. J. Lewis and B. F. G. Johnson, *Advances in Inorganic Chemistry*, Emeleus and Sharpe (Ed.), 1981, **24**, 225.
35. See *Comprehensive organometallic chemistry*, G. Wilkinson and F. G. A. Stone (Eds.). Oxford, 1982, Vol. 4, p. 6.
36. J. D. Atwood, *Inorganic and organometallic reaction mechanisms*, Brooks and Cole, 1985.

Cluster Complexes as Homogeneous Catalysts and Catalyst Precursors

Wayne L. Gladfelter and Kevin J. Roesselet

7.1. Introduction

Among the numerous reasons for the excitement in the area of metal cluster chemistry has been the interest in probing their capabilities as homogeneous catalysts. Very reasonable arguments have been put forth as to why the potential of a cluster should be great for certain types of reactions.[1-3] Reactions requiring a considerable degree of change in ligand environment for one metal, for instance the successive addition of several units of H_2 to a substrate, might be aided by the presence of adjacent metals. Novel bonding modes that are available could lead to new reactions or low energy routes for known transformations. We will examine details of selected studies of catalytic reactions involving a variety of substrates. Reviews of the experimental work in cluster catalyzed reactions have appeared.[4,5,6]

The majority of compounds discussed in this chapter have three or more metal atoms with some evidence of direct metal-metal bonds. The question of the existence of such bonds in the presence of bridging ligands always clouds the issue, but no differentiation is made here. Several significant reactions involving dinuclear species are also discussed.

The organization of the chapter is based on the structure of the cluster involved in the catalysis. Considering the wide variety of structures possible with metal clusters, some clarification of this is in order. The first section involves studies of clusters that are saturated in their stable state and for which the metals are bound together primarily through the M—M bonds. As will be seen, most of the clusters of this type are hydrido carbonyl clusters. The second group of clusters are those which have a bridging ligand capable of enforcing the nuclearity of the cluster. Among the ligands most valuable in this class of clusters are alkylidyne and phosphinidene groups. The third group of clusters is comprised of compounds that are electronically unsaturated in their stable state and those which are activated photochemically or by the addition of some other promoter that leads to a catalytically active unsaturated species. This section also includes some of the examples of using clusters as a stable source of active monomers.

Within each of these sections the various catalytic reactions observed for the particular class of clusters will be described. The final section of the chapter describes some of the comparisons between the reactivity of clusters and monomers. Some brief comments on the methods used to establish the nuclearity of the catalytically active species will be included.

7.2. Classification of Catalyst Precursors Based on Structure

7.2.1. Binary Metal Carbonyl and Hydrido Carbonyl Clusters

Perhaps because of their ready availability, most of the studies using clusters as catalyst precursors have utilized this class of compounds, especially $Ru_3(CO)_{12}$, $Rh_4(CO)_{12}$, $H_4Ru_4(CO)_{12}$, $[HRu_3(CO)_{11}]^-$, and some mixed-metal analogs such as $H_2FeRu_3(CO)_{13}$ and $H_3NiRu_3Cp(CO)_9$. All of these compounds are thermally stable; several are stable in air. As described elsewhere in this book they can be prepared in good yields and in large quantities.

7.2.2.1. Water-Gas Shift Catalysis

Equation (7.1) shows the reaction of water and CO which can be catalyzed by a large number of metal carbonyls.[6]

$$H_2O + CO \rightarrow H_2 + CO_2 \tag{7.1}$$

The most detailed studies involving cluster carbonyls have been reported for ruthenium. $Ru_3(CO)_{12}$ itself is insoluble in aqueous media; it does, however, react under such conditions to form polynuclear anionic hydrido complexes such as $[HRu_3(CO)_{11}]^-$ and $[H_3Ru_4(CO)_{12}]^-$. The formation of these anions involves the well-known nucleophilic attack of hydroxide on a coordinated carbonyl ligand. The intermediate metal carboxylic acid (or metal carboxylate ion) rapidly loses CO_2 leading to a metal hydride or a carbonylmetalate, depending on the pH of the solution and the pKa of the M—H species (Scheme 7.1).

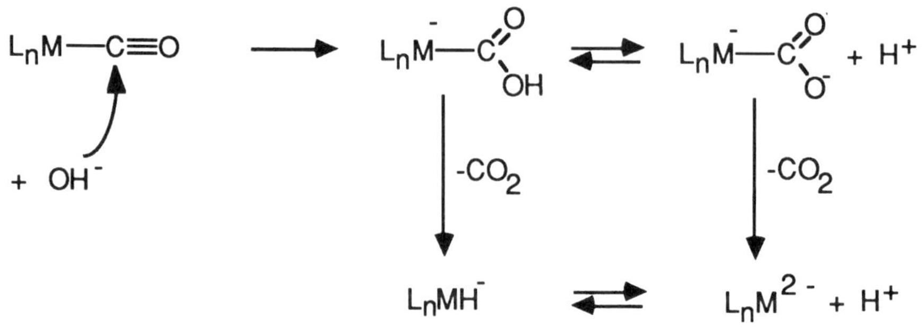

Scheme 7.1. Hydroxide Attack on Metal Carbonyls

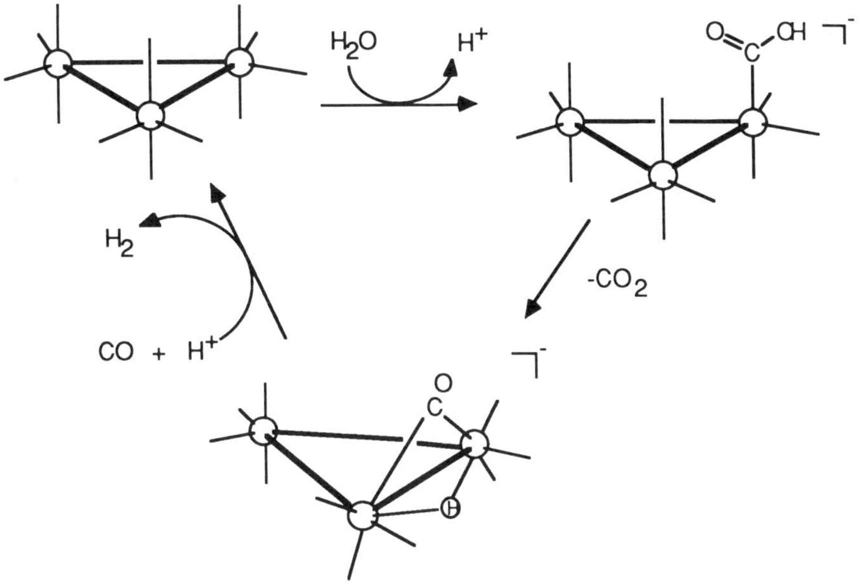

Scheme 7.2. Water-Gas Shift Catalysis Via Trinuclear Clusters

Much of the work by Ford and co-workers[7,8] focused on a variety of ruthenium carbonyl clusters [activity was also observed for $Ir_4(CO)_{12}$, $Re_2(CO)_{10}$, $H_3Re_3(CO)_{12}$, and $Rh_6(CO)_{16}$] as the catalyst precursors in alkaline, aqueous ethoxyethanol maintained at $100°C$ under 0.9 atm of CO. The rates were generally slow (around 3–4 turnovers/day), but the activity was long lasting. Only small differences in rates were observed among the three related clusters $Ru_3(CO)_{12}$, $H_2Ru_4(CO)_{13}$, and $H_4Ru_4(CO)_{12}$, and when normalized on the basis of the number of metal atoms, the rates were the same. Infrared and ^1H NMR spectroscopy of the solutions revealed the presence of $[HRu_3(CO)_{11}]^-$ and $[H_3Ru_4(CO)_{12}]^-$ in amounts that were dependent on the conditions of the reaction. The kinetics showed that the reaction was first order in total ruthenium concentration as well as in the partial pressure of CO. These results led Ford to propose mechanisms that were based on either a trinuclear cluster (Scheme 7.2), a tetranuclear cluster (Scheme 7.3), or some combination of both. The steps in Schemes 7.2 and 7.3 are based on known stoichiometric reactions.

In the course of studying the reactivity of $[HRu_3(CO)_{11}]^-$, Shore and co-workers provided strong evidence that the significant catalytic pathway involved the trinuclear cluster.[9–11] Central to the arguments was the discovery of the hydridic character of $[HRu_3(CO)_{11}]^-$ in the presence of a CO atmosphere. Especially relevant to the water-gas shift reaction was the observation of equation (7.2), and that no $Ru_3(CO)_{12}$ (and little H_2) were formed if CO is left out of the reaction.

$$[HRu_3(CO)_{11}]^- + H_2O + CO \rightarrow H_2 + Ru_3(CO)_{12} + OH^- \qquad (7.2)$$

The equilibrium between the K^+ salts of $[HRu_3(CO)_{11}]^-$ and $[H_3Ru_4(CO)_{12}]^-$,

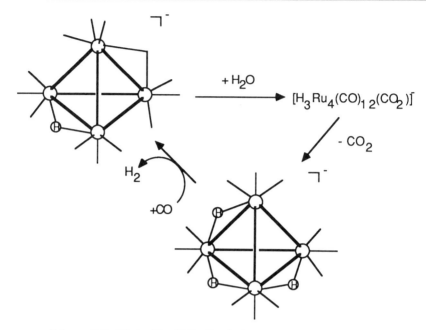

Scheme 7.3. Water-Gas Shift Catalysis Via Tetranuclear Clusters

equation (7.3) (which probably proceeds through $[HRu_4(CO)_{13}]^-$), was observed and provides a ready path from trinuclear to the tetranuclear clusters.

$$[H_3Ru_4(CO)_{12}]^- + 3CO \rightarrow [HRu_3(CO)_{11}]^- + 1/3Ru_3(CO)_{12} + H_2 \quad (7.3)$$

In a very clever experiment Shore placed a heated Pd disk between the catalytic reactor and a Toepler pump.[10] Since Pd metal is selectively permeable towards H_2, the equilibrium shown in equation (7.3) was driven to the right. When this was conducted with an active catalyst solution, only $[HRu_3(CO)_{11}]^-$ was observed by spectroscopy and the activity of the solutions increased.

Under these basic conditions Ford and co-workers[12] noted that the mixed-metal cluster, $H_2FeRu_3(CO)_{13}$, gave the most active solutions (around 10 turnovers/day based on the concentration of the original cluster). Similar rates were obtained from mixtures of $Fe(CO)_5$ and $Ru_3(CO)_{12}$ or $H_4Ru_4(CO)_{12}$, and the infrared spectra of the solutions indicated that the species present in basic media were the same regardless of the catalyst precursor. The nature of the activating influence of iron remains unknown, but it seems likely that species such as $[HFeRu_3(CO)_{13}]^-$ and $[H_3FeRu_3(CO)_{12}]^-$ are involved in the catalytic cycle.

Ruthenium complexes in acidic solution also catalyze the water-gas shift reaction, but the nature of the species present is not well established. Based primarily on the ^1H NMR chemical shift of the most abundant species present in the catalytically active solutions, Ford and co-workers[13] proposed that a dinuclear intermediate containing a bridging hydride was present. Under the standard conditions of their experiment ($[Ru]_{total} = 0.036\ M$, $P_{CO} = 0.9$ atm, $T = 100°C$, $[H_2SO_4] = 0.25$

M, $[H_2O] = 8.0\ M$, diglyme solvent), the presence of cationic metal carbonyl complexes was suggested, and they proposed the formulation $[HRu_2(CO)_{9-x}(OR_2)_x]^+$, where OR_2 represents diglyme or H_2O. The currently proposed catalytic cycle involves dinuclear cations and neutral species throughout.

7.2.1.2. Olefin Hydrogenation and Isomerization with $H_4Ru_4(CO)_{12}$ and Its Close Relatives

The tetraruthenium cluster, $H_4Ru_4(CO)_{12}$, has been used as a homogeneous catalyst in many studies. In this section the work involving the parent cluster is described as well as the numerous studies involving its phosphine-substituted analogs. Also included in this section are the studies of isoelectronic tetranuclear clusters that have been shown to hydrogenate and isomerize olefins catalytically.

Ethylene Hydrogenation with $H_4Ru_4(CO)_{12}$ The work of Doi and co-workers[14] on the hydrogenation of ethylene using $H_4Ru_4(CO)_{12}$ is the best starting point because of the simplicity of the substrate (no isomerization can occur) and the completeness and quantitative nature of the kinetic investigation. The glass apparatus used in the experiments allowed the introduction of the gases into the closed system, and the rate of the reaction was monitored by periodic analysis of the reactant and product using gas chromatography. Typical conditions (which could be precisely controlled and monitored during the reaction) were $T = 72°C$, $P_{H_2} = 100$ torr, $P_{C_2H_4} = 100$ torr, $[H_4Ru_4(CO)_{12}] = 0.4$ mM, solvent = heptane (5 mL), and gave a rate of 0.58 turnovers/min. The results indicated the catalysis:

1. was first order in $[H_4Ru_4(CO)_{12}]$,
2. exhibited saturation kinetics for increasing pressures of both H_2 and C_2H_4, and
3. was inversely dependent on the pressure of added CO.

Experiments involving D_2 gave a value of k_H/k_D of 1.22, but also showed that H/D exchange on the cluster and the ethylene was an order of magnitude faster than the rate of hydrogenation. The sequence of chemical reactions shown in equations (7.4) through (7.7) was used to model quantitatively the kinetic results.

$$H_4Ru_4(CO)_{12} \rightleftarrows CO + H_4Ru_4(CO)_{11} \tag{7.4}$$

$$H_4Ru_4(CO)_{11} + H_2 \rightleftarrows H_6Ru_4(CO)_{11} \tag{7.5}$$

$$H_4Ru_4(CO)_{11} + C_2H_4 \rightleftarrows H_3Ru_4(CO)_{11}(C_2H_5) \tag{7.6}$$

$$H_3Ru_4(CO)_{11}(C_2H_5) + H_2 \rightarrow H_4Ru_4(CO)_{11} + C_2H_6 \tag{7.7}$$

In essence, the vacant site created by CO dissociation from $H_4Ru_4(CO)_{12}$ can be reversibly scavenged by H_2, equation (7.5), or CO, equation (7.4), but productive catalysis occurs only after the reversible insertion of C_2H_4 into the Ru—H bond, equation (7.6). This step is followed by the rate-determining hydrogenolysis of the ethyl group, equation (7.7). Independent evidence supporting the reversible formation of $H_6Ru_4(CO)_{11}$, equation (7.5), was obtained by examining the electronic absorption spectrum of $H_4Ru_4(CO)_{12}$ under H_2. The reversible shift from 366 to 373 nm under hydrogen is consistent with a reaction occurring, but it unfortunately yields no data addressing the formula or structure of the product.

Other Hydrogenations and Isomerizations with $H_4Ru_4(CO)_{12}$ Chronologically, most of the catalytic studies involving higher alkenes and $H_4Ru_4(CO)_{12}$ were reported prior to the ethylene study described earlier. It is, however, particularly interesting to review these earlier qualitative to semiquantitative data in light of the previous mechanism. We should mention that various aspects of this mechanism, especially the intermediacy of $H_4Ru_4(CO)_{11}$ and $H_3Ru_4(CO)_{11}(R)$, were suggested[15-17] prior to the work of Doi and co-workers, but not supported with any quantitative treatment.

A general observation is that replacement of the hydrogens on ethylene with alkyl or aryl groups slows all alkene reactions. While numbers are difficult to come by, it appears that the rate of isomerization of 1-pentene to *cis*- and *trans*-2-pentene is approximately 1 turnover/min, and that hydrogenation is observable but much slower. This value was obtained under similar conditions to those used for ethylene except for the absence of H_2; under H_2 the rate of isomerization was even slower [consistent with the unproductive formation of a species such as $H_6Ru_4(CO)_{11}$]. In all studies using $H_4Ru_4(CO)_{12}$ as a catalyst, CO inhibition was found, which is consistent with the initial step being reversible CO dissociation.

Both the nature and number of phosphine and phosphite ligands used to replace one to four of the carbonyls on $H_4Ru_4(CO)_{12}$ affect the rate of isomerization of 1-pentene. Scheme 7.4 shows the structures for the substituted series $H_4Ru_4(CO)_{12-n}(L)_n$ ($n = 1-4$).[18]

All of the monosubstituted clusters, $H_4Ru_4(CO)_{11}(L)$, were found to have greater activity [2–3 turnovers/min at 70°C for L = $P(OEt)_3$] than $H_4Ru_4(CO)_{12}$ itself, while all of the more highly substituted compounds exhibited greatly diminished activity. Within the series $H_4Ru_4(CO)_{11}(L)$ the isomerization rate increases in the order $PPh_3 < P(OPh)_3 < P(OEt)_3$. Mechanistic studies of CO substitution reactions on clusters have often shown that replacement of the first CO with a phosphine often increases the rate of substitution for the second CO by increasing the equilibrium constant for the second CO dissociation.[19] Such an effect could be responsible for the increased activity of $H_4Ru_4(CO)_{11}(L)$ compared to $H_4Ru_4(CO)_{12}$. The slower isomerization rates for larger ligands and the diminished activity for the multiply substituted clusters could easily be related to the increased crowdedness affecting steps such as the olefin insertion or the final hydrogenolysis of the Ru—R bond.

The rate of isomerization of 1-pentene by $H_4Ru_4(CO)_{11}(L)$ was also found to increase as the polarity of the solvent was increased.[20] Based on initial rates the following series was established; $CHCl_3 > C_6H_6 >$ toluene > cyclohexane > mesitylene. For L = $P(OEt_3)_3$, a sevenfold change in rate was found between $CHCl_3$ and mesitylene. The results were interpreted by invoking a solvent-assisted CO dissociation step.

Interpretation of the rates of the hydrogenation of alkynes by $H_4Ru_4(CO)_{12}$ and its substituted derivatives was complicated by irreversible reaction of the clus-

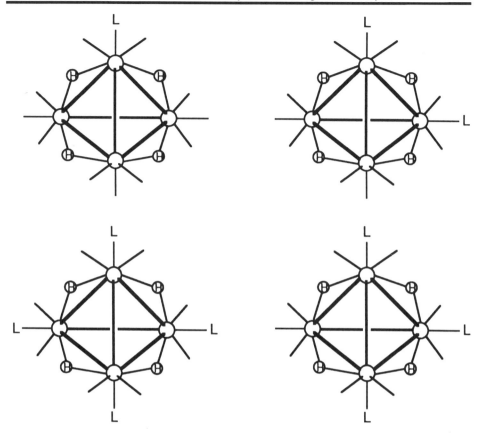

Scheme 7.4. Structures of $H_4Ru_4(CO)_{12-n}(L)_n$ ($n = 1-4$)

ter with the substrates.[21,22] The data obtained in the early reaction stages, however, is consistent with the earlier picture. Cyclohexanone hydrogenation was found to be catalyzed rapidly (10 turnovers/min) by $H_4Ru_4(CO)_{12}$ at 100°C and 100 atm of H_2 pressure in THF. Despite the vigorous conditions the catalyst was recovered unchanged, and a kinetic analysis revealed the reaction was first order with respect to the hydrogen pressure, the ketone concentration, and the concentration of the catalyst. The observed solvent dependence was so great that catalysis in hydrocarbon solvents was barely observable. Such a strong difference may imply the presence of polar or even ionic intermediates, consistent with the polar nature of the substrate itself.

The tetrasubstituted cluster, $H_4Ru_4(CO)_8[P(n\text{-Bu})_3]_4$, was found to catalyze the selective transfer of hydrogen from isopropanol to the C=O of α,β-unsaturated aldehydes.[23] Whereas the use of $Ru_3(CO)_{12}$, $H_4Ru_4(CO)_{12}$, and $[H_3Ru_4(CO)_{12}]^-$ resulted in low activity and conversion of the cluster into other species, $H_4Ru_4(CO)_8[P(n\text{-Bu})_3]_4$ was recovered unchanged. The higher activity (5 turnovers/h at 82°C) allowed a kinetic analysis to be completed. The rate law, rate $= k_{obs}[H_4Ru_4(CO)_8[P(n\text{-Bu})_3]_4][\text{crotonaldehyde}][\text{isopropanol}]/[P(n\text{-Bu})_3]$, suggested that $P(n\text{-Bu})_3$ dissociation from an intact cluster was important. Surprisingly, the use of d_8-isopropanol did lead to d_2-crotyl alcohol, but no H/D exchange with the cluster hydrides.

In the related $Ru_3(CO)_{12}$-catalyzed hydrogen transfer from isopropanol to benzylideneaniline ($PhCH=NPh$) to give acetone and N-benzylaniline, a rate of 16 turnovers/h at 82°C was found.[24] The intermediate, $HRu_3(\eta^2\text{-}\mu_3\text{-}PhN=CPh)(CO)_9$, was isolated and structurally characterized, and could be recharged in the catalytic reactor and quantitatively recovered.

Many clusters have been prepared recently based on the bonding analogy between a H^+ and a PPh_3Au^+ fragment. The clusters, $H_3Ru_4[M(PPh_3)](CO)_{12}$ and $H_2Ru_4[M(PPh_3)]_2(CO)_{12}$ where M=Cu and Au were found to catalytically isomerize 1-pentene to cis- and trans-2-pentene.[25] At 35°C the gold-containing clusters were found to be twice as active as $H_4Ru_4(CO)_{12}$ under identical conditions. The inhibition of this reaction by CO suggests a similarity to the mechanism of catalysis by $H_4Ru_4(CO)_{12}$. More work is necessary to understand how the gold is enhancing the rate.

Several studies on the use of $H_4Ru_4(CO)_8[(-)\text{-diop}]_2$ as a catalyst for the chiral reduction of organic carbonyl groups have appeared.[26–30] In some of these studies, questions regarding the nuclearity of these catalysts were not addressed, while in those involving the reduction of carboxylic acids, metal carbonyl phosphine acetates were the proposed intermediates.

Catalysis with Tetranuclear Clusters Isoelectronic with $H_4Ru_4(CO)_{12}$ The synthetic advances in cluster chemistry have led to a wide variety of tetrahedral structures having the same 60-electron count as $H_4Ru_4(CO)_{12}$, and several of these have been employed as homogeneous catalysts. One set of mixed-metal compounds that has been extensively studied contain a CpNi fragment replacing one of the $HM(CO)_3$ (M=Ru, Os) apices. $H_3NiRu_3Cp(CO)_9$, $H_3NiOs_3Cp(CO)_9$, and several of their phosphine-substituted derivatives were found to catalyze the isomerization and hydrogenation of alkenes, alkynes, and dienes.[31–34] The reactions were studied by charging individual ampules with the substrates, catalyst, and solvent (usually octane), and, after a given time at 120°C, the products were analyzed by gc and tlc. While it is very difficult to obtain usable kinetic information from this approach, an overview of the reaction can be developed. For instance, the presence of CO in the gas mixture always inhibited the reactions, and terminal olefins were much more readily hydrogenated than internal olefins. The osmium-containing cluster was robust and little decomposition was observed over several hours, whereas the ruthenium analog was extensively decomposed to several organometallics within 40 min. It is difficult to quote a turnover rate for a typical reaction because many of the values changed as a function of reaction time. Several of the reactions with slower rates appeared to have an induction period.

The cycle shown in Scheme 7.5 for hydrogenation was suggested and also shows one of the cluster degradation products. As in the earlier studies of $H_4Ru_4(CO)_{12}$, phosphine substitution had varying effects on the reaction rates. Once again, while the data are consistent with the cluster remaining intact during the catalytic cycle, it does not prove such is the case.

Perhaps the most interesting comparisons to $H_4Ru_4(CO)_{12}$ arise from results obtained in a study of the homonuclear osmium analog, $H_4Os_4(CO)_{12}$, and several

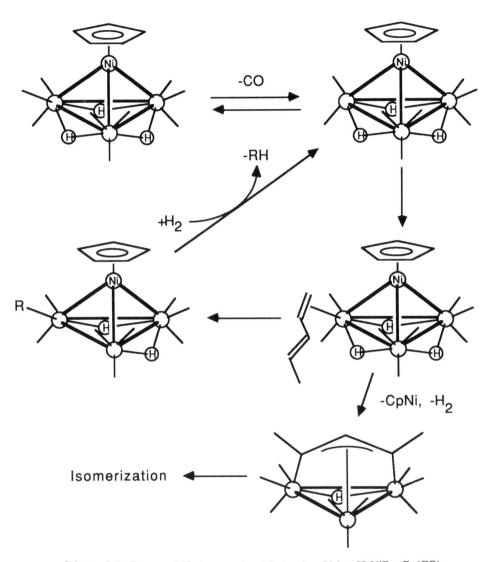

Scheme 7.5. Proposed Hydrogenation Mechanism Using H$_3$NiRu$_3$Cp(CO)$_9$

related tetranuclear osmium clusters.[35,36] In the kinetic study of the hydrogenation of styrene at 140°C and 800 torr of H$_2$, the catalysis rate was found to be first order in styrene and H$_2$ [at 1.2 M styrene and 0.112 mM H$_4$Os$_4$(CO)$_{12}$ the rate was 1.45 turnovers/min]. Unlike the ruthenium system, however, the rate of this reaction displayed a complex dependence on the concentration of the cluster which prevented the authors from making any quantitative evaluation of the mechanism. For both H$_4$Os$_4$(CO)$_{12}$ and H$_3$Os$_4$(CO)$_{12}$(I) (the latter being the most active of the clusters studied with a rate of 9.7 turnovers/min at the previous conditions) the turnover frequency increased as the concentration of the starting cluster was decreased. Because any equilibrium involving fragmentation should be more favored at lower total cluster concentrations, this was taken as evidence for the occurrence of fragmentation yielding highly active species of lower nuclearity. As with the ruthenium systems, added CO eventually inhibited the reaction.

The comparison between $H_4Ru_4(CO)_{12}$ and $H_4Os_4(CO)_{12}$ highlights some of the difficulties in this area. For instance, the osmium catalysis was found to be very sensitive to the reactor design and stirring rate, factors which affect the efficiency of H_2 transfer between the gas and solution phase. It may be that the complex dependence of the rate on the cluster concentration is related to this reactor design sensitivity. No such effect was found in the ruthenium system. Some of the differences between the Ru and Os clusters could also be due to the much higher temperature ($140°C$) and different substrate (styrene) used with $H_4Os_4(CO)_{12}$ compared to $H_4Ru_4(CO)_{12}$ (ethylene at $72°C$).

Interesting studies involving a number of mixed-metal clusters have also appeared. The initial rate for hydrogenation of styrene with $Co_2Rh_2(CO)_{12}$, for instance, was found to be about twice that for $Co_3Rh(CO)_{12}$, while $Co_4(CO)_{12}$ was inactive under the mild conditions used.[37] High activity and selectivity were likewise obtained for the hydrogenation of 2-cyclohexenone by $H_2Ru_2Rh_2(CO)_{12}$ relative to $H_4Ru_4(CO)_{12}$ and $Rh_4(CO)_{12}$.[38] The nature of the interplay of various metals in the cluster is not well understood.

7.2.1.3. Catalysis Involving $[HRu_3(CO)_{11}]^-$

Aside from the studies suggesting the involvement of $[HRu_3(CO)_{11}]^-$ in the water-gas shift catalysis, this anion has been used as a catalyst or catalyst precursor in several other reactions. A separate discussion of its role in the hydrogenation of CO at elevated temperatures and pressures is left to Section 7.2.3.5. Hydrogenation of ethylene and propylene (15 bar partial pressure) occurs at $25°C$ and 20 bar H_2 at an average rate of 0.5 turnover/min in DMF.[39,40] At the end of the reaction an unidentified red ruthenium carbonyl was present, which reverted back to $[HRu_3(CO)_{11}]^-$ upon being treated in an atmosphere of CO and H_2. As with other hydrogenations involving saturated carbonyl clusters, CO strongly inhibits the rate of hydrogenation. When, however, the temperature was raised, in the presence of CO, hydroformylation catalysis began. Under typical conditions ($100°C$, 26 bar CO, 13 bar H_2, 13 bar C_2H_4) the average rate was just over 1 turnover/min. With propylene the rate dropped by a factor of 20, and the normal to iso product ratio was in the range of 15 to 20.

A study of the deuterium distribution in propanal formed by the hydroformylation of ethylene using D_2 showed that the formyl hydrogen was 98% deuterated.[41] The methyl group was 70% to 80% monodeuterated and the methylene showed small amounts (5% to 12%) of deuterium incorporation. The catalytic cycle shown in Scheme 7.6 was proposed to account for the bulk of the deuterium distribution, and was also consistent with some stoichiometric reactions.

For instance, the reaction of C_2H_4 (3 atm) with $[HRu_3(CO)_{11}]^-$ at $25°C$ followed by protonation gave the fully characterized μ-acyl, $HRu_3[C(O)Et](CO)_{10}$,[42] presumably via the anion having the structure shown in the catalytic cycle. As with most hydroformylation studies, the deuterium labeling differences between the methyl and methylene carbons is primarily a reflection of the relative rates

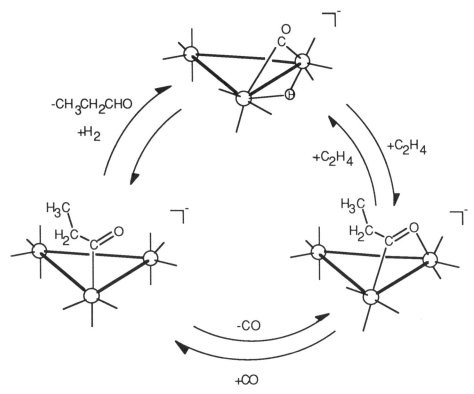

Scheme 7.6. Proposed Mechanism for the Hydroformylation of Olefins Using [HRu$_3$(CO)$_{11}$]$^-$

of reaction of the intermediate metal-alkyl. Rapid CO insertion into the M—R bond compared to the rate of β-hydrogen elimination will lead to regiospecific labeling on the methyl group and in the formyl position. As the authors pointed out, however, this labeling study is only consistent with a cluster-catalyzed reaction and does not exclude other processes. Further analysis of the mechanism will require careful kinetic studies.

Hydrosilylation, silacarbonylation,[40,43] and silyl formate[44] syntheses [equations (7.8), (7.9), and (7.10)] have been reported to be catalyzed by [HRu$_3$(CO)$_{11}$]$^-$ under conditions very similar to those reported earlier.

$$Et_3SiH + CH_2{=}CH_2 \rightarrow CH_3{-}CH_2{-}SiEt_3 + CH_2{=}CH{-}SiEt_3 \qquad (7.8)$$

$$CO + Et_3SiH + CH_2{=}CH_2 \rightarrow CH_3{-}CH{=}CHOSiEt_3 \qquad (7.9)$$

$$CO_2 + Et_3SiH \rightarrow Et_3Si{-}O{-}C(O)H \qquad (7.10)$$

Silanes such as Et$_3$SiH were found to react reversibly with [HRu$_3$(CO)$_{11}$]$^-$ according to equation (7.11), with the product having two sigma bound SiEt$_3$ ligands.

$$[HRu_3(CO)_{11}]^- + 2Et_3SiH \rightarrow [HRu_3(SiEt_3)_2(CO)_{10}]^- + H_2 + CO \quad (7.11)$$

While $[HRu_3(SiEt_3)_2(CO)_{10}]^-$ was proposed to be important in each of these reactions, relatively few details have yet been published on the chemistry of this interesting cluster.

Several reports have appeared describing the use of $[HRu_3(SiEt_3)_2(CO)_{10}]^-$, which is formed from $[HRu_3(CO)_{11}]^-$, for catalyzing novel chemical reactions involving alkyl isocyanates. In the following reaction, one of the isocyanate oxygens is removed by formation of the silanol while five isocyanates are coupled to give the [4,5] spiroheterocyles, equation (7.12).[45,45] The temperature of the reaction in THF was 120°C, and the time required depended on the R group of the isocyanate. With R = Me, a 41% yield was obtained after 25 h, whereas a comparable yield for R = n-Bu required 60 h.

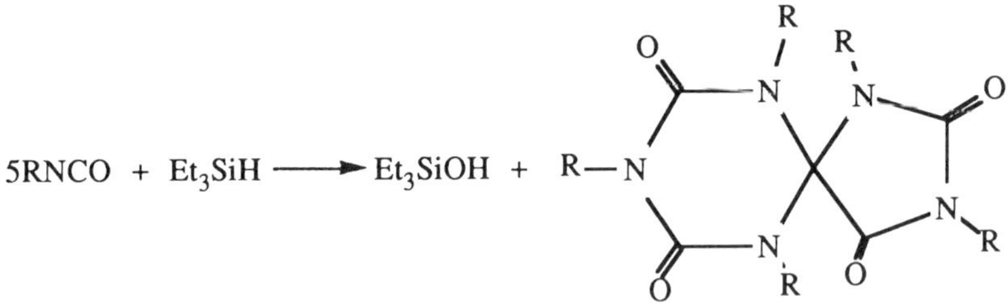

$$5RNCO + Et_3SiH \longrightarrow Et_3SiOH + R—N \quad (7.12)$$

Replacing Et_3SiH in equation (7.12) with H_2 (50 bar) and changing the catalyst to the tetranuclear anionic cluster, $[H_3Ru_4(CO)_{12}]^-$, resulted in the reductive coupling of only two isocyanates, equation (7.13).[47] After 20 h, 230 turnovers of MeNCO to the dimer were observed.

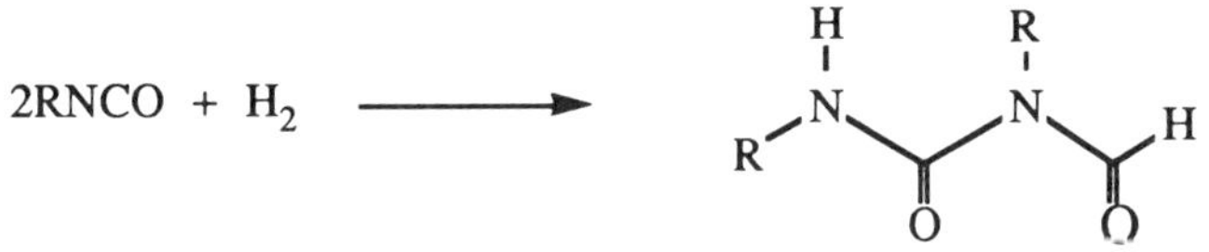

$$2RNCO + H_2 \longrightarrow \quad (7.13)$$

In an interesting extension of this, reductive coupling was found by adding phenylacetylene to the reaction. Under identical conditions approximately 50 turnovers 5-benzylidene hydantoins were formed in 24 h, equation (7.14).[48] Several polynuclear clusters of ruthenium were found to catalyze this reaction at similar rates, whereas $RuCl_3$ itself was inactive.

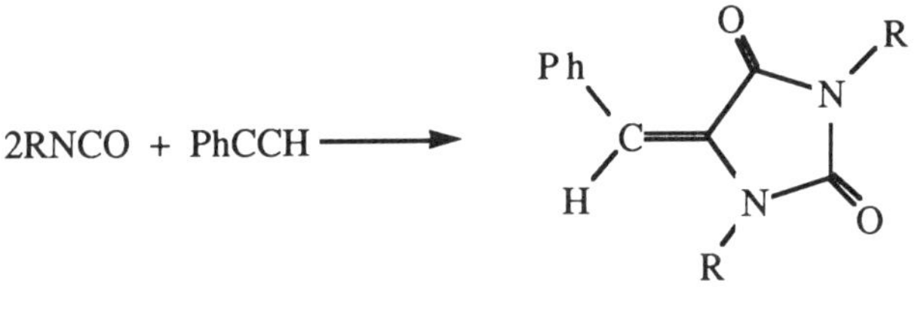

$$2RNCO + PhCCH \longrightarrow \quad (7.14)$$

At this point very little is known about the catalyst in these reactions. It is, however, noteworthy that several studies[49] of the reactions of alkyl isocyanates with hydrido clusters, specifically $H_2Os_3(CO)_{10}$, have found that insertion into the M—H bond does occur.

7.2.1.4. Oxidations using $Rh_6(CO)_{16}$

The cluster $Rh_6(CO)_{16}$ has been found to be an effective catalyst for the conversion of aliphatic ketones to carboxylic acids with molecular oxygen.[50–53] This reaction has been studied thoroughly and deserves mention as an example of the type of study necessary to establish meaningful mechanistic conclusions. The complex was initially found to catalytically oxidize CO to CO_2 in the presence of stoichiometric O_2, a reaction that occurred most efficiently in ketone solvents. Analysis of the active solutions revealed that they contained carboxylic acids derived from the solvent in yields that likewise indicated a catalytic reaction. In a typical reaction, $Rh_6(CO)_{16}$ (10^{-2} mmol) suspended in 10 mL cyclohexanone and stirred at 100°C under 34 atm pressure (3:1 O_2:CO) produced ~1000 mmol adipic acid.[50] The reaction was found, following initiation, to proceed at a rate independent of oxygen pressure and to be strongly inhibited by radical scavengers.[51] These results taken together suggest a free-radical mechanism. Careful analysis of the side products (especially lactone formation), temperature dependence, and solvent effects revealed no qualitative difference from data obtained from uncatalyzed runs, known to proceed via peracids. Similar results were obtained for reactions conducted with $Re_2(CO)_{10}$ as the catalyst. The overall mechanistic inference drawn was that the metal carbonyl species serves to accelerate the decomposition of the peracid rather than initiation via O_2 activation.[52]

The exact nature of the hexarhodium species under catalytic conditions has yet to be determined. The cluster is insoluble in cyclohexanone under ambient conditions, but becomes soluble during the reaction. Undissolved cluster could be filtered from these solutions; the filtrate remained catalytically active and homogeneous. At the end of a run the remaining red solution contained no $Rh_6(CO)_{16}$ initially, but the cluster could be regenerated by exposure to high temperatures and CO pressures. Careful analysis of the red solutions was not reported, but lower nuclearity carboxylate species were suggested as likely in the presence of the acid products.[51] Such a claim requires further investigation, however, in light of the observed increase in acid yields with increased mole fraction of CO.[53] While the higher CO pressures are liable to rupture Rh—Rh bonds, known rhodium carboxylate compounds are known to reform $Rh_6(CO)_{16}$ under such conditions. Thus, while the reaction is truly catalytic in cluster in the sense that it can be recovered from the reaction unchanged, some unidentified species is obviously responsible for the observed reactivity.

7.2.1.5. Hydrogenation of Carbon Monoxide

Some of the earliest interest in homogeneous catalysts arose from the notion that they might offer a way to selectively reduce CO. Such chemistry could produce hydrocarbons for use as fuels, or perhaps olefins or oxygenates for the synthesis of other chemicals. The use of heterogeneous catalysts continues to be actively explored for similar reductions, but generally suffers a lack of selectivity, save for the production of methane and methanol. The use of metal carbonyl clusters to catalyze this reaction can be broken into two regimes based upon the pressure at which the reaction is run. Reactions run at low pressures of CO tend to exhibit very low activity, which in many cases is thought to be due to the formation of metal. Alternatively, high H_2 and CO pressures achieve more reasonable rates, and it is in this area that homogeneous catalysts are most likely to play a role.

Union Carbide has been particularly active in this area, reporting several patented systems that lead to methanol, ethanol, and especially ethylene glycol.[54] In the rhodium chemistry, a typical reaction is run at 20,000 psig and 250°C. The precatalyst may be added in a variety of forms, $Rh(CO)_2(acac)$ or $Rh_6(CO)_{16}$, among others.[54,55] Although many minor products are observed, selectivity to oxygenates such as glycol is good. Spectroscopic studies of the reaction solutions indicated a mixture of high nuclearity carbonyls. Infrared investigation of a number of rhodium precursors [including the mononuclear $Rh(CO)_2(acac)$] at temperatures and pressures approaching the optimal catalytic conditions detected mainly $[Rh_5(CO)_{15}]^-$ and $[Rh(CO)_4]^-$. Increased temperatures broadened the spectra considerably, however, making any identification of the actual catalytic species ambiguous. An impressive series of high pressure ^{13}C NMR studies at lower temperatures ($<-40°C$) clearly indicate the pentanuclear cluster as the predominant carbonyl species.[56] A high resolution probe situated in a titanium alloy pressure vessel was especially constructed for these experiments. Further indication of the involvement of intact rhodium clusters is the observation that the robust species $[Rh_6C(CO)_{15}]^{2-}$, $[Rh_9P(CO)_{21}]^{2-}$, and $[Rh_{17}S_2(CO)_{32}]^{3-}$ [56,57] also catalyze polyol formation. While slower than the $Rh(CO)_2(acac)$ system, these reactions occurred at conditions mild enough that the charged clusters were the only detectable species by IR. Taken together, these results seem to imply cluster catalysis, but the detailed kinetic and mechanistic studies necessary to confirm this have yet to be reported. The broader application of such specialized spectroscopic techniques under extreme conditions will continue to be useful in this connection.

A second system deserving attention begins with a tetrairidium cluster precatalyst in $NaCl/AlCl_3$ melts.[58] Muetterties and co-workers initially found such systems capable of producing a number of aliphatic hydrocarbons with ethane as the predominant reaction product. This result may be contrasted with those obtained for $Ir_4(CO)_{12}$[59] in hydrocarbon solutions or for Ir metal[60] catalysts, both of which lead primarily to methane as the hydrocarbon product. The static reaction system investigated consisted of a 3:1 H_2:CO gas mixture over an $Ir_4(CO)_{12}$ catalyst (1:1000 cluster:CO) in molten $NaCl\cdot2AlCl_3$ solvent. Reactions were carried out at 180°C and 1.5 atm in sealed tubes and were essentially complete after 12 to 24 hours. Ethane to methane ratios fell from around 10:1 after 3 hours to 1:2 after 12 hours, an effect attributed to cracking by $AlCl_3$.

Later studies of this system under flow conditions have led to controversy over the mechanism of the hydrogenation. Muetterties first studied product distributions obtained by passing the gas mixture through the molten catalyst/salt bed.[58b] Saturated hydrocarbons ranging from C_1 to C_8 as well as HCl were detected, with propane and isobutane the major components. The distribution was dependent on temperature and flow rate; longer contact times (lower flow) resulted in higher yields of ethane, consistent with observations from the sealed tube reactions. The most significant mechanistic point in this report was the failure to detect methyl chloride in the product gases; likewise, added CH_3Cl had no effect on the reaction.

It is at this point that a serious discrepancy occurs—Collman and co-workers have found[61] that methyl chloride (probably derived from methanol) apparently plays an important role in the chemistry of the system. Attempts to reproduce the earlier flow reaction resulted in large amounts ($\sim$25%) of methyl chloride. More to the point, addition of CH_3Cl to the reagent gases resulted in enhanced activity: an immediate increase in methane production and a subsequent steady increase in ethane were observed. Additives such as formaldehyde and ethylene gave results that were similarly used to invoke these species as likely intermediates in hydrocarbon production. Larger yields of methane, slower overall rates, and the observations cited earlier led to the conclusion that the two systems had different catalysts, despite their close similarity.

There is other evidence that different catalysts may be responsible for this puzzling behavior, although the investigations make few definite comparisons as far as the nature of these species. There is support throughout for a homogeneous system: a number of heterogeneous iridium-based catalysts were demonstrated to show dramatically different behavior. Muetterties reports the recovery of some $Ir_4(CO)_{12}$ following the sealed tube reactions; infrared studies following the flow reactions indicated a new oxidized carbonyl species, a result confirmed by Collman. In this connection, it was found that $Ir(CO)_3Cl$ as a precursor not only led to an almost identical catalytic reaction, but also resulted in similar infrared spectra.

The role of aluminum halide is not rigorously addressed for these reactions, apart from its part as a rather unusual solvent. Collman's work in particular supports a chloroiridium carbonyl as the active catalyst, as well as the involvement of CH_3Cl. Aluminum trichloride obviously serves as the chloride source; it also serves as sole repository for the oxygen removed from carbon monoxide. Mechanistic involvement is less apparent than these stoichiometric concerns: an Ir—C—O—Al interaction to activate the CO bond is implied but has not been carefully studied. Considerations such as these should prove useful in future attempts to design catalytic systems and illustrate the potential for catalysis in nontraditional media.

A related system involves the hydrogenation of CO with $Os_3(CO)_{12}$ as catalytic precursor in molten boron tribromide.[62] Under sealed tube conditions as given previously, a mixture of hydrocarbons dominated by methane was observed. In this case, however, significant amounts of CH_3Br and CH_3CH_2Br were also detected. The final osmium-containing product was identified as $Os_2(CO)_6Br_2$, which produced similar hydrocarbon–alkyl bromide mixtures when used as the catalyst precursor. Initial rates are quite rapid, but decrease by an order of magnitude as the dimer becomes the predominant metal species in solution. It is tempting to propose an intact trinuclear catalyst for the faster regime, but solid evidence is lacking. Substitution of BCl_3 as the solvent gave only hydrocarbon products, consistent with the iridium/$AlCl_3$ system.

7.2.2. Clusters Stabilized by Strong Bridging Ligands

One class of compounds that merit attention contain bridging groups that are strongly bound to the metals. These groups often have the effect of maintaining the integrity of the cluster even under the forcing conditions often required for catalysis. This will be an important consideration in cases where the goal is an intact cluster catalyst in systems particularly hostile to metal-metal bonds, for

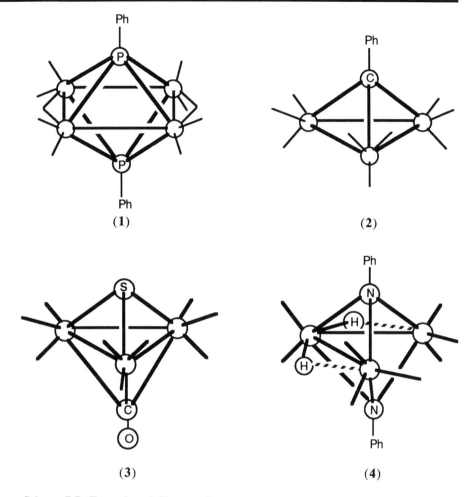

Ph

(1)

(2)

(3)

(4)

Scheme 7.7. Examples of Clusters Containing Strongly Bridging Ligands. 1) $Co_4(\mu_4$-PPh$)_2$(CO$)_{10}$, 2) $Co_3(\mu_3$-CPh)(CO$)_9$, 3) $Os_3(\mu_3$-S)(CO$)_{10}$, 4) $H_2Ru_3(\mu_3$-NPh$)_2$(CO$)_9$

example high pressures of CO. Several examples of such clusters will be examined in the following sections and are illustrated in Scheme 7.7.

7.2.2.1. Hydroformylation by Cobalt Alkylidyne and Phosphinidene Systems

The clusters $Co_4(\mu_4$-PPh$)_2$(CO$)_{10}$ (**1**) and $Co_3(\mu_3$-CPh)(CO$)_9$ (**2**) were found to be catalytically active under conditions typically used in hydroformylations by Co_2(CO$)_8$.[63] Conversion of 1- and 2-pentene to aldehydes, for example, occurred in a fairly high normal-to-branched ratio at temperatures around 100°C and pressures of 400 to 1200 psig. Several hydroformylations, however, were performed at milder conditions than those required for Co_2(CO$)_8$. Furthermore, the clusters were recovered in high yield after a large number of turnovers. While detailed spectroscopic and kinetic results were not reported, this evidence taken together seemed to indicate catalysis by the intact clusters. A subsequent study[64] involving $Co_4(\mu_4\text{-PPh})_2(CO)_8(PPh_3)_2$ and $Co_4(\mu_4\text{-PPh})_2(CO)_{10}$ lent support to this assertion, since the starting clusters were the only species detectable by HPLC or TLC following hydroformylation.

A related report[65] by Seyferth and co-workers should be compared with this system. As part of an attempt to evaluate polymers derived from $Co_3(\mu_3\text{-}CAr)(CO)_9$, $(Ar = p\text{-}C_6H_4C(O)C(CH_3)=CH_2, p\text{-}C_6H_4CH=CH_2)$, as hydroformylation catalysts, the $Co_3(\mu_3\text{-CPh})(CO)_9$ system was reevaluated. Under very similar conditions, however, only a moderate amount (40–60%) of the starting cluster was recovered. Infrared studies of the catalytic solutions, moreover, confirmed the presence of other metal carbonyls, most likely $Co_2(CO)_8$ and $HCo(CO)_4$. Experiments were carried out using $Co_2(CO)_8$ as the catalyst precursor in concentrations corresponding to those expected from the unrecovered alkylidyne cluster. No change in selectivity or IR spectral characteristics was observed relative to the results using the cluster precursor. The polymers derived from the functionalized clusters displayed the same activity as the discrete cluster system, further supporting cluster decomposition as the source of the actual catalyst.

The point of divergence in these systems is obviously the nuclearity of the catalyst. On one level, Seyferth's work illustrates the critical point that a minor concentration of a fragment with a much greater reactivity relative to the parent cluster may account for the observed catalysis, a topic which will receive further attention in Section 7.2.3.5. With respect to this particular set of studies, however, it may be unwise to implicate $Co_2(CO)_8$ (or some other fragment) as the catalyst in any of the cases except $Co_3(\mu_3\text{-CPh})(CO)_9$. Conditions inducing the partial decomposition of the alkylidyne clusters may not disrupt the bisphosphinidene systems, for instance, since the latter contain two strongly bridging ligands rather than one. This feature is emphasized by the addition of phosphines to catalytic runs using $Co_4(\mu_4\text{-PPh})_2(CO)_8(PPh_3)_2$ and $Co_4(\mu_4\text{-PPh})_2(CO)_{10}$.[64] Under the hydroformylation conditions used, $Co_2(CO)_8$ is known to form $HCo(CO)_3(PPh_3)$ and lead to high yields of alcohols. Very little alcohol is formed in the cluster reactions, however, and together with the aforementioned high yield of cluster recovery support the involvement of an intact catalyst.

Further investigations involving other trinuclear complexes,[66] however, appear to indicate that a single bridge may be sufficient to enforce cluster nuclearity in some cases. Hydroformylation reactions utilizing the heteronuclear clusters (5) through (10) appeared to lead to fragmentation for (10) only, a conclusion based on comparison to the activity of $Co_2(CO)_8$ and high yield isolation of the clusters as the sole metal-containing products. Styrene is hydroformylated by (5), (7), and (8); high cluster recovery and the mild 60°C reaction temperature make declusterification seem extremely unlikely.

Clearly the interplay of various structural features requires additional study. Work incorporating second row metals seems to indicate, for instance, that it may be possible to take advantage of stronger metal-metal bonds in these systems.[67,68] The maximum number of bridging ligands possible would appear to lend additional stability. Finally, potential involvement of the bridging ligand itself in the catalytic cycle is a poorly understood component.

In another connection, the studies cited in this section demonstrate some of the considerations involved in establishing cluster catalysis. While cluster recovery and structural information are important components, careful spectroscopic and kinetic studies are crucial. Comparative analysis of the activities of likely fragments, when known, with that of the cluster will also be fruitful, as demonstrated in this discussion and in a further example later in the chapter. Finally, it is important to critically examine some of the earlier claims of cluster catalysis with the object of establishing or disproving these claims with further data.

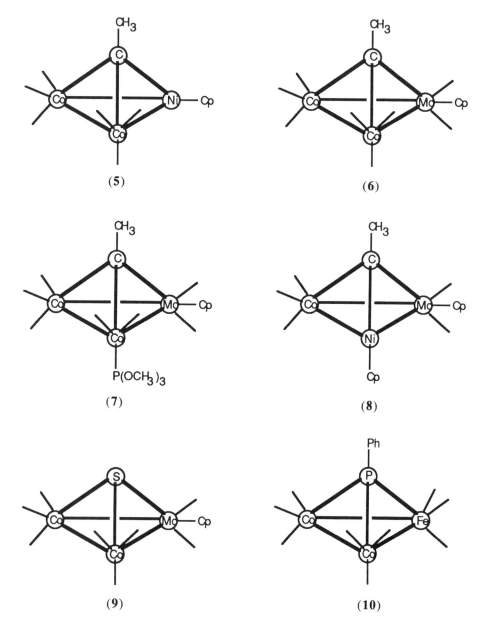

7.2.2.2. Hydrogenation by Heteronuclear Ruthenium Clusters

A wide variety of trinuclear clusters of the type $M_3(\mu_3\text{-}E)$, (**11**)–(**13**), have been investigated as possible hydrogenation catalysts.[67] For styrene and 2-pentene, turnover numbers ($\sim$2/h), mild conditions (60°C and 60 atm), and high recovery of the cluster were possible, provided E = PR and at least one ruthenium atom was present in the complex. The catalytically active clusters could be separated and reused, the active fractions being the parent complex and two others with the same cluster geometry formed by side reactions at the phosphorus ligand. Alkylidyne clusters were only active in cases where disruption to monomers occurred. Likewise, the sulfur-capped complexes (**13**) were much poorer catalysts, polymerizing the styrene substrate extensively.

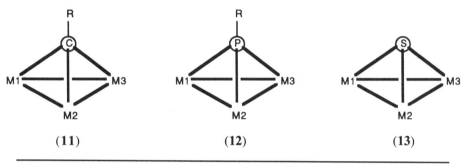

(**11**)   (**12**)   (**13**)

Compound	R	M1	M2	M3
11a	CH_3	$Co(CO)_3$	$Co(CO)_3$	$Co(CO)_3$
11b	CH_3	$Co(CO)_3$	NiCp	$MoCp(CO)_2$
11c	CH_3	$Co(CO)_3$	$FeH(CO)_3$	$MoCp(CO)_2$
12a	Ph	$RuH(CO)_3$	$RuH(CO)_3$	$Ru(CO)_3$
12b	Ph	$Ru(CO)_3$	$Co(CO)_3$	$Co(CO)_3$
12c	CH_3	$Ru(CO)_3$	$Co(CO)_3$	$Co(CO)_3$
12d	CH_3	$Ru(CO)_3$	$Ru(CO)_3$	$CoH(CO)_3$
12e	CH_3	$Ru(CO)_3$	$Fe(CO)_3$	$CoH(CO)_3$
12f	CH_3	$Fe(CO)_3$	$Fe(CO)_3$	$CoH(CO)_3$
12g	CH_3	$Fe(CO)_3$	$Co(CO)_3$	$WCp(CO)_2$
13a	—	$Ru(CO)_3$	$Co(CO)_3$	$Co(CO)_3$
13b	—	$Ru(CO)_3$	$Co(CO)_3$	$MoCp(CO)_2$

The conditions required for catalysis in this case are interesting. First, it may be noted that this is a case similar to that discussed in the previous section, in that a single CR bridging ligand is insufficient to maintain cluster nuclearity. More interesting, however, is the interplay of metals for these heterometallic complexes. The effects of varying metal composition in similar hydrogenations were explored briefly in an earlier section; in this case the presence of Ru atoms in the cluster is vital to the activity of the catalyst.

7.2.2.3. Hydrogenation by Ruthenium Arylimido Systems

Recently improved syntheses of triruthenium bisarylimido clusters[69] have allowed the investigation of these compounds as catalysts. $Ru_3(\mu_3\text{-}NPh)_2(CO)_9$, for instance, was found to catalyze the hydrogenation of styrene or 3,3-dimethylbutene at a moderate rate (0.5 turnover/h) under 50 psig H_2 at 100°C.[70] The metal complex isolated from these reactions is $H_2Ru_3(\mu_3\text{-NPh})_2(CO)_8$ (**4**) which can be synthesized directly from the reaction of the nonacarbonyl with H_2 in the absence of olefin. This dihydrido compound has been shown to be the actual catalyst precursor. A set of crossover experiments was performed to determine whether cluster fragmentation was important in these reactions. Catalysis by an equimolar $H_2Ru_3(\mu_3\text{-NPh})_2(CO)_8$-$H_2Ru_3(\mu_3\text{-NC}_6H_4OMe)_2(CO)_8$ mixture, for instance, failed to yield any $H_2Ru_3(\mu_3\text{-NC}_6H_4OMe)(\mu_3\text{-NPh})(CO)_8$ via arylimido scrambling. Furthermore, this unsymmetric cluster catalyzed the hydrogenation without forming either of the symmetric clusters. Crossover experiments have not been used extensively in the evaluation of cluster catalysis, but in cases such as this their potential is obvious.

7.2.2.4. Transalkylation of Amines by Osmium Sulfido Systems

Recently the cluster $Os_3(\mu_3\text{-S})(CO)_{10}$ (**3**) was reported[71] to catalyze the transalkylation of amines, equation (7.15), a potentially valuable means of generating unsymmetric tertiary amines. The triosmium complex reacted with NMe_3 at 125°C to give the carbene-containing cluster $H_2Os_3S(CO)_8(CHNMe_2)$ (**14**). When placed in a sealed tube containing a large excess of NEt_3 and NPr_3 at 143°C, this complex catalyzed transalkylation. A roughly statistical mixture of NEt_3, NEt_2Pr, $NEtPr_2$, and NPr_3 was produced in a 16-h reaction.

$$NR_3 + NR'_3 \longleftrightarrow NR_2R' + NRR'_2 \qquad (7.15)$$

The proposed mechanism (Scheme 7.8) of related stoichiometric reactions involves dehydrogenation of the incoming tertiary amine forming a β-dialkylamino alkyl ligand (**15**). Reversible transfer of the dialkylamino group to the aminocarbene ligand through (**16**) would allow equilibration of the nitrogen-bound alkyl groups. Studies under catalytic conditions showed the formation of $[R_3NH][HOs_3(\mu_3\text{-S})(CO)_9]$ which was also an active metathesis catalyst. While further studies will serve to establish the significance of the cluster in this reaction, the ability of these clusters to withstand the high temperatures involved is very likely reinforced by the triply bridging sulfur ligand. The recently reported[72] clusters $Os_3(\mu_3\text{-S})_2(CO)_9$ and $H_2Os_3(\mu_3\text{-S})_2(CO)_8$, analogous in structure to the bisarylimido triruthenium complexes discussed in Section 7.2.2.3, also promise to be interesting in this connection.

7.2.3. Activated Carbonyl Clusters

A major problem restricting the application of metal carbonyl clusters in catalysis is the relatively severe conditions required to effect the desired reactivity. In this section three approaches to the activation of these clusters will be considered.

7.2.3.1. Unsaturated Clusters

The most significant results involve the study of the cluster $H_2Os_3(CO)_{10}$, which is both electronically and sterically unsaturated. It was found to catalytically hydrogenate 1-hexane slowly (<1 turnover/h) at 50°C and 50 psig H_2;[73] significant amounts of isomerization were also reported. The proposed mechanism

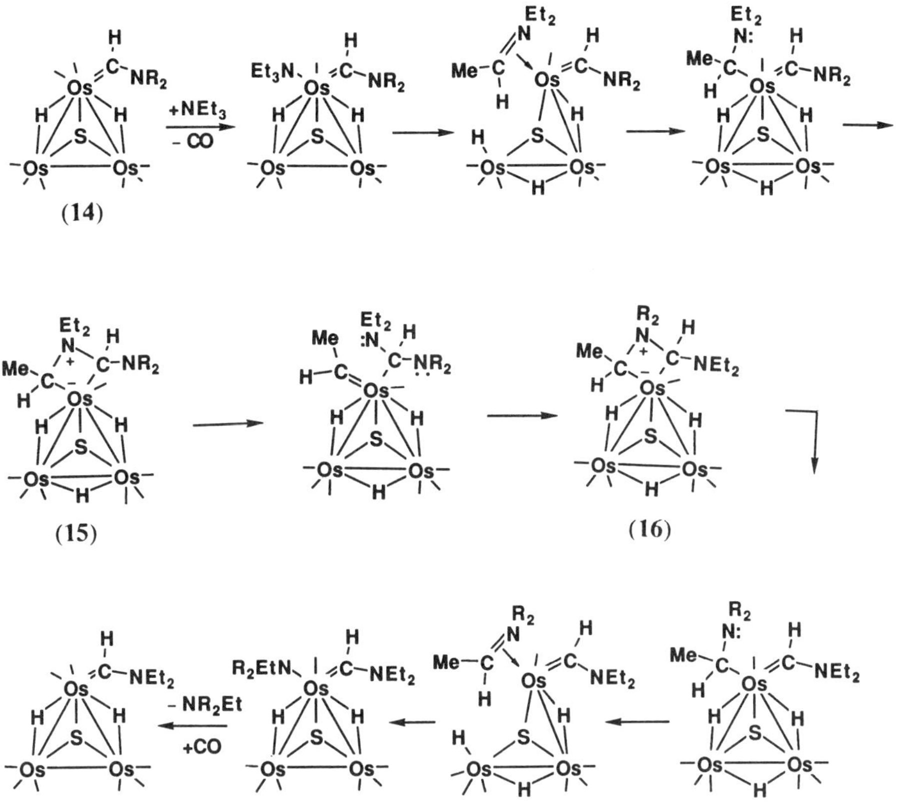

Scheme 7.8. Proposed Transalkylation Mechanism

is outlined in Scheme 7.9 and was supported by the isolation of the alkyl complex (18) when the olefin was diethyl fumarate. The isomerization reaction was studied independently,[74] and the kinetics were found to be first order in the triosmium cluster. Taken together, these studies provide one of the strongest cases for a catalytic reaction involving an intact cluster throughout the cycle.

Clusters analogous to (18) are the result of reactions with maleic anhydride, ethyl acrylate, and ethyl diazo acetate.[73] The stability of these species probably results from the coordination of the β-carbonyl, forming an unstrained ring and leaving the cluster electronically saturated. Secondary stabilization involving an agostic[75] C—H—Os interaction was observed in the absence of potential coordinating groups in the formation of $HOs_3(CH_2R)(CO)_{10}$, (R=H,[76] Me[77]). Other clusters containing alkyl ligands supported by secondary interactions were prepared by the reaction of $H_2Os_3(CO)_{10}$ with α,β-unsaturated aldehydes,[78] methyl vinyl ether,[79] phenyl vinyl sulfide,[80] and acetylenes.[81] While none of these complexes has been demonstrated to be part of a catalytic cycle, they provide a variety of structural types from which potential intermediates for such cycles may be proposed.

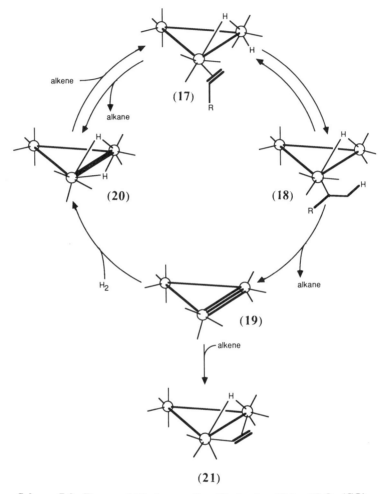

Scheme 7.9. **Proposed Hydrogenation Mechanism Using H₂Os₃(CO)₁₀**

7.2.3.2. Activation by Anions

A second approach invovles the utilization of anions to labilize CO ligands. While used primarily for ligand substitution studies to date, several notable reports have appeared applying the effect to catalytic studies.

Labilization of CO by Acetate and Alkoxides   Recent studies[82-87] of the interaction of anions with $Ru_3(CO)_{12}$ have demonstrated that the carbonyl ligands are efficiently labilized. Examples of these reactions will be examined in greater detail elsewhere in the text; in the context of cluster catalysis, however, CO labilization provides necessary open coordination sites. Lavigne and Kaesz have utilized this reaction to efficiently promote phosphine substitution.[82] It was found, for instance, that PPN(OAc) is an excellent catalyst for the monosubstitution of triphenylphosphine on $Ru_3(CO)_{12}$. Other anions provide milder catalysts and fail to give the pure monosubstituted product. Hydride sources were subsequently[83] found to catalyze substitution reactions as well.

Ford and co-workers have explored the reaction of methoxide with $Ru_3(CO)_{12}$, which can also promote subsequent substitution chemistry.[84] The resulting cluster, $[Ru_3(CO)_{11}(CO_2Me)]^-$, was activated toward phosphite substitution with a half-life three orders of magnitude smaller than that observed for the uncatalyzed reaction. The proposed mechanism for the reaction invokes reversible CO dissociation as the first step, consistent with labilization by the acyl anion. The enhanced reactivity of $[Ru_3(CO)_{11}(CO_2Me)]^-$ to ^{13}CO exchange has been shown by Darensbourg and co-workers.[85] Reaction with H_2, moreover, leads to $[HRu_3(CO)_{11}]^-$ and HCO_2Me under mild conditions.[86]

Olefin Hydrogenation and Isomerization Promoted by Isocyanate

The studies cited earlier established that anions can labilize CO ligands and provide open coordination sites on a cluster. This is an important consideration for catalysis in which reactants such as olefins or dihydrogen require such sites for activation. Recent work has shown that rapid olefin hydrogenation can be catalyzed by ruthenium clusters that are promoted by anions and, in particular, isocyanate.[88] Solutions of $[Ru_3(\mu_2\text{-}NCO)(CO)_{10}]^-$ (**22**), for instance, upon saturation with H_2 followed by addition of olefin immediately catalyzed olefin hydrogenation. In a typical reaction, a flask containing 1.4 mM cluster under 11 psig H_2 was charged with 0.38 M olefin at 25.0°C and exhibited a rate of 5.2 turnover/min. No induction period was observed following addition of olefin, and the rate of hydrogen uptake remained linear for several hundred turnovers. Infrared spectroscopic studies of the catalytic solution revealed that only $[Ru_3(\mu_2\text{-}NCO)(CO)_{10}]^-$ could be correlated to the catalytic activity. Other species detected as the activity eventually decreased were $[HRu_3(CO)_{11}]^-$, $[H_3Ru_4(CO)_{12}]^-$, and $[H_2Ru_4(NCO)(CO)_{12}]^-$; this mixture also forms rapidly when (**22**) was allowed to react with H_2 in the absence of olefin. No reaction occurred between the cluster and olefin in the absence of H_2. The catalyst selectively reduced terminal, unactivated olefins; isomerization of 1-pentene to cis- and trans-2-pentene was observed during its hydrogenation.

The experimentally derived rate law for the catalysis was $\partial[H_2]/\partial t = k_{obs}$ $[\mathbf{22}]^{1/2}[H_2]$. It is important to note that the fractional cluster order in this case does not necessarily imply cleavage of M—M bonds; it simply implies $[Ru_3(\mu_2\text{-}NCO)(CO)_{10}]^-$ fragments into two particles. This may involve cluster fragmentation or simple CO dissociation. The reaction was strongly inhibited by CO addition. The observed deuterium isotope effect of $k_H/k_D = 1.5$ was consistent with a rate-determining oxidative addition of dihydrogen. A reaction sequence consistent with these data is shown in equations (7.16)–(7.19).

$$[Ru_3(NCO)(CO)_{10}]^- \leftrightarrow CO + [Ru_3(NCO)(CO)_9]^- \qquad (7.16)$$

$$[Ru_3(NCO)(CO)_9]^- + H_2 \rightarrow [H_2Ru_3(NCO)(CO)_9]^- \qquad (7.17)$$

$$[H_2Ru_3(NCO)(CO)_9]^- + \text{olefin} + CO \rightarrow [Ru_3(NCO)(CO)_{10}]^- + \text{alkane} \quad (7.18)$$

A mechanism consistent with the kinetics is shown in Scheme 7.10.

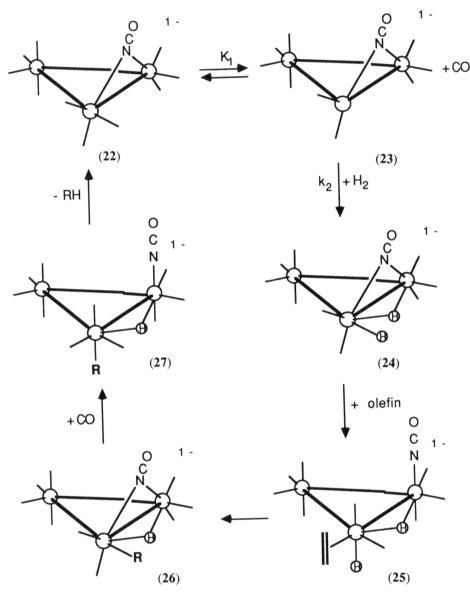

Scheme 7.10. Proposed Mechanism for Alkene Hydrogenation by Ruthenium and Osmium Isocyanate Clusters

Due to the rapid rate of catalysis, none of the proposed triruthenium interme-diates could be isolated or observed. Four related osmium compounds, however, were successfully isolated.[89] $[Os_3(NCO)(CO)_{11}]^-$ and $[Os(\mu_2\text{-NCO})(CO)_{10}]^-$ were prepared in the same fashion as the ruthenium analogs. The struc-ture of the decacarbonyl cluster was established by comparison to the structurally characterized $[Os_3(\mu_2\text{-}NO)(CO)_{10}]^-$. The new anionic dihydrido cluster $[H_2Os_3(NCO)(CO)_{10}]^-$ was prepared directly from $H_2Os_3(CO)_{10}$ and PPN(NCO). This cluster readily reacted with olefins such as maleic anhydride to give the fourth new cluster, $[HOs_3(NCO)(R)(CO)_9]^-$, where R is a terminally bound alkyl. A crystallographic characterization of the compound where R is succinoyl anhydride revealed the structure to be (26).

While less active than the ruthenium system, the isocyanato osmium clusters also catalyzed the hydrogenation. The major species present following catalysis was $[HOs_3(NCO)(R)(CO)_9]^-$, emphasizing its relationship to the analogous structure shown in Scheme 7.10: upon heating in THF, the alkyl complex reductively eliminated R—H, a reaction that must occur to complete the catalytic cycle.

7.2.3.3. Photochemically Activated Systems

Photochemistry has always played an important role[90] in metal carbonyl chemistry; it is no surprise that studies relevant to catalysis have appeared. A large number of examples of the activation of sterically and electronically saturated complexes have been reported. For mononuclear metal carbonyls, photolysis commonly leads to the selective dissociation of CO, while binuclear carbonyls can exhibit a combination of both CO elimination and M—M bond cleavage.[91] In each case, however, reactive fragments are produced that may become involved in a catalytic cycle. The number of studies specifically involving the photochemistry of metal clusters is much smaller, with only a few reports of photocatalysis utilizing such species. Several significant examples will be discussed in the following sections.

Labilization of CO Ligands Photolysis of $H_4Ru_4(CO)_{12}$ in the presence of donor ligands led to clean CO substitution under mild conditions.[92] When conducted in the presence of an olefin such as 1-pentene, however, photolysis led to catalytic isomerization at a rapid rate (>2000 turnovers/h) at $25°C$. This process was found to be catalytic in photons, that is, a single photon could lead to as many as 300 isomerization cycles. The reaction was suppressed by addition of a CO atmosphere, consistent with a dissociative mechanism. Addition of 10 psig H_2 to the system resulted in slow (60 turnovers/h) catalytic hydrogenation. Work by Doi[93] has demonstrated a similar reaction occurs with ethylene. The report contained extensive kinetic and mechanistic details analogous to those for the thermal reaction[14] discussed in an earlier section. Indeed, the properties of the photochemical and thermal reaction are so similar the same mechanism is proposed [equations (7.4)–(7.7)], except for means of initially generating the unsaturated active species $H_4Ru_4(CO)_{11}$. Such an assertion is well supported by comparing the details of the photocatalytic study to the kinetic results from the thermal hydrogenation. Although the means of liberating CO differ, the kinetics of the reactions are qualitatively the same; both are inhibited by CO, both exhibit deuterium-hydrogen exchange on ethylene at a rate faster than ethane formation; both have a similar kinetic isotope effect. Photogeneration of the active catalyst in this case has the added benefit of allowing extremely mild conditions to be employed, making subsequent thermally induced cluster fragmentation unlikely.

In this connection it is also appropriate to mention two recent reports[94,95] on the photodissociation of CO from $Os_3(CO)_{12}$ and $Ru_3(CO)_{12}$ with near-UV radiation. While the catalytic potential of this specific transformation has not yet been explored, the substitution chemistry is analogous to that discussed earlier for $H_4Ru_4(CO)_{12}$ and holds the possibility of further cluster-based systems.

Metal-Metal Bond Cleavage   The cleavage of dinuclear metal complexes by photochemical means to give reactive 17-electron fragments is a well-documented reaction.[91] The analogous photolysis of a single metal-metal bond in a cluster could lead to a tethered diradical species for which recombination should be facile.[96] Accordingly, few examples of such a process leading to useful chemistry exist. Cleavage producing a nonradical intermediate (**28**) has been invoked by Wrighton to explain an apparent associative substitution of $Ru_3(CO)_{12}$ at 90 K.[95]

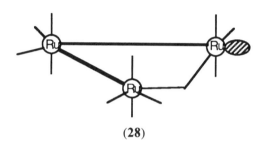

(28)

Low energy photoexcitation of $Os_3(CO)_{12}$ has been found to lead to inefficient fragmentation of the cluster.[94] Long wavelength irradiation of the analogous ruthenium cluster in the presence of CO or C_2H_4 leads almost exclusively to the fragments $Ru(CO)_4L$ and $Ru_2(CO)_8L$ at 195 K. In the presence of PPh_3, however, the predominant product is $Ru_3(CO)_{11}PPh_3$.[95] Broad band irradiation of $Ru_3(CO)_{12}$ at room temperature leads almost completely to mononuclear complexes in the presence of two electron donors. These fragments demonstrate activity as isomerization[97] and hydrosilation catalysts.[98]

Likewise, fragmentation dominates the photochemistry of $Fe_3(CO)_{12}$ in solution under ambient conditions[95]; the facility of such reactions has led to their investigation as possible catalyst precursors.[97-99] Excitation of $Fe_3(CO)_{12}$ with visible light in the presence of alkenes, for instance, produced an extremely active isomerization catalyst.[100] Thirty seconds of intense laser radiation at 515 nm was found to isomerize 1-pentene at a turnover rate of $\sim10^3$/min, among the fastest measured for a homogeneous catalyst. Fairly selective hydrosilation was observed at similar rates.[98] Since the photoactivity of $Fe(CO)_5$ was very similar, a mononuclear catalyst was proposed for the reaction. This contention has been further supported by more direct evidence; in ethylene saturated solutions, for instance, visible irradiation of $Fe_3(CO)_{12}$ yields $Fe(CO)_5$, $Fe(CO)_4(C_2H_4)$, and $Fe(CO)_3(C_2H_4)_2$. Of these, the latter alone demonstrates rapid isomerization of 1-pentene. Other catalytically active systems[100] derived from $M_3(CO)_{12}$ (M = Fe, Ru) may also involve such mononuclear tricarbonyl units, although further detailed investigations are still required.

In cases where the same active catalyst can apparently be generated from a mononuclear or multinuclear precursor, clusters demonstrate several advantages. First, clusters often exhibit absorptions in the visible region of the spectrum, whereas the appropriate monomer requires UV excitation to effect the desired chemistry. While this is of some practical benefit in itself, it also permits the utilization of potential organic substrates that are sensitive to the higher energy radiation themselves. A second useful property of many metal clusters is their relative stability and ease of handling. Polynuclear metal carbonyls, for example, are generally nonvolatile solids relatively insensitive to air or moisture. Appropriate mononuclear counterparts, on the other hand, often require more specialized handling or additional ligands for stability. In this respect, then, the cluster serves as a convenient way to introduce an active monomer to the system, a concept which will be further discussed in Section 7.2.3.5.

Isomerization by Fe—M Dimers   The photochemical isomerization of allylbenzene by $[HFeM(CO)_9]^-$ (M = Cr, Mo, W) (**29**) was reported recently.[101] This dinuclear complex consists of $M(CO)_5$ and $Fe(CO)_4$ units bridged by a hydride. The reaction proceeded under mild irradiation from fluorescent room light, and it was suggested that the slow catalysis ($\sim$4 turnovers/h for M = Cr, Mo) involved an intact dinuclear species (Scheme 7.11). Recognizing the substantial amount of literature that reports M—M bond cleavage occurs upon photolysis of such species, much effort was directed at discounting the presence of mononuclear complexes as the active catalysts. Based on earlier thermal fragmentation studies of the dimer, $[HFe(CO)_4]^-$ and $[M(CO)_5]$ were examined for catalytic activity, as were other less likely fragments such as $[Fe(CO)_4]^-$ and $[HM(CO)_5]^-$. This systematic study demonstrated that the observed reactivity could be attributed to no mononuclear complex reasonably derived from $[HMFe(CO)_9]^-$. While built upon negative evidence, the conclusion illustrates the value of this technique, which can be used effectively in conjunction with other methods to establish a mechanism. The obvious difficulty connected with extending this exhaustive methodology to larger clusters, particularly heterometallic species, lies in the corresponding increase in the number of plausible fragments to be investigated.

7.2.3.4. Clusters with Labile Ligands

Both of these studies by Muetterties and co-workers begin with clusters containing ligands other than CO. The starting materials for the first study were a series of nickel isocyanide complexes.[102] This family of compounds is able to catalyze the reduction of acetylenes, isonitriles, and nitriles. $Ni_4(CNR)_7$ (**33**) was the most important among these very reactive complexes. $Ni_4(CNR)_7$ was found to react with acetylenes to give the structurally characterized adduct, $Ni_4(CNR)_4(acetylene)_3$, which under 1 atm of H_2 catalyzes the hydrogenation of diarylacetylenes and dialkylacetylenes. The rates approached 1 turnover/min and this cluster could be recovered intact after several hours of catalysis. Several mononuclear complexes were tested and found to be inactive under the same reaction conditions. At higher reaction temperatures (90°C), the isocyanide ligands themselves were hydrogenated to t-butylamine and t-butylmethylamine. The nickel ends up in the metallic state, and one of the most troublesome points that had to be addressed was whether or not heterogeneous catalysis was responsible for the products observed. Nickel metal was prepared by two separate means and found

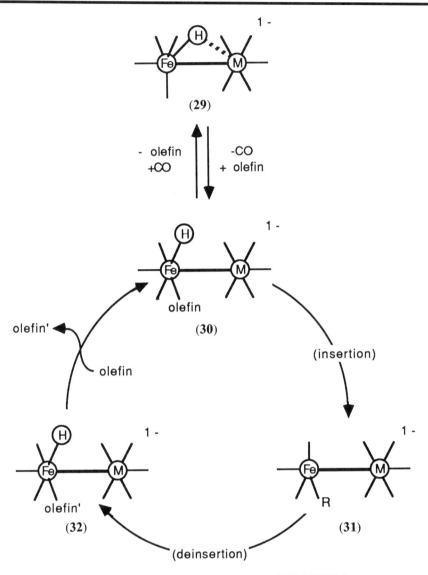

Scheme 7.11. Olefin Isomerization by [HFeM(CO)$_9$]$^-$

to be qualitatively different in reactivity compared to the isocyanide complexes. Of the isocyanide reductions that were studied the most interesting example, and indeed the first example of homogeneous catalytic reduction of an isocyanide, is shown in equation (7.19).

$$4 \text{ Ni(CNR)}_4 + \text{H}_2 \xrightarrow{\text{Ni}_4(\text{CNR})_7} 9 \text{ RNHCH}_3 + \text{Ni}_4(\text{CNR})_7 \qquad (7.19)$$

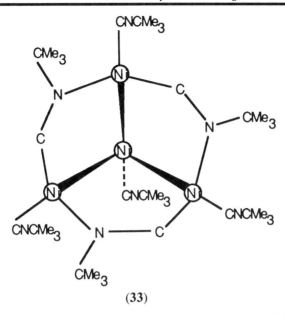

(33)

The mechanisms of these catalytic hydrogenations are still not well defined, but the unusual bonding of the bridging isocyanide to the polynuclear metal complex was proposed to play an important role. Acetonitrile was also reduced to ethylamine, but the reaction became heterogeneous after one turnover. The rate was the slowest of the reductions of any of the triply bonded species, and very little additional information is available to address the mechanism.

Another group of polynuclear complexes that has been studied by Muetterties and co-workers[103] contain only phosphite and hydride ligands on rhodium atoms. This work begins with the complex $\{(H)_2Rh[P(O-i-C_3H_7)_3]_2\}_2$ which was used to catalytically hydrogenate acetylenes to the *trans*-alkenes. At 20°C the reaction was found to be totally stereoselective; however, the activity (1 turnover/min) lasted only five minutes. At that point further reduction continued, but the product now contained primarily *cis*-alkene which was shown to result from the hydrogenation catalyzed by a mononuclear complex. The importance of this study is the clear definition between the two reaction domains (mononuclear vs. dinuclear) based on the stereochemistry of the resulting product. Virtually all catalytic hydrogenations of alkynes by mononuclear systems generate *cis*-alkenes. The mechanism elucidated for generating the *trans* isomer is shown in Scheme 7.12. The unique stereochemistry is proposed to result in the hydrogen migration to the μ_2-η^2 alkyne to give the bridging vinyl complex. The stereochemistry of this complex was confirmed by X-ray crystallographic studies. Final reductive elimination would require formation of the *trans* isomer.

7.2.3.5. Clusters as Sources of Active Monomers

This section discusses several cases in which the cluster serves as a precursor from which catalytically active monomeric species are derived under reaction conditions. In other words, the role of the metal cluster is that of a stable storehouse for a more reactive mononuclear fragment.

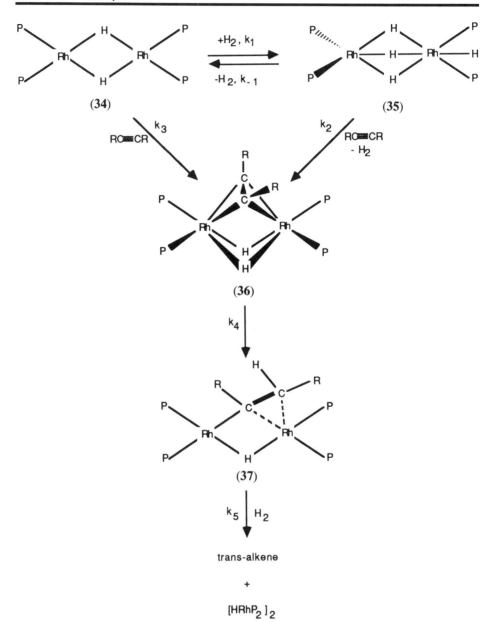

(34)   (35)

(36)

(37)

trans-alkene

+

[HRhP$_2$]$_2$

Scheme 7.12. Stereoselective Acetylene Hydrogenation by $\{(H)_2Rh[P(O-i-C_3H_7)_3]_2\}_2$

Hydrogenation of CO by Ruthenium   Knifton[104] and Dombek[105] have extensively explored the use of ruthenium carbonyls under high gas pressures to catalyze
the reduction of CO to ethylene glycol, ethanol, and methanol. The most impressive results involve the use of halides, especially iodide, to promote the catalysis.
This reaction has been thoroughly studied using *in situ* infrared spectroscopy and

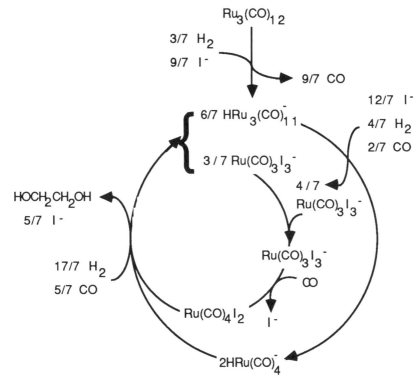

Scheme 7.13. Glycol Formation by Halide-Promoted Ruthenium Species

kinetics, allowing a viable mechanism for the reaction to be proposed. Typical conditions for a catalytic run were 12,000 psig and 220°C in sulfolane solutions. The metal could be charged as $Ru_3(CO)_{12}$ or one of many mononuclear precursors; iodide was introduced as either the sodium or organic anion salt. Under optimized conditions, the spectroscopic and kinetic studies indicated the presence of $[HRu_3(CO)_{11}]^-$ and $[RuI_3(CO)_3]^-$ in a 2:1 ratio. The reaction shown in equation (7.20) occurs even under mild conditions and was found to be responsible for the formation of these two species. Scheme 7.13 illustrates the complexity of the catalytic cycle proposed.

$$7/3Ru_3(CO)_{12} + H_2 + 3I^- \rightarrow 2[HRu_3(CO)_{11}]^- + [RuI_3(CO)_3]^- + 3CO$$

$$(7.20)$$

As just shown, it has been proposed that $[RuI_3(CO)_3]^-$ reacts with CO to eliminate I^- and form $RuI_2(CO)_4$, the carbonyls on this complex being susceptible to nucleophilic attack. Model studies found that even under CO, $[HRu_3(CO)_{11}]^-$ was not capable of donating hydride to form the crucial formyl complex. $[HRu(CO)_4]^-$ is effective for donating hydride, however, and while it is not detected in the catalytic reaction, small amounts were presumed to result from the reaction of $[HRu_3(CO)_{11}]^-$ with high pressures of CO.

Hydrogenation of CO by Mixed Metal Systems   An interesting modification[106] of the system discussed in the preceding section has been reported to lead to greatly improved selectivity toward ethylene glycol formation. In one case, small amounts of $Rh(CO)_2(acac)$ were added to the system; under reaction conditions this was converted to $[Rh(CO)_2I_2]^-$. While this addition did not affect the overall rate of glycol production, methanol production was suppressed. The proposed explanation for this observation was oxidation of the additive to $[Rh(CO)_2I_4]^-$, which then reacted with $[HRu(CO)_4]^-$ to form a rhodium formyl complex. The change in selectivity would result from a preference for the formyl (or subsequent intermediate such as a hydroxylmethyl or hydroxymethylidene) to migrate to a second CO rather than reductively eliminate methanol.

A related study[107] reports a new acetic acid synthesis directly from synthesis gas. As above, the system relies on a tetraalkylphosphonium halide melt. Maximum acetic acid production is achieved with a $Ru_3(CO)_{12}/CoI_2$ catalyst precursor in a 2:1 ratio. The proposed mechanism involves a ruthenium formyl in this case, which goes on to reductively eliminate methanol. In the presence of HI and $[Co(CO)_4]^-$ formed under the reaction conditions, a cobalt acetyl species is produced which goes on to eliminate acetic acid. To optimize the selectivity for acid formation it was necessary to balance the relative rates of the Ru catalyzed methanol production and Co catalyzed carbonylation so the concentration of methanol remained small.

The chemistry proposed in these systems does not seem to involve clusters in any of the crucial bond-forming steps: $Ru_3(CO)_{12}$ apparently serves only as a source of reactive mononuclear fragments. The potential of synergistic behavior in heterometallic precursor systems is also an important aspect of this chemistry.

Closely related to these CO reductions are studies on the hydroformylation of formaldehyde to glycolaldehyde ($HOCH_2CHO$), a presumed intermediate in the ethylene glycol synthesis.[108,109] Both studies used $Rh_4(CO)_{12}$ as the catalyst precursor with either $CoCl_2$ or PPh_3/HI as a cocatalyst. The conditions required high pressures of CO and H_2 (100 atm) and temperatures around 100°C. Methanol was always the principal side product and the selectivity to glycolaldehyde was sensitive to the nature and quantity of the cocatalyst.

Infrared spectroscopy indicated the formation of anionic pentarhodium clusters such as $[Rh_5(CO)_{15}]^-$ during catalysis, but further details on this complex reaction have yet to be established. It was suggested that one important role of the cocatalyst was to control the oxidation state of the rhodium. In the mixed Rh/Co system, after all of the Co and Rh were reduced to $[Co(CO)_4]^-$ and $[Rh(CO)_4]^-$, the catalytic action ceased.[108]

7.3. Summary and Comments

The focus of this chapter is on studies of catalytic processes yielding some information about the mechanism of the reaction. In these closing comments, we add some thoughts on comparing clusters to monomers and on the studies necessary to prove cluster catalysis.

Questions regarding the mechanisms of catalytic reactions continue to prompt many researchers to study both monometallic and polymetallic homogeneous catalysts. One fundamentally important issue to consider involves defining the similarities and differences between mononuclear and polynuclear catalysts. To properly address this question, one must first establish mechanisms, as best one can, and secondly, compare the results with those found for suitable mononuclear complexes. In such comparisons, it is appropriate that as many of the variables be kept constant as possible while the nuclearity of the catalyst is changed. In other words, polynuclear metal carbonyls such as $[HRu_3(CO)_{11}]^-$ should be compared to a related mononuclear complex such as $[HRu(CO)_4]^-$ rather than a mononuclear phosphine complex such as $RhH(CO)(PPh_3)_3$. Some of these comparisons have been made within the chapter, but far more are needed to understand the similarities and differences of mononuclear and polynuclear metal complexes.

Several descriptions of experiments that are needed to prove cluster catalysis have been put forth in earlier reviews. In the most rigorous sense, a chemical reaction mechanism can never be proved. The choice of guidelines defining what information is needed for a mechanism to become known will lead to controversy, but they are useful to place our efforts in perspective. In this regard the following quote from a textbook on organometallic chemistry perhaps best describes what is needed.

> "...to discover the mechanism of a multistep catalytic reaction, the rate laws of individual steps must be determined independently. When the rate and equilibrium parameters for these steps are assembled and shown to account quantitatively for the overall catalytic behavior, the mechanism is said to be 'known.' "[110]

Only a few metal-catalyzed reactions have met this rigorous requirement, and no studies involving clusters have achieved this degree of completion. Indeed, there are likely to be relatively few systems that will ever be amenable to such a detailed analysis.

Regarding the specific need to address the nuclearity of the active catalyst, some experiments (i.e., dependence of the rate on the cluster concentration) will be more helpful than others, but the specific interpretation of such results may vary from one cluster to another. The example of a single experiment that would prove an intact cluster is operating throughout a catalytic cycle is the observation of asymmetric induction in the product using a cluster whose chirality is determined only by its differences among the metals. For instance, a tetranuclear cluster with four unique apices (different metals or nonmetals) would exist in two enantiomeric forms. Vahrenkamp and co-workers have succeeded in synthesizing and resolving chiral clusters.[111] Unfortunately, after the incredible effort to systematically prepare such compounds, there is no guarantee that the cluster will catalyze a reaction involving a prochiral substrate. In this chapter, we have seen numerous examples of reactions that proceed with ethylene or terminal olefins, but which are completely ineffective with more highly substituted olefins. Vahrenkamp and co-workers have found several encouraging stoichiometric reactions[112] using methyl-N-acetyl-2-aminopropenoate which upon hydrogenation and subsequent hydrolysis yields the amino acid alanine.

The determination of catalytic reaction mechanisms involving metal clusters is difficult, and no one should expect quick and easy answers. This situation bears some similarity to the early problems encountered in the study of now famous catalysts such as $RhCl(PPh_3)_3$. In the years before the reaction mechanism of this catalyst was elucidated, numerous studies were undertaken and much work focused on the number of phosphines bound to the metal in the active catalyst. Just as this problem was eventually clarified, we can anticipate solutions to the "number of metals in the active catalyst" problem in the future.

References

1. R. M. Laine, *J. Mol. Catal.*, 1982, **14**, 137.
2. R. Ugo and P. Psaro, *J. Mol. Catal.*, 1983, **20**, 53.
3. E. L. Muetterties and M. J. Krause, *Angew. Chem.*, 1983, **95**, 135.
4. L. Markó and A. Vizi-Orosz, in *Metal clusters in catalysis*, B. C. Gates, L. Guczi and H. Knözinger (Eds.). Amsterdam: Elsevier, 1986, Ch. 5.
5. P. Braunstein and J. Rose, in *Stereochemistry of organometallic and inorganic compounds*, I. Bernal (Ed.). Amsterdam: Elsevier, 1988, Vol. 3.
6. G. Süss-Fink and F. Neumann, in *The Chemistry of the Metal-Carbon Bond*, Vol. 5, F. R. Hartley (Ed.). New York: Wiley, 1989, Ch. 7.
7. P. C. Ford, *Acc. Chem. Res.*, 1981, **14**, 31.
8. (a) R. M. Laine, R. G. Rinker and P. C. Ford, *J. Am. Chem. Soc.*, 1977, **99**, 252.
   (b) C. Ungermann, V. Landis, S. A. Moya, H. Cohen, H. Walker, R. G. Pearson, R. G. Rinker and P. C. Ford, *J. Am. Chem. Soc.*, 1979, **101**, 5922.
9. J. C. Bricker, C. C. Nagel and S. G. Shore, *J. Am. Chem. Soc.*, 1982, **104**, 1444.
10. J. C. Bricker, C. C. Nagel, A. A. Bhattacharyya and S. G. Shore, *J. Am. Chem. Soc.*, 1985, **107**, 377.
11. M. W. Payne, D. L. Leussing and S. G. Shore, *J. Am. Chem. Soc.*, 1987, **109**, 617.
12. P. C. Ford, R. G. Rinker, C. Ungermann, R. M. Laine, V. Landis and S. A. Moya, *J. Am. Chem. Soc.*, 1978, **100**, 4595.
13. P. Yarrow, H. Cohen, C. Ungermann, D. Vandenberg, P. C. Ford and R. G. Rinker, *J. Mol. Catal.*, 1983, **22**, 239.
14. Y. Doi, K. Koshizuka and T. Keii, *Inorg. Chem.*, 1982, **21**, 2732.
15. M. Valle, D. Osella and G. A. Vaglio, *Inorg. Chim. Acta*, 1976, **20**, 213.
16. G. A. Vaglio, D. Osella and M. Valle, *Trans. Met. Chem.*, 1977, **2**, 94.
17. G. A. Vaglio and M. Valle, *Inorg. Chim. Acta*, 1978, **30**, 161.
18. S. A. R. Knox and H. D. Kaesz, *J. Am. Chem. Soc.*, 1971, **93**, 4594.
19. D. J. Darensbourg and B. J. Baldwin-Zuschke, *J. Am. Chem. Soc.*, 1982, **104**, 3906.
20. P. Michelin Lausarot, G. A. Vaglio and M. Valle, *Trans. Met. Chem.*, 1979, **4**, 39.
21. P. Michelin Lausarot, G. A. Vaglio and M. Valle, *Inorg. Chim. Acta*, 1977, **25**, L107.
22. P. Michelin Lausarot, G. A. Vaglio and M. Valle, *Inorg. Chim. Acta*, 1979, **36**, 213.
23. S. Bhaduri and K. Sharma, *J. Chem. Soc. Chem. Commun.*, 1988, 173.
24. A. Basu, S. Bhaduri, K. Sharma and P. G. Jones, *J. Chem. Soc. Chem. Commun.*, 1987, 1126.
25. J. Evans and G. Jingxing, *J. Chem. Soc. Chem. Commun.*, 1985, 39.
26. P. Frediani, U. Matteoli, M. Bianchi, F. Piacenti and G. Menchi, *J. Organomet. Chem.*, 1978, **150**, 273.
27. C. Botteghi, S. Gladiali, M. Bianchi, U. Matteoli, P. Frediani, P. G. Vergamini and E. Benedetti, *J. Organomet. Chem.*, 1977, **140**, 221.
28. M. Bianchi, G. Menchi, F. Francalanci, F. Piacenti, U. Matteoli, P. Frediani and C. Botteghi, *J. Organomet. Chem.*, 1980, **188**, 109.

29. M. Bianchi, U. Matteoli, G. Menchi, P. Frediani, S. Pratesi, F. Piacenti and C. Botteghi, *J. Organomet. Chem.*, 1980, **198**, 73.
30. M. Bianchi, U. Matteoli, P. Frediani, G. Menchi, F. Piacenti, C. Botteghi and M. Marchetti, *J. Organomet. Chem.*, 1983, **252**, 317.
31. M. Castiglioni, E. Sappa, M. Valle, M. Lanfranchi and A. Tiripicchio, *J. Organomet. Chem.*, 1983, **241**, 99.
32. M. Castiglioni, R. Giordano, E. Sappa, A. Tiripicchio and M. T. Camellini, *J. Chem. Soc. Dalton Trans.*, 1986, 23.
33. M. Castiglioni, R. Giordano and E. Sappa, *J. Organomet. Chem.*, 1987, **319**, 167.
34. M. Castiglioni, R. Giordano and E. Sappa, submitted for publication.
35. R. A. Sánchez-Delgado, J. Puga and M. Rosales, *J. Mol. Catal.*, 1984, **24**, 221.
36. R. A. Sánchez-Delgado, A. Andriollo, J. Puga and G. Martín, *Inorg. Chem.*, 1987, **26**, 1867.
37. D. Labroue and R. Poilbanc, *J. Mol. Catal.*, 1977, **2**, 329.
38. F. Piacenta, U. Matteoli, M. Bianci, P. Frediani and G. Menchi, Proceedings, XIX Congresso, Nazionale di Chimica Inorganica; IV Congresso Nazionale di Catalisi; Santa Margherita di Pula-Cagliari; October 1986, 389.
39. G. Süss-Fink, *J. Organomet. Chem.*, 1980, **193**, C20.
40. G. Süss-Fink and J. Reiner, *J. Mol. Catal.*, 1982, **16**, 231.
41. G. Süss-Fink and G. Herrmann, *J. Chem. Soc. Chem. Commun.*, 1985, 735.
42. C. E. Kampe, N. M. Boag and H. D. Kaesz, *J. Am. Chem. Soc.*, 1983, **105**, 2896.
43. G. Süss-Fink, *Angew. Chem. Int. Ed. Engl.*, 1982, **21**, 73.
44. G. Süss-Fink and J. Reiner, *J. Organomet. Chem.*, 1981, **221**, C36.
45. G. Süss-Fink, G. Herrmann and U. Thewalt, *Angew. Chem. Int. Ed. Engl.*, 1983, **22**, 880.
46. G. Herrmann and G. Süss-Fink, *Chem. Ber.*, 1985, **118**, 3959.
47. G. Süss-Fink and G. Herrmann, *Angew. Chem.*, 1986, **98**, 568.
48. G. Süss-Fink, G. F. Schmidt and G. Herrmann, *Chem. Ber.*, 1987, **120**, 1451.
49. (a) R. D. Adams and N. M. Golembeski, *J. Organomet. Chem.*, 1979, **171**, C21. (b) R. D. Adams, N. M. Golembeski and J. P. Selegue, *Inorg. Chem.*, 1981, **20**, 1242.
50. G. D. Mercer, J. S. Shu, T. B. Rauchfuss and D. M. Roundhill, *J. Am. Chem. Soc.*, 1975, **97**, 1967.
51. G. D. Mercer, W. B. Beaulieu and D. M. Roundhill, *J. Am. Chem. Soc.*, 1977, **99**, 6551.
52. D. M. Roundhill, M. K. Dickson, N. J. Dixit and B. P. Sudha-Dixit, *J. Am. Chem. Soc.*, 1980, **102**, 5538.
53. M. K. Dickson, B. P. Sudha and D. M. Roundhill, *J. Organomet. Chem.*, 1980, **190**, C43.
54. (a) R. L. Pruett and W. W. Walker, Union Carbide Corp., U.S. Patents 3 833 634 (1974) and 3 957 857 (1976). (b) J. L. Vidal, Z. C. Mester and W. E. Walker, Union Carbide Corp., U.S. Patent 4 115 428 (1978). (c) L. A. Cosby, R. A. Fiato and J. L. Vidal, Union Carbide Corp., U.S. Patent 4 115 428 (1978).
55. J. L. Vidal and W. E. Walker, *Inorg. Chem.*, 1987, **109**, 4518.
56. (a) B. T. Heaton, J. Jonas, T. Eguchi and G. A. Hoffman, *J. Chem. Soc. Chem. Commun.*, 1981, 331. (b) B. T. Heaton, L. Strona, J. Jonas, T. Eguchi and G. A. Hoffman, *J. Chem. Soc. Dalton Trans.*, 1982, 1159.
57. R. C. Schoening, J. L. Vidal and R. A. Fiato, *J. Mol. Catal.*, 1981, **13**, 83.
58. (a) G. C. Demitras and E. L. Muetterties, *J. Am. Chem. Soc.*, 1977, **99**, 2796. (b) H.-K. Wang, H. W. Choi and E. L. Muetterties, *Inorg. Chem.*, 1981, **20**, 2661.
59. (a) M. G. Thomas, B. F. Beier and E. L. Muetterties, *J. Am. Chem. Soc.*, 1976, **98**, 4645. (b) R. A. Schunn, G. C. Demitras, H. W. Choi and E. L. Muetterties, *Inorg. Chem.*, 1981, **20**, 4023.

60. M. A. Vannice, *J. Catal.*, 1975, **37**, 462.

61. J. P. Collman, J. I. Brauman, G. Tustin and G. S. Wann III, *J. Am. Chem. Soc.*, 1983, **105**, 3913.

62. H. W. Choi and E. L. Muetterties, *Inorg. Chem.*, 1981, **20**, 2664.

63. (a) R. C. Ryan, C. U. Pittman, Jr. and J. P. O'Connor, *J. Am. Chem. Soc.*, 1977, **99**, 1986. (b) C. U. Pittman, Jr. and R. C. Ryan, *Chem. Technol.*, 1978, **8**, 170.

64. C. U. Pittman, Jr., G. M. Wilemon, W. D. Wilson and R. C. Ryan, *Angew. Chem. Int. Ed. Engl.*, 1980, **19**, 478.

65. H. P. Withers, Jr. and D. Seyferth, *Inorg. Chem.*, 1983, **22**, 2931.

66. M. G. Richmond, M. Absi-Halbi and C. U. Pittman, *J. Mol. Catal.*, 1984, **22**, 367.

67. D. Mani and H. Vahrenkamp, *J. Mol. Catal.*, 1985, **29**, 305.

68. E. Roland and H. Vahrenkamp, *Organometallics*, 1983, **2**, 183.

69. (a) J. A. Smieja and W. L. Gladfelter, *Inorg. Chem.*, 1986, **25**, 2667. (b) J. A. Smieja, J. E. Gozum and W. L. Gladfelter, *Organometallics*, 1987, **6**, 1311.

70. J. A. Smieja, J. E. Gozum and W. L. Gladfelter, *Organometallics*, 1986, **5**, 2154.

71. (a) R. D. Adams, H. Kim and S. Wang, *J. Am. Chem. Soc.*, 1985, **107**, 6107. (b) R. D. Adams, J. E. Babin, H. S. Kim, J. T. Tanner and T. A. Wolfe, *J. An. Chem. Soc.*, 1990, **112**, in press.

72. R. D. Adams, J. E. Babin and M. Tasi, *Inorg. Chem.*, 1986, **25**, 4514.

73. J. B. Keister and J. R. Shapley, *J. Am. Chem. Soc.*, 1976, **98**, 1056.

74. A. J. Deeming and S. Hasso, *J. Organomet. Chem.*, 1975, **88**, C21.

75. M. Brookhart and M. L. H. Green, *J. Organomet. Chem.*, 1983, **250**, 395.

76. (a) R. B. Calvert, J. R. Shapley, A. J. Schultz, J. M. Williams, S. Suib and G. D. Stucky, *J. Am. Chem. Soc.*, 1978, **100**, 6240. (b) R. B. Calvert and J. R. Shapley, *J. Am. Chem. Soc.*, 1978, **100**, 7726.

77. M. Cree-Uchiyama, J. R. Shapley and G. M. St. George, *J. Am. Chem. Soc.*, 1986, **108**, 1316.

78. A. J. Arce, Y. DeSanctis and A. J. Deeming, *J. Organomet. Chem.*, 1985, **295**, 365.

79. E. Boyar, A. J. Deeming, A. J. Arce and Y. DeSanctis, *J. Organomet. Chem.*, 1984, **276**, C45.

80. E. Boyar, A. J. Deeming, K. Henrick, M. McDartlin and A. Scott, *J. Chem. Soc. Dalton Trans.*, 1986, 1431.

81. B. F. G. Johnson, J. Lewis, T. I. Odiaka and P. R. Raithby, *J. Organomet. Chem.*, 1981, **216**, C56.

82. G. Lavigne and H. D. Kaesz, *J. Am. Chem. Soc.*, 1984, **106**, 4647.

83. G. Lavigne, N. Lugan and J.-J. Bonnet, *Inorg. Chem.*, 1987, **26**, 2345.

84. M. Anstock, D. Taube, D. C. Gross and P. C. Ford, *J. Am. Chem. Soc.*, 1984, **106**, 3696.

85. D. J. Darensbourg, R. L. Gray and M. Pala, *Organometallics*, 1984, **3**, 1928.

86. D. J. Taube, A. Rokicki, M. Anstock and P. C. Ford, *Inorg. Chem.*, 1987, **26**, 526.

87. D. E. Fjare, J. A. Jensen and W. L. Gladfelter, *Inorg. Chem.*, 1983, **22**, 1774.

88. J. L. Zuffa, M. L. Blohm and W. L. Gladfelter, *J. Am. Chem. Soc.*, 1986, **108**, 552.

89. J. L. Zuffa and W. L. Gladfelter, *J. Am. Chem. Soc.*, 1986, **108**, 4669.

90. G. L. Geoffroy and M. S. Wrighton, *Organometallic photochemistry*. New York: Academic Press, 1979.

91. T. J. Meyer and J. V. Casper, *Chem. Rev.*, 1985, **85**, 187.

92. J. L. Graff and M. S. Wrighton, *J. Am. Chem. Soc.*, 1980, **102**, 2123.

93. (a) Y. Doi, S. Tamura and K. Koshizuka, *Inorg. Chim. Acta*, 1982, **65**, L63. (b) Y. Doi, S. Tamura and K. Koshizuka, *J. Mol. Catal.*, 1983, **19**, 213.

94. J. G. Bentsen and M. S. Wrighton, *J. Am. Chem. Soc.*, 1987, **109**, 4518.

95. J. G. Bentsen and M. S. Wrighton, *J. Am. Chem. Soc.*, 1987, **109**, 4530.

96. (a) G. L. Geoffroy and R. A. Epstein, *Inorg. Chem.*, 1977, **16**, 2795. (b) R. A. Epstein, T. R. Gaffney, G. L. Geoffroy, W. L. Gladfelter and R. S. Henderson, *J. Am. Chem. Soc.*, 1979, **101**, 3847.

97. Y.-M. Wuu, J. G. Bentsen, C. G. Brinkley and M. S. Wrighton, *Inorg. Chem.*, 1987, **26**, 530.

98. R. G. Austin, R. S. Paonessa, P. J. Giordano and M. S. Wrighton, *Adv. Chem. Ser.*, 1978, **168**, 189.

99. J. C. Mitchener and M. S. Wrighton, *J. Am. Chem. Soc.*, 1981, **103**, 975.

100. (a) J. L. Graff, R. D. Sanner and M. S. Wrighton, *J. Am. Chem. Soc.*, 1979, **101**, 273. (b) J. L. Graff, R. D. Sanner and M. S. Wrighton, *Organometallics*, 1982, **1**, 837. (c) V. V. Kane, J. R. C. Light and M. C. Whiting, *Polyhedron*, 1984, **4**, 533.

101. P. A. Tooley, L. W. Arndt and M. Y. Darensbourg, *J. Am. Chem. Soc.*, 1985, **107**, 2422.

102. E. L. Muetterties, E. Band, A. Kokorin, W. R. Pretzer and M. G. Thomas, *Inorg. Chem.*, 1980, **19**, 1552.

103. R. R. Burch, A. J. Shusterman, E. L. Muetterties, R. G. Teller and J. M. Williams, *J. Am. Chem. Soc.*, 1983, **105**, 3546.

104. J. F. Knifton, *J. Am. Chem. Soc.*, 1981, **103**, 3959.

105. (a) B. D. Dombek, *J. Am. Chem. Soc.*, 1981, **103**, 6508. (b) B. K. Warren and B. D. Dombek, *J. Catal.*, 1983, **79**, 334.

106. B. D. Dombek, *Organometallics*, 1985, **4**, 1707.

107. J. F. Knifton, *Chem. & Eng. News*, May 5, 1986, 43.

108. M. Marchionna and G. Longoni, *J. Mol. Catal.*, 1986, **35**, 107.

109. M. Marchionna and G. Longoni, *Gazz. Chim. Ital.*, 1986, **116**, 453.

110. J. P. Collman, L. S. Hegedus, J. R. Norton and R. G. Finke, *Principles and applications of organotransition metal chemistry*, Mill Valley, CA: University Science Books, 1987, p. 525.

111. (a) F. Richter and H. Vahrenkamp, *Chem. Ber.*, 1982, **115**, 3243. (b) M. Müller and H. Vahrenkamp, *Chem. Ber.*, 1983, **116**, 2748. (c) B. Blumhofer and H. Vahrenkamp, *Chem. Ber.*, 1986, **119**, 683.

112. D. M. Mani, H.-T. Schacht, A. Powell and H. Vahrenkamp, *Organometallics*, 1987, **6**, 1360.

Organo-Transition Metal Cluster Chemistry: Bibliography of Reviews 1965–1988

Michael I. Bruce

8.1. Introduction

The preparation of this text provides a timely and convenient opportunity to collect together the large number of reviews that have been produced in this area. The field of metal clusters in general has crossed established boundaries so that workers whose main interest may be in molecular beam chemistry, solid-state chemistry, catalysis, biological chemistry, or enzyme studies now have cause to know about some of the developments in this field. In this chapter, reviews on binuclear systems or the atom-bridged cubane-like arrays that occur in nature have been excluded, as these have been the subject of separate volumes (M. H. Chisholm, Ed., *Reactivity of metal-metal bonds*, ACS Symposium Series 155, American Chemical Society, Washington, D.C., 1981; F. A. Cotton and R. A. Walton, *Multiple bonds between metal atoms*, Wiley, New York, 1982; L. Que, Jr., Ed., *Metal clusters in proteins*, ACS Symposium Series No. 372, American Chemical Society, Washington, D.C., 1988).

While some of the references appearing in this chapter may be cited in one (or more) of the foregoing chapters, it is hoped that this chapter proves to be a useful reference (or cross-reference) to the review literature in the field.

This summary is limited to organometallic cluster complexes of the transition metals and encompasses the scope of the book of which it is part. It is divided into several subsets by topic, several obvious divisions being by element, by ligand, and by size, but further discussion has considered the various theories that have been developed to explain the bonding in a variety of clusters. Nowhere is the connection with main group chemistry more apparent, for it was the polyhedral boranes and the related carboranes, followed by metalloborane and metallocarborane complexes, which inspired efforts to improve our understanding of the bonding characteristics of atom clusters. Later, Hoffmann's isolobal concept,[1] which so clearly interrelates metal-containing units with each other and with their organic counterparts, was used to direct synthetic approaches to a multitude of new cluster complexes.[2]

The other extreme is reactions catalyzed by metals, metal surfaces, and metallites. It is not possible to include every survey dealing with aspects of heterogeneous catalysis, and we have chosen to list those which relate the molecular basis of reactivity to the atomic structure. It was Muetterties who, fifteen years ago, first enumerated the many points of resemblance between adsorbed (chemisorbed) molecules on metal surfaces and ligands on metal clusters, particularly those which interact with two, three, or more metal atoms.[3] The plenitude of reviews on this topic serve to indicate the current interest in the use of this analogy to further our understanding of reactions occurring on metal surfaces. One particular application which has commanded attention in a world faced with dwindling supplies of fossil fuels is the conversion of carbon monoxide and hydrogen mixtures (syngas) to hydrocarbons and oxygenates by various modifications of the well-known but imperfectly understood Fischer-Tropsch and related reactions. Many of these reactions occur at more than one metal center, and this is an area having an obvious relationship with molecular metal cluster chemistry.

Also documented are applications of various spectroscopic and other physico-chemical techniques to the elucidation not only of structures, but also of reactions. The latter encompass "simple" ligand substitutions, as well as ligand rearrangements, inter-ligand reactions, and metal cluster rearrangements.

The following includes all major articles known to the compiler that have described various aspects of transition metal cluster chemistry appearing in the major review journals in English, from 1965 until 1988. Some reviews in other languages that have been noted in the course of preparation of this survey have been included, but this part of the compilation is not complete.

8.2. Books

There are few general books on cluster chemistry, although advanced inorganic chemistry texts contain introductions to the subject. The most useful of these are:

F. A. Cotton and G. Wilkinson, *Advanced inorganic chemistry*, 5th ed. New York: Wiley, 1988, Ch. 23: Metal-metal bonds and metal atom clusters.

N. N. Greenwood and A. Earnshaw, *Chemistry of the elements*, Oxford, Pergamon, 1984, Ch. 6.4: Boranes; Ch. 6.6: Metallocarboranes; and various references at the end of chapters on each Periodic Group of the transition elements.

J. E. Huheey, *Inorganic chemistry*, 2nd ed. New York: Harper and Row, 1978, Ch. 14: Inorganic rings, chains, cages and clusters. Metal clusters, pp. 636–649.

K. F. Purcell and J. C. Kotz, *Inorganic chemistry*. Philadelphia: Saunders, 1977, Ch. 18: Molecular polyhedra: Boron hydrides and metal clusters. Metallocarboranes, pp. 1020–1025; Metal-metal bonds and metal clusters, pp. 1026–1049.

At present, the best general introductions for the intending cluster chemist are the following collections:

B. F. G. Johnson (Ed.), *Transition metal clusters.* New York: Wiley, 1980.
M. Moskovits (Ed.), *Metal clusters.* New York: Wiley-Interscience, 1986.

Any account of this type could not omit the extensive references to organometallic chemistry that are included in the encyclopedia work:

G. Wilkinson, F. G. A. Stone and E. W. Abel, (Eds.), *Comprehensive organometallic chemistry*, 9 vols., Oxford: Pergamon, 1982.

The well-known Gmelin compilation now includes volumes describing in detail the organometallic chemistry of some (but so far, not all) transition metals.

Gmelin handbook of inorganic chemistry, 8th ed. Berlin: Springer-Verlag.

References later to these compilations are abbreviated COMC and Gmelin, respectively.

8.3. Collections of Reviews

Special issues of journals have contained collections of reviews of aspects of metal cluster chemistry. In many cases these have been presented at conferences, and may also contain accounts of specific research results, which are not included here. These include:

Gazz. Chim. Ital., 1979, **109** (5) [papers given at 3rd European Conference on Inorganic Chemistry, Cortona, Italy, April 1978].
Phil. Trans. R. Soc. London, 1982, **A308** (1) [contributions to meeting on Metal Clusters in Chemistry, London, 1981]. Later published in book form: J. Lewis and M. L. H. Green, (Eds.), *Metal clusters*, Cambridge U.P., 1986.
Izvest. Sibir. Otdel. Akad. Nauk SSSR, Ser. Khim. Nauk, 1982, **4** (9) [papers given at an All-Union Discussion Seminar on Chemistry of Clusters, USSR, 1981].
Polyhedron, 1983, **3** (12) [B. F. G. Johnson, (Ed.), Symposium-in-print, "Recent advances in the structure and bonding in cluster compounds"].
Koord. Khim., 1984, **10** (7) [papers given at 1st All-Union Conference on Clusters in Catalysis, USSR, 1983].
Usp. Khim., 1985, **54** (4); *Russ. Chem. Rev.*, 1985, **54** (4) [papers given at 2nd All-Union Conference on Chemistry of Clusters, USSR, 1984].
Zh. Vses. Khim. O-va. im D. I. Mendeleev (J. All-Union Mendeleev Chem. Soc.), 1987, **32** (1) [accounts of Russian research given at a conference in 1986].
Polyhedron, 1988, **7** (10/11) [M. H. Chisholm (Ed.), Symposium-in-print, "Reactivity of bridging hydrocarbyl ligands," contains many contributions concerning metal clusters].
New J. Chem., 1988, **12** (7) [a contemporary reflection of activities in metal cluster chemistry].

Polyhedron, 1988, **7** (22/23) [R. D. Adams and W. A. Herrmann, (Ed.), "The chemistry of heteronuclear clusters and multimetallic catalysts," proceedings of a symposium, Königstein, September 1987].

Many hard-cover compilations of articles grouped around particular themes are also available. Individual reviews are referenced in the classified list. Some examples are:

American Chemical Society (ACS) Symposia

No. 155 *Reactivity of metal-metal bonds*, M. H. Chisholm, (Ed.), 1981.

No. 211 *Inorganic chemistry: Towards the 21st century*, M. H. Chisholm, (Ed.), 1983 [section on Non-classical Coordination Compounds (metal-metal bonds and clusters)].

No. 232 *Rings, clusters and polymers of main group elements*, A. H. Cowley, (Ed.), 1983.

No. 328 *Industrial chemicals via C₁ processes*, D. R. Fahey, (Ed.), 1987.

Chemistry for the future, H. Grünewald, (Ed.) [Proceedings of the 29th IUPAC Conference, Cologne, Germany, June 1983].

Structure and bonding, G. A. Somorjai and M. A. van Hove, 1979, Vol. 38 [Issue devoted to Adsorbed Monolayers on Solid Surfaces].

Homogeneous and heterogeneous catalysis, Yu. Yermakova and V. Likholobov (Eds.), VNU Science Press, Utrecht, 1986 [Proceedings of the fifth international symposium on relations between homogeneous and heterogeneous catalysis, Novosibirsk, July 1986]. Section 3 contains 23 papers on catalysis by metal clusters and dispersed metal particles.

8.4. Annual Surveys

Organo-transition metal clusters are most commonly found in Groups 6–11; the organometallic chemistry of these elements has been surveyed on an annual basis in the *Journal of Organometallic Chemistry* since 1964, and most references to new discoveries in the area are included. Table 8.1 summarizes the locations of these reviews covering the period from 1975. The same publisher also produces *Coordination Chemistry Reviews*, which include similar regular surveys of the coordination chemistry, and therefore a considerable amount of related cluster chemistry.

Similarly, the Royal Society of Chemistry's Specialist Periodical Reports on *Organometallic Chemistry* [F. G. A. Stone and E. W. Abel (Eds.)] has been produced since 1971, and has contained sections on organo-transition metal cluster complexes as follows:

Ch. 4   Carbaboranes, including their metal complexes
Ch. 8   Metal carbonyls [including polynuclear species]
Ch. 9   Organometallic compounds containing metal-metal bonds.

The last chapter in each volume contains a summary of diffraction (X-ray, neutron, and electron) studies of organometallic compounds, including cluster complexes.

Table 8.1 ■ Annual Surveys of Organometallic Chemistry

Year	Cr,Mo,W	Mn,Tc,Re	Fe,Ru,Os	Ru,Os	Co,Rh,Ir	Ni,Pd,Pt	Cu,Ag,Au
1975	143 385	126 383	151 1		138 229	126 431	138 405
1976	223 49	147 239	183 281		167 135	147 335	158 413
1977		176 307	223 117		176 339	167 265	
1978	180 205	189 129	274 241		211 279	196 175	
1979	196 79	211 177	223 273		230 1	211 397	
1980	237 95	237 61			230 99	324 283	
			Fe				
1981	257 105	242 205	274 331	245 409	242 241	337 431	
1982		261 69	283 405	274 457	261 103	357 51	
1983		17*365	278 205	318 297	278 1		
1984		318 83	298 77	318 409	305 1		
1985		318 121	318 157	351 89	324 57		
1986		357 25	343 1	351 145	351 215		
1987			360 319				

Structures: 1975: *126* 1; 1976: *151* 313; 1977: *167* 361; 1978: *196* 295; Heterometal clusters: 1980–1981: *251* 417; 1982–1983: *17** 399.
* Volume 17 in *J. Organomet. Chem. Library* series. Other references are volume, page of *J. Organomet. Chem.*

8.5. Bibliography of Reviews

The major part of this chapter collects together the large number of reviews that have been produced, enabling readers to have ready access to the substance of the literally thousands of research communications and papers that describe this chemistry. This survey is divided into 16 subsets by topic, some of which are further divided. Entries can be found under the following headings, and some cross-referencing has also been necessary:

A   Metal clusters: general chemistry
B   Metal clusters: reactions
C   Metal clusters: physical methods
    1 Structural studies
    2 Spectroscopic methods
    3 Electrochemistry
    4 Photo- and thermo-chemistry
D   Chemistry of metal-metal bonds in relation to clusters
E   Theoretical studies (mainly bonding)
F   Polynuclear metal carbonyls
G   Organometallic clusters by Periodic Group
H   Heterometallic clusters
I   Organometallic clusters by ligand
    1 Hydride
    2 Carbene, carbyne, isocyanide
    3 Unsaturated hydrocarbons (excluding alkynes)
    4 Alkynes
    5 Group 15 ligands
    6 Group 16 ligands
J   Clusters with main-group atoms (including interstitial)
K   Metal-boron clusters
    1 Metalloboranes
    2 Metallocarboranes
L   Naked metal clusters (gas phase, matrix isolated)
M   Metal clusters in catalysis
    1 Cluster complexes in solution
    2 Supported clusters
    3 Alloys
N   Metal clusters and Fischer-Tropsch chemistry
O   Surface chemistry
P   Metal clusters and surfaces

Not included are references to the chemistry of clusters containing main-group elements alone (boranes, carbon clusters, Zintl anions, etc.), the cubane systems of predominantly biochemical interest, halide and chalcogenide clusters of the early transition metals, the fascinating compounds discovered by Corbett and his group, or so-called one-dimensional complexes.

An indication of the depth of treatment can be obtained from the length of the review (inclusive pages given) and the number of references (given in parentheses after the page numbers). However, the latter is often a minimum number, as no

Table 8.2 ▪ Organometallic Cluster Syntheses

Complex	Reagents	Reference*
trans-$(Mo_6Cl_8)Cl_4(PBu_3)_2$	Mo_6Cl_{12}: PBu_3	OMS, 1988, *4*, 93
all trans-$(Mo_6Cl_8)Cl_2Et_2(PBu_3)_2$	$(Mo_6Cl_8)Cl_4(PBu_3)_2$: $AlEt_3$	OMS, 1988, *4*, 93
trans,mer-$(Mo_6Cl_8)ClEt_3(PBu_3)_2$	$(Mo_6Cl_8)Cl_2Et_2(PBu_3)_2$: $AlEt_3$	OMS, 1988, *4*, 94
trans-$(W_6Cl_8)Cl_4\{P(n\text{-}C_5H_{11})_3\}_2$	W_6Cl_{12}: $P(n\text{-}C_5H_{11})_3$	OMS, 1988, *4*, 93
all trans-$(W_6Cl_8)Cl_2Et_2\{P(n\text{-}C_5H_{11})_3\}_2$	$(W_6Cl_8)Cl_4\{P(n\text{-}C_5H_{11})_3\}_2$: $AlEt_3$	OMS, 1988, *4*, 94
trans,mer-$(W_6Cl_8)ClEt_3\{P(n\text{-}C_5H_{11})_3\}_2$	$(W_6Cl_8)Cl_2Et_2\{P(n\text{-}C_5H_{11})_3\}_2$: $AlEt_3$	OMS, 1988, *4*, 94
$Nb_3(CO)_7(\eta\text{-}C_5H_5)_3$	$Nb(CO)_4(\eta\text{-}C_5H_5)$: UV	Brauer, *3*, 1859
$Mn_3(\mu\text{-}H)_3(CO)_{12}$	$Mn_2(CO)_{10}$: (i) KOH, (ii) H_3PO_4	IS, 1970, *12*, 43 Brauer, *3*, 1973
$Mn_3(\mu\text{-}H)(\mu_3\text{-}B_2H_6)(CO)_{10}$	$Mn_3(CO)_{10}$: (i) $NaBH_4$, (ii) H_3PO_4	IS, 1980, *20*, 240
$Mn_4(\mu_3\text{-}SPh)_4(CO)_{12}$	$MnBr(CO)_5$: $Sn(SPh)Bu_3$	IS, 1989, *25*, 117
$Re_3(\mu\text{-}H)_3(CO)_{12}$	$Re_2(CO)_{10}$: (i) $NaBH_4$, (ii) H_3PO_4	IS, 1977, *17*, 66
$Re_4(\mu\text{-}H)_4(CO)_{12}$	$Re_2(CO)_{10}$: H_2	IS, 1978, *18*, 60
$\{Re(\mu_3\text{-}OH)(CO)_3\}_4$	$Re_2(CO)_{10}$: H_2O	Brauer, *3*, 2026
$Fe_3(CO)_{12}$	$Fe(CO)_5$: (i) KOH, (ii) MnO_2	OMS, 1965, *1*, 95 IS, 1963, *7*, 193 Brauer, *3*, 1828
$[Fe_3(\mu\text{-}H)(CO)_{11}]^-$	$Fe(CO)_5$: (i) NEt_3, (ii) HCl $Fe(CO)_5$: (i) $NaBH_4$, (ii) HOAc, (iii) [ppn]Cl	IS, 1966, *8*, 181 IS, 1980, *20*, 218
$[Fe_3(CO)_{11}]^{2-}$	$Fe_3(CO)_{12}$: (i) KOH, (ii) HOAc, (iii) [ppn]Cl $Fe_3(CO)_{12}$: (i) KOH, (ii) [ppn]Cl	IS, 1980, *20*, 222 IS, 1986, *24*, 157
$[Fe_4(CO)_{13}]^{2-}$	$Fe_3(CO)_{12}$: (i) $NaC_{10}H_8$, (ii) [ppn]Cl $Fe(CO)_5$: (i) py, (ii) [ppn]Cl	IS, 1982, *21*, 66
$Fe_4(\mu_3\text{-}CO)_4(\eta\text{-}C_5H_5)_4$	$\{Fe(CO)_2(\eta\text{-}C_5H_5)\}_2$: reflux in xylene	Brauer, *3*, 1872
$[Fe_4(\mu\text{-}S)_6(\eta\text{-}C_5H_5)_4]^{2+}$	$\{Fe(CO)_2(\eta\text{-}C_5H_5)\}_2$: S_8	IS, 1982, *21*, 44
$[Fe_4(\mu\text{-}S)_5(\eta\text{-}C_5H_5)_4][PF_6]$	$Fe_4(\mu\text{-}S)_6(\eta\text{-}C_5H_5)_4$: (i) O_2, PF_6^-	IS, 1982, *21*, 45
$Fe_4(\mu\text{-}S)_6(\eta\text{-}C_5H_5)_4$	$[Fe_4(\mu\text{-}S)_5(\eta\text{-}C_5H_5)_4][PF_6]$: $NaBH_4$	IS, 1982, *21*, 42
$Ru_3(CO)_{12}$	$RuCl_3 \cdot xH_2O$: Na(acac)/CO/H_2 $RuCl_3 \cdot xH_2O$: (i) CO, (ii) Zn/CO	IS, 1972, *13*, 92 Brauer, *3*, 1831 IS, 1976, *16*, 47 Brauer, *3*, 1831 IS, 1976, *16*, 45
$Ru_3(CO)_{11}(NCMe)$	$[Ru_3O(OAc)_6(OH)_3][OAc]$: CO (1 atm)	OMS, 1988, *4*, 234
$Ru_3(CO)_{10}(NCMe)_2$	$Ru_3(CO)_{12}$: Me_3NO, MeCN	OMS, 1988, *4*, 235
$[Ru_3(\mu\text{-}H)(CO)_{11}]^-$	$Ru_3(CO)_{12}$: Me_3NO, MeCN $Ru_3(CO)_{12}$: (i) $NaBH_4$, (ii) $[NEt_4]Br$	IS, 1986, *24*, 168

(continued)

Table 8.2 Continued ▪ **Organometallic Cluster Syntheses**

Complex	Reagents	Reference*
$Ru_3(\mu\text{-}NO)_2(CO)_{10}$	$Ru_3(CO)_{12}$: NO	IS, 1976, *16*, 39
$[Ru_3(\mu\text{-}NO)(CO)_{10}]^-$	$Ru_3(CO)_{12}$: [ppn]NO$_2$	IS, 1983, *22*, 165
$Ru_3(\mu\text{-}H)(\mu_3\text{-}MeCCCHCHMe)(CO)_9$ $\Big\}$ $Ru_3(\mu\text{-}H)(\mu_3\text{-}MeCCHCHMe)(CO)_9$	$Ru_3(CO)_{12}$: 1,3-pentadiene	OMS, 1988, *4*, 253
$Ru_3(\mu\text{-}H)(\mu_3\text{-}C_2Bu^t)(CO)_9$	$Ru_3(CO)_{12}$: HC$_2$Bu^t	OMS, 1988, *4*, 256
$Ru_3(\mu\text{-}H)_2(\mu_3\text{-}MeC_2Et)(CO)_9$	$Ru_3(CO)_{12}$: 1,3-pentadiene, H$_2$	OMS, 1988, *4*, 258
$Ru_3(\mu_3\text{-}MeCCEtCPhCPh)(\mu\text{-}CO)_2(CO)_6$	$Ru_3(\mu\text{-}H)(\mu_3\text{-}MeCCHCHMe)(CO)_9$: C$_2Ph_2$	OMS, 1988, *4*, 260
$Ru_4(\mu\text{-}H)_4(CO)_{12}$	$Ru_3(CO)_{12}$: H$_2$	OMS, 1988, *4*, 242
$[ppn][Ru_4(\mu\text{-}H)_3(CO)_{12}]$	$Ru_4(\mu\text{-}H)_4(CO)_{12}$: (i) KOH, (ii) [ppn]Cl	OMS, 1988, *4*, 242
$Os_3(CO)_{12}$	OsO$_4$: CO	IS, 1972, *13*, 93; Brauer, *3*, 1832
$[ppn][Os_3(\mu\text{-}H)(\mu\text{-}CO)(CO)_{10}]$	$Os_3(CO)_{12}$: KOH, [ppn]Cl	IS, 1989, *25*, 193
$Os_3(CO)_{11}(NCMe)$	$Os_3(CO)_{12}$: Me$_3$NO, MeCN	OMS, 1988, *4*, 234
$Os_3(CO)_{10}(NCMe)_2$	$Os_3(CO)_{12}$: Me$_3$NO, MeCN	OMS, 1988, *4*, 236
$Os_3(\mu\text{-}NO)_2(CO)_{10}$	$Os_3(CO)_{12}$: NO	IS, 1976, *16*, 40
$[ppn]_2[Os_4(\mu\text{-}H)_2(CO)_{12}]$	$Os_4(\mu\text{-}H)_4(CO)_{12}$: (i) KH, (ii) [ppn]Cl	OMS, 1988, *4*, 244
$Os_6(CO)_{17}(NCMe)$	$Os_6(CO)_{18}$: Me$_3$NO, MeCN	OMS, 1988, *4*, 238
$Os_6(CO)_{16}(NCMe)_2$	$Os_6(CO)_{18}$: Me$_3$NO, MeCN	OMS, 1988, *4*, 239
$Co_3(\mu_3\text{-}CX)(CO)_9$ X = Cl	$Co_2(CO)_8$: CCl$_4$	IS, 1980, *20*, 224; OMS, 1965, *1*, 153; Brauer, *3*, 1930
Br	$Co_2(CO)_8$: CBr$_4$	OMS, 1965, *1*, 153
Me	$Co_2(CO)_8$: CCl$_3$CH$_3$	OMS, 1965, *1*, 153
H	$Co_2(CO)_8$: CHBr$_3$	IS, 1980, *20*, 224
Ph	$Co_3(\mu_3\text{-}CH)(CO)_9$: HgPh$_2$	IS, 1980, *20*, 224
Co$_2$Et	$Co_2(CO)_8$: CCl$_3$CO$_2$Et	IS, 1980, *20*, 224
NHMe	$Co_3(\mu_3\text{-}CCO_2Et)(CO)_9$: (i) HPF$_6$, (ii) NH$_2$Me	IS, 1980, *20*, 224
CO$_2$Bu^t	$Co_3(\mu_3\text{-}CCl)(CO)_9$: (i) AlCl$_3$, (ii) Bu^{t}OH	IS, 1980, *20*, 224
$Co_4(CO)_{12}$	$Co_2(CO)_8$: Co(acac)$_2$/H$_2$ $\Big\}$: Co(2-Et-hexanoate)$_2$/H$_2$	OMS, 1965, *1*, 103; Brauer, *3*, 1834
$Rh_4(CO)_{12}$	{Rh(μ-Cl)(CO)$_2$}$_2$: CO $\Big\}$ {Rh(μ-Cl)(CO)$_2$}$_2$: NaHCO$_3$/CO Cu/CO	IS, 1977, *17*, 115; Brauer, *3*, 1836
	RhCl$_3$: (i) CO/Cu/NaCl, (ii) CO/H$_2$O	IS, 1980, *20*, 209

Rh₆(CO)₁₆	Rh₂(OAc)₄: CO/H₂O	IS, 1976, *16*, 49
	Rh₂(OAc)₄: CO/HBF₄/PrⁱOH }	Brauer, *3*, 1837
	RhCl₃: CO	
[Rh₆C(CO)₁₅]²⁻	K₃RhCl₆: CO/CHCl₃/KOH	IS, 1980, *20*, 212
[Rh₁₂(CO)₃₀]²⁻	Rh₄(CO)₁₂: NaOAc/H₂O	IS, 1980, *20*, 215
[Rh₃(μ₃–CH)(μ₃–CO)₂(η–C₅H₅)₃]⁺	{Rh(CO)(η–C₅H₅)}₂(μ–CH₂): HBF₄	Brauer, *3*, 1932
Ir₄(CO)₁₂	Na₂IrCl₆: (i) NaI, (ii) CO, (iii) K₂CO₃/CO	IS, 1972, *13*, 95
{Pt(μ₃–I)Me₃}₄	K₂PtCl₆: MeMgI	IS, 1967, *10*, 71
		Brauer, *3*, 1921
Cu₆(μ₃–H)₆(PR₃) (R = Ph, tol)	CuCl(PR₃): LiAlH₄	IS, 1979, *19*, 87
MnFe₂(μ₃–Te)(CO)₈(η–C₅Me₅)	Fe₂(CO)₉: {Mn(CO)₂(η–C₅Me₅)}₂Te	OMS, 1986, *3*, 304
[FeRu₃(μ–H)(CO)₁₃]⁻	Ru₃(CO)₁₂: [ppn][FeH(CO)₄]	IS, 1982, *21*, 60
FeRu₃(μ–H)₂(CO)₁₃	Ru₃(CO)₁₂: [ppn]₂[Fe(CO)₄]	IS, 1982, *21*, 58
FeOs₃(μ–H)₂(CO)₁₃	Os₃(μ–H)₂(CO)₁₀: Fe(CO)₅	IS, 1982, *21*, 63
Fe₃Au(μ–COMe)(CO)₁₀(PPh₃)	Fe₃(μ–H)(μ–COMe)(CO)₁₀: AuMe(PPh₃)	OMS, 1986, *3*, 312
RuOs₃(μ–H)₂(CO)₁₃	Os₃(μ–H)₂(CO)₁₀: Ru₃(CO)₁₂	IS, 1982, *21*, 64
[Ru₃Co(CO)₁₃]⁻	Ru₃(CO)₁₂: [ppn][Co(CO)₄]	IS, 1982, *21*, 61
Ru₃Au(μ–COMe)(CO)₁₀(PPh₃)	Ru₃(μ–H)(μ–COMe)(CO)₁₀: AuMe(PPh₃)	OMS, 1986, *3*, 312
Ru₄Ag(μ₃–H)₃(CO)₁₂(PPh₃)	[ppn][Ru₄(μ–H)₃(CO)₁₂]: (i) [Ag(NCMe)₄][PF₆], (ii) PPh₃	OMS, 1986, *3*, 319
Ru₄Ag₂(μ₃–H)₂(CO)₁₂(PPh₃)₂	[ppn]₂[Ru₄(μ–H)₂(CO)₁₂]: (i) Ag(NCMe)₄][PF₆], (ii) PPh₃	OMS, 1986, *3*, 315
Ru₄Cu(μ₃–H)₃(CO)₁₂(PPh₃)	[ppn][Ru₄(μ–H)₃(CO)₁₂]: (i) [Cu(NCMe)₄][PF₆], (ii) PPh₃	OMS, 1986, *3*, 319
Ru₄Cu₂(μ₃–H)₂(CO)₁₂(PPh₃)₂	[ppn]₂[Ru₄(μ–H)₂(CO)₁₂]: (i) [Cu(NCMe)₄][PF₆], (ii) PPh₃	OMS, 1986, *3*, 315
Ru₄Au(μ₃–H)(μ–H)₂(CO)₁₂(PPh₃)	[ppn][Ru₄(μ–H)₃(CO)₁₂]: AuCl(PPh₃)	OMS, 1988, *4*, 250
Ru₄Au₂(μ₃–H)(μ–H)(μ–dppm)(CO)₁₂	[ppn]₂[Ru₄(μ–H)₂(CO)₁₂]: Au₂(μ–dppm)Cl₂	OMS, 1988, *4*, 248
Os₃Co(μ–H)₂(μ–CO)(CO)₉(η–C₅H₅)	Os₃(μ–H)₂(CO)₁₀: Co(CO)₂(η–C₅H₅)	IS, 1989, *25*, 195
Os₃Co(μ–H)₃(CO)₉(η–C₅H₅) }		
Os₃Co(μ–H)₄(CO)₉(η–C₅H₅) }	Os₃(μ–H)₂(CO)₁₀: Co(CO)₂(η–C₅H₅), H₂	IS, 1989, *25*, 195

* IS Inorganic Syntheses; OMS Organometallic Syntheses; Brauer Brauer, G., ed., *Handbuch der Präparativen Anorganischen Chemie*, 3rd ed., Enke: Stuttgart (1981).

account has been taken of multiple citations appearing under the same reference number, or (in most cases) of additional references appearing, for example, with tabulated data. Grouping of reviews has been based mainly on content and title, subject to inspection in most cases.

8.6. Organometallic Cluster Syntheses

Finally, we include a list of tried and tested syntheses of metal cluster complexes often used as precursors, as given in various volumes of *Inorganic Syntheses* and *Organometallic Syntheses* (Table 8.2); space does not permit such a survey being extended to the primary literature. The syntheses are tabulated in order of Periodic Group, and indicate the precursors required.

8.7. Author Index for Cluster Review Bibliography

Acknowledgment

I am especially grateful to Dr. N. N. Zaitseva for help in tracking down and translating much of the Russian literature.

References

1. R. Hoffmann, *Angew. Chem.*, 1982, **94**, 725; *Angew. Chem. Int. Ed. Engl.*, 1982, **21**, 711.
2. F. G. A. Stone, *Angew. Chem.*, 1984, **96**, 85; *Angew. Chem. Int. Ed. Engl.*, 1984, **23**, 89.
3. E. L. Muetterties, *Bull. Soc. Chim. Belge*, 1975, **84**, 959.

A. General chemistry of metal clusters

A.1	Cluster complexes containing opened transition metal polyhedra	Albers MO, Robinson DJ, Coville NJ, *Coord Chem Rev*, 1986, **69**, 127–258 (357).
A.2	Covalent polynuclear compounds of transition and nontransition metals	Bochkarev MN, *Koord Khim*, 1984, **10**, 673–679 (16).
A.3	Organometallic cluster chemistry	Bradley JS, in Moskovits M, ed, *Metal Clusters*, Wiley: New York (1986), Ch 5, pp 105–130 (60).
A.4	Molecular clusters: materials, architectures, conclusions	Braunstein P, *Nouv J Chim*, 1986, **10**, 365–386 (281).
A.5	High- and low-valence metal cluster compounds: a comparison	Cotton FA, *ACS Symp Ser*, 1983, **211**, 209–219 (-).
A.6	Transition metal compounds containing clusters of metal atoms	Cotton FA, *Quart Rev*, 1966, **20**, 389–401 (43).
A.7	Cubane clusters	Garner CD, in Johnson BFG, ed, *Transition Metal Clusters*, Wiley: New York (1980), Ch 4, pp 265–344 (132).
A.8	Synthesis of monometallic and multimetallic clusters	Geoffroy GL, in Gates BC, Guczi L, Knözinger H, eds, *Metal Clusters in Catalysis*, Elsevier: Amsterdam (1986), Ch 1, pp 1–19 (60).
A.9	Chemistry of cluster compounds—the new trend in inorganic chemistry	Gubin SP, *Izvest Sib Otd AN SSSR, Ser Khim Nauk*, 1982, **9** (4), 3–7 (-).
A.10	Cluster chemistry—achievements and prospects	Gubin SP, *Zh Vses Khim O-va im D I Mendeleeva*, 1987, **32**, 3–11 (20).
A.11	Three-membered metallacycles	Gubin SP, *Usp Khim*, 1985, **54**, 529–555; *Russ Chem Rev*, 1985, **54**, 305–322 (169).
A.12	The chemistry of stabilized clusters	Iggo JA, Mays MJ, Taylor PL, *Phil Trans R Soc London*, 1982, **A308**, 27–34 (21).
A.13	Ligand-stabilized metal clusters: structure, bonding, fluxionality, and the metallic state	Kharas KCC, Dahl LF, *Adv Chem Phys*, 1988, **70** Pt 2, 1–43 (143).
A.14	Transition metal cluster compounds	King RB, *Prog Inorg Chem*, 1972, **15**, 287–473 (382).
A.15	Metal clusters revisited	Lewis J, *Chem Brit*, 1988, **24**, 795–800 (-).
A.16	Clusters provide unusual chemistry	Maugh TH, *Science*, 1983, **220**, 592–595 (4).

B.5 Fluxional molecules: reversible thermal intramolecular rearrangements of metal carbonyls — Cotton FA, Hanson BE in de Mayo P, ed, *Rearrangements in Ground and Excited States*, Academic: New York (1980), Vol 2, Ch 12, 379–421 (109).

B.6 Some reactions of metal clusters — Deeming AJ, in Johnson BFG, ed, *Transition Metal Clusters*, Wiley, New York (1980), Ch 6, pp. 391–469 (154).

B.7 Molecular rearrangements in polynuclear transition metal complexes — Evans J, *Adv Organomet Chem*, 1977, **16**, 319–347 (107).

B.8 Ligand mobility in clusters — Johnson BFG, Benfield RE, in Johnson BFG, ed, *Transition Metal Clusters* Wiley: New York (1980), Ch 7, pp 471–543 (103).

B.9 Transformation of organic substrates on metal cluster complexes — Kaesz HD, Knobler CB, Andrews MA, van Buskirk G, Szostak R, Strouse CE, Lin YC, Mayr A, *Pure Appl Chem*, 1982, **54**, 131–143 (23).

B.10 Reactivities of metal clusters — Lavigne G, Kaesz HD, in Gates BC, Guczi L, Knözinger H, eds, *Metal Clusters in Catalysis*, Elsevier: Amsterdam (1986), Ch 4, pp 43–88 (168).

B.11 Peculiarities of ligand coordination and activation on several metal centers in clusters — Maksakov VA, Gubin SP, *Koord Khim*, 1984, **10**, 689–700 (23).

B.12 The fluxionality of organic ligands on metal clusters — Mann BE, COMC, Vol. 3, Ch 20.20, pp 164–167 (24).

B.13 Intermetallic intramolecular exchange of carbon monoxide and related groups — Mann BE, COMC, Vol 3, Ch 20.9, pp 151–163 (65).

B.14 Selective reactions of transition metals and their complexes — Muetterties EL, *Inorg Chim Acta*, 1981, **50**, 1–9 (31).

B.15 Molecular features of metal cluster reactions — Muetterties EL, Burch RR, Stolzenberg AM, *Ann Rev Phys Chem*, 1982, **33**, 89–118 (112).

B.16 Kinetic studies of thermal reactivities of metal-metal bonded carbonyls — Poë A, *ACS Symp Ser*, 1981, **155**, 135–166 (82).

B.17 Kinetics of reactions of metal carbonyl clusters — Poë AJ, in Moskovits M, ed, *Metal Clusters*, Wiley: New York (1986), Ch 4, pp 53–103 (166).

B.18 Metal exchange in organometallic cluster compounds — Vahrenkamp H, *Comments Inorg Chem*, 1985, **4**, 253–267 (62).

B.19 Basic metal cluster reactions

Vahrenkamp H, *Adv Organomet Chem*, 1983, **22**, 169–208 (212).

C. Physical methods applied to the study of metal clusters

C1. Physical studies of metal cluster complexes
See also: I1.1, I1.9, I1.11.

C1.1 Metal–metal bonds and covalent atomic radii of transition metals in their pi-complexes and polynuclear carbonyls

Bir'yukov BP, Struchkov YuT, *Usp Khim*, 1970, **39**, 1672–1686; *Russ Chem Rev*, 1970, **39**, 789–798 (56).

C1.2 Index of structures determined by diffraction methods [to 1981: includes cluster complexes]

Bruce MI, COMC, Vol 9, pp 1209–1520.

C1.3 Structure of metal cluster complexes

Farrar DH, Goudsmit RJ, in Moskovits M, ed, *Metal Clusters*, Wiley: New York (1986), Ch 3, pp 29–51 (84).

C1.4 Cluster materials [structures of metal clusters]

Fedorov VE, Gubin SP, *Zh Vses Khim O-va im D I Mendeleeva*, 1987, **32**, 31–36 (86).

C1.5 Structures of metal clusters

Geoffroy GL, in Gates BC, Guczi L, Knözinger H, eds, *Metal Clusters in Catalysis*, Elsevier: Amsterdam (1986), Ch 2, pp 21–31 (8).

C1.6 Computer graphics in the study of metal cluster compounds

Henrick K, McPartlin M, Morris J, *Angew Chem*, 1986, **98**, 843–850; *Angew Chem Int Ed Engl*, 1986, **25**, 853–860 (41).

C1.7 Structural inorganic chemistry and diffraction methods: metal-ligand bonds in polynuclear complexes and on metal surfaces

Mason R, *Pure Appl Chem*, 1973, **33**, 513–526 (43).

C1.8 Structural organotransition metal chemistry

Mason R, Mingos DMP, *MTP Int Rev Sci, Inorg Chem, Ser II*, 1975, **11**, 121–176 (244).

C1.9 Some structural systematics in metal carbonyl cluster chemistry

McPartlin M, Mingos DMP, *Polyhedron*, 1984, **3**, 1321–1328 (27).

C1.10 Stereochemistry of metal cluster compounds

Penfold BR, *Perspectives Struct Chem*, 1968, **2**, 71–149 (181).

C1.11 The structure of metal cluster compounds

Raithby PR, in Johnson BFG, ed, *Transition Metal Clusters*, Wiley: New York (1980), Ch 2, pp. 5–192 (309).

(continued)

C4.4	Thermochemistry of metal-metal bonds	Connor JA, Skinner HA, *ACS Symp Ser*, 1981, **155**, 197–205 (29).
C4.5	Photochemistry of metal-metal bonds (dimeric only)	Meyer TJ, Caspar JV, *Chem Rev*, 1985, **85**, 187–218 (113).
C4.6	Photochemistry of metal-metal bonded transition metal complexes	Wrighton MS, Graff JL, Luong JC, Reichel CL, Robbins JL, *ACS Symp Ser*, 1981, **155**, 85–110 (74).

D. Chemistry of metal-metal bonds in relation to clusters

Book: Cotton FA, Walton RA, *Multiple Bonds Between Metal Atoms*, Wiley: New York (1982).

D.1	Metal-metal bonds in transition metal compounds	Baird MC, *Prog Inorg Chem*, 1968, **9**, 1–159 (898).
D.2	Bonding in coordination compounds containing metal-metal bonds	Bulkin BJ, Rundell CA, *Coord Chem Rev*, 1967, **2**, 371–384 (85).
D.3	Anything one can do, two can do, too—and it's more interesting	Chisholm MH, *ACS Symp Ser*, 1981, **155**, 17–39 (54).
D.4	Chemical reactions of metal-metal bonded compounds of the transition elements	Chisholm MH, Rothwell IP, *Prog Inorg Chem*, 1982, **29**, 1–72 (238).
D.5	Quadruple bonds and other multiple metal-metal bonds	Cotton FA, *Rev Pure Appl Chem*, 1967, **17**, 25–40 (-).
D.6	Strong homonuclear metal-metal bonds	Cotton FA, *Acc Chem Res*, 1969, **2**, 240–247 (49).
D.7	Discovering and understanding multiple metal-to-metal bonds	Cotton FA, *Acc Chem Res*, 1978, **11**, 225–232 (87).
D.8	Quadruple bonds and other multiple metal-to-metal bonds (R Soc Chem Centenary Lecture)	Cotton FA, *Chem Soc Rev*, 1975, **4**, 27–53 (127).
D.9	Synergistic interplay of experiment and theory in studying metal-metal bonds of various orders (Nyholm Lecture)	Cotton FA, *Chem Soc Rev*, 1983, **12**, 35–51 (29).
D.10	Multiple metal-metal bonds	Cotton FA, *J Chem Ed*, 1983, **60**, 713–720 (75).
D.11	Coordination compounds with metal-to-metal bonds: the constructive interaction of theory and experiment	Cotton FA, *Pure Appl Chem*, 1980, **52**, 2331–2337 (23).
D.12	Metal-metal multiple bonds and metal clusters: new dimensions and new opportunities in transition metal chemistry	Cotton FA, *ACS Symp Ser*, 1981, **155**, 1–16 (58).

(continued)

E.9   Nature of chemical bonding and electronic structure in systems with metal-metal bonds   Klyagina AP, Levin AA, *Koord Khim*, 1984, **10**, 579–587 (61).

E.10   Electronic structure of transition metal cluster compounds with weak- and strong-field ligands   Kostikova GP, Korol'kov DV, *Usp Khim*, 1985, **54**, 591–618; *Russ Chem Rev*, 1985, **54**, 344–360 (137).

E.11   Characteristics of the electronic structures of transition metal cluster complexes   Kostikova GP, Korol'kov DV, *Zh Vses Khim O-va im D I Mendeleeva*, 1987, **32**, 55–60 (38).

E.12   Clusters: stoichiometry, structure, and bonding electrons   Lemenovskii DA, *Izvest Sib Otd AN SSSR, Ser Khim Nauk*, 1982, **9** (4), 8–14 (38).

E.13   Electronic structures of transition metal cluster complexes   Manning MC, Trogler WC, *Coord Chem Rev*, 1981, **38**, 89–138 (406).

E.14   Electron-counting procedures in clusters of the iron triad   McPartlin M, *Polyhedron*, 1984, **3**, 1279–1288 (29).

E.15   Polyhedral skeletal electron-pair approach   Mingos DMP, *Acc Chem Res*, 1984, **17**, 311–319 (45).

E.16   Recent developments in theoretical organometallic chemistry   Mingos DMP, *Adv Organomet Chem*, 1977, **15**, 1–51 (245).

E.17   Theoretical and structural studies on organometallic cluster molecules   Mingos DMP, *Pure Appl Chem*, 1980, **52**, 705–712 (15).

E.18   Bonding in molecular clusters and their relationship to bulk metals   Mingos DMP, *Chem Soc Rev*, 1986, **15**, 31–61 (59).

E.19   Theoretical models of cluster bonding   Mingos DMP, Johnston RL, *Struct Bonding*, 1987, **68**, 29–87 (183).

E.20   Electron counting in clusters: a view of the concepts   Owen SM, *Polyhedron*, 1988, **7**, 253–283 (202).

E.21   Chemical bonding, kinetics, and the approach to equilibrium structures of simple metallic, molecular, and network microclusters   Phillips JC, *Chem Rev*, 1986, **86**, 619–634 (45).

E.22   Boranes and heteroboranes: a paradigm for the electron requirements of clusters?   Rudolph RW, *Acc Chem Res*, 1976, **9**, 446–452 (83).

E.23   The structure of transition metal cluster compounds and limits of applicability of the electron counting rules for polyhedral molecules   Slovokhotov YuL, Struchkov YuT, *Usp Khim*, 1985, **54**, 556–590; *Russ Chem Rev*, 1985, **54**, 323–343 (150).

E.24   A simple model of superaromatic clusters and the scope of electron calculation schemes   Slovokhotov YuL, Struchkov YuT, *Koord Khim*, 1984, **10**, 597–602 (28).

E.25   The bonding in boron and transition metal cluster compounds   Stone AJ, *Polyhedron*, 1984, **3**, 1299–1306 (18).

E.26   Structural and bonding patterns in cluster chemistry   Wade K, *Adv Inorg Chem Radiochem*, 1976, **18**, 1–66 (220).

E.27   Some bonding considerations [for metal clusters]   Wade K, in Johnson BFG, ed, *Transition Metal Clusters*, Wiley: New York (1980), Ch 3, pp 193–264 (153).

E.28   Electrons in transition metal cluster carbonyls   Woolley RG, in Johnson BFG, ed. *Transition Metal Clusters*, Wiley: New York (1980), Ch 9, pp 607–659 (50).

F. Polynuclear metal carbonyls

[See also entries in Section G under individual Groups]

F.1   The chemistry of transition metal carbonyls: structural considerations   Abel EW, Stone FGA, *Quart Rev*, 1969, **23**, 325–371 (209).

F.2   The chemistry of transition metal carbonyls: synthesis and reactivity   Abel EW, Stone FGA, *Quart Rev*, 1970, **24**, 498–552 (360).

F.3   Large metal carbonyl clusters (LMCC)   Chini P, *J Organomet Chem*, 1980, **200**, 37–61 (101).

F.4   Synthesis of large anionic carbonyl clusters as models for small metallic crystallites   Chini P, *Gazz Chim Ital*, 1979, **109**, 225–240 (57).

F.5   The closed metal carbcnyl clusters   Chini P, *Inorg Chim Acta Rev*, 1968, **2**, 31–51 (223).

F.6   Some aspects of the chemistry of polynuclear metal carbonyl compounds   Chini P, *Pure Appl Chem*, 1970, **23**, 489–503 (72).

F.7   Tetranuclear carbonyl clusters   Chini P, Heaton BT, *Topics Current Chem*, 1977, **71**, 1–70 (253).

F.8   High nuclearity metal carbonyl clusters   Chini P, Longoni G, Albano VG, *Adv Organomet Chem*, 1976, **14**, 285–344 (122).

F.9 μ_2-Bridging carbonyl systems in transition metal complexes   Colton R, McCormick MJ, *Coord Chem Rev*, 1980, **31**, 1–52 (162).

F.10   Metal carbonyls: some new observations in an old field   Cotton FA, *Prog Inorg Chem*, 1976, **21**, 1–28 (36).

F.11   Higher nuclearity carbcnyl clusters   Heaton BT, *ACS Symp Ser*, 1983, **211**, 227–234 (39).

(continued)

G6.8   Trinuclear clusters of the early transition elements   Müller A, Jostes R, Cotton FA, *Angew Chem*, 1980, **92**, 921–928; *Angew Chem Int Ed Engl*, 1980, **19**, 875–882 (57).

G7. *Mn, Tc, Re*

G7.1   Technetium and rhenium [metal carbonyls and their hydride and halide derivatives; also cubane clusters]   Boag NM, Kaesz HD, COMC, Vol 4, Ch 30.2, pp 162–170 (86).

G7.2   Rhenium clusters in inorganic chemistry: structures and metal-metal bonding   Perrin A, Sergent M, *New J Chem*, 1988, **12**, 337–356 (181).

G7.3   Chemistry of technetium cluster compounds   Spitsyn VI, Kuzina AF, Oblova AA, Kryuchkov SV, *Usp Khim*, 1985, **54**, 637–670; *Russ Chem Rev*, 1985, **54**, 373–393 (106).

G7.4   Manganese [references to trinuclear and cubane clusters]   Treichel PM, COMC, Vol 4, Ch 29, pp 1–159 (649).

G7.5   Ligand-induced redox reactions of low oxidation state rhenium halides and related systems in nonaqueous solvents   Walton RA, *Prog Inorg Chem*, 1976, **21**, 105–127 (81).

G8. *Fe, Ru, Os*

Books: Gmelin, System-nummer 59, Iron
Vol 36, pt B1 (1975): iron-cobalt carbonyls, pp 200–205
    pt B2 (1976): cluster compounds with one Fe(CO)$_3$ group, pp 194–199
    pt C1 (1977): binuclear iron carbonyls [including cluster compounds containing Fe$_2$(CO)$_n$ groups, pp 209–222]

    pt C7 (1984): polynuclear iron clusters
Gmelin, System-number 63, Ruthenium (1970)
[limited account of chemistry of Ru$_3$(CO)$_{12}$, pp 483–489]

G8.1   Chemistry of triosmium carbonyl cluster compounds and its implications for catalysis   Adams RD, *Acc Chem Res*, 1983, **16**, 67–72 (27).

G8.2   The synthesis, structures, bonding, and unusual reactivity of sulphido-osmium carbonyl cluster compounds   Adams RD, *Polyhedron*, 1985, **4**, 2003–2025 (46).

G8.3   The structure, bonding, and transformation behavior of iminium, aminocarbene, and aminocarbyne ligands in triosmium cluster complexes   Adams RD, Babin JE, Kim H-S, *Polyhedron*, 1988, **7**, 967–978 (39).

(continued)

G8.4	Novel reactions of metal carbonyl cluster compounds	Adams RD, Horvath IT, *Prog Inorg Chem*, 1985, **33**, 127–181 (200).
G8.5	Osmium carbonyls and related compounds	Adams RD, Selegue JP, COMC, Vol 4, Ch 33.1, pp 968–976 (72).
G8.6	[Osmium] Cluster compounds	Adams RD, Selegue JP, COMC, Vol 4, Ch 33.3, pp 1023–1057 (174).
G8.7	Generation and reactivity of ketene ligands on triosmium clusters	Bassner SL, Geoffroy GL, Rheingold AL, *Polyhedron*, 1988, **7**, 791–805 (22).
G8.8	Carbidocarbonyl clusters of iron	Bradley JS, *Phil Trans R Soc London*, 1982, **A308**, 103–113 (18).
G8.9	Some reactions of ruthenium cluster carbonyls under mild conditions	Bruce MI, *Coord Chem Rev*, 1987, **79**, 1–43 (174).
G8.10	Ruthenium: Introduction [includes cluster syntheses and fluxional behavior]	Bruce MI, COMC, Vol 4, Ch 32.1, pp 651–659 (60).
G8.11	Ruthenium carbonyls and related compounds	Bruce MI, COMC, Vol 4, Ch 32.2, pp 661–690 (136).
G8.12	Chemistry and reactivity of dodecacarbonyltriruthenium	Bruce MI, COMC, Vol 4, Ch 32.5, pp 843–887 (204).
G8.13	Polynuclear ruthenium carbonyl complexes	Bruce MI, COMC, Vol 4, Ch 32.6, pp 889–908 (80).
G8.14	Ruthenium complexes containing other metals	Bruce MI, COMC, Vol 4, Ch 32.8, pp 923–929 (36).
G8.15	Electron transfer-catalyzed substitution reactions of metal cluster carbonyls	Bruce MI, in Chanon M, Julliard M, Poite JC, eds, *Paramagnetic Organometallic Species in Activation/Selectivity, Catalysis* [NATO ASI Series, Vol C257], Kluwer: Dordrecht (1989), pp 407–422 (46).
G8.16	Dodecacarbonyltriruthenium	Bruce MI, Stone FGA, *Angew Chem*, 1968, **80**, 460–465; *Angew Chem Int Ed Engl*, 1968, **7**, 427–432 (74).
G8.17	Reactions of triosmium clusters with organic compounds	Burgess K, *Polyhedron*, 1984, **3**, 1175–1225 (223).
G8.18	Phosphido-bridged iron group clusters	Carty AJ, *ACS Adv Chem Ser*, 1982, **196**, 163–193 (44).
G8.19	Compounds with iron-metal bonds and clusters	Chini P, in Koerner von Gustorf EA, Grevels F-W, Fischler I, eds, *Organic Chemistry of Iron*, Academic: New York (1981), Vol 2, pp 189–282 (539).

(continued)

G8.34   Advances in platinum metal carbonyls and their substituted derivatives. I. Ru and Os carbonyls   Tripathi SC, Srivastava SC, Mani RP, Shrimal AK, *Inorg Chim Acta*, 1975, **15**, 249–290 (327).

G9. Co, Rh, Ir

Book: Gmelin, System-nummer 58, Cobalt (1972)
[Co₃ pp 127–174; Co₄ pp 175–199; Co₅ pp 200–202; Co₆ pp 202–218; Co₈ pp 213–215; Co₁₂ p 215]

See also: G8.31

G9.1	Compounds derived from alkynes and carbonyl complexes of cobalt	Dickson RS, Fraser PJ, *Adv Organomet Chem*, 1974, **12**, 323–377 (209).
G9.2	The chemistry, structure, and metal-metal bonding in compounds of rhodium(II)	Felthouse TR, *Prog Inorg Chem*, 1982, **29**, 73–166 (353).
G9.3	Photoinduced declusterification of cobalt carbonyls	Geoffroy GL, Epstein RA, ACS *Adv Chem Ser*, 1978, **168**, 132–146 (49).
G9.4	Rhodium compounds without hydrocarbon ligands. Polynuclear carbonyl complexes	Hughes RP, COMC, Vol 5, Ch 35.2.2, pp 317–339 (80).
G9.5	Cobalt compounds without hydrocarbon ligands [including polynuclear carbonyls]	Kemmitt RDW, COMC, Vol 5, Ch 34.2, pp 3–47 (222).
G9.6	Alkylidyne-enneacarbonyltricobalt and other alkylidyne-cobalt cluster complexes	Kemmitt RDW, COMC, Vol 5, Ch 34.3.9, pp 162–177 (37).
G9.7	Cobalt cluster compounds containing η5-ligands	Kemmitt RDW, COMC, Vol 5, Ch 34.4.5, pp 259–261 (11).
G9.8	Polynuclear iridium complexes	Leigh GJ, Richards RL, COMC, Vol 5, Ch 36.4, pp 614–620 (41).
G9.9	Tetrahedral cobalt carbonyl clusters with heteroatoms	Marko L, *Gazz Chim Ital*, 1979, **109**, 247–253 (45).
G9.10	The potential utility of transition metal-alkyne complexes and derived cluster compounds as reagents in organic synthesis	Nicholas KM, Nestle MO, Seyferth D, in Alper H, ed, *Transition Metal Organometallics in Organic Synthesis*, Academic: New York (1978), Vol 2, pp 1–63 (200).
G9.11	Methinyltricobalt enneacarbonyl compounds	Palyi G, Piacenti F, Marko L, *Inorg Chim Acta Rev*, 1970, **4**, 109–121 (94).
G9.12	Tricobaltcarbon, an organometallic cluster	Penfold BR, Robinson BH, *Acc Chem Res*, 1973, **6**, 73–80 (64).

G9.13   Tetrahedral carbonylcobalt clusters — Schmid G, *Angew Chem*, 1978, **90**, 417–424; *Angew Chem Int Ed Engl*, 1978, **17**, 392–400 (42).

G9.14   Chemistry of carbon-functional alkylidynetricobalt nonacarbonyl cluster complexes — Seyferth D, *Adv Organomet Chem*, 1976, **14**, 97–144 (89).

G9.15   Advances in platinum metal carbonyls and their substituted derivatives. II. Rh, Ir, Pd, and Pt carbonyls — Tripathi SC, Srivastava SC, Mani RP, Shrimal AK, *Inorg Chim Acta*, 1976, **17**, 257–290 (463).

G9.16   Rhodium carbonyl cluster chemistry under high pressures of carbon monoxide and hydrogen — Vidal JL, Schoening RC, Walker WE, *ACS Symp Ser*, 1981, **155**, 61–83 (22).

G10. *Ni, Pd, Pt*

Book: Gmelin, System-nummer 57, Nickel, Vol. 17, pt 2 (1974) [pp 372–392 Polynuclear nickel complexes]

See also: G8.31, G9.15

G10.1   Dinuclear complexes of the platinum metals containing a metal-metal bond — Baranovskii IB, Shchelokov RN, *Zh neorg Khim*, 1978, **23**, 3–17 (136)

G10.2   Platinum carbonyls and their use in homogeneous catalysis — Clark, HC, Jain VK, *Coord Chem Rev*, 1984, **55**, 151–204 (288).

G10.3   Carbonyl-phosphine clusters of palladium and platinum — Eremenko NK, Mednikov EG, Gubin SP, *Koord Khim*, 1984, **10**, 617–624 (24).

G10.4   Phosphinepalladium and phosphineplatinum carbonyl cluster compounds — Eremenko NK, Mednikov EG, Kurasov SS, *Usp Khim*, 1985, **54**, 671–693; *Russ Chem Rev*, 1985, **54**, 394–407 (69).

G10.5   Homopolynuclear and heteropolynuclear platinum carbonyl complexes — Hartley FR, COMC, Vol 6, Ch 39.1, pp 474–491 (120).

G10.6   Nickel tetracarbonyl [includes reduction to polynuclear nickel carbonyl anions] — Jolly PW, COMC, Vol 6, Ch 37.2, pp 3–14 (139).

G10.7   Palladium(I) and cluster complexes — Maitlis PM, Espinet P, Russell MJH, COMC, Vol. 6, Ch. 38.3, pp 265–278 (63).

G10.8   Synthesis of three-, four-, and ten-nuclear carbonylphosphine palladium clusters by reduction of palladium acetate with carbon monoxide — Mednikov EG, Eremenko NK, Gubin SP, *Koord Khim*, 1984, **10**, 711–714 (9).

(*continued*)

G10.9	Homonuclear cluster compounds of platinum	Mingos DMP, Wardle RWM, *Transition Met Chem*, 1985, **10**, 441–459 (76).
G10.10	Palladium(I) complexes in coordination chemistry and catalysis	Temkin ON, Bruk LG, *Usp Khim*, 1983, **52**, 206–243; *Russ Chem Rev*, 1983, **52**, 117–137 (163).

G11. *Cu, Ag, Au*

Books: Gmelin, System-nummer 60, Copper, Suppl. pt 4 (1986) [pp 192–253 Polynuclear copper complexes]
Gmelin, System-nummer 62, Gold, Suppl. (1980) [pp 275–291 Polynuclear gold and heterometallic clusters]

G11.1	Gold in bimetallic molecular clusters	Braunstein P, Rosé J, *Gold Bull*, 1985, **18**, 17–30 (113).
G11.2	New types of organometallic complexes of gold	Grandberg KI, *Koord Khim*, 1984, **10**, 646–655 (32).
G11.3	Homonuclear and heteronuclear cluster compounds of gold	Hall KP, Mingos DMP, *Prog Inorg Chem*, 1984, **32**, 237–325 (226).
G11.4	Gold compounds: X-ray structural and Mössbauer data	Melnik M, Parish RV, *Coord Chem Rev*, 1986, **70**, 157–257 (323).
G11.5	Complementary spherical electron density model for coordination compounds [includes clusters of gold with interstitial atoms]	Mingos DMP, *Pure Appl Chem*, 1987, **59**, 145–154 (21).
G11.6	Gold cluster compounds	Mingos DMP, *Gold Bull*, 1984, **17**, 5–12 (26).
G11.7	Some theoretical and structural aspects of gold cluster chemistry	Mingos DMP, *Phil Trans R Soc London*, 1982, **A308**, 75–83 (27).
G11.8	Structure and bonding in cluster compounds of gold	Mingos DMP, *Polyhedron*, 1984, **3**, 1289–1297 (40).
G11.9	Some aspects of the chemistry of organotin hydrides and of Group 1B arylmetal cluster compounds	Noltes JG, *J Organomet Chem*, 1975, **100**, 177–187 (95).
G11.10	Chemistry of organocopper clusters	Noltes JG, *Phil Trans R Soc London*, 1982, **A308**, 35–45 (17).
G11.11	Compounds of gold in unusual oxidation states	Schmidbaur H, Dash KC, *Adv Inorg Chem Radiochem*, 1982, **25**, 239–266 (124).
G11.12	Preparation and properties of gold cluster compounds	Steggerda JJ, Bour JJ, van der Velden JWA, *Receuil, J R Neth Chem Soc*, 1982, **101**, 164–170 (35).

G11.13	Dynamics of 3c-2e bonded aryl groups in copper, silver, and gold clusters	van Koten G, Noltes JG in Tsutsui M ed, *Fundamental Research in Homogeneous Catalysis*, Plenum: New York (1979), Vol 3, pp 953–968 (18).
G11.14	Copper and silver [includes cluster complexes]	van Koten G, Noltes JG, COMC, Vol 2, Ch 14, pp 709–763 (255).

H. Heterometallic clusters

See also: G8.13, G11.1, G11.3, I4.5, J.11, M1.2

H.1	New approaches to the chemistry of di- and tri-metal complexes	Ashworth TV, Chetcuti MJ, Farrugia LJ, Howard JAK, Jeffery JC, Mills R, Pain GN, Stone FGA, Woodward P, *ACS Symp Ser*, 1981, **155**, 299–313 (31).
H.2	Heterometallic clusters in catalysis	Braunstein P, Rosé J, *Stereochem Organomet Inorg Compounds*, 1988, **3**, (320).
H.3	Synthesis, molecular dynamics and reactivity of mixed-metal clusters	Geoffroy GL, *Acc Chem Res*, 1980, **13**, 469–476 (29).
H.4	Thermal and photochemical reactivity of $H_2FeRu_3(CO)_{13}$ and related mixed-metal clusters	Geoffroy GL, Foley HC, Fox JR, Gladfelter WL, *ACS Symp Ser*, 1981, **155**, 111–134 (38).
H.5	Mixed-metal clusters	Gladfelter WL, Geoffroy FL, *Adv Organomet Chem*, 1980, **18**, 207–273 (178).
H.6	New ways to heterometallic clusters. Synthesis of iron-rhodium cluster series	Gubin SP, Mikova NM, Tsybenov MTs, Lopatin VE, *Koord Khim*, 1984, **10**, 625–633 (18).
H.7	Laws governing the directed synthesis and structure of some types of heterometallic clusters	Pasynskii AA, Eremenko IL, *Sov Sci Rev B, Chem*, 1987, **10**, 443–483 (65).
H.8	Chemical construction of heterometallic magnetoactive clusters	Pasynskii AA, Eremenko IL, *Zh Vses Khim O-va im D I Mendeleeva*, 1987, **32**, 88–95 (35).
H.9	Synthesis and structure of chromium-containing heterometallic clusters	Pasynskii AA, Eremenko IL, Gasanov GSh, Orazsakhatov B, Kalinnikov NT, Shklover VE, Struchkov YuT, *Koord Khim*, 1984, **10**, 634–645 (25).

(continued)

H.10	Directed synthesis and structure of sterically strained antiferromagnetic metal clusters	Pasynskii AA, Eremenko IL, Kalinnikov VT, Buslaev YuA, *Izvest Sib Otd AN SSSR, Ser Khim Nauk*, 1982, **9** (4), 88–96 (18).
H.11	Compounds with heteronuclear bonds between transition elements	Roberts DA, Geoffroy GL, COMC, Vol 6, Ch 40, pp 763–877 (245).
H.12	Selective metal-ligand interactions in heterometallic transition metal clusters	Sappa, E, Tiripicchio A, Braunstein P, *Coord Chem Rev*, 1985, **65**, 219–284 (219).
H.13	Zero-valent platinum complexes and their role in the synthesis of di-, tri-, and tetra-nuclear metal compounds	Stone FGA, *Inorg Chim Acta*, 1981, **50**, 33–42 (75).
H.14	Ligand-free platinum compounds	Stone FGA, *Acc Chem Res*, 1981, **14**, 318–325 (63).
H.15	Novel routes to heteronuclear metal clusters containing rhodium	Stone FGA, *Phil Trans R Soc London*, 1982, **A308**, 87–93 (24).
H.16	Synthetic and structural studies on transition element cluster compounds with bridging carbene or carbyne groups	Stone FGA, *Proc 29th IUPAC Congr*, Cologne, 1983, pp 149–154 (21).
H.17	The alkylidyne compounds $(\eta\text{-}C_5H_5)(OC)_2W{=}CC_6H_4Me\text{-}4$, a reagent for synthesizing complexes with bonds between tungsten and other metals	Stone FGA, *ACS Symp Ser*, 1983, **211**, 383–397 (29).
H.18	A new approach to the synthesis of organometallic compounds relevant to catalysis	Stone FGA, in Shapiro BL, ed, *Organometallic Compounds*, Texas A&M UP: College Park (1983), pp 1–28 (34).
H.19	Heteronuclear cluster compounds	Vahrenkamp H, *Phil Trans R Soc London*, 1982, **A308**, 17–26 (10).

I. Organometallic clusters by ligand

II. *Hydrides*

II.1	Structures of transition metal hydride complexes	Bau R, *Acc Chem Res*, 1979, **12**, 176–183 (63).
II.2	Transition metal polyhydride complexes	Hlatky GG, Crabtree RH, *Coord Chem Rev*, 1985, **65**, 1–48 (292).
II.3	The hydrido-transition metal cluster complexes	Humphries AP, Kaesz HD, *Prog Inorg Chem*, 1979, **25**, 145–221 (212).

(continued)

I2.8   Zerovalent transition metal complexes of organic isocyanides   Yamamoto Y, *Coord Chem Rev*, 1980, **32**, 193–233 (172).

I3. *Unsaturated hydrocarbons (except alkynes)*

I3.1   Transition metal clusters with pi-acid ligands   Johnston RD, *Adv Inorg Chem Radiochem*, 1970, **13**, 471–533 (386).

I3.2   Approaches to the synthesis of pentalene via metal complexes   Knox SAR, Stone FGA, *Acc Chem Res*, 1974, **7**, 321–328 (48).

I3.3   Bi- and polynuclear complexes of transition metals synthesized on the basis of σ-vinyl derivatives of metals   Rybinskaya MI, Rybin LV, Yur'ev VP, *Koord Khim*, 1984, **10**, 656–665 (30).

I4. *Alkynes*

I4.1   Structural chemistry and reactivity of cluster-bound acetylides: close relatives of the carbides?   Carty AJ, *Pure Appl Chem*, 1982, **54**, 113–130 (49).

I4.2   Nucleophilic addition at μ3-alkyne clusters leading to carbon-carbon bond formation   Deeming AJ, Manning PJ, *Phil Trans R Soc London*, 1982, **A308**, 59–66 (25).

I4.3   Alkyne- and aryne-transition metal complexes   Mason R, Thomas KM, *Ann New York Acad Sci*, 1974, **239**, 225–236 (38).

I4.4   Alkyne-substituted transition metal clusters   Raithby PR, Rosales MJ, *Adv Inorg Chem Radiochem*, 1985, **29**, 169–247 (471).

I4.5   Alkyne-substituted homometallic and heterometallic carbonyl clusters of the iron, cobalt, and nickel triads   Sappa E, Tiripicchio A, Braunstein P, *Chem Rev*, 1983, **83**, 203–239 (338).

I5. *Clusters containing Group 15 ligands*

I5.1   Metal-metal bond making and breaking in binuclear complexes with phosphine bridging ligands   Balch AL, *ACS Symp Ser*, 1981, **155**, 167–185 (34).

J.19 Mixed metal-carbon clusters and metal carbides — Olah GA, Surya Prakash GK, Williams RE, Field LD, Wade K, *Hypercarbon Chemistry*, Wiley: New York (1987), Ch 4, pp 111–137 (104).

J.20 Advances in the chemistry of organometallic polynuclear compounds containing σ-bonded metals — Razuvaev GA, *J Organomet Chem*, 1980, **200**, 243–257 (61).

J.21 P, As, Sb, and Bi multiply bonded systems with low coordination number—their role as complex ligands — Scherer OJ, *Angew Chem*, 1985, **97**, 905–924; *Angew Chem Int Ed Engl*, 1985, **24**, 924–943 (85).

J.22 Three-dimensional metallic clusters with internal nonmetal atoms — Soloveichuk GL, Bulychev BM, Semenenko KN, *Koord Khim*, 1983, **9**, 1585–1616 (136).

J.23 Metal carbide clusters — Tachikawa M, Muetterties EL, *Prog Inorg Chem*, 1981, **28**, 203–238 (70).

J.24 The interface of main group and transition metal cluster chemistry — Whitmire KH, *J Coord Chem*, 1988, **17**, 95–203 (413).

K. Metallaboranes and metallacarboranes

Books: Adams, RM, ed, *Boron, Metallaboron Compounds and Boranes*, Interscience: New York (1964).
Grimes RN, *Carboranes*, Academic: New York (1970).
Grimes RN, ed, *Metal Interactions with Boron Clusters*, Plenum: New York (1982).

K.1 New chemistry of metallocarboranes and metalloboranes — Callahan KP, Hawthorne MF, *Pure Appl Chem*, 1974, **39**, 475–495 (47).

K.2 Metallacarboranes and metal-boron clusters in organometallic synthesis — Grimes RN, *Pure Appl Chem*, 1982, **54**, 43–58 (52).

K.3 Metallacarboranes and metallaboranes — Grimes RN, COMC, Vol 1, Ch 5.5, pp 459–542 (260).

K.4 Polyhedral boranes, carboranes, and carbametallic boron hydride derivatives — Hawthorne MF, *Endeavour*, 1966, **25**, 146–153 (40).

K.5 Electrochemistry of boron compounds — Morris JH, Gysling HJ, Reed D, *Chem Rev*, 1985, **85**, 51–76 (202).

K6 Polyhedral metallaboranes, metallacarbaboranes, and metalla-heteroboranes with the (η-C_5H_5)Fe fragment in the polyhedron — Zakharkin LI, Kobak VV, Zhigareva GG, *Usp Khim*, 1986, **55**, 974–998; *Russ Chem Rev*, 1986, **55**, 531–545 (74).

(continued)

K1. *Metallaboranes*

Books: Gmelin, system-nummer 13, Boron
Descriptions of transition metal derivatives of polynuclear boranes and carboranes are contained in the following volumes: Part 2, Section 1 (1974); Part 3, Section 11 (1975); Part 6, Section 3 (1975); 1st Suppl, Vol 1 (1980), Vol 3 (1981); 2nd Suppl, Vol 2 (1982).

K1.1	Metal-rich ferra- and cobalta-boranes. Mimics of organometallic clusters	Fehlner TP, *New J Chem*, 1988, **12**, 307–316 (83).
K1.2	Borane anion ligands—new bonding combinations with metals	Gaines DF, Fischer MB, Hildebrandt SJ, Ulman JA, Lott JW, *ACS Adv Chem Ser*, 1976, **150**, 311–317 (24).
K1.3	Compounds with bonds between a transition metal and boron	Gilbert KB, Boocock SK, Shore SG, COMC, Vol 6, Ch 41.1, pp 879–945 (289).
K1.4	Synthesis, structures, and reactions of metalloboranes	Greenwood NN, *Pure Appl Chem*, 1977, **49**, 791–800 (40).
K1.5	Heteroatom cluster compounds incorporating polyhedral boranes as ligands	Greenwood NN, *ACS Symp Ser*, 1983, **211**, 333–347 (8).
K1.6	Molecular tectonics: the construction of polyhedral clusters (Liversidge Lecture)	Greenwood NN, *Chem Soc Rev*, 1984, **13**, 353–374 (45).
K1.7	The design and synthesis of novel polyhedral metalloboranes	Greenwood NN, *Proc 29th IUPAC Congr, Cologne*, 1983, pp 131–134 (2).
K1.8	The synthesis, structure, and chemical reactions of metalloboranes	Greenwood NN, *Pure Appl Chem*, 1977, **49**, 791–801 (40).
K1.9	Metallaboranes 1983	Greenwood NN, *Pure Appl Chem*, 1983, **55**, 1415–1430 (77).
K1.10	Metallaborane cluster compounds	Greenwood NN, *Pure Appl Chem*, 1983, **55**, 77–87 (21).
K1.11	Novel cluster interactions in metalloboranes	Greenwood NN, *ACS Symp Ser*, 1983, **232**, 125–138 (17).
K1.12	Metalloboranes and metal-boron bonding	Greenwood NN, Ward IM, *Chem Soc Rev*, 1974, **3**, 231–271 (58).
K1.13	Structure and stereochemistry in metalloboron cage compounds	Grimes RN, *Acc Chem Res*, 1978, **11**, 420–427 (58).
K1.14	The role of metals in borane clusters	Grimes RN, *Acc Chem Res*, 1983, **16**, 22–26 (30).
K1.15	Small metalloboron cage compounds as analogues of metal clusters. Unifying concepts of bonding	Grimes RN, *Ann NY Acad Sci*, 1974, **239**, 180–192 (66).

(continued)

K2.24	Carboranes and metallocarboranes	Snaith R, Wade K, in *MTP Int Rev Sci, Ser 2, Inorg Chem*, Butterworth: London (1975), Vol 1, pp 95–134 (1977).
K2.25	Transition metal-carborane complexes	Todd LJ, *Adv Organomet Chem*, 1970, **8**, 87–115 (49).
K2.26	Recent developments in the study of carboranes	Todd LJ, *Pure Appl Chem*, 1972, **30**, 587–598 (27).
K2.27	Metallocarboranes: structural studies in recent years	Yanovskii AI, *Usp Khim*, 1985, **54**, 881–902; *Russ Chem Rev*, 1985, **54**, 515–531 (78).
K2.28	Structural chemistry of metallocarboranes [of Co, Fe, Pt, Re]	Yanovskii AI, Struchkov YuT, *Khim Svyaz Str Mol*, 1984, 83–96 (21).
K2.29	Metallocarboranes	Zakharkin LI, Kalinin VN, *Usp Khim*, 1974, **43**, 1207–1240; *Russ Chem Rev*, 1974, **43**, 551–573 (142).
K2.30	Structure of organometallic compounds with metallachains, metallacycles, and metallaframeworks	Zakharov LN, Struchkov YuT, *Izvest Sib Otd AN SSSR, Ser Khim Nauk*, 1982, **9** (4), 14–29 (48).
K2.31	Closo-borate anions as a means of synthesizing new coordination compounds	Zakharova IA, *Coord Chem Rev*, 1982, **43**, 313–324 (20).

L. Naked metal clusters (gas-phase, matrix-isolated)

L.1	Structure and electronic relations between molecular clusters and small particles: an essay to the understanding of very dispersed metals	Basset J-M, Ugo R, *Aspects Homogen Catal*, 1977, **3**, 137–183 (168).
L.2	Clusters: bridging the gas and condensed phases [ion chemistry]	Castleman AW, Keesee RG, *Acc Chem Res*, 1986, **19**, 413–419 (60).
L.3	Unsupported small metal particles: preparation, reactivity, and characterization	Davis SC, Klabunde KJ, *Chem Rev*, 1982, **82**, 153–208 (309).
L.4	Structural models for clusters produced in a free jet expansion	Farges J, de Feraudy MF, Raoult B, Torchet G, *Adv Chem Phys*, 1988, **70** Pt 2, 45–74 (38).
L.5	The gas-phase characterization of the molecular electronic structure of small metal clusters and cluster oxidation	Gole JL, in Moskovits M, ed, *Metal Clusters*, Wiley: New York (1986), Ch 6, pp 131–185 (156).
L.6	Study of the genesis, structure, and reactions of small metal clusters using a rotating cryostat [naked clusters by evaporation]	Howard JA, Mile B, *Acc Chem Res*, 1987, **20**, 173–179 (82).

(continued)

L.7 Molecular surface chemistry: reactions of gas-phase metal clusters — Kaldor A, Cox DM, Zakin MR, *Adv Chem Phys*, 1988, **70** Pt 2, 211–261 (135).

L.8 Theoretical aspects of metal atom clusters [in the gas phase] — Koutecky J, Fantucci P, *Chem Rev*, 1986, **86**, 539–587 (360).

L.9 Cluster beam chemistry—from atoms to solids — Martin TP, *Angew Chem*, 1986, **98**, 197–211; *Angew Chem Int Ed Engl*, 1986, **25**, 197–211 (90).

L.10 Clusters of [ligand-free] transition metal atoms — Morse MD, *Chem Rev*, 1986, **86**, 1049–1109 (577).

L.11 Application of matrix isolation to the study of metal clusters with a postscript on the reactivity of clusters in supersonic beams — Moskovits M, in Moskovits M, ed, *Metal Clusters*, Wiley: New York (1986), Ch 7, pp 185–217 (100).

L.12 Clusters of metals in a graphite matrix and their catalytic properties — Novikov YuN, Vol'pin ME, *Zh Vses Khim O-va im D I Mendeleeva*, 1987, **32**, 69–75 (43).

L.13 Cobalt, nickel, and copper naked metal clusters and olefin chemisorption models — Ozin GA, *Coord Chem Rev*, 1979, **28**, 117–142 (45).

L.14 Very small metallic and bimetallic clusters: the metal cluster-metal-surface analogy in catalysis and chemisorption processes — Ozin GA, *Catal Rev—Sci Eng*, 1977, **16**, 191–286 (93).

L.15 Metal atom matrix chemistry. Correlation of bonding with chemisorbed molecules — Ozin GA, *Acc Chem Res*, 1977, **10**, 21–26 (32).

L.16 Dispersed metal clusters from metal vapour chemistry — Ozin GA, Andrews MA, in Gates BC, Guczi L, Knözinger H, eds, *Metal Clusters in Catalysis*, Elsevier: Amsterdam (1986), Ch 7, pp 265–356 (186).

L.17 Ligand-free metal clusters — Ozin GA, Mitchell SA, *Angew Chem*, 1983, **95**, 706–727; *Angew Chem Int Ed Engl*, 1983, **22**, 674–694 (140).

L.18 Magnetic properties of ultradispersed (cluster) particles — Piskorskii VP, Lipanov AM, Balusov VA, *Zh Vses Khim O-va im D I Mendeleeva*, 1987, **32**, 47–50 (44).

L.19 Cluster-globule metallic phase [concept and definition of metal clusters] — Semenenko KN, *Zh Vses Khim O-va im D I Mendeleeva*, 1987, **32**, 24–30 (12).

L.20 Vapour-phase method for synthesis of metal cluster catalysts — Sergeev VA, Vasil'kov AYu, Lisichkin GV, *Zh Vses Khim O-va im D I Mendeleeva*, 1987, **32**, 96–100 (54).

L.21 From polynuclear complexes to colloidal metals — Vargaftik MN, *Zh Vses Khim O-va im D I Mendeleeva*, 1987, **32**, 36–42 (66).

M. Metal clusters in catalysis

Books: Gates, BC, Guczi L, Knözinger H, eds, *Metal Clusters in Catalysis*, Elsevier: Amsterdam (1986) [see below].

Yermakov Yu, Likholobov V, eds, *Homogeneous and Heterogeneous Catalysis* (Proc. 5th Int Symp. Relations between Homogen. Heterogen. Catal., Novosibirsk, July 1986), VNU Science Press: Utrecht (1986) [Pt 3: Catalysis by metal clusters and dispersed metal particles].

M1. *Homogeneous catalysis*

M1.1	The water gas-shift reaction: homogeneous catalysis by ruthenium and other metal carbonyls	Ford PC, *Acc Chem Res*, 1981, **14**, 31–37 (34).
M1.2	The homogeneous hydrogenation of carbon-carbon multiple bonds with heteronuclear platinum clusters	Fusi A, Ugo R, Psaro R, Braunstein P, Dehand J, *Phil Trans R Soc London*, 1982, **A308**, 125–130 (13).
M1.3	Transition metal clusters as catalysts	Huttner G, *Nachr Chem Tech Lab*, 1979, **27**, 261–263 (15).
M1.4	Metal clusters and cluster catalysis	Jackson SD, Wells PB, Whyman R, Worthington P, in Kemball C, Dowden DA, eds, *Catalysis*, R Soc Chem: London (1981), Ch 3, pp 75–99 (125).
M1.5	Stereochemically opened clusters of heavy d elements in redox catalysis	Korolkov DV, *Izvest Sib Otd AN SSSR, Ser Khim Nauk*, 1982, **9** (4), 54–73 (15).
M1.6	Criteria for identifying transition metal cluster-catalyzed reactions	Laine RM, *J Mol Catal*, 1982, **14**, 137–169 (87).
M1.7	Recent developments in the homogeneous catalysis of the water gas-shift reaction	Laine RM, Wilson RB, *Aspects Homogen Catal*, 1984, **5**, 217–240 (71).
M1.8	Principal laws governing the catalysis of the conversions of unsaturated hydrocarbons by metal carbonyl clusters	Magomedov GK-I, *Koord Khim*, 1984, **10**, 893–900 (33).
M1.9	Homogeneous catalysis by metal clusters	Marko L, Vizi-Orosz A, in Gates BC, Guczi L, Knözinger H, eds, *Metal Clusters in Catalysis*, Elsevier: Amsterdam (1986), Ch 5, pp 89–120 (116).
M1.10	Molecular metal clusters as catalysts	Muetterties EL, *Catal Rev*, 1981, **23**, 69–83 (42).
M1.11	Metal clusters in catalysis. Reduction of triple bonds	Muetterties EL, *Bull Soc Chim Belge*, 1976, **85**, 451–470 (-).

(continued)

M1.12	Metal clusters in catalysis. Selective hydrogenation of triple bonds with organometallic transition metal compounds	Muetterties EL, *Pure Appl Chem*, 1978, **50**, 941–950 (36).
M1.13	Metal clusters in catalysis. Clusters as models for chemisorption processes and heterogeneous catalysis	Muetterties EL, *Bull Soc Chim Belge*, 1975, **84**, 959–986 (95).
M1.14	Hydrocarbon reactions at metal centers	Muetterties EL, *Chem Soc Rev*, 1982, **11**, 283–320 (102).
M1.15	Metal cluster-catalyzed hydrocarbon activation	Muetterties EL, in Ishii Y, Tsutsui M, eds, *Fundamental Research in Homogeneous Catalysis*, Plenum: New York (1978), Vol 2, pp 1–10 (-).
M1.16	Catalysis by molecular metal clusters	Muetterties EL, Krause MJ, *Angew Chem*, 1983, **95**, 135–148; *Angew Chem Int Ed Engl*, 1983, **22**, 135–148 (106).
M1.17	Metal cluster catalysis	Pittman CU, Ryan RC, *ChemTech*, 1978, **8**, 170–175 (51).
M1.18	Metal clusters and catalysis	Shapley JR, *Strem Chemiker*, 1978, **6**, 3–8 (26).
M1.19	Transition metal cluster complexes as catalysts	Smith AK, Basset J-M, *J Mol Catal*, 1977, **2**, 229–241 (55).
M1.20	New catalysts—reactions through transition metal clusters	Süss-Fink G, *Nachr Chem Tech Lab*, 1988, **36**, 1110–1113 (25).
M1.21	Transition metal carbonyl cluster chemistry: some new aspects of carbon monoxide catalysis	Ugo R, Psaro R, *J Mol Catal*, 1983, **20**, 53–79 (119).
M1.22	Industrial aspects of cluster chemistry	Whyman R, *Phil Trans R Soc London*, 1982, **A308**, 131–140 (17).
M1.23	Metal clusters in catalysis	Whyman R, in Johnson BFG, ed, *Transition Metal Clusters*, Wiley: New York (1980), Ch 8, pp 545–606 (130).

M2. *Catalysis by supported clusters*

Book: Gates BC, Guczi L, Knözinger H, eds, *Metal Clusters in Catalysis*, Elsevier: Amsterdam (1986) (also referenced as *Stud. Surf. Sci. Catal.*, 1986, **29**) contains an extensive section on the characterization of supported clusters.

6. Characterization of supported metal clusters by physical methods:
Knözinger H, Vibrational spectroscopies, Ch 6.2, pp 129–172 (155).
Knözinger H, Optical spectroscopy, Ch 6.3, pp 173–186 (36).
Knözinger H, Magnetic resonance, Ch 6.4, pp 187–207 (82).

Guczi L, Photoelectron spectroscopies, Ch 6.5, pp 209–219 (40).

Guczi L, Mössbauer spectroscopy, Ch 6.6, pp 221–230 (17).

Pettifer RF, X-Ray absorption spectroscopy, Ch 6.7, pp 231–258 (29).

Knözinger H, Thermoanalytical methods, Ch. 6.8, pp 259–264 (12).

9. Supported metal catalysts prepared from molecular metal clusters: organometallic surface chemistry.

Gates BC, Metal clusters on functionalized supports, Ch. 9.1, pp 415–425 (42).

Psaro R, Ugo R, Metal clusters on unfunctionalized inorganic oxides, Ch. 9.2, pp 427–496 (277).

Gates BC, Supported metal cluster catalysts for alkene conversion, Ch. 9.3, pp 497–507 (20).

Maire G, Supported metal catalysts prepared from molecular clusters: activities for hydrogenolysis and skeletal isomerization of hydrocarbons, Ch. 9.4, pp 509–530 (56).

Knözinger H, Gates BC, CO hydrogenation catalysis and supported metal clusters, pp 531–545 (52).

10. Guczi L, Supported bimetallic catalysts derived from molecular metal clusters, pp 547–574 (98).

M2.1 [Catalytic applications of] Polynuclear complexes on the surfaces of supports

M2.2 Immobilized transition metal carbonyls and related catalysts [includes polymer-clusters]

M2.3 Catalysis by supported clusters: two examples of catalytic reactions that involve a molecular cluster frame

M2.4 Comparative catalytic activity of supported clusters

M2.5 Clusters in heterogeneous catalysis

M2.6 Metal clusters in zeolites

Arzamaskova LN, Ermakov YuI, *Zh Vses Khim O-va im D I Mendeleeva*, 1987, **32**, 75–81 (51).

Bailey DC, Langer SH, *Chem Rev*, 1981, **81**, 109–148 (308).

Basset J-M, Besson B, Choplin A, Theolier A, *Phil Trans R Soc London*, 1982, **A308**, 115–124 (48).

Brenner A, in Moskovits M, ed, *Metal Clusters*, Wiley: New York (1986), Ch 9, pp 249–281 (114).

Ermakov YuI, Arzamaskova LN, Kuznetsov VL, *Koord Khim*, 1984, **10**, 877–886 (40).

Gallezot P, in Moskovits M, ed, *Metal Clusters*, Wiley: New York (1986), Ch 8, pp 219–247 (107).

(continued)

M2.7	Supported metal cluster catalysis	Gates BC, in Moskovits M, ed, *Metal Clusters*, Wiley: New York (1986), Ch 10, pp 283–310 (68).
M2.8	Metallic clusters in polymer matrices ('cluspol')	Gubin SP, Kozobudskii ID, *Usp Khim*, 1983, **52**, 1350–1364; *Russ Chem Rev*, 1983, **52**, 766–774 (62).
M2.9	Supported bimetallic catalysts derived from molecular metal clusters	Guczi L, in Gates BC, Guczi L, Knözinger H, eds, *Metal Clusters in Catalysis*, Elsevier: Amsterdam (1986), Ch 10, pp 547–574 (98).
M2.10	Cluster-derived supported catalysts and their use	Ichikawa M, *Chem Tech*, 1982, 674–680 (11).
M2.11	Metal clusters and zeolites	Jacobs PA, in Gates BC, Guczi L, Knözinger H, eds, *Metal Clusters in Catalysis*, Elsevier: Amsterdam (1986), Ch 8, pp 357–414 (198).
M2.12	Metal cluster complexes and heterogeneous catalysis: a heterodox view	Moskovits M, *Acc Chem Res*, 1979, **12**, 229–236 (74).
M2.13	Problems in the study of supported metal catalysts	Slinkin AA, *Usp Khim*, 1980, **49**, 771–788; *Russ Chem Rev*, 1980, **49**, 404–413 (96).
M2.14	Cluster and polynuclear heterogeneous metal complex catalysts	Yuffa AYa, Lisichkin GV, *Usp Khim*, 1986, **55**, 1452–1479; *Russ Chem Rev*, 1986, **55**, 825–842 (166).

M3. Bimetallic catalysts and alloys

M3.1	Structure and catalytic properties of palladium-silver and palladium-gold alloys	Allison EG, Bond GC, *Catal Rev*, 1972, **7**, 233–289 (194).
M3.2	Importance of electronic ligand effects in metal alloy catalysis	Burch R, *Acc Chem Res*, 1982, **15**, 24–31 (76).
M3.3	Structure of bimetallic clusters [solid state]	Sinfelt JH, *Acc Chem Res*, 1987, **20**, 134–139 (47).
M3.4	Catalysis by alloys and bimetallic clusters	Sinfelt JH, *Acc Chem Res*, 1977, **10**, 15–20 (43).

N. Metal clusters and Fischer-Tropsch chemistry

Books: Anderson RB, *The Fischer-Tropsch Synthesis*, Academic: New York (1984).

Falbe J, ed, *New Syntheses with Carbon Monoxide*, Springer: Berlin (1980).

Keim W, *Catalysis in C₁ Chemistry*, Reidel: Dordrecht (1983).

Kugler EL, Steffgen FW, eds, *Hydrocarbon Synthesis from Carbon Monoxide and Hydrogen*, ACS: Washington (1979) [ACS Adv. Chem. Ser., Vol. 178].

N.1 Mechanism of hydrocarbon synthesis over Fischer-Tropsch catalysts
Biloen P, Sachtler WMH, *Adv Catal*, 1981, **30**, 165–214 (84).

N.2 Model studies of metal-catalyzed CO reduction
Casey CP, Neumann SM, Andrews MA, McAlister DR, *Pure Appl Chem*, 1980, **52**, 625–632 (31).

N.3 Homogeneous catalytic hydrogenation of carbon monoxide: ethylene glycol and ethanol from synthesis gas
Dombek BD, *Adv Catal*, 1983, **32**, 326–416 (219).

N.4 Advances in Fischer-Tropsch chemistry
Dry ME, *Ind Eng Chem, Prod Res Dev*, 1976, **15**, 282–285 (-).

N.5 The mechanism of the Fischer-Tropsch reaction and the initiated hydropolymerization of alkenes, from radiochemical and kinetic data
Eidus Y, *Usp Khim*, 1967, **36**, 824–846; *Russ Chem Rev*, 1967, **36**, 338–351 (125).

N.6 The Fischer-Tropsch synthesis: molecular weight distribution of primary products and reaction mechanism
Henrici-Olivé G, Olivé S, *Angew Chem*, 1976, **88**, 144–149; *Angew Chem Int Ed Engl*, 1976, **15**, 136–141 (21).

N.7 Organometallic aspects of the Fischer-Tropsch synthesis
Herrmann WA, *Angew Chem*, 1982, **94**, 118–129; *Angew Chem Int Ed Engl*, 1982, **21**, 117–130 (48).

N.8 A technological perspective for catalytic processes based on synthesis gas
King DL, Cusumano JA, Garten RL, *Catal Rev*, 1981, **23**, 233–259 (58).

N.9 Metal carbonyl catalysts of the synthesis of organic compounds from carbon monoxide and molecular hydrogen
Lapidus AL, Savel'ev MM, *Usp Khim*, 1988, **57**, 29–49; *Russ Chem Rev*, 1988, **57**, 17–28 (165).

N.10 The Fischer-Tropsch reaction
Masters C, *Adv Organomet Chem*, 1979, **17**, 61–103 (115).

N.11 Mechanistic features of catalytic carbon monoxide hydrogenation reactions
Muetterties EL, Stein J, *Chem Rev*, 1979, **79**, 479–491 (93).

N.12 The development of catalytic synthesis of organic compounds from carbon monoxide and hydrogen
Nefedov BE, Eidus YaT, *Usp Khim*, 1965, **34**, 630–652; *Russ Chem Rev*, 1965, **34**, 272–284 (214).

N.13 A comprehensive mechanism for the Fischer-Tropsch synthesis
Rofer-DePoorter CK, *Chem Rev*, 1981, **81**, 447–474 (416).

(continued)

N.14   Metal carbonyl clusters in the catalytic hydrogenation of carbon monoxide   Zwart J, Snel R, *J Mol Catal*, 1985, **30**, 305–352 (220).

O. Surface chemistry

Books: Albert MR, Yates JT, *The Surface Scientist's Guide to Organometallic Chemistry*, ACS: Washington (1986).

Anderson JR, *Structure of Metallic Catalysts*, Academic: New York (1975).

Anderson JR, ed, *Chemisorption and Reactions on Metallic Films*, Academic: New York (1971), Vols 1, 2.

Basset J-M: Gates BC, Candy J-P, Choplin A, Leconte M, Quignard F, Santini C, eds, *Surface Organometallic Chemistry: Molecular Approaches to Surface Catalysis* [NATO ASI Series, Vol C231], Kluwer: Dordrecht (1988).

Ertl G, Kuppers J, *Low Energy Electrons and Surface Chemistry*, Verlag Chemie: Weinheim (1974).

Gomer R, ed, *Interactions on Metal Surfaces*, Springer: Berlin (1975).

Rhodin TN, Ertl G, eds, *The Nature of the Surface Chemical Bond*, North Holland: Amsterdam (1978).

Somorjai GA, *Chemistry in Two Dimensions: Surfaces*, Cornell U.P.: Ithaca (1981) [Ch 7, 8].

Thompson SJ, Webb RN, *Heterogeneous Catalysis*, Wiley: New York (1968).

Rideal EK, *Concepts in Catalysis*, Academic: New York (1968).

Gomer BC, Katzer JR, Schint GCA, *Chemistry of Catalytic Processes*, McGraw-Hill: New York (1979).

O.1   Surface organometallic chemistry: a new approach to heterogeneous catalysis   Basset J-M, Choplin A, *J Mol Catal*, 1983, **21**, 95–108 (22).

O.2   The mechanism of the hydrogenation of unsaturated hydrocarbons on transition metal catalysts   Bond GC, Wells PB, *Adv Catal*, 1964, **15**, 91–226 (161).

O.3   Ultraviolet photoelectron spectroscopy of gases adsorbed on metal surfaces   Bradshaw AM, Cederbaum LS, Domcke W, *Struct Bonding*, 1975, **24**, 133–169 (105).

O.4 — The structure of adsorbed gas monolayers — Buchholz JC, Somorjai GA, *Acc Chem Res*, 1976, **9**, 333–338 (43).

O.5 — Surface structures of adsorbed gases on solid surfaces: a tabulation of data reported by low-energy electron diffraction studies — Castner DG, Somorjai GA, *Chem Rev*, 1979, **79**, 233–252 (437).

O.6 — Infrared spectra of chemisorbed molecules — Eischens RP, *Acc Chem Res*, 1972, **5**, 74–80 (32).

O.7 — Elementary processes at gas/metal interfaces — Ertl G, *Angew Chem*, 1976, **88**, 423–432; *Angew Chem Int Ed Engl*, 1976, **15**, 391–400 (81).

O.8 — Chemisorption on transition metal surfaces — Ertl G, *Gazz Chim Ital*, 1979, **109**, 217–224 (41).

O.9 — Surface science and catalysis — Ertl G, *Pure Appl Chem*, 1980, **52**, 2051–2060 (21).

O.10 — Carbon monoxide adsorption on transition metals — Ford RR, *Adv Catal*, 1970, **21**, 51–150 (212).

O.11 — Reaction mechanisms in heterogeneous catalysis (metal surfaces) — Gault FG, *Gazz Chim Ital*, 1979, **109**, 255–269 (75).

O.12 — Model catalytic studies over metal single crystals — Goodman DW, *Acc Chem Res*, 1984, **17**, 194–200 (43).

O.13 — Structure of solid surfaces — Kesmodel LL, Somorjai GA, *Acc Chem Res*, 1976, **9**, 392–398 (56).

O.14 — Molecular organometallic chemistry on surfaces: reactivity of metal carbonyls on metal oxides — Lamb HH, Gates BC, Knözinger H, *Angew Chem*, 1988, **100**, 1162–1179; *Angew Chem Int Ed Engl*, 1988, **27**, 1127–1144 (71).

O.15 — Surface reactivity: heterogeneous reactions on single crystal surfaces — Madix RJ, *Acc Chem Res*, 1979, **12**, 265–270 (30).

O.16 — Coordination and activation of simple molecules on metal surfaces — Mason R, Wyn-Roberts M, *Inorg Chim Acta*, 1981, **50**, 53–58 (30).

O.17 — Stereochemistry in the coordination chemistry of metal surfaces — Muetterties EL, *Isr J Chem*, 1980, **20**, 84–92 (55).

O.18 — The coordination chemistry of metal surfaces — Muetterties EL, *ACS Symp Ser*, 1981, **155**, 273–297 (31).

O.19 — A coordination chemist's view of surface science — Muetterties EL, *Angew Chem*, 1978, **90**, 577–590; *Angew Chem Int Ed Engl*, 1978, **17**, 545–558 (60).

O.20 — Coordination chemistry of metal surfaces and metal complexes — Muetterties EL, *Pure Appl Chem*, 1980, **52**, 2061–2066 (12).

O.21 — The organometallic chemistry of metal surfaces — Muetterties EL, *Pure Appl Chem*, 1982, **54**, 83–96 (21).
(continued)

O.22	Formation of ad-layers and clusters on condensation of metal vapors on solid surfaces	Niedermayer R, *Angew Chem*, 1975, **87**, 233–239; *Angew Chem Int Ed Engl*, 1975, **14**, 212–218 (17).
O.23	New perspectives in surface chemistry and catalysis (R Soc Chem Tilden Lecture)	Roberts MW, *Chem Soc Rev*, 1977, **6**, 373–391 (40).
O.24	Crystallographic dependence in the surface chemistry of tungsten	Rye RR, *Acc Chem Res*, 1975, **8**, 347–354 (49).
O.25	The fuzzy interface between surface chemistry, heterogeneous catalysis and organometallic chemistry	Schaeffer III HF, *Acc Chem Res*, 1977, **10**, 287–293 (73).
O.26	Reactions on single-crystal surfaces	Somorjai GA, *Acc Chem Res*, 1976, **9**, 248–256 (42).
O.27	Active sites in heterogeneous catalysis	Somorjai GA, *Adv Catal*, 1977, **26**, 1–68 (54).
O.28	The surface chemical bond	Somorjai GA, *Angew Chem*, 1977, **89**, 94–101; *Angew Chem Int Ed Engl*, 1977, **16**, 92–99 (55).
O.29	The surface structure of and catalysis by platinum single crystal surfaces	Somorjai GA, *Catal Rev*, 1972, **7**, 87–120 (43).
O.30	Molecular ingredients of heterogeneous catalysis (R Soc Chem Centenary Lecture)	Somorjai GA, *Chem Soc Rev*, 1984, **13**, 321–349 (38).
O.31	Active sites for hydrocarbon catalysis on metal surfaces	Somorjai GA, *Pure Appl Chem*, 1978, **50**, 963–969 (17).
O.32	Adsorbed monolayers on solid surfaces	Somorjai GA, van Hove MA, *Struct Bonding*, 1979, **38**, 1–136 (781).
O.33	Dynamics of chemical processes at surfaces	Tully JC, *Acc Chem Res*, 1981, **14**, 188–194 (35).
O.34	Catalysis from the point of view of surface chemistry	Weinberg WH, *Surv Prog Chem*, 1983, **10**, 1–59 (92).
O.35	Surface science studies of catalysis: classification of reactions	Zaera F, Gellman AJ, Somorjai GA, *Acc Chem Res*, 1986, **19**, 24–31 (43).

P. Metal clusters and metal surfaces

P.1	Relations between metal clusters and metal surfaces	Ertl G, in Gates BC, Guczi L, Knözinger H, eds, *Metal Clusters in Catalysis*, Elsevier: Amsterdam (1986), Ch 11, pp 577–604 (67).
P.2	The relationship between metal carbonyl clusters and supported metal catalysts (Meldola Medal Lecture)	Evans J, *Chem Soc Rev*, 1981, **10**, 159–180 (94).

P.3 Theoretical studies of metal clusters as models in surface chemistry

Messmer RP, *Gazz Chim Ital*, 1979, **109**, 241–246 (15).

P.4 Metal clusters. Bridges between molecular and solid state chemistry

Muetterties EL, *C & E News*, 1982 Aug 30, 28–41 (15).

P.5 Clusters and surfaces

Muetterties EL, Rhodin TL, Band E, Brucker CF, Pretzer WR, *Chem Rev*, 1979, **79**, 91–137 (295).

P.6 Metal clusters and metal surfaces

Muetterties EL, Wexler RM, *Surv Prog Chem*, 1983, **10**, 61–128 (228).

P.7 Clusters (Dowden-type) in homogeneous metallic catalyst systems

Yatsimirskii VK, *Izv Sib Otd AN SSSR, Ser Khim Nauk*, 1982, **9** (4), 131–132 (6).

Subject Index

Chapters 1–7 are indexed here. Chapter 8 stands on its own as an index of reviews. The notation t indicates a table.

Formula Index

The formulas of individual compounds listed in the text of chapters 1–7 are presented here. References to tables are based on metal nuclearity rather than individual formulas.

M2

[see tables p 164, 373–375]

$AuCr(CO)_3(Cp)(H)(PPh_3)$ 138
$AuMo(CO)_3(Cp)(H)(PPh_3)$ 138
$AuW(CO)_3(Cp)(H)(PPh_3)$ 138
$Co_2(CO)_6(PhC_2Ph)$ 162
$Co_2(CO)(C_5H_5)_2(NO)$ 13
$Co_2(CO)_2(C_5H_5)_2^-$ 13
$Co_2(CO)_6$ 126
$Co_2(CO)_6(PPh_2C_6H_{13})_2$ 248
$Co_2(CO)_6(PPh_2OEt)_2$ 248
$Co_2(CO)_8$ 125, 126, 137, 150, 162, 189, 312, 314, 324, 344
$Co_2(CO)_2(Cp)_2$ 13
$Co_2(CO)_4(Cp^*)$ 122
$CoAu(CO)_4(PPh_3)$ 131
$CoMo(CO)_5(MeC_2Ph)(Cp)$ 162
$CoRh(CO)_6$ 126
$CoRh(CO)_7$ 126
$CoW(CO)_5(MeC_2Ph)(Cp)$ 162
$CrCo(AsMe_2)(CO)_8$ 148
$CrFe(CO)_9(H)^-$ 355
$CrMn(CO)_9(AsMe_2)$ 148
$CrMo(CO)_7(AsMe_2)(Cp)$ 148
$CrRe(CO)_9(AsMe_2)$ 148
$CrRh(CO)_5(COD)(PBu^t)_2$ 138
$CrW(CO)_7(AsMe_2)(Cp)$ 148
$Fe_2(C_5H_5)_2(NO)_2$ 13
$Fe_2(CO)_6(C_2R)(SBu^t)$ 145
$Fe_2(CO)_6(PPh)(PR_2H)^-$ 248
$Fe_2(CO)_6(PPh_2)(H)^-$ 248
$Fe_2(CO)_6(PPh_2)_2$ 248
$Fe_2(CO)_6(PR_2)_2$ 150
$Fe_2(CO)_6(RPCPhCPh)$ 219
$Fe_2(CO)_6(S)_2$ 142

$Fe_2(CO)_6(S)_2^{2-}$ 143
$Fe_2(CO)_6(S_2)$ 155
$Fe_2(CO)_6(SMe)_2$ 207
$Fe_2(CO)_4(Cp)_2$ 207
$Fe_2(CO)_5(PPh_2)_2(CHO)^-$ 248
$Fe_2(CO)_9$ 3, 4, 123–125, 145, 149
$Fe_2(CO)_7(GeR_2)$ 147
$Fe_2(CO)_8(GeR_2)$ 147
$Fe_2(NO)_4(I)_2$ 12
$Fe_2(NO)_4(SR)$ 12
$Fe_2(CO)_5(PPh_2)(Cp)$ 147
$Fe_2(CO)_6(PR)$ 149
$Fe_2(CO)_6(PRCl)(Cl)$ 149
$Fe_2(CO)_7(SnR_2)_2$ 147
$Fe_2(CO)_8(SnR_2)_2$ 147
$Fe_2(CO)_4(Cp)$ 126
$FeCo(CO)_7(PRH)$ 150
$FeCo(CO)_8^-$ 124
$FeCo(CO)_7(PRBr)$ 148
$FeMo(CO)_9(H)^-$ 355
$FeW(CO)_6(C\text{-tol})(Cp)$ 158
$FeW(CO)_9(H)^-$ 355
$Ir_2(CO)_2(PPh_2)_2(PPh_3)_2$ 14
$Mn_2(CO)_{12}$ 185
$Mn_2(CO)_{10}$ 122, 137, 191, 307, 324
$Mn_2(CO)_9(NCMe)$ 137
$Mn_2(CO)_9(L)$ 191
$MnCr(CO)_{10}^-$ 132
$MnFe(CO)_7(Cp)$ 130
$MnMo(CO)_{10}^-$ 124, 132
$MnMo(CO)_7(PR_2Ph)$ 152
$MnPt(CO)_2(CS)(PMe_2Ph)_2(Cp)$ 128
$MnRe(CO)_9(NCMe)$ 138
$MnRh(CO)_4(Cp)(Cp^*)$ 134
$MnW(CO)_{10}^-$ 132